THE HISTORY OF
SOVIET AIRCRAFT
FROM 1918

Vaclav Nemecek

Willow Books
Collins
8 Grafton Street, London
1986

Willow Books
William Collins Sons & Co Ltd
London● Glasgow● Sydney
Auckland● Toronto● Johannesburg

First published in Great Britain 1986

Nemecek, Vaclav
    The history of Soviet aircraft from 1918
    1. Aeronautics – Soviet Union – History
    1. Title II. Schoenmaker, Wim
629.133'09   TL515
ISBN 0 00 218033 2

Produced for Willow Books by Key Publishing
Ltd, 1 Wothorpe Road, Stamford, Lincs., PE9
2JR.

Filmset by Arty Type, Whittlesey, Peterborough,
with colour process by PRS Ltd, 4 Roger Street,
London WC1.

Printed in Great Britain by William Clowes Ltd,
Beccles, Suffolk.

2

INTRODUCTION

I FIRST OBTAINED a copy of Vaclav Nemecek's 'Sovetska Letadla' in 1970 and was struck by the magnificent collection of photographs which it included, even though, in many cases, the reproduction left a lot to be desired. I was, however, extremely disappointed to realise that the mastering of the Chez language would be quite beyond me and the details of the text remained a mystery for some years.

In due course a German edition was published as 'Sowjet Flugzeuge' and in this instance the reproduction of the photographs was marginally improved and I was extremely fortunate in finding that my old friend, Tet Williams, was prepared to undertake the enormous task of translating the text from German into English. Over the next few years an English translation was published in the small circulation Bulletin of the Russian Aviation Research Group of Air Britain.

Through the good offices of Wim Schoenmaker I was then able to establish contact with Vaclav and obtain his support for the idea of a publication of his work in English. With the co-operation of Frank Ward at Key Publishing Ltd we set about editing and updating the text for Vaclav's approval and Wim Schoenmaker set about the task of covering the later aircraft not included in the original book. This time we have been able to insert the photographs in the proper place in the text and to reproduce them in sufficient size to do justice, at last, to Vaclav's magnificent collection, supplemented where necessary.

As an aircraft enthusiast I find it difficult not to be struck by the parallels between the trials and tribulations, successes and failures of Soviet aircraft designers and the similar vicissitudes suffered by their colleagues in the West. It is very clear from Vaclav's fascinating tale that Soviet designers were innovative and resourceful and pioneered features which often became standard throughout the world.

Soviet aircraft were not simplified copies of Western designs, as they are sometimes portrayed. Even when an attempt was made to catch up on the development of strategic bombers immediately after the war with the notorious copying of the Boeing B-29, the actual task of reverse engineering an aircraft of this size and complexity in the time scale in which it was performed was itself an achievement of considerable magnitude.

It is a pity that Soviet authorities feel it is necessary to release such sparse information on a number of aircraft which can no longer be of any possible military significance. You will note, for example, that aircraft such as the Ilyushin Il-40, Tupolev Tu-91, Tupolev Tu-98 and Ilyushin Il-40 which were demonstrated to a Western delegation in 1956 are still, nearly 30 years later, known only by a single photograph or, in the case of the Il-40, only by photographs of models.

Would it be too optimistic to hope that the wider interest in Soviet aeronautical achievement that may be generated by the publication in English of Nemecek's book will meet with a response from the Soviet authorities and encourage them to de-classify and release information when it ceases to be of any military significance?

In some cases, of course, particularly in the case of pre-war and wartime prototypes, the records have been irretrievably lost, although it is amazing how, on a number of occasions, photographs have eventually reappeared.

It is a great pleasure to me to have helped in some small way to make Vaclav's great work on Soviet aircraft available to a wider public and I hope that you, the reader, will share this enjoyment.

Nigel Eastaway

Editor, Bulletin of The Russian Aviation Research Group of Air Britain.

3

★ CONTENTS

Acknowledgements

Key Publishing Ltd gratefully acknowledge the invaluable assistance given by Wim Schoenmaker and Nigel Eastaway in the production of this book. Thanks also to photographic contributors Zdenek Novotny, Miroslav Balous, Bruce Rigelsford, Ken Ellis, Pieter Dekker, Karel Masojidek, Duncan Cubitt, M B Passingham, Jan Cech, Vaclav Jukl, J P Alexander, William Green, Frantisek Kunik, Peter Valent and Donald Hannah.

CHAPTER 1

Developments up to 1928

FIGHTERS USED in the defence of the State against enemy air attacks and simultaneously providing a guaratee of aerial supremacy, always occupied a central position of interest for the Red Air Force and Soviet designers.

Already, in the first critical months of the existence of the Soviet Union, commanders of the Air Force showed their anxiety to maintain fighter units at an acceptable military and technical level, although the general standards in this sphere were very low. Soviet designers did their utmost to catch up with the great advances made by Western powers, but this was impossible.

They did design a few fighters, but these were experiments rather than aircraft good enough to be put into service. Fighters date fast, and certainly with the situation and resources of the time these aircraft could not be built nor put into production quickly enough.

The Soviet Government decided on a prompt if expensive solution to the problem. They bought foreign fighters. In the period 1922-24 a hundred British Martinsyde F-4 and thirty Italian Ansaldo A-1 Ballida were bought.

But more important was the purchase of 200 Dutch Fokker D-XI fighters through a private trading company. These Fokker machines became popular not only because of their good qualities (300 metric horse power Hispano-Suiza 8Fb producing a maximum speed of 255kph) but also because of their long life. The last D-XI were withdrawn from the Red Air Force in 1930. A year earlier they had been put into service in combats over the Chinese-Eastern railway which had been attacked by Chinese troops.

The Fokkers soon replaced the outdated frontline fighters of various brands. Among the models replaced we find other foreign 'planes – several French SPAD S-7, some being actual French deliveries and others licensed Russian productions. The Moscow 'Dux' plant had begun licensed production of S-7 in Spring 1917, before the

October Revolution, and produced about 100 machines. After the Revolution production had to be halted, owing to lack of Hispano-Suiza engines. The Russian SPAD S-7 were powered by Hispano-Suiza 8Aa engines of 180mhp with a maximum speed of 210kph.

The Defence Commissariat published a design competition for a fighter in 1921 and two models were tested in 1923-4. But the tests confirmed that the Soviet Union had been right to buy abroad; neither model was good enough to be put into service with the units. The faster machine was the I-1 biplane of D P Grigorovich which made its first flight in January 1924, achieving 230kph. It had the American Liberty engine of 400mhp and was produced in the national aircraft plant No.1 in Moscow. The initial "I" (for Istrebitel = fighter) was used for the first time in the designation of this model.

The second fighter was MK-21 Rybka (Little Fish) designed by V L Korvin, N G Mickhelson and M M Shishmarev. This was built in the former Anatra plants in Taganrog. The MK-21 was originally designed as a float fighter. As the floats were unsuccessful, the aircraft flew with land undercarriage – wheels or skids. Both I-1 and MK-21 were biplanes with wooden fuselages and both remained at the prototype stage.

It is said that the history of Soviet fighters begins on August 23, 1923. On this day a new

Below: Incomplete fuselage of Grigorovich's I-1 biplane fighter.

The product of three designers was MK-21 known as 'Rybka' or 'Little Fish'.

fighter took off for the first time – N N Polikarpov's low-wing monoplane I1-400 which was built entirely of wood. It was an especially courageous design for the times, confirming the boldness of Polikarpov's creative imagination.

The design was no simple matter. On the first flight, with K K Artsoylov at the controls, the machine reared suddenly at about 20m and fell to the ground. The reason was soon discovered after fresh calculations and wind tunnel experiments. It was, in fact, the common ailment of aircraft of that time – the centre of gravity was located too far to the rear, behind the centre of buoyancy, roughly in 52% of the mean aerodynamic chord (20%-30% were normal for the time).

The second variant, I1-400b, was tested by A I Shukov and proved faultless in this respect. A series of 33 aircraft was ordered but even production models had their problems. There was always a tendency for the aircraft to pitch down and it could not easily be brought out of a flat spin. Flying with I1-400b always required the full attention of pilots.

The designation described characteristics of the aircraft. "I" stands for Istrebitel (fighter), "L" the American Liberty engine, and 400 the metric horsepower. Production aircraft were given the Soviet M-5 engines, a licensed production of the Liberty. These were first designated I-1M5, that is, "first fighter with M-5". Later, this designation was simplified to I-1. The speed of 264kph was noteworthy. Take-off weight was 1,530kg and the aircraft was fast, but there was room for considerable improvement.

I-1 was an interesting experiment. Although it resulted in series production the increase in combat strength of the Red Air Force was meagre, for the aircraft were never actually put into service with fighter units.

One piece of history was made, however, when M M Gromov used an I-1 for the first parachute jump in the USSR on June 23, 1927.

First Soviet designed fighter taken on by the Air Force and put into production was the I-2 biplane, designed by D P Grigorovich and derived from the I-1 biplane. There were problems with I-2. On his return from the first flight in September 1924, test pilot A I Shukov announced that the cockpit was too narrow, the visibility limited etc.

Below: IL-400b was a development of Polikarpov's bold attempt at a monoplane fighter.

I-2 was the first Soviet-built fighter to enter service with the Red Air Force.

Nevertheless only slight modifications were made and the I-2 was immediately put into production.

If we include the later I-2bis variant as many as 211 examples of this aircraft were built from 1925. The flaw was still the narrowness of the cockpit, for the two Vickers 7.7mm machine guns were mounted on the sides of the fuselage and took a lot of room. It was also difficult to get out of a flat spin.

Grigorovich had to redesign the aircraft in 1925. The new I-2bis had new control surfaces, the cockpit was broader and the two weapons were mounted over the engine. Test pilots Shukov, M M Gromov and A F Anisimov were satisfied with the I-2bis and the new variant soon replaced I-2 in production.

All the machines had M-5 engines. Maximum speed of the production aircraft was 232kph but without armament and with special propellers it could reach 257kph – quite a good performance for the time. The I-2bis remained in series production until the beginning of the first Five Year Plan (1926 to 1929).

The Defence Commissariat of the USSR, encouraged by the relative success in development and series production of I-2 aircraft, published a decree in April 1925 according to which the outdated fighter models of foreign provenance were to be continuously replaced. The designers were exhorted to create new, more efficient aircraft for series production during the period of the first Five Year Plan.

P O Sukhoi, director of a design group at AGOS TsAGI, began work on a suitable fighter in Spring 1926. Designation of the project was ANT-5 from the initials of A N Tupolev, director of AGOS. Military designation was I-4.

Sukhoi made consistent use of all-metal construction, mainly dural corrugated sheet. I-4 was a sesquiplane, the upper wing was strut-braced to the fuselage while the lower wing was entirely cantilever and could be dismantled in order to achieve a higher speed. Engines for the first example were imported Gnome-Rhone Jupiter IV of 480mhp while armament consisted of two synchronised machine guns in the fuselage to the rear of the engine.

Below: I-2bis was a redesigned I-2 with wider cockpit and M-5 engine.

Sukhoi's I-4 (ANT-5) first flew in 1927 and stayed in production for seven years.

The first prototype was completed in Summer 1927. From July to September 1927 the pilots Gromov, Anisimov and A B Yumashev put the aircraft successfully through plant and government tests in the Scientific and Research Institute of the Red Air Force. The performances were not exceptional for the time, but a good average; maximum speed 257kph at low level, climb performance 5,000m in 10.9 minutes and service ceiling 7,650m. The I-4's one special quality was its incredible life span despite being exposed to variable terrain and weather conditions in the USSR.

The first production I-4 were put into service with the fighter branch in 1928 and stayed there until 1937. Some 370 I-4 were built before production came to an end in 1934, seven years after the first flight. Production aircraft were powered by licence-built Jupiter engines, designated M-22, with a take-off performance of 480mhp.

In 1931 a few examples of I-4bis were produced. They were pure high-wing monoplanes with mechanical slats and Jupiter VIs of 490mhp.

But the maximum speed was only 260kph and the other qualities were apparently not so much better as to warrant a change in production.

I-3 followed I-4, although one would expect it to be the other way round. The Aviatrust design group OSS, directed by N N Polikarpov, announced I-3 in 1927, basically a redesign of his two-seat fighter 2I-N1 as a single-seat machine. The I-3 was a simple biplane in composite construction with the German BMW-VIz of 500mhp. It was technologically quite simple and, after successful government test in Winter 1927-8, was put into production.

About 400 aircraft were serially produced. At first they were given the original BMW-BIz engine, later the licence-built M-17 of the same power. Standard armament was two fixed machine guns. Maximum speed at low level was 283kph, but the aircraft was fairly heavy at 1,863kg take-off weight and therefore not very manoeuvrable.

I-3 and I-4 were the first fighter models to be built and found suitable for series produciton during the first years of the Five Year Plan.

Below: I-3 followed I-4 in production and about 400 were constructed from 1928.

CHAPTER 2

Early Five Year Plan Fighters

OPENING OF THE first Soviet Five Year Plan in 1928 marked a real turning point in the national economy and in the whole of the country. Such a state of affairs found general expression in the armament industry, and in particular the aircraft industry, for the precise aims in this sphere were Soviet self-sufficiency and independence from foreign capitalist countries.

In the initial phase of transition from individual productions to real series production there were many difficulties and the development and production of fighters did not proceed as smoothly as had been expected. But the Red Air Force insisted on having these machines, which were delivered according to the 1927 agreement between the Air Force and the technical committee of Aviatrust. Aviatrust had promised to design new, faster and more manoeuvrable aircraft which had the prospect of quite long service in the fighter units.

A N Tupolev was to design the 1-5 fighter in 1928. It was to have a French Gnome-Rhone Jupiter-VI or Soviet built M-36 engine. Tupolev prepared the project as ANT-12 but he had so much bomber design work that he had to abandon it. The designation I-5, however, was to appear again.

By 1928 a great urgency was felt to develop fighter aeroplanes. In summer 1929, N N Polikarpov of the group OSS, designed a new fighter biplane which was to meet the increased demands of the Air Force. It was to be of wooden construction with Jupiter-VI engine and two synchronised machine guns.

The GPU, at that time entrusted with the supervision of aircraft design, were of the opinion that the work was taking too long. In September 1929 Polikarpov was interned together with a number of other designers and leading personalities of the aircraft industry. The internees were formed into a group, the so-called Vnutrennaya Tyurma ("house arrest"), in December 1929 in

No 7 hangar of Moscow plant No 39 V R Menshinskii.

Here the internees continued their specialist work as designers, draughtsmen, stress analysts etc, rigorously guarded by a rigorous government in order that they should meet an early dateline. D P Grigorovich, the camp veteran, was responsible for design and in public announcements authorities designated the Vnutrennaya Tyurma as the Central Design Bureau TsKB.

In this environment Polikarpov produced another fighter sketch which Grigorovich then took over for the real design work. The machine was known as VT-11 and on April 29, 1930, B L Bukhgolts was able to complete the first flight. It was a classic biplane of composite construction with Jupiter VII engine of 450mhp. Engine cylinders were individually cowled and on the sides of the fuselage were two synchronised PV-1 machine guns.

In May 1930 the second prototype, "Klim Voroshilov", was produced, named in honour of

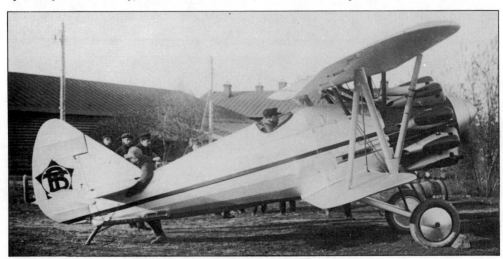

VT-11, first prototype of the I-5, with 450mhp Jupiter VII engine.

I-6 flew before the VT-11 (I-5) but only two were built.

K J Voroshilov who personally supported the design work. This had a low altitude Jupiter VI engine. The third prototype, "Podarok XVI Partsyezdu" (gift to the 16th Party Assembly), had a Soviet M-15 engine of 480mhp enclosed in a NACA-type cowling and was flight tested on July 1, 1930. The VT-11 were put into production for routine duties immediately after their first successful flight tests and were designated 1-5.

I-5 were produced for six years, as many as 800 being constructed. The production aircraft underwent several modifications: for example, the cylinder cowling was replaced by simple Townend rings to aid cooling. The engines were M-22 and maximum speed was 286kph. An altitude of 5,000m was reached in 10.1 minutes and a roll of 360 degrees could be flown in 9.5 seconds (on the 1-4 it was 11.5 seconds).

Manoeuvrability was excellent.

The 1-5 of the last series had four machine guns, two in the fuselage and two in the upper wing. They were among the most popular fighters of the thirties and were frequently used in experiments of a varied nature. In summer 1941 several 1-5 were sighted among the destroyed machines on the Soviet airfields.

Those assistants of Polikarpov who had not been interned continued work on his concept for a fighter with wooden monocoque fuselage. The prototype, designated 1-6, was in the air before the first VT-11, matching the latter's performance and qualities. But 1-5 was given more backing and only two 1-6 were built.

The I-5 delivery delay was bridged in 1932 by the purchase of prototype aircraft and licence construction of German Heinkel HD-37c biplanes,

An I-5 in series form. Some 800 were constructed over a six-year period.

introduced as I-7. The German originals had BMW-VI of 500/730mhp while Soviet constructions had M-17 engines. In all, 134 1-7 were built and they remained on the production programme until 1934.

Speed was 290mph, boosted to 320kph without the armament of two standard machine guns. The I-7 were only intended to be a stand-by, and after the introduction of I-5 were promptly removed from service.

Continuing with the I numbers we come to model I-8, a tiny interceptor biplane designed by Tupolev with the number ANT-13 and the name Shokey (Jockey).

In the course of 1928 Tupolev had been on a mission to Krupp's in Essen, returning with several samples of nickel-chromium steel and stainless steel. After technical experiments the stainless steel was used for the wing spars of ANT-13. Engine used was the American twelve-cylinder Curtiss V-1570 Conqueror of 625-700mhp.

M M Gromov test flew the prototype I-8 on December 12, 1930, and was specially pleased with it. In the course of tests, speed was measured at 303kph – the first time that an aircraft had exceeded 300kph in the USSR. But it remained at prototype stage because the Air Force regarded the I-5 as their standard fighter and did not wish to introduce further models. Furthermore, they did not intend to produce under licence any engine of the Conqueror class.

Little is known about any other fighter designs of this time, for most of the information was destroyed. In 1932 and 1933 several designs were executed. I-9 was to have been a biplane with M-30, M-31, M-32, M-37 or M-38 engines of 500-600mhp. But the engines were not completed and the aircraft also remained at the drawing board stage.

Another design was produced concurrently with I-9. This was Grigorovich's single-seat heavy fihter with two M-22 engines. All we know about the I-10 is that it was a high-wing monoplane in all electron construction with an M-41 engine.

I-11 and I-13 fighters were conceived by Polikarpov. The in-line M-34 engine of 750mhp was to be mounted on the I-11, the I-13 was to get the American Wright Cyclone SGR-1820/F-3 of 710mph. These unrealistic projects paved the way for Polikarpov from I-5 to the future I-15.

The designation I-12 was used for a two-engine fighter of V N Chernyshov of TsAGI. Details about this machine are found in the section on fighters with recoilless cannon.

Around 1932, commanders and scientific theoreticists of the Red Air Force worked out the prospects for further development of the fighter branch and the tactical uses to which fighters could be put in the near future. The principles established at the time remained unshaken throughout the thirties and even up to the beginning of the forties.

Soviet military theorists worked on the assumption that those separate, sometimes opposite, qualities demanded of an aircraft (high speed, manoeuvrability, control, manipulation at the horizontal and vertical level, heavy efficient armament etc) could only with great difficulty be reconciled when it came to the design of a fighter, and perhaps such features could not in fact be reconciled with one another at all.

According to stipulations of the time the Soviet fighter branch was to consist of a precisely collaborating team with high-speed horizontal operating fighter monoplanes and manoeuvrable vertical fighter biplanes. The high-speed, heavy armed monoplanes were to attack the enemy and force them to fight or to be pursued. The idea was certainly good and theoretically well based, but it was difficult to put into practice.

Soviet fighter pilots were intensively trained for this collaborative work and were very much in control of the situation when taking part in peacetime practices. But in a real combat situation, with the quick change of formations and circumstances, no close collaboration was possible. The resulting individual operations certainly showed up the good qualities of the various fighter types, but also their deficiencies when not in close collaboration.

Experiences in battles in Spain, on the River Khalkhin-Goll in the Far East and in the 1939 Finnish War confirmed the existence of this weak spot in Soviet thinking. But designers were obliged to follow this 1932 theory of two co-ordinating fighter branches throughout the thirties.

So two different types of fighter were in service during this period – the *manevrennye istrebiteli* or manoeuvrable fighters and the *skorostnye istrebiteli* or high-speed fighters. In the first category biplanes were predominant and in the second came the low-wing monoplanes. This separation of the two fighter categories had several results. The first was favourable in that Soviet designers were the first to develop and put into production the cantilever, low-wing monoplane with retractable undercarriage. The second result was unfavourable – in Summer 1941 it proved almost catastrophic. The Red Air Force had been putting fighter biplanes into service over too long a period. By 1941 they were the only air force, apart from Italy, still using fighter biplanes on a large scale.

Biplanes, of course, constituted the domain of N N Polikarpov. In February 1933 he began the design of a new model, for which military designation I-15 was used, although in design papers the machine was called TsKB-3.

Polikarpov made use of experience from the design of fighter I-5 and incorporated details prepared for project I-13. The I-15 was a classic biplane in composite construction, with fabric covered wooden wings and steel tube fuselage. Centre of the upper wing could be pulled down so as to offer the pilot a better forward view. The undercarriage legs were semi-cantilever with faired wheels and engine was the American

I-7 were licenced constructions of Germany's Heinkel HD-37c biplane.

Wright Cyclone SGR-1820/F-3 of 715mhp which was cowled by a Townend ring. The first stage of flight testing, begun by Y P Chkalov in October 1933, took only a month and was concluded by a successful Government test.

At the beginning of 1934 the I-15 was put into production. There were some difficulties as engines of Soviet origin in the performance class of the Cyclone were not yet available. A series production of Cylone was promptly prepared under licence, but the Soviet M-25, which also produced 715mhp, could only be mounted in the final series of I-15. The first series of 404 aircraft received the less powerful M-22 engines of 480mhp while 59 were built with Cyclones and only 270 of the final series were given the M-25.

Armament consisted of two fixed PV-1 machine guns initially, but fighters of the final series were given four PV-1 at the expense of smaller fuel tanks. Each weapon had 750 rounds.

Unfortunately the majority of I-15 (with M-22 engines) could still only achieve 320kph maximum speed, though with other engines it reached up to 365kph at 3,000m altitude.

I-15 had good altitude performances: on November 21, 1935, V K Kokkinaki reached 14,575m in an I-15 with no armament and hardly any fittings, the pilot sitting on a plywood seat. Kokkinaki had certainly beaten the altitude record set up by the Italian, Renato Donati (14,442m in a Caproni Ca-113 biplane on April 11, 1934) but his performance could not be recognised by the FAI for the USSR was not yet a member.

In November 1936 the first twenty-five I-15 with Soviet volunteer pilots were sent to Spain to help the Republican government. Collective delivery of the two models, I-15 and the later I-15bis, reached 550 aircraft, known in Spain as Chato.

The I-15 were about on a par with the German Heinkel He-51 biplanes. The Italian Fiat CR-32, which fought on the side of Franco (along with

Below: First flown in October 1933, Polikarpov I-15 fighters were among aircraft sent to Spain in 1936 to assist Republicans against Franco.

I-15ter of I-153 featured retractable undercarriage and kinked upper wing.

the He-51 of the Condor Legion), were rather better aircraft especially as regards manoeuvrability. Compared with the Messerschmitt Bf-109B, put into service later on, these I-15 were slow and weakly armed. They only prevailed because of their manoevrability and their performance in vertical combat. I-15 had more success in China, being delivered to the Chinese Air Force in 1937.

It was in 1937 that Soviet plants delivered the first aircraft of an improved series I-15bis or I-152. This variant was designed and tested in 1936. The designers were able to secure an improved M-25A engine of 750mhp and Polikarpov altered the lines in order to make better use of it. The upper wing now formed an integral part over the fuselage with the engine surrounded by a broad ring, similar to the NACA ring but featuring a lockable front. Undercarriage legs were cantilever and armament was increased to four PV-1 and later to ShKAS machine guns. Each weapon was provided with 650 rounds.

Some 2,408 I-15bis were produced and several could be seen in June 1941 on Soviet airfields.

Improvements were soon made with regard to manoeuvrability and speed. In 1938 the prototype I-15ter or I-153 was test flown with M-25V engine of 750mhp. Shortly afterwards further prototypes were built which could take the more powerful M-62R engines of 800/900mhp. When comparing the I-15 and I-15bis, the greatest novelty is the retractable undercarriage. Both legs were withdrawn in a rearwards direction into the underside of the fuselage, the wheels being turned through 90° until they lay flat. As on all the other Soviet models, skids could be mounted instead of wheels. In this case the undercarriage struts remained rigid.

I-153 had four fixed synchronised ShKAS machine guns, firing along canals lying between the engine cylinders. As on the I-15 and I-15bis, there were carriers for four 25kg or two 50kg bombs situated under the lower wings.

The upper wing of I-153 had a kink, resulting in the designation *Chajka* (Seagull).

Test examples of I-153 easily reached a speed of 440kph at 4,600m altitude and their climb performance and manoeuvrability surpassed all contemporary biplanes. Fully-armed production models were slower, reaching only 430kph at the same altitude, but even that was high for a biplane. At the beginning of 1939 priority production was given to these aircraft, and as early as May the first I-153 were being flown with field units.

The new I-153 were used particularly in the Far East, where Japanese provocations on the frontier between Mongolia and Mandshukuo had degenerated into open fighting in summer 1939. Here there were heavy air combats, often involving 150 fighters in one engagement. The situation was at first unfavourable to the Red Air Force, for the Japanese had put into service their own new, low-wing monoplanes Nakajima Ki-26 (Nate). So the Soviets promptly introduced their I-16 monoplanes and the new I-153.

Soviet pilots employed a strategy which, at the beginning, was particularly effective. The I-153 approached an enemy with extended undercarriage and at about 250kph. The Japanesee were expecting a familiar I-15 and made the usual military preparations. Not until the last minute, before combat was engaged, did the Soviet pilots retract undercarriage, give full throttle and surprise the Japanese with their speed and fire efficiency.

A few such shocks developed respect for the Soviet biplanes. Japanese fighter pilots often avoided the old I-15, suspecting them to be I-153 in disguise.

I-153GK was a high-altitude variant in the I-15 series with pressurised cabin.

Chajkas also fought in the Finnish War in winter 1939-40. Many aircraft of the I-153 type were assigned in Summer 1941 to front-line service against the German powers. I-153 were superior in speed, but it was their manoeuvrability that really helped them and the designation cropped up in German reports as late as 1943.

The I-153, with 3,437 examples, were the most numerous variants in the family I-15/I-152/I-153 which totalled 6,578. The last variant to be delivered (1940) was I-153BS. This had two UBS machine guns of 12.7mm calibre. A smaller number of I-153P were issued (P for *Pushka* = cannon) which had two 20mm ShVAK guns each. Only a few examples of the high-altitude variant I-153GK were built. These aircraft, constructed in 1940-1, had a pressurised cabin to Polikarpov's or J Shcherbakov's design. With supercharged M-62TK engines service ceilings of 11,800m were reached.

The "manoeuvrable" fighter biplane was not only supported by the highest authorities in the Red Air Force but even forced on the country. In the period 1939-40 the I-153 biplane was redesigned in Polikarpov's bureau in order to increase performance to the utmost. At the beginning of 1939 Polikarpov began to design the biplane I-190; in summer the first machine was test flown.

It was an aerodynamically and technically improved variant of the I-153 with the fourteen-cylinder, double-row radial M-88 of 950mhp. The second prototype (I-190TK) was designed as a high-altitude pursuit fighter with pressurised cabin and supercharged M-88TK engine. The I-190TK was able to reach altitudes of 12,400m and still maintain its combat efficiency. Further development gave the I-190 prototypes speeds of 490kph in 1940/41.

At the beginning of 1941 one of the prototypes met with an accident and that provided an occasion to halt further design work. In any case,

Below: I-15bis variants were fitted with improved M-25A engines.

Sukhoi's I-14 (ANT-31) prototype monoplane fighter of 1933.

Ramjet experiments were carried out with I-152 (above) and I-153 (below), cylindrical motors being attached to the lower wings. They made 74 flights without incident.

more powerful and more promising monoplanes had been put into production.

Work on I-195 was also halted. This aircraft was designed and built in 1940 but not completed. With a double-row M-90 radial engine of 1,500mhp it was calculated that the aircraft would have reached 580kph, making it the fastest biplane up to that time. The I-190 and I-195 were to have two machine guns and two cannon apiece.

Aircraft of the family I-15/I-153 were often used for experimental purposes. For example, the inventor engineer I A Merkulov tested his first ramjet engines on models 152 and 153. Merkulov approached the Technical Council of the Commissariat for the Aviation Industry in July 1939 with his project for a ramjet which would serve as an auxiliary engine for fighters. In particular, this engine was to increase horizontal speed and climb performance over a short period. The Technical Council submitted Merkulov's project to experts who gave their consent to the construction as well as to tests on the ground and in the air. Merkulov's first ramjet engine was the DM-1 *(Dopolnitelnii Motor* = booster engine). It consisted of a hollow cylinder of 400mm diameter and 1,500mm length, built as a dural shell and streamlined on the inside accordingly. In September 1939 they were able to run DM-1 for the first time on a test stand at the Central Airfield of Moscow. In October three improved DM-2 were built and tested. As it was well known that the ramjet required a certain flying speed to start it, Merkulov built a makeshift wind-tunnel of 15.5m length and 1m diameter for the ground tests. The engine could be run in this tunnel at air speeds of up to 450kph. but the DM-2 was only tested at a speed of 120kph with a thrust of 10kp.

In December 1939 two DM-2 were seen mounted beneath the lower wings of an I-152 fighter. These engines were first ignited in the air. on January 25, 1940, before a commission of the Commissariat for the Aviation Industry; pilot was P J Loginov, later to become head of Civil Aviation. At a speed of 320kph the engines were started up, producing a thrust corresponding to 100-120mhp and giving a speed increase of about 20kph. The DM-2 engines drew long trails of flame which created great excitement in the streets of Moscow. A few fire engines even drove to the airfield in order to extinguish the supposedly burning aircraft.

In September 1940 an I-153 was flown with two DM-2 and increased speed by 33kph. In October 1940 new DM-4 of 500mm diameter were built, their performance corresponding to 300mhp at 440kph, increasing the aircraft speed by about 50kph. I-152 and I-153 made 74 experimental flights with the booster engines DM-2 and DM-4 without disturbance or accident.

There was even a machine specially designed and built for Merkulov's boosters. A A Borovkov and I F Florov designed a completely cantilever biplane, No. 7211, in their bureau OKB-7 in 1937.

It was a small aircraft with spindle fuselage reminiscent of the American racing aircraft Gee Bee, for in both models the cockpit was located in the keel fin. With its M-85 engine of 800mhp, No. 7211 reached a speed of 416kph and had outstanding climb performance of 5,000m in 4.5 minutes and a ceiling of 13,000m.

This interesting machine was test flown on June 1, 1937, by P M Stefanovskii who gave a very favourable report. But the Red Air Force had it tested more thoroughly, and in the course of their examination test pilot E J Preman met his death when the engine suddenly failed on a landing approach.

As the flaw lay with the engine and not with the airframe, it was decided to continue with design. Thus arose the cantilever I-207 biplane, an aircraft specially designed for booster engines DM-2 or DM-4. I-207 had better lines than No. 7211, but it was driven by an M-62 engine of 850mhp, which increased maximum speed to 426kph but reduced altitude performance; 5,000m attained in 6.2 minutes and the ceiling was only 9,200m. A few prototypes were built with various engine cowlings. I-207 was then taken on in the experimental series but later discarded.

These were the manoeuvrable fighter biplanes of the thirties. We now return to 1932 and design assignment No. 2 for high-speed fighters. This was tackled by three design groups, once in AGOS TsAGI and twice in OSSTsKB.

In AGOS TsAGI, P O Sukhoi was entrusted with the creation of a high-speed, low-wing fighter monoplane with strong cannon armament. The design name was ANT-31, the military name I-14.

Sukhoi conceived the machine as a cantilever low-wing monoplane with all-metal monocoque fuselage. The metal skin on the fuselage was stressed while on the wings Sukhoi used a light corrugated metal. The undercarriage was retractable. Armament was to be either a synchronised PV-1 machine gun and two recoilless APK-37 cannon, or two PV-1 and two ShVAK cannon. As they had not yet procured the cannon, a corresponding weight was mounted on the prototype and mock guns were mounted on the wing leading edge.

In May 1933 the first I-14 prototype was test flown with a British Bristol VS-2 Mercury of 570mhp. The results were not too reassuring. At 5,000m altitude the maximum speed was only 40kph more than I-15 (i.e. speed of 384kph). At an altitude of 3,000m and under the I-14 was quite a bit slower because the engine was too weak for an aircraft of this class.

Sukhoi built the second prototype I-14bis or I-142 with Wright Cyclone radial engine of 640mhp. On February 12, 1934, the I-14bis was test flown and speed increased to 414kph, climb performance being 5.9 minutes to 5,000m. But not everything was good. In curving flight the horizontal tail unit was in the turbulent region of the wing and the machine became difficult to control.

AGOS TsAGI undertook a number of experiments and in 1936 the rear fuselage was designed anew, solving the problem. By the time I-142 was test flown the ShVAK guns were at production stage so they were mounted along with two APK-11 cannon.

This version of I-14 was a fairly good aircraft and so an experimental series of 55 machines was ordered. But after production of the 18th aircraft construction was halted, for there now existed another fighter. The design of this had begun under more favourable conditions.

The first prototype of this more successful rival was called TsKB-12 and test flown on November 31, 1933, by V P Chkalov. Soon these machines became known worldwide under the military designation I-16 and later under various nicknames.

Polikarpov designed his TsKB-12 with the smallest possible dimensions in order to achieve light weight and slight torque. Wing span was only 9m, the length 6m and wing surface only 14.6sq m. The short, spindle-shaped fuselage was a plywood shell; the wing had two spars of tubular steel with dural webs; ribs were of dural and there was fabric covering.

Noteworthy were unusually long ailerons and the streamlined link from wings to fuselage. The pilot sat in a relatively narrow cockpit with transparent enclosure; the whole could be pushed forward. In the centre of the enclosure they mounted a piece of telescopic apparatus for the machine gun.

A nine-cylinder M-22 of 450/480mhp and metal propeller served the prototype which had retractable undercarriage. Armament consisted of two synchronised and two non-synchronised fixed ShKAS machine guns, each with 90 rounds.

Chkalov soon completed the test flying and subsequent plant and Government tests. The results were rather disappointing, maximum speed at low altitude being 360kph and climb rate 5,000m in 9.4 minutes. The weak engine was to blame, as had been the case on the I-15, for as yet none of the more powerful series radial engines were available. Nevertheless, the I-16 was quickly put into production with its M-22, and in the second half of 1934 the first I-16-Model 1 were put into the units.

For the Air Parade of May 1, 1935, several groups, each consisting of five I-16-Model 1, flew over Red Square in Moscow, exciting among foreign observers about as much attention as rocket weapons in more recent times. These were the first production-built modern fighter monoplanes in the world with retractable undercarriage. A noteworthy achievement in the field of Soviet engineering.

The Red Air Force were aware of the shortcomings of I-16-Model 1. Nevertheless, they demanded prompt series production in order that pilots could complete their training on the new aircraft as quickly as possible.

It was quite an art to fly an I-16. The front section of the fuselage which bore the engine was too close to the centre of gravity. The pilot's cockpit, on the other hand, was located too far to the rear, which produced a centre of gravity with 45%-50% of the profile chord. Longitudinal stability was insufficient and the pilot had to hold the flight control the whole time.

Take-off and landing were not that simple either. Undercarriage suspension was hard, the aircraft rebounding vigorously whenever it encountered uneven ground and showing a tendency to nose over. Retraction of the undercarriage also caused difficulties; the pilot had to turn a hand crank 44 times before retraction was complete. Cranking was made with the right hand which also held the control-stick and therefore the aircraft flew in a slightly undulatory fashion during the operation. This undulatory movement was indeed a distinguishing feature of the I-16.

On Febuary 18, 1934, Chkalov test flew the prototype of the second variant of I-16, the TsKB-12bis. This machine had a suitable engine, the Wright Cyclone R-1820/F-3 of 715mhp, which featured a quite original cowling with separate air intake holes for each cylinder and regulating discs for the air intake. With this engine and the new metal AV-1 propeller, TsKB-12bis reached 437kph at 3,000m on the second flight, becoming top fighter of the time in the world. The heavy engine also pushed the centre of gravity further forward, improving flying qualities considerably. And climb capacity was much improved, 5,000m reached in 5.9 minutes.

TsKB-12bis was quickly put into production and, since most of the components were identical with those of I-16-Model 1, the new I-16-Model 4 was soon ready for delivery. With M-25 engine, production aircraft reached 455kph at 4,000m.

Unfortunately it was not possible to effect a speedy distribution of these powerful fighters throughout the country and at first they could only operate from the larger airfields. This was because of inadequate liaison between the directors of aircraft deployment and the directors of airfield construction. Most Soviet military airfields of the time were designed for biplanes. The I-16 needed at least 300m for take-off and 230m for landing and the government did not publish their Act for enlargement of airfields until July 1935. Meanwhile, much time had been lost.

Further variants of I-16 soon followed. I-16-Model 5 was like Model 4 but the pilot seat was given armoured plating of 9mm thickness which increased the dead weight by 40kg. The I-16-Model 6 of 1937 was in service over a wide area. It had the M-25A engine of 750mhp which allowed a maximum speed with full armament of 440kph at 3,000m. If fixed skids were mounted, maximum speed sank to 385kph.

Production of I-16 in every variant form was so rapid that by 1937 the aircraft constituted the backbone of the fighter units. The two fighter branches were able to work together effectively, though the good performance of I-16 led to experiments around 1936 with the idea of eliminating co-ordinatory work. In this period they reduced production of the I-15 in favour of the I-16 to only 1.4%. But they soon resumed their former practice.

In 1937 the new I-16-Model 10 were delivered. At first glance these variants could be distinguished from the older models by two long upper coverings to the rear of the engine. Under these were the two fixed synchronised ShKAS machine guns, which strengthened the hitherto relatively weak armament. There were 650 rounds per gun.

The weapons increased take-off weight from 1,660kg to 1,716kg, so the more powerful M-25V engine of 750mhp was fitted. Another new feature was the improved windscreen, now made broader and not so unpleasantly close to the pilot's head when the cockpit was shut. In spite of this improvement, pilots continued to fly with the cockpit roof open. The I-16 Model 10 featured for the first time retractable skis.

Landing speed of I-16 was relatively high at 120kph so experiments were made with landing flaps. On prototype TsKB-29 of 1936 shorter ailerons were used in order to make room for pneumatically operated landing flaps. The undercarriage was also pneumatically operated by way of experiment and a Cyclone F-3 engine yielded favourable results. But these novelties were not introduced to the production aircraft.

Above: I-16-Model 4, seen here on display in Milan, reached 455kph at 4,000m with an M-25 engine.

Below: A flight of I-16-Model 10 with two synchronised machine guns lying on top of the more powerful M-25V engine.

More important were the innovations in armament. Tests were made with heavy cannon armament on various fighter models but most were unsuccessful. So in 1936 interest was concentrated on cannon armament of the well-tried I-16. It bore in its wings two ShVAK 20mm cannon and, over the engine, two synchronised machine guns. Flying weight of this 1-16P increased to 1,640kg and the speed was now 444kph. But this cannon-armed machine was not actually built until 1938 when it was given M-25V engines. It flew without machine guns and with only wing-mounted cannon.

Full armament was mounted in the production aircraft I-16-Model 17 of 1938, but in this case the cannon were synchronised and the machine guns free-shooting. The new armament and equipment increased weight and impaired manoeuvrability and climb performance. For example, I-16-Model 17 had a take-off weight of 1,810kg and needed a full 8.9 minutes to reach 5,000m altitude – about as long as the first I-16-Model 1. At 1,000m altitude Model 10 effected a half-roll in 17.6 seconds; the older Model 4 only needed 14.3 seconds. Speed was only marginally increased, the original 440kph rising to 445. Service ceiling on Model 1 reached 7,200m and on Model 4 9,300m, but subsequently showed a tendency to decrease.

Meanwhile, foreign altitude performances had improved and it became necessary to design a variant for combats at great altitudes. The prototype I-16TK of 1939 solved this problem by mounting an M-25VTK engine with supercharger. The supercharging produced a speed of 494kph at 8,600m and the ceiling rose to 10,000m. A small series was run.

Even at that time it was clear that the M-25 engines were inadequate. Improved performances were only possible with the new M-62R engines of 920mhp. These were mounted for the first time on the I-16 Model 18 fighters in 1939. I-16-Model 18 were armed with four machine guns and no other weapons. But the engines were heavy and weight had to be reduced. Fuel supply was cut from 425 litres to 255 litres and the range dropped from 800km to not quite 600km.

Nevertheless, weight increased to 1,830kg, though speed also increased to 464kph and climb performance improved by 310m per minute. Wing load of the new Sixteen was greater than on any of the earlier variants; it increased from 92kg per sq m on Model 1 to 125.7kg per sq m and was to rise still further.

Wing loading of the subsequent variant reached 131.5kg per sq m. Of all the I-16 models this I-16-Model 24 of 1939 was produced in the greatest numbers. The M-62R engine was retained, but

armament was strengthened to reach the striking power of Model 17 – two ShVAK cannon and two ShKAS machine guns. The interior fuel tanks were still small, but two auxiliary tanks, each for 100 litres, could be mounted under the wing, bringing the range up to 1,000km again. Flying weight increased to 1,910kg.

The M-62R kept climb performance at an acceptable level, I-16-Model 24 reaching an altitude of 5,000m in 5.8 minutes, a better performance than Model 4's. It reached a speed of 490kph at 4,000m and the service ceiling was 11,000m.

In 1939 M-63 engines of 900mhp were tried on Models 28, 29, and 30, but performances were weaker, maximum speed at 3,000m altitude being only 462kph and service ceiling 9,100m. But the take-off weight was greater than that of any other I-16 variant at 1,940kg.

The I-16-Model 24 fighters were certainly the best available to the USSR in 1939 and 1940, and in fact till the summer of 1941, for none of the new, more powerful fighter models were available in large enough numbers for routine service.

Soviet fighter pilots grew accustomed to the unusual qualities of I-16 and became expert at handling them. Years later, when new models were introduced, they were reluctant to part with their Sixteens. The nicknames given these ma-

chines by airmen indicated a certain contradiction of atitude; the I-16 was called either *Jasterbok* (Hawk) or *Ishak* (Donkey).

Much has been written about I-16 service in the Spanish Civil War. *Mosca* (Small Fly) was their popular name on the Republican side, but the machines became known worldwide under the name given them by the Nationalists – *Rata* (Rat).

In the past the Soviet Union has painted too rosy a picture of the contribution made in Spain by the I-16. In practice there were some problems. However, one thing is clear. The 475 I-16-Model 6 and I-16-Model 10 delivered by the USSR to help fight Franco's Air Force and the Italian and German units on Franco's side did, in fact, constitute an enormous help. Without them the Republican Air Force would not have been able to defend themselves for so long.

The first I-16 were brought on the cargo boats Rostov, Neva and Volga directly into the Spanish harbours of Cartagena and Alicante. Later, when the National Navy blockaded these sites, aircraft were brought by rail from the French ports of Le Havre and Bordeaux and assembled in Catalonia.

Often just airframes were delivered to Spain where the Wright Cyclone R-1820-F54 engines were added. The biggest assembly and repair plants were constructed near Alicante. As I-16's technology was not particularly complex they even tried to buid the machines in Spain under licence but did not get very far. Only about twenty I-16 fighters were built and ten two-seat UTI-4 trainers.

First I-16 seen in the Spanish sky were the "6" models, put into service in November 1936 in the regions of Valdemoro, Sesena and Esquivias for the greater counter-attack. In Spring 1936 the machines were mostly combined to form Fighter Squadron 31. This group was composed of seven flying sections, each of 15 machines.

For the I-16 the German Heinkel He-51 biplanes constituted no problem, but the manoeuvrable Italian Fiat CR-32 were particularly redoubtable adversaries when their pilots knew how to fly them. Republican airmen preferred the tactics of frontal attack in a closed order against the enemy formation, making use of higher horizontal and vertical speeds to prevent the CR-32 from engaging in a dog-fight.

The Fiat CR-32 was a more dangerous opponent to the I-16 than the first Messerschmitt Bf 109B which was put into service by the Condor Legion in 1937. The German machines, with Jumo 210 engines of 610mhp and three MG-17,

Left: An I-16-Model 17 in Finnish colours. This version had greater armament but performance was impaired.

could not keep pace with the I-16; they were slower, more weakly armed and had no armouring. On the other hand they could make a half roll in 15.5 seconds, 2.1 seconds better than I-16-Model 10.

By the time the Spanish Civil War came to an end, Franco's men had captured several I-16. These *Ratas* served in the Spanish Air Force until May 1943; some had a still longer term in the trainer branch. The last I-16-Model 10 flew with the original M-25V engine in the aviation school at Moren up to July 1952, carrying Air Force designation C-8.

The outcome of the Spanish Civil War brought home to the Soviet Air Force the bitter truth – they had relied too long on the possibility of further development of I-16. By 1939 the I-16 had virtually reached the limit of their technical potential and no M-62 or M-63 engine could work any more wonders in a 1932 airframe. But Messerschmitt's Bf 109 was only at the first stage of development and the Bf 109E variant, delivered from 1939 onwards, was in every respect superior to later variants of I-16.

Further experience was garnered in 1939 during combats on the river Khalkhin-Gol where they fought the well-armed and armoured I-16 against the manoeuvrable Japanese Nakajima Ki-27 which also had a good climb capacity. Here the honours were more even and the Japanese spoke respectfully of the I-16-Model 10, calling it *Abu* (Gad-fly). One I-16 brought to the Japanese by a Mongolian pilot was carefully studied and tested.

The *Ishak* I-16 retained their well-established place in Soviet aviation history. Between 1934 and 1940 a total of 6,554 examples of I-16 were built in all the variant forms, 737 with cannon armament (models 16, 17 and 24). In 1941 I-16 construction was resumed for a short time to add a further 450. Over 7,000 aircraft of one type constituted a world record.

It is less well known that the I-16 was first in

another field. On August 20, 1939, a group of five I-16, led by N I Zvonarev, discharged a volley of rocket missiles at a group of Japanese fighters and brought down two aircraft from a great distance. This was the first fighter-to-fighter combat with rocket projectiles (if we discount the operation of French fighters with Le Pieur rockets used to shoot down balloons in World War 1).

The origin of non-guided Soviet rocket missiles for use in air combat can be traced back to 1920 when two artillery officers, V A Artemyev and N I Tikhomirov, took on the problem. After a while two groups for rocket research were formed, one in Leningrad and one in Moscow. Artemyev's Leningrad group achieved the first successes in 1928 when several test missiles were discharged. From the Leningrad group there arose the so-called *Gasodinamicheskaya Laboratoriya* (laboratory concerned with the dynamics of gases). The work of this laboratory was supported by G K Orjonikidze and later Marshal M N Tukhachevskii.

As early as 1931 the laboratory director, B S Petropavlovskii, designed two basic variants of a rocket missile with solid propellant and calibres of 75.82 and 132mm. Both variants were intended for attacking aerial and ground targets.

In 1933 the Moscow and Leningrad laboratories amalgamated to form an institute with the name *Reaktivnii Nauchnoissledovatelskii Institut* (Scientific and Research Institute for Reaction).

The 75mm missile, intended for aerial combat, was to enable fighters to destroy targets at up to 6,000m distance. It was to break up groups of enemy aircraft and then destroy them individually. The heavy missiles of 82 and 132mm were to be put into service on bombers and combat aircraft against ground targets.

The RS-75 missiles (*Reaktivnii Snaryad* = jet missile) were tried out between July and December 1937 south of Moscow. Use was made of small target 'planes released by R-5 biplanes at a certain altitude. The I-16 crews achieved a good number of hits but nevertheless modifications had to be made. By 1938 one could say that design work had been concluded. I-15 and I-16 fighters could carry up to eight RS-75 missiles which were mounted on simple T-pieces under the wings. This was much better than the complicated frame construction of the early attempts.

The RS-75 received their baptism of fire in Summer 1939. At that time it was not yet clear to the Japanese how their aircraft had been destroyed. So the world first learned of the missiles in Summer 1941 on the occasion of an encounter with the Germans. At the time these missiles were used in particular by Il-2 aircraft, but were better known as a weapon of the artillery in their BM-16, a framework version mounted on armoured cars or ZIS lorries. The RS missiles originally intended for aerial combat proved excellent against ground targets. Later only the 82 and 132mm missiles were used, named RS-82 and RS-132.

Left: To remain competitive in high-altitude combat the I-16TK of 1939 had a supercharged M-25VTK engine which pushed speed to 494kph at 8,600m with a ceiling of 10,000m.

CHAPTER 3

Fighters with Recoilless Cannon

IN THE 'THIRTIES the Soviet Air Force devoted their attentions to the use of recoilless cannon for aerial combat; they were the first Air Force in the world to do so. The weapon, now indispensible for ground attack, was at the time a relative novelty.

Inventor L V Kurchevskii achieved particular success at the end of the 'twenties with his recoilless cannon. These were known among experts in the USSR under the designation DRP *(Dynamo Reaktivnaya Pushka* = dynamic reaction cannon). The mode of operation was simple – the cannon shot two discharges at the same time in opposite directions – combat discharge forwards and a compensatory discharge backwards. Since the cannon fired in two directions, there was no recoil, and therefore no difficulties in design of the aircraft parts on which the cannon was mounted.

At the end of the 'twenties the Red Army gave these cannon a thorough test. Marshal Tukhachevskii supported development of the weapon and instigated the use of DRP as aircraft armament. In his opinion, cannon had particular importance for interceptors since they could shoot from a greater distance at large bombers than had been possible using 7.62mm machine guns. Unfortunately, the cannon could only fire a single round.

At the beginning of 1931 two DRP-76 cannon of 76.2mm calibre were tested under the wings of the I-4 fighter (ANT-5). The weapons were only fired at ground targets but the outcome was satisfactory. Soon it would be possible to put into service a new machine – D P Grigorovich's TsKB No.7 monoplane – which was specially designed for cannon.

Grigorovich used the forward fuselage of an I-5 fighter, extending as far as the rear of the cockpit, and added a new tail in dural skin construction. The strut-braced wings had an all-metal skeleton of Enersh 6 with stainless steel and fabric covering. The tail unit, with high horizontal stabiliser, was unusual, for the horizontal surfaces were given a strong dural sheet covering with reinforcing strips. These surfaces were just above the tail of flame from the two DRP-76 cannon. These were mounted under the wing on the wing/undercarriage struts.

Besides the cannon, TsKB No.7 possessed a fixed PV-1 machine gun for fire direction. As the cannon only had one round the pilot had to aim carefully, using tracer ammunition of the machine gun which was also a safeguard in the event of combat after firing of the cannon. However, an encounter with enemy fighters was not expected, for the TsKB No.7 was intended for home defence and protection of the sector outside the compass of standard fighters.

The prototype TsKB No.7 was tested in 1931/32 and several modifications had to be made on the aircraft and cannon before the model was put into production. The seventy machines built in 1932 were taken on by the Red Air Force as I-Zs and were the first fighters in the world to have their particular equipment. Maximum speed was 300kph and a few I-Zs took part in experiments with parasite fighters.

The production I-Z models had M-22 engines, as had the prototype, but with simple Townend cowling instead of helmet-like cowling of individual cylinders.

But the DRP-76 cannon's greatest disadvantage remained – it could still only fire a single round. L V Kurchevskii worked on modernisation of the weapon, producing the automatic APK-4 *(Avtomaticheskaya Pushka Kurchevskogo)* of 76.2mm calibre which could fire six to ten rounds at a slow rate.

In 1934 D P Grigorovich designed the new fighter DG-52 – not a makeshift design like TsKB No.7, but a purpose-built low-wing cantilever monoplane in all-metal construction with monocoque fuselage and retractable undercarriage. Under the wing, in an unusual cowling, were two APK-4 and under the broad cowling of the Cyclone engine was a ShKAS machine gun. Maximum speed with cannon was 360-380kph at 2,500m or 410kph at 3,000m without cannon.

The prototype showed directional instability which was eliminated by the mounting of a long tail fin on the upper side of the fuselage. This tail fin is also a characteristic of the 200 production aircraft which were put into service for home defence with the fighter branch as IP-1 *(Istrebitel Pushechnii* =cannon fighter). Production aircraft were given M-27V engines of 750mhp.

In 1934 Grigorovich tried to achieve higher performances on his cannon fighter by reducing the wing area from 20.0sq m to 16.4 and modifying the cowling of the Cyclone F-3. Thus arose the prototype DG-53 which reached a speed of 385kph, or 435kph without cannon. This variant was taken on as IP-4. Grigorovich continued his work and on variant DG-53bis with ShVAK and ShKAS guns, but the type remained unfinished.

These APK-4 and newer APK-11 45mm calibre

TsKB No.7, prototype of the I-Z. Only one round was carried in each of two cannon which were fixed to the main wing/undercarriage struts.

Above: Some 200 IP-1 (DG-52) with a pair of APK-4 cannon under the wing were put into service for home defence.

Below: Grigorovich's DG-53 cannon fighter was taken on as IP-4 and achieved greater speed by a reduction in wing area and modified engine cowling.

cannon were found to be unsuitable for aerial combat because of their slow rate of fire and inadequate supply of ammunition; the production ShVAK were more successful. ShVAK then replaced the APK cannon on the IP-1, but after modification its performance was lower than I-16 variants. IP production was halted.

Grigorovich himself was working on the DG-54 or IP-2 at that time. This was a relatively large, all metal, low-wing monoplane with Hispano-Suiza Xbrs of 830mhp which was supposed to reach as much as 520kph at 3,000m. APK armament was replaced by ShVAK automatic cannon and in the wings were no fewer than ten fixed machine guns. But though DG-54 was almost completed by 1936, it was never quite finished and there are no photographs extant.

During this period, when interest was fast diminishing in Kurchevskii's cannon, changes were also made in the armament of other models originally intended to take APK-4 or APK-11 (e.g. P O Sukhoi's I-14 fighter).

Several other aircraft remained at the prototype stage. There was, for instance, the interesting tailless fighter BICh-18 of B I Cheranovskii, a low-wing monoplane with parabolic form wing into which were mounted APK-11 cannon. The engine was to be an M-22.

Designers S A Lavochkin and S N Lyushin designed a fighter LL in 1935. It was an aerodynamic low-wing monoplane with a smooth fuselage. The pilot's seat was to be sunk into the fuselage and he was to look out through a periscope. In winter 1935 the fuselage mock-up was built. It was examined carefully by General J I Alksnis, then commander of the Red Air Force. He found the cockpit too narrow and visibility so limited that he did not recommend construction.

After the first experiments with DRP-76 cannon in I-4 fighters, authorities considered the use of even more powerful weapons of this type involving greater calibre, longer firing range and greater destructive power. It was even believed that such weapons could be used against difficult ground targets.

In December 1931 a discussion was held at TsAGI, in the course of which aircraft and weapon designers, together with representatives of the Red Air Force, laid down clear design stipulations which initiated design of a 102mm calibre cannon and corresponding aircraft.

L V Kurchevskii developed the APK-100 cannon and, using the first blueprints, the drawing office AGOS TsAGI was entrusted with design of the aircraft.

A group of young designers under the direction of V N Chernyshov designed a special machine with the name ANT-23 and military designation I-12. Chernyshov wanted to make special use of the long exhaust barrels of the APK-100 cannon. He mounted it in little pods on the all-metal wing, further lengthening the exhaust barrels by creating them out of 170mm diameter waterpipes; wall thickness was now 1.5mm and the cannon also became the tail booms.

The short fuselage compartment was also pro-duced in all-metal and had a Bristol Jupiter VI of 420/525mhp in the nose and another in the tail, so there were tractor and pusher propellers. Cockpit was between the two engines, an arrangement which did not crop up again until seen on the Dutch Fokker fighter, D-XXIII.

The prototype ANT-23 was test flown in 1934 by I F Kozlov. It was designated *Baumanskii Komsomolets* by the designers, in honour of a Socialist, Bauman of the Tzar's time, who had lived and worked near TsAGI. This district of the town was also called after Bauman.

Test flying was not an easy task as Chernyshov's creative audacity proved greater than his technical experience. The machine was too heavy and slow. Speed did not exceed 300kph and the APK-100 cannon were not without flaws.

Kozlov remarked immediately on the dangerous position of the pilot between two engines and stressed the machine's total lack of airworthiness. The pilot, or at least his parachute, would be torn to pieces by the rear propeller, which had no locking device. In the event of an emergency landing the two engines might crush him. Kozlov's fears proved justified. In a firing trial one cannon exploded in the air and heavily damaged the controls. Kozlov could not climb out and had to make an emergency landing on a grass field. Luckily he was unhurt, but after that all work was halted on I-12.

A A Arkhangelskii's group at TsAGI began design of a machine with two APK-100 cannon in 1932, but followed an easier path. ANT-29 was an elegant aircraft with flat sheet covering and two Hispano-Suiza 12Ybrs engines, each of 860mhp and given the name M-100. ANT-29 embodied several concepts which were taken up a little later for design of the medium high-speed SB-2 bomber. It may even be said that ANT-29 was the ancestor of ANT-40 (SB-2). But the authorities pressed for production of the SB-2 bomber and work on ANT-29 had to be postponed for a while.

The first ANT-29 was test flown in February 1935. The fuselage was very flat with a high nose from which barrels of the two APK-100 projected. The cannon were located in the under section of the fuselage extending as far as the rear cabin where the machine gunner also did the loading. Exhausts of the cannon then converged into a single tube that had its muzzle to the rear of the fuselage under the tail unit. In contrast to other cannon fighters, ANT-29 possessed the advantage of having weapons which were accessible during flight.

The Red Air Force designated this machine DIP (*Dvukhmestnii Istrebitel Pushechnii* = two-seat cannon fighter). On tests in 1935 the machine reached 352kph at 4,000m, which was not a bad performance. Unfortunately there was some longitudinal instability.

At this time ANT-46, prototype of the two-seat heavy fighter DI-8, was also tested. This, too, was a design of Arkhangelskii, a conversion of the airframe of bomber SB-2 for fighter purposes. The machine had two APK-100 cannon in the wings,

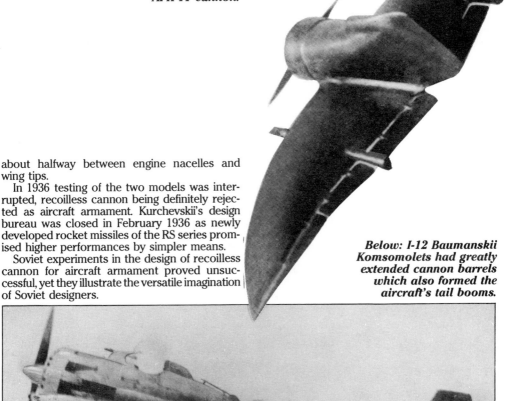

about halfway between engine nacelles and wing tips.

In 1936 testing of the two models was interrupted, recoilless cannon being definitely rejected as aircraft armament. Kurchevskii's design bureau was closed in February 1936 as newly developed rocket missiles of the RS series promised higher performances by simpler means.

Soviet experiments in the design of recoilless cannon for aircraft armament proved unsuccessful, yet they illustrate the versatile imagination of Soviet designers.

Below: I-12 Baumanskii Komsomolets had greatly extended cannon barrels which also formed the aircraft's tail booms.

Below: Twin APK-100 cannon were installed in the lower fuselage of ANT-29 which was designated DIP by the Red Air Force. One of its main advantages was that both weapons were accessible for servicing during flight.

CHAPTER 4

Multi-Seat Fighters

FOR MANY years there were attempts in the USSR, as well as in other countries, to solve the problem of the two-seat fighter. The designers tried to provide rear defence for the fighter by accommodating a machine gunner. But the gunner plus the weapon plus the ammunition increased weight so much that performances were seriously reduced and the prototypes were mostly rejected.

Collaboration between pilot and gunner had also proved very difficult. Nevertheless, from time to time a two-seat fighter model was put into production and new machines were designed; each, it was imagined, would be **the** design which had been so long awaited. Unfortunately almost every one ended in the same disappointment.

The first Soviet two-seat fighter appeared in 1925 under the designation 2I-N1. It was designed in N N Polikarpov's bureau. The name 2I-N1 denotes a two-seat fighter with a Napier engine, in this case a Napier Lion of 450 metric horsepower. It was a biplane in all-wood construction with two fixed machine guns and a flexible twin machine gun. N V Filipov tested the aircraft in March and April 1926 and reached a speed of 262kph, 30kph more than the single-seat fighter I-2bis).

But the Red Air Force had no immediate need for machines like this, and the prototype had no successors. Later its designation was changed to

DI-1 (*Dvukhmestnii Istrebitel* = two-seat fighter). Polikarpov used the modified airframe to make the single-seat fighter I-3 and in 1929, by back development, two-seat fighter, DI-2, was made from the single-seat I-3. DI-2 had an M-17 engine and achieved 280kph. This aircraft also remained

at the prototype stage.

Two years later, D P Grigorovich's two-seat DI-3 fighter met the same fate. This aircraft was designed at TsKB. In contrast to the conventional DI-1 and DI-2, the DI-3 had an unusually shaped fuselage tail with twin rudder. In this way the machine gunner would secure an unhindered area of fire to the rear. The prototype DI-3 was tested from August 1931 onwards and reached 272kph with a German BMW-VI engine of 500 metric horse-power. The aircraft had good flying qualities and a limited construction was undertaken. The Soviet Air Force did not accept it for its fighter groups.

DI-4 also remained at the prototype stage. This aircraft was a strongly braced high-wing monoplane designed in the BNK bureau (*Byuro Novych Konstrukcii* = bureau of new designs). BNK was created in the years 1932 and 1933 and was under the direction of Frenchman Andre Laville. The engine was an American Curtiss V-1570 Conqueror of 600mhp which gave the aircraft a speed of 320kph.

One model that did go into production was the robust biplane DI-6 or TsKB-11, again a two-seater. It was designed by V P Yatsenko. Between May and November 1935 the TsKB-11 completed government tests. It had a Wright Cyclone SGR-1820-F3 engine and was taken on by the fighter

Left: The first Soviet two-seat fighter was Polikarpov's DI-N1 of 1925, powered by a Napier Lion engine.

Below left: DI-2 was a conversion of the single-seat I-3 but made no impression on air force decision makers.

Below: A limited construction was undertaken of Grigorovich's DI-3, seen here on skis. None went into air force service.

branch. The 200 production aeroplanes, which had been given M-25 engines from 1937, were also equipped with two fixed machine guns and had at their disposal a flexible ShKAS under a glazed turret. The small dimensions of the aircraft are noteworthy, wing span being only about 24cm greater and fuselage 1m longer than I-15.

Maximum speed of 372kph at 3,000m was not bad for a two-seat biplane in 1935. But by 1939 this was found to be inadequate for front-line service, even more so by 1941. In battles with the Japanese on the Khalkin-Gol river and over Khasan lake the DI-6 were successful, but here the element of surprise played a great part. At first the Japanese imagined that DI-6 was merely a variant of the I-153 fighter, for both aircraft had the retractable undercarriage.

In summer 1941 several DI-6 fighters on the Soviet airfields were destroyed by German attacks.

In 1936, alongside delivery of the DI-6 fighter, delivery was also made of the low-attack variant DI-6Sh or TsKB-38 with four machine guns in the lower wings and additional armour. Up to four 25kg bombs could be mounted under the lower wings. These modifications increased dead weight from 1,360 to 1,434kg. Among further variants was the simplified DI-6bis or Samolet 21 of 1937, with fixed faired undercarriage and M-25B engine. For fighter training DI-6T was built, an aircraft with dual control.

Roughly parallel with development of the DI-6 biplane ran A N Tupolev's two-seat, low-wing fighter monoplane ANT-45, but design was interrupted in 1936. A further aircraft from Tupolev's KOSOS-TsAGI bureau was the two-engined ANT-46 or DI-8, already mentioned in the chapter about fighters with recoilless cannon.

DI-8 was really a variant of the SB-2 bomber with two Gnome-Rhone 14Krsd engines, each of 800 metric horse-power and armament of two APK-100 cannon in the wings and four fixed ShKAS machine guns in the fuselage nose. On flight tests in 1935 speeds of 400kph at 4,000m were measured, but the aircraft were not put into production owing to the tense situation over preparation of

SB-2 bombers.

All the two-seat fighters covered up to now were thoroughly conventional machines. But one model was completely different. This was the two-seat fighter Sigma of A S Moskalev, designed and built in the OKB-31 bureau in Voronesh.

Moskalev wanted to make the aircraft as compact as possible for the sake of manoeuvrability. He also wanted to keep the area of fire free for the flexible rear machine gun. So Sigma was constructed as a tailless aircraft with outboard rudder fins on the trapezoidal wing. The fuselage was short, with one engine in the nose and a machine-gun turret in the tail.

It was originally planned to have an Hispano-Suiza 12Ybrs but this engine was not given to the designer. Moskalev had to make do with the Soviet M-34 engine of 750 metric horse-power. This had no reduction gear so the propeller had to be four-bladed to provide sufficient ground clearance. Moreover, it was not possible to mount the automatic cannon as had been planned and they had to make do with two synchronised and one flexible machine gun.

To keep the forms of the all-metal aircraft as smooth as possible, aerodynamic surface cooling was mounted. At lower speeds, especially for take-off and for landing approach, a small retractable radiator was to be used. The undercarriage was also retractable.

In 1935 Sigma was ready for flight, but the main administration of the aviation industry regarded the aircraft as too dangerous and used any pretext for delay. As a result it was not much flown and testing halted completely in 1936. So it was not possible to ascertain whether the estimated 500kph speed could, in fact, be reached.

In the twenties, and especially the thirties, multi-seat fighter cruisers were designed in fairly large numbers. They were intended primarily as escorts to the large bombers and it was planned to use them as protection on daylight attacks. These aircraft were relatively large machines with numerous flexible weapons and a range to match that of the bombers. At the time several models of this type were designed and built, notably in France, but a few models were to be found in other countries including the USSR.

The first fighter cruiser of Soviet provenance was the all-metal, low-wing monoplane KR-6 (*Krejser* = cruiser) of 1930. It was no more than a variant of the two-engined reconnaissance aircraft ANT-7. The KR-6 was given two M-17 engines, each of 550 metric horse-power, and two flexible twin machine guns (PV-2). With a crew of two the machine reached 240kph. Several KR-6 were built and put into trainer service, later being re-equiped for reconnaissance or used as civil machines in the Arctic.

There were plans for a high-speed fighter cruiser to be completed in 1933, and the Red Air Force had high hopes for it. A A Arkhangelski's group, under the direction of Tupolev, were working on the cantilever low-wing monoplane ANT-21, one of the first in a new line. The first

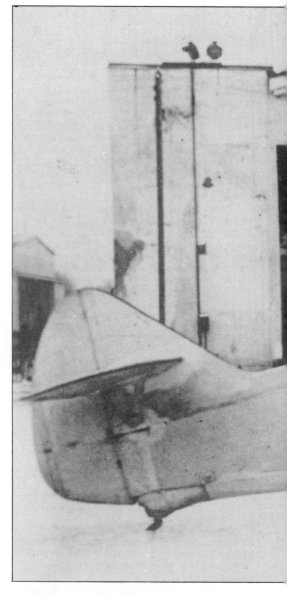

Above: Some 200 examples of Yatsenko's DI-6 joined the Red Air Force from 1935 onwards but by 1941 were relying heavily on the element of surprise for successful engagements.

Right: Among the variants of DI-6 was the simplified DI-6bis or Samolet 21. It had a fixed undercarriage and M-25B engine.

ANT-21 had two M-17 engines, each of 500/680 metric horse-power, retractable undercarriage and twin rudder. This design marked a transition from the angular Tupolev aircraft to the more modern models with rounded contours. ANT-21 still had corrugated sheet covering but the whole surface was covered with fabric to reduce drag. It had two twin PV-2 machine guns in the nose and dorsal position.

The Red Air Force took on ANT-21 as Mi-3 *(Mnogomestnii Istrebitel = multi-seat fighter)*. Among test fliers the machine was known as Mit-rich. Test flights were executed in summer 1933 without any difficulties arising and maximum speed was fairly good at 350kph. In September 1933 an attempt was made to increse speed but violent flutter from aileron and elevator affected the whole of the wing and fuselage, making the aircraft unmanageable.

These difficulties were experienced world-wide whenever attempts were made to approach the 400kph mark. TsAGI had to make every effort to shed light on these symptoms and remove the causes.

The second Mi-3 had a single rudder and was powered by two AM-34RN, each of 775mhp. This aircraft had much better flying qualities, but already its development had become more a question of prestige than of practical application, for in the meantime the Air Force had lost interest.

A few designs for fighter cruisers remained on the drawing board, e.g. ANT-34 designed in 1934. This was a modern monoplane with two Wright Cyclone engines. D P Grigorovich designed the DG-56 in 1936 as a three-seater with two Hispano-Suiza 12Ybrs producing an estimated speed of 438kph at 3,000m. Military designation was LK-3 *(Legkii Krejser = light cruiser)*.

Another machine of this class was actually constructed. G-38 was a three-seat fighter developed by the Civil Aviation group in Leningrad. Designers were P A Ivensen and V I Korovin under the directorship of P I Grokhovskii. Design was completed in September 1934 as a mid-wing monoplane in twin boom construction. The wings were made entirely of wood as were the long tail booms which formed an extension of the engine nacelles. A short crew compartment was of dural while armament consisted of two 20mm ShVAK cannon, four ShKAS machine guns (all fixed) and a flexible twin machine gun. The prototype had two Gnome-Rhone K-14 Mistral Major engines, each of 850mhp.

By the end of 1936 the prototype G-38 was completed. It had clean smooth lines, small dimensions (wing span was only 13.6m) and everything indicated that it would be a success. Unfortunately it was at that time that Grokhovskii's group was dissolved and the aircraft was destroyed, together with all designs and photographs.

The reason given was that the aircraft had a faulty design; it was said that landing speed would have been too high because the wing had

160 kg/sq m loading. But such assertions could not be proved, nor could it be ascertained if the maximum speed of 550kph was attainable or not. It is possible that with the G-38 the Soviets might well have obtained, at a far earlier date, an aircraft of the same class as the Fokker G-1.

In other countries, too, experiments with fighter cruisers were unsuccessful. So in the thirties the problem remained – how to provide long-range defence of large bombers by conventional means. In the USSR they worked on another scheme for protection – the parasite fighter which was transported by the bomber itself.

Fighter cruiser ANT-21 was taken into service as Mi-3. The first example (below) suffered handling problems at speeds approaching 400kph and although the second Mi-3 (above) was better no further development seemed worthwhile.

Below: Pioneer of the multi-seat fighter cruiser concept was KR-6 which appeared in 1930 as a variant of ANT-7.

CHAPTER 5

Experiments with Parasite Fighters

ENGINEER V S Vakhmistrov was a scientific worker at the Red Air Force's Institute for Technical Research and Science. On June 1, 1930, he wrote a letter to General Alksnis, head of the Air Force, proposing the use of parasite fighter aircraft as an escort for heavy bombers of the TB class. Incursions could then be made deep into enemy territory far beyond fighter range.

Vakhmistrov's plan was for the bombers to take their own escorts on the wings and under the fuselage. In the event of an enemy attack the fighters would separate from the mother aircraft, parry the attack and then reattach themselves. They might also be used for constant supervision of air space and for defensive supervision over the Soviet Union, tasks far beyond the normal fighter.

It was not an original thought for the Germans had already carried out similar experiments for the protection of airships in the First World War. After the war the English did the same, and then the Americans. In every case, however, it was a question of the defence of airships, and here the hangarage of fighters caused relatively few problems. But with other aircraft as carriers the operation was more difficult.

Vakhmistrov was inspired through the commission he received in 1930 to design a target aeroplane which could fly freelance without an engine, change its position, loop the loop, glide and turn etc. Thus the fighter pilot was to receive better conditions for gunnery training, for the normal towed targets could only be flown straight ahead. Vakhmistrov designed a small aircraft or, rather a big model of an aircraft which was put on the upper wing of the reconnaissance aircraft R-1; at a suitable altitude the model was separated and released. The method of engaging and releasing prompted the parasite fighter.

General Alksnis approved Vakhmistrov's plan and stipulated which institutes should help carry it out. The TsAGI institute were to produce calculations for streamlining and stability while at Monino airfield the real technical work and flight testing were to take place.

The twin-engined heavy bomber TB-1 was chosen as carrier aircraft and 1-4 served as fighters. All the necessary connections and releases were operated from the seat of the second pilot.

Two fighters were pulled by means of a cable by two teams of men over a wooden ramp onto the wings of the TB-1 and there made fast. The aircraft were connected to the bomber by two locks on the undercarriage axles. These had to be released by the two pilots. In addition there was a supporting strut under the tail of the fighter which was to be released by the pilots shortly before separation. The whole combination was called *Samolet-Zveno* (aircraft-aircraft group) and received the abbreviation Z-1.

On December 3, 1931, there was excitement on Monino airfield as Vakhmistrov's Circus Z-1 took off on its first flight. Pilot of the carrier aircraft was A I Zalevskii while in the fighter on the right sat V P Chkalov and on the left A I Anisimov.

Vakhmistrov was with his assistant, Morozov, in the front machine gun turret to direct manoeuvres. Originally he was to have flown as second pilot to unlock the fighters, but at the last minute the airfield commander ordered that only someone with a licence for heavy machines was to occupy the seat. Vakhmistrov wasn't qualified so A R Sharapov was chosen but could only be briefed superficially in the necessary manipulations.

The ruling was certainly justified, but almost led to an accident. In flight the fighter pilot should have first released the supporting strut, and only then was the second bomber pilot to detach him from the mother aircraft. As Vakhmistrov gave the signal, Sharapov was so excited that he unlocked the undercarriage axle of Chkalov's aircraft without giving him time to release the strut. Chkalov's 1-4 reared up but he instantly recognised the danger and set free. On the other hand, the separation of Anisimov's fighter took place in a completely normal way.

Samolet Zveno (ZI) comprised a TB-1 bomber and two I-4 fighters.

This moment of drama supplied an answer to the question of what would happen if the aircraft did not separate immediately? It was shown that they could take off at irregular intervals. Take-off from a flying aircraft was certainly a great event in aviation history and all three pilots, along with Vakhmistrov, were awarded the Order of the Red Star.

On December 19 Marshal Tukhachevskii was given results of the first test and he ordered that work should be continued. Vakhmistrov was to perfect the technique of separation as far as possible and increase the range of Z-1 from 800-1,000km.

The Z-1 group then made several flights with other crews as well. Once, after trouble with the separation mechanism, the whole group managed to land unscathed. Pilot of the bomber was P M Stefanovskii. On another flight the group made a practice attack en route from Moscow to Kiev. The bomber dropped practice bombs over the target, the fighters separated and then escorted their mother aircraft to Moscow.

In September 1933 group Z-1a flew for the first time. This consisted of a TB-1 bomber and two I-5 fighter biplanes. In August 1934 group Z-2 made its appearance. Carrier aircraft was the four-engined TB-3 bomber and the fighters were three I-5, one of which was engaged over the fuselage. In autumn 1934 Vakhmistrov tested attachment of a fighter under the wing. The first such group was the Z-3, consisting of a TB-3 and two I-Z fighter monoplanes.

So the first stage of development was concluded, the technique of take-off from a flying carrier aircraft having been tested by a relatively large number of pilots. The Red Air Force now began to count tactically on this system but there was yet

Below: A wooden ramp was used for loading I-5 fighters on to the wing of a TB-3 bomber to make up Z-2. This group first flew in August 1934.

another problem to be resolved – that of re-stowing under the carrier aircraft.

It was clear to Vakhmistrov that fighters could not return to holdfasts on the wings. A new technique had to be developed, preferably making use of a trapeze. A similar technique had already been successfully tested on American airships whereby the pilot tried to hook into the horizontal pole of the trapeze.

In Winter 1934-5 Vakhmistrov and the pilot who had been picked for the purpose made preparations. Fighter and test pilot Vasilii Stepanchenok – known to his friends at Monino airfield as "Vaska the artiste" – took off daily with his I-Z. It carried a curved guiding pole with an attachment hook over the fuselage on the struts and Stepanchenok practised approach to the carrier TB-3. Later a trapeze was to be built in between the undercarriage struts of TB-3, but on practice flights a cable was stretched between them, strung with brightly coloured pennons. Stepanchenok's training consisted of trying to tear off these pennons one after the other with the hook on his aeroplane.

On March 23, 1935, the first attachment took place. That patient TB-3 took off from Monino airfield and when aloft the trapeze was let down out of the fuselage so that the horizontal pole was lower than the wheels of the undercarriage. Stepanchenok followed and quickly climbed to rendezvous at 2,000m. The I-Z fighter aimed to get between the undercarriage of the bomber, matched speed and attached itself carefully but securely on the trapeze. The safety lock clamped down and the two machines were connected. So there arose the Zveno Z-5. The pair flew round the airfield a few times, then landed separately.

Further experiments improved the technical

Above: SPB under the wing of a TB-3. SPB were dive bomber variants of the I-16.

Left: An I-5 of the Z-2 combination with tail free and ready for release of the main undercarriage clamps.

Below: Pictured during Z-5 experiments, an I-Z fighter dangles on the trapeze under a TB-3.

side and in November 1935 they reached a climax with a gigantic group of not less than six aircraft which flew attached. This group was called *Aviamatka* (Mother Aircraft).

The TB-3, piloted by P M Stefanovskii, took off with two 1-5 biplanes over the wings and two 1-16 low-wing monoplanes below on November 20, 1935, and climbed to 2,000m. On the flight, Stepanchenok's I-Z fighter was overtaken and attached itself to the mother aircraft. The Z-6 was filmed and photographed to record the historic moment, then all the fighters separated simultaneously from the mother aircraft and landed together with it.

Vakhmistrov was enthusiastic about these successes and managed to win support from the highest circles of the Air Force. In 1936 he began to design a giant bomber and a fighter for its defence. The bomber was to be tailless and take not less than six fighters. By 1937 the fighter prototype was almost finished. It was a variant of the I-17, with shorter wings, less lifting surface and greater wing load. It had no undercarriage, only a retractable hook. The aircraft did not need to reduce its speed for landing as it would never land on the ground.

But in 1937 Marshal Tukhachevskii was arrested, followed by General Alksnis. All design work supported by them had to be halted, and this included the tailless bomber and fighters.

Thereafter, Vakhmistrov was only able to experiment with normal production machines. In July 1937 he put together a new Zveno. It was a variant of Z-6, consisting of the TB-3 bomber in newer form with AM-34 engines and two 1-16 fighters (dive-bomber variant SPB) under the wings. It was called Zveno Z-6SPB. On practice flights pilots A S Nikolayev and I A Tabarovskii scored 90% direct hits aiming at a target with the dimensions of a destroyer.

Following the pattern of Z-6, a squadron was assembled of six TB-3 and twelve SPB under the direction of A V Shubikov in Yevpatoriya in the last months before the war. In summer 1941 a group like this carried out the attack on the Danube bridge at Negru Voda, Rumania. The Zveno took off from an airfield on the Black Sea, the dive-bombers separated not far from the target and dropped their two 250kg bombs. Then all the separated machines returned to base, the dive bombers serving as escort. This was the first and only time this singular weapon was used.

Experimental activitiy of the inventor reached a climax in November 1939 with the flight of Zveno Z-7. This time the TB-3 with the AM-34 engines carried three 1-16 fighters under the wings and fuselage. But by now some drawing offices had already designed long-range fighters that were to protect the bombers in a simpler way. Vakhmistrov's experiments came to an end.

Soviet involvement with parasite fighter aircraft lasted nearly ten years, but the results remained quite meagre despite the high financial and intellectual means at the Air Force's disposal. This was not only due to technical inaccessibility

Climax of experiments in multiple groupings was the spectacular Z-6 Aviamatka (Mother Aircraft) ensemble consisting of a TB-3 carrier, two I-5 biplanes above the wings, two I-16 monoplanes below and an I-Z on the trapeze. First flight was in November 1935 when all five fighters successfully separated. Pictured right is the I-Z at its moment of release.

but also because of the unfavourable internal political situation of the USSR in the last years of the thirties.

After the results of American experiments with parasite jet fighters in the forties and fifties it can be claimed with a certain amount of certainty that this bomber escort method was not practicable on a great scale.

CHAPTER 6

Experiments with Fighters in the 1930s

WE NOW RETURN to the basic category of fighters, that is the classic one-seat model. We know how far the USSR had gone in the development of such machines, up to the production aircraft I-15, I-15bis, I-153 and I-16. There existed several other prototypes and projects in which the designers tried to increase the fighting power yet further.

But it must be said immediately that efforts to create better fighters in the thirties brought no success. So for a long time the I-16 fighters and their numerous variants represented the technical zenith in this sphere. Not even Polikarpov managed to repeat the success of I-16 with another model.

Some months after design work had begun on the TsKB-12, Polikarpov received a personal commission from Stalin for the design of a one seat fighter which could fly at 500kph. It was a demanding task but Polikarpov took it on — anyway, he couldn't very well turn it down!

In TsKB a modern one-seat fighter was produced. This aircraft, even judged by international criteria, can be considered the first modern fighter of this class at the onset of the Second World War. It was the prototype TsKB-15 which had been flown for the first time on September 1, 1934, by V P Chkalov before the prototype Spitfire, Hurricane or Bf 109.

It was a slim machine with noticeably broad fairings between fuselage and wings, and powered by the French Hispano-Suiza 12 Ybrs engine of 760mhp. The wings were all-metal while the fuselage was entirely of wood. The TsKB-15 did not possess any armament but there was provision for two cannon and a machine gun.

On flight tests a speed of 455mph was reached. More was simply not possible with the engine and Chkalov complained in particular about the narrow cockpit.

A second variant, TsKB-19, was tested. It was powered by the M-100 engine of 760mhp, a Soviet copy of the Hispano-Suiza. This aircraft had a built-in cannon and four fixed machine guns in the wings. The Red Air Force gave TsKB-19 the designation I-17, but only a few prototypes were constructed because the aircraft could never reach the desired speed. A prototype was exhibited in 1936 in the Paris Aerosalon. It had, at that time, a propeller with unique twin blades. The radiators were interesting — two cylindrical blocks which could be retracted.

Polikarpov designed several more fighter monoplanes with retractable undercarriage. In 1935 he designed the TsKB-25 or I-19 with Gnome-Rhone 14 Krsd two-row radial engine and an estimated speed of 475kph. The desired 500kph was finally reached by TsKB-33 in 1936. This aircraft had an HS 12 Ybrs with condenser cooling, armament consisting of three machine guns, one of which was in the propeller axle. From TsKB-19 came the TsKB-43 of 1936. It had an HS 12 Ycrs engine and was to reach a speed of 520kph.

Polikarpov's activitiy in the design of fighters reached a peak in the thirties with the I-180. Design had already begun in the last months of 1937 but work did not proceed smoothly. In the spring of 1938 the main administration of the aircraft industry had intervened and halted design of I-180 which had derived from the two seat reconnaissance aircraft Ivanov. The I-180 was relatively light — only 1,800kg at take-off — and was to have the M-87A engine, a two-row radial developed by S K Tumanskii from the series of French Gnome-Rhone 14K. This M-87A accomplished 850mhp.

As there was dissatisfaction with the Ivanov reconnaissance aircraft, the designer was to devote his attentions more to a development of

Modern-looking TsKB-15 first flew on September 1, 1934 – before the Hurricane and Spitfire.

the 1-16, an aircraft of proven worth. So in winter 1938 arose the 1-180-1, a little more robust than other machines of this time and more stream-lined than the I-16.

The Red Air Force expected a lot of this model and counted on it, along with the use of all l-16 variants. Even the test pilot Chkalov was impatient to assess the new machine's qualities.

On December 15, 1938, when the temperature was 26 degrees below zero, he tried the aircraft for the first time. The engine was overcooled, and as he approached the airfield after a short flight, the motor at low rotation broke down suddenly.

The aircraft slowed at low altitude, stalled and splintered on the ground. Chkalov was killed.

Design continued despite Chkalov's accident. In Spring 1939 the second prototype was ready but that aircraft, too, was wrecked on the test flight when the pilot, T P Suzi, unaccountably dived almost vertically into the ground from 10,000m. This I-180-2 had an M-87B engine.

Another prototype appeared in 1939, the I-180-3 with M-88P engine of 1,000mhp. Its structure was this time nearer to that of the Ivanov. Flight tests began on February 25, 1939, and showed 585kph maximum speed. One of its pilots, S P Suprun, was injured when an undercarriage strut

Below: Polikarpov's prototype I-180 with M-87A two-row radial engine.

gave way on landing; another, A G Proshakov, got into an uncontrollable flat spin and had to save himself by parachute.

The tragic series of accidents brought serious consequences for Polikarpov and his collaborators. First, the most highly-placed state and party personalities evinced distrust, although Polikarpov had, up to that time, received the highest honours and distinction. These failures marked the beginning of great difficultites in Polikarpov's life and work. For some of his collaborators the consequences were yet more serious. Director of the main administration of the aviation industry, Belyaykin, director of the aircraft plant, Ushachev, and Polikarpov's deputy and director of model production, D L Tomashevich, were all arrested.

A court of inquiry found no concrete causes for the accidents of Proshakov and Suzi, and an experimental series was produced – ten I-180S aircraft with M-88R engines of 1,000mhp with reduction gear. They were armed with two UBK and two synchronised ShKAS machine guns, and reached 571mph.

But the verdict on the aircraft was negative. At the time of testing of the 1-180S machines, war had already broken out in Western Europe and the Red Air Force were more exacting in their requirements for combat aircraft. The assembled variant I-180Sh with 1,100mhp M-88 was not test flown after this, although it was almost ready for flight.

Other Soviet designers designed and constructed fighters at this time, but not one model reached production stage. In the Scientific Research Institute of Civil Aviation, the Italian Robert L. Bartini was working. In spring 1930 he delivered to the TsKB the project for a one-seat fast aircraft, STAL-6. After permission, the prototype

was constructed and was ready to fly in autumn 1933.

The STAL-6 was a cantilever low-wing monoplane of composite construction with especially clear lines. In the nose was the American Curtiss V-1570 Conqueror engine of 660/680mhp. The fuselage was a steel-tube frame with plywood casing, the wings were entirely of steel, casing of the front edge and upper surface being a double layer of stainless steel plate, Enersh 6. Between the two layers, surface cooling of the engine was arranged.

The undercarriage was single-track with a retractable wheel under the fuselage and two supporting struts under the wing tips. The cockpit, too, was unusual in that its roofing did not project beyond the contours of the fuselage.

A B Yumashev and P M Stefanovskii tested the STAL-6. Yumashev landed after the first flight in a thick cloud of vapour, and it became apparent that the cooling had to be improved. Also, the view from the cockpit caused considerable difficuties for the pilot. These things apart, performance was remarkably high. In August 1934 the STAL-6 reached a speed of 420kph at low altitude and rate of climb was 21m a second.

Bartini tried in vain to find a market for his design and G K Orjonikidze was first to win support with the building of a military variant STAL-8. This time the fuselage was a steel-plate shell, the engine was an M-100A of 860mhp and two ShKAS machine guns were to be built in. The designer expected a maximum speed of 620kph at 3,000m and the aircraft was almost ready by Autumn 1934. But the Air Force showed no more interest so it remained uncompleted.

The speed expected from STAL-8 was certainly high, but at the same time a Soviet designer con-

ceived a one-seat fighter which was to fly at 1,000kph!

He was A S Moskalev, whom we already know as the creator of Sigma. The superfast fighter bore the name *Strela* (Missile). It was a tailless aeroplane whose wings had a Gothic outline, similar to that of the present supersonic aircraft Concorde. The engine, which has not been described any more fully, was hidden in the wing centre-section and was to power two contra-rotating propellers by remote control. The pilot was to sit assymmetrically near the propeller axle-shaft.

The commission of the armaments industry who were to investigate this design were unfamiliar with the principles of aerodynamics of higher speeds. Only after several pieces of research work by TsAGI experts in the years 1934-1936 was Moskalev allowed to construct a small experimental model to test the qualities of a Gothic wing.

By Spring 1937, in only seventy days, Moskalev designed and constructed in Voronezh the experimental model L. It was a miniature monoplane with only 3m span, 6.15m long and powered by an MV-4 engine of 140mhp. The first flights took place in Voronezh, before the aircraft was brought to the TsAGI airfield and tested by the pilots Rybko, Gusarov and Kudrin.

Flying with such a tiny aircraft with extremely small aspect ratio was an adventure. Even the 20 degrees approach angle on take off and landing, which today is quite normal, was an unexpected surprise at that time. The climbs, turns and other figures demanded full concentration. At speeds under 310kph the unpleasant qualities of a Gothic wing were more in evidence than the favourable qualities which first showed at higher speeds. As these difficulties troubled too many of the test pilots, the design of Strela was dismissed as too fantastic and development was halted in 1937.

But Moskalev was full of new ideas! In 1939, he built another interesting aircraft, SAM-13. This time he had found his inspiration in the Dutch Fokker D-23 fighter. Moskalev's SAM-13 was an all-wood, low-wing monoplane. Two tail booms projected backwards from the wings and in the centre was a fuselage pod. An MV-6 engine of 220mhp fitted in the nose and another in the tail. The pilot sat between the two engines. In contrast to the Fokker D-23 there was a single fin which lay in the slipstream.

In 1940 M L Gallaj was able to test the first SAM-13. The qualities in all phases of flying were especially unpleasant; even horizontal attitude created difficulties. Moreover, an error in design prevented complete retraction of the nose wheel. Therefore Gallaj could only reach 590kph which was, however, fairly good as the expected speed was 600kph.

SAM-13 was further tested, for this machine was regarded as a preliminary to a later fighter. In summer 1941, SAM-13 was to take part in a speed race for light aircraft in the USSR. Unfortunately June 22, 1941, came round and the aircraft was destroyed for reasons of safety.

In this survey of Soviet fighter prototypes we also find a machine developed by the designer of later bombers and ground attackers, S V Ilyushin. It was the small, low-wing monoplane, TsKB-32, which had been constructed in 1936 and taken over by the Air Force as I-21.

The TsKB-32 was built primarily for speed. To reduce resistance there was surface cooling of the engine, an M-34 of 810mhp, and the machine reached a speed of 520kph. But other flying qualities were not so good, especially because of the relatively heavy flying weight of 2,000kg. In spite of this some I-21 were ordered in a small experimental series. Before work could begin, a halt was called because of the great vulnerability of surface cooling under combat conditions.

One-seat fighters were also designed in the TsAGI drawing office. These were projects ANT-32 and ANT-47 which were not carried out.

Only after 1938 did the Soviet designers, in their new groups, manage to create better fighters. Then the machines played a large part in the so-called Great War of the Fatherland of the Soviet People in the years 1941 to 1945.

Left: Italian designer Bartini produced his STAL-6 within TsKB between 1930 and 1933. An unusual feature was the cockpit canopy which did not project beyond the fuselage contours.

A New Generation of Fighters

WE HAVE SEEN that all efforts to produce a new pursuit fighter to replace the I-16 and I-15 to I-153 types by 1938 were in vain. Even the promising I-180 was a disappointment. The I-180 had already been a new generation aircraft with high speed in level flight, good climb rate and manoeuvrability at a relatively higher wing-loading than usual.

During 1939/40 numerous fighters were produced in the USSR with more or less similar characteristics. From such a large number it was then possible to select the best types to form the standard equipment of the fighter squadrons.

At that time aircraft development in the USSR underwent a complete re-organisation. Most of the earlier large groups were disbanded and several young designers or assistants of the famous chief constructors were given the opportunity to set-up their own design bureaux.

Inner political wrangling during 1936 and 1937 brought about a definite but unjustified distrust in the work of the old constructors. This was one reason why assistance was given to the new groups.

In the first days of 1939 a meeting took place in the Kremlin involving all aircraft and engine manufacturers. Leaders of the State and the Party – Stalin, Molotov, Kaganovich and others – instructed the constructors to develop new aircraft for all purposes to modernise the whole of the Red Air Fleet.

Subsequently several smaller meetings were called at short intervals, split into the different categories of military aircraft. In the discussion with Stalin, no less than eleven development groups were given the go-ahead to produce new aircraft types. Not all got past the project stage but many were remarkable, and some provided unique solutions.

One rule was common to all groups. Through lack of Dural, aircraft had to be constructed mostly in wood or composites. This was somewhat of a disadvantage, but it did have one asset. During the first stage of the war almost the complete aircraft industry was evacuated and thanks to this form of construction, work in the new plants could be started in record time.

Characteristics and performance of those aircraft were not far behind all-metal planes. Only one aspect of performance was bad – the range. The wooden spars and ribs needed too much room on the inside, so limited space remained for fuel tanks. Consequently, the single-seat fighters had only one hour endurance, i.e. 600-700km range.

A S Yakovlev made his fighter debut with the I-26, prototype of the Yak-1, in 1940. Modern features included under-fuselage cooling tunnel, retractable undercarriage and variable pitch propellor.

First fighter to arrive for testing, the I-28, was abandoned after two prototypes.

During the first stages of this development, in the years 1939/40, classic front-line single-seat fighters were demanded and built as direct successors to the I-15/I-16 series. In the second stage, covering 1940/41, more finance and time was given to development of other aircraft types – long-range fighters, high-altitude fighters, special constructions etc.

Development of new fighters proceeded on a lavish scale. The circumstances of the following months meant, however, that these were only built as prototypes, and only those of the first stage were put into production.

First design group to produce its aircraft was led by V P Yatsenko. The prototype I-28 was of all-wooden construction with W shape wings and a double row radial M-87A engine of 950mhp. Armament was concentrated under the engine cowling and consisted either of two ShVAK cannon and two ShKAS machine guns or two ShVAK cannon and one UBS machine gun.

The first prototype arrived at the test airfield on April 30, 1939, and made its first flight on June

10, piloted by P M Stefanovsky. The aircraft was light, with 2,660kg take-off weight and attained 545kph at 6,000m. All was going well. On June 10 Stefanovsky tested the critical dive speed and as a result the elevator was torn off. The aircraft went into a wild spin and the pilot was thrown from his cabin. He was saved by his parachute.

The second prototype I-28 entered flight testing in August 1939 and reached 587kph with the 1,000mhp M-87B. The State Commission was not satisfied with the aircraft and did not accept it.

More attention and assistance was given to those fighter types for which V M Klimov built the new 1,050mhp M-105 engine and especially the cannon variant M-105P. These were Soviet developments of the French Hispano-Suiza 12Y, which were produced in the USSR under licence as the M-100. The M-105P had reduction gears and provision for the 20mm ShVAK cannon.

On January 13, 1940, A S Yakovlev's I-26 prototype was ready and test flights began with Y I Pointkovsky at the controls. Three months later, on March 30, 1940, another new prototype was test flown. This was the single-seat I-22 designed by S A Lavochkin, V P Gorbunov and M I Gudkov.

Yakovlev, a young and ambitious designer, was well known in the USSR through his sporting aircraft. With the I-26 and the only slightly older BB-22 high-speed reconnaissance aircraft, he made his debut in the military aircraft field.

The I-26 fighter was a low-wing monoplane of composite construction, with wooden wings and metal fuselage which was covered in Dural sheet over the centre section, and with fabric at the rear. The tail unit was of Dural frame with fabric covering. Many construction details were modern, such as the cooling tunnel under the fuselage, retractable undercarriage, and a three-blade variable pitch air-screw. Armament consisted of one ShVAK and two ShKAS above the engine.

Lavochkin and his colleagues projected the I-22 in their spare time, and only after discussions at the Kremlin was he able to put together his own design group and work independently.

Construction of the I-22 was entirely of wood. Plywood from Siberian birch trees was used, soaked in synthetic resin, heated and then pressed into the required shape. Such plywood was known as Delta-Drevesina. Armament of the I-22 was heavy – one 23mm cannon on the engine and two adjusdtable UBS machine guns. Yet the weight, in contrast to this heavy armament, was surprisingly low at 2,986kg (the I-26 had a weight of 2,895kg).

Performance was also similar. Maximum speed of the I-26 was 600kph, that of the I-22, 605 at 5,000m. During pre-production development both aircraft were provided with 1,180/1,240mhp M-105PF. The upper level for these engines dropped, however, from the usual 4,000m to as low as 2,700m. This meant that the optimum fighting altitude was about 3,000m, which in the war with Germany was the most common.

Both machines were put into production at the end of 1940 but the first aircraft did not reach training schools until the beginning of Summer 1941. Both variants were produced with different armament. The standard configuration always had the ShVAK motor cannon, plus one or two fixed ShKAS machine guns or only one UBS machine gun.

The I-22 was further modified for its production run as I-301. When, at the beginning of 1941, the USSR changed its designation system to incorporate the names of the chief designers, I-26 became Yak-1, and I-301 became LaGG-3. Retroactively, I-22 became LaGG-1. From then, uneven numbers were used for fighters and even numbers for all other categories.

The outsider compared with the two successful types I-22 and I-26 remained the single-seat I-21 of M M Paschinin. Designation I-21 became available after the TsKB-32 was rejected in 1937, and was once again given to Paschinin in 1940. The I-21, with its M-105P engine, was slower than its rivals (537kph at 5,000m), was not armour plated and its symetrical wing profile resulted in unpleasant flight characteristics. In general shape, I-21 was similar to I-26, but lower.

At that time, Polikarpov continued development of his unlucky I-180 series under the designation I-185. The prototypes were built concurrently in Spring 1941.

First was the I-185R(02), which used several components from the I-180. This prototype, though, was not completed, since Polikarpov could not obtain the promised M-90 engine from A D Shvezov. This engine was a twin-radial of 1,500mhp, but its development was fraught with difficulties which were never completely overcome. The test programme was continually postponed, and the R(02) was finally scrapped in April 1940. Polikarpov wanted to use a particularly narrow NACA cowling with air cooling. Armament of the R(02) was to consist of two adjustable UBS and two ShKAS machine guns, as well as two 250kg bombs. Maximum speed was expected to be 715kph at 7,300m.

Alas, Polikarpov had no luck either with the second prototype, I-185RM(03). The machine made its maiden flight on March 10, 1940, and it had similar lines to the R(02) and the same proposed armament. Power plant was a prototype of the M-81 from Shvezov. It produced 1,200mhp, but after bad teething troubles had to be reconstructed. The new configuration became later well-known as the M-82. As a result of the use of M-81, test flights with RM(03) had to be interrupted and the aircraft only attained a speed of 500kph.

The new 1,330mhp M-82 did not become available until Spring 1941. Polikarpov used it for his prototypes I-185-I and I-185-ID. Both reached 625kph at 6,550m and carried three ShVAK cannon with 500 rounds each, and could also accommodate under the wings four 100kg bombs or eight RS-82 rockets. Test flights with these fighters proved better but did not end in success as too many modifications were still required to the engines.

Events of June 1941 interrupted development of the I-185 for a long time.

Types mentioned up to now were pure frontline fighters with an optimum fighting altitude of 3,000-6,000m. In a further stage, high-altitude

LaGG-3 was projected by S A Lavochkin and his colleagues in their spare time as I-22. Construction was entirely of wood, making substantial use of Siberian birch ply which was pressed into shape.

fighters were developed, and these were intended as interceptors against enemy bomber groups.

The development group of A I Mikoyan and M I Gurevitch was instructed in December 1939 to construct a single-engine, single-seat interceptor. First prototype of the I-200 was designed and built in a record time of four months. On April 5, 1940, test pilot A N Yekatov took the aircraft into the air for the first time. By April 24, Yekatov had already reached 648.5 kph at 6,900m, and shortly afterwards 651 kph at 7,000m. These speeds represented top performance for battle aircraft of the time.

One pre-qualification for such performance was the high-altitude engine AM-35A of A A Mikulin, a 12-cylinder engine in V-shape which could produce 1,200mhp up to 7,200m. This engine was relatively heavy which gave the aircraft an empty weight of 2,620kg. Armament had to be sacrificed and it was thought that for intercepting duties a UBS and two ShKAS machine guns would be sufficient.

The I-200 was of composite construction. The front fuselage up to the end of the cabin consisted of a steel frame with fabric covering, while the rear was of wood; central wing section was of Duralumin, the outer sections of wood.

Flight characteristics were favourable and the aircraft was put into production in August 1940. Progress, however, was slow and the first production aircraft never attained the performance of the prototypes. Nevertheless maximum speed of 628khp at 7,000m remained quite good, as did its service ceiling of 12,000m. In Spring 1941, I-200 was re-designated as the MiG-1. Only 100 were built.

Mikoyan and Gurevich had to improve the construction in winter 1940/41. Especially, the complex technology had to be simplified, the airframe had to be strengthened to give a longer service life and many details of internal fittings had to be improved. These modifications resulted in the MiG-3. Its take-off weight at 3,350kg was heavier as against 3,070kg of MiG-1, but it was more robust and had a range almost double that of its predecessor – 1,250km as against 730km.

Two versions of Polikarpov's I-185 – fitted with an M-71 engine (far left) and featuring a modified fuselage (left).

Handling of the aircraft was more difficult, however, and servicing before and after a flight took much longer.

The fighters of Mikoyan and Gurevich had an optimum fighting altitude of between 7,000 and 8,000m. Designer P O Sukhoi wanted to go one better and built a single-seat fighter for aerial battles at 10,000m and above. In Autumn 1939 he designed a single-seat fighter, the I-330, with an M-105P engine and two TK-2 turbo-chargers. Test flying began in summer 1940.

The I-330 was a low-wing aeroplane with a plywood fuselage shell, wing and tail-plane of Dural, and with a rearward retractable undercarriage. By the first flights, I-330 already attained 500kph close to the ground and 641kph at 10,000m. Alas, these performances were rare, as the turbochargers proved very unreliable. Since the aircraft showed promise, testing continued with and without turbo-charging until Summer 1941. During evacuation eastwards, the aircraft was destroyed. At that time it had designation SU-1. Armament consisted of a single ShVAK cannon and two ShKAS machine guns. Range was 720km.

A high-performance aircraft among the high-altitude fighters of the time was expected from the twin-engine, two-seat VI-100, designed by V M Petlyakov. VI meant *Vysotny Istrebitel* = high-altitude fighter. Petlyakov projected this aircraft in 1938 for two M-105P engines with TK-3 turbo-chargers and a pressurised cabin, divided for the pilot and the MG-operator. Both crew could get into the cabin through trapdoors under the seats, which could also be used for an emergency exit. Armament consisted of four ShVAK cannon and a moveable, remotely-controlled ShKAS machine gun.

Construction began in 1939 at which time the aircraft represented the ultimate in fighters, as machines with pressurised cabins were not being built anywhere else. By Autumn 1939 the VI-100 was almost ready for its first flight. Unfortunately, the Red Air Fleet had no immediate use for such complicated fighter aircraft.

Petlyakov was instructed to make the airframe suitable for a high-altitude bomber. The hybrid made its first flight on December 22, 1939, no longer a fighter but not yet a bomber. Through further development emerged the horizontal and dive-bomber Pe-2.

These types returned in a fighter role for a short time. At the beginning of Summer 1941, Petlyakov converted some Pe-2 into heavy interceptors. They had no dive-brakes, but received two fixed ShVAK and two UBK machine guns in the bomb housing.

During aerial battles over Moscow, several Pe-3 and the improved Pe-3bis had proved successful. Their maximum speed was 540kph at 5,000m.

At that time, war in Western Europe was already well advanced and commanders-in-chief of the Red Air Fleet were in a position to study experiences of the first few months and consequently adjust their plans for the future.

Much was written and spoken about the German destroyer, the Messerschmitt Bf 110, whose

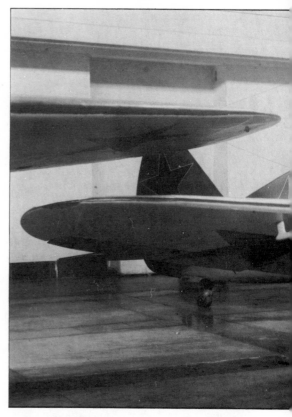

battle strength was even more exaggerated by German propaganda. One fact was clear nonetheless – the use of day-bombers without escort protection over enemy territory was not possible. Thus the Air Force demanded from constructors, long-range escort fighters.

Such orders were given to the design groups of Polikarpov and Mikoyan and Gurevich. Alas it was too late. The prototypes were ready by June 1941 and test flown, but could not be completed until 1942/43 when conditions were much less favourable. For the new escort fighters, it was intended to use A A Mikulin's new engine, the 12-cylinder AM-37 of 1,300/1,400mhp.

Polikarpov's aircraft was named TIS(A) which meant *Tyazhelyi Istrebitel Soprovozhdeniya* or heavy escort fighter. It was ready for its first flight before June 1941 and even made a few test flights. Performance was remarkable, maximum speed near the ground was 522kph and it reached 652kph at 7,400m. The prototype only had four fixed ShKAS machine guns with 2,000 rounds of ammunition each, and one machine gun for defence at the rear, while the production series were intended to have two fixed ShVAK and one ShK-37mm cannon. Such armament was fixed to the prototype in 1943 when it was tested again.

At the new works of Polikarpov, the second prototype TIS(MA) was built in 1943/44. The shape remained the same, featuring slim fuselage with short two-seat cabin, twin ailerons and retractable undercarriage, though the better AM-39 engine of 1,900mhp was installed and armament

Improved version of Mikoyan and Gurevich's MiG-1 was the more robust MiG-3. It suffered handling and servicing problems.

Polikarpov's heavy escort fighter, the twin-engined TIS(A), made a few test flights in 1941, achieving a maximum speed of 652kph at 7,400m. It was not tested again until 1943.

numbered two ShK cannon and two UBK machine guns. The prototype was flown in late 1943.

The interest of the Air Force in longer range fighters did not last long. The war and production possibilities changed much and influenced the fate of the second escort fighter, the DIS of Mikoyan and Gurevich. In contrast to the two-seat all-metal low-wing monoplane of Polikarpov, the DIS *(Dvukhmotornyi Istrebitel Soprovozhdeniya* = twin engined escort fighter) was a single-seat monoplane with W-wing shape, made completely from wood. Two ShK cannon were built into the short front fuselage and, and six ShVAK machine guns into the central wing section. The machine could also take bombs, torpedos or cannon, making it a universal fighting aircraft.

It was considered a serious contender and allocated the production designation MiG-5. The first DIS aircraft was test flown shortly before the outbreak of war. It gave a maximum speed of 610kph and its range was 2,300km, longer than that of the TIS(A)'s 1,000-1,700km. Unfortunately there was no opportunity to put this performance into practice. The develoment group was evacuated and the first DIS prototype was destroyed.

Not until 1942 were Mikoyan and Gurevich in a position to recommence work on the DIS. The ASh-82F engine of 1,550/1,700mhp, was now available which had better performance and serviceability than the AM-37. The new DIS used these twin-row radial engines, had a new-shape fuselage and armament of two VYa-23mm cannons, two UBK and four ShKAS machine guns. It attained 600kph at 5,000m which was reached in 6.3mins, and had a range of 2,500km.

All these were good results. At that time though, production capacity was full and the Defence Committee did not want to introduce new types. A few months later, the lack of escort fighters to protect long-range aircraft was recognised, but by then it was already too late for the DIS.

Endeavours to introduce a long-range fighter thus remained without success. Development of new fighters just before the outbreak of World War II produced some remarkable designs which had no counterpart in any other part of the world and demonstrated the inventiveness of Soviet aircraft constructors. The reason why such aircraft were developed lay in the fact that in the 1930s Soviet fighters were split into two groups – fast aircraft and manoeuvrable aircraft.

The impossibility of combining both characteristics in a classic design led to thoughts of producing a variable machine which could, at will, be changed from a manoeuvrable aircraft to a fast fighter. Modifications consisted basically of increasing or decreasing the wing area, and thus the wing loading, climb rate and manoeuvrability.

In the West similar aircraft were also built, but these were purely experimental and had no use in practical service. In the USSR variable aircraft were built for service.

In 1939, two constructors, V V Nikitin and V V Shevchenko, leaders of development bureau OBK-30, submitted a design. The aircraft was to be a high-wing monoplane with a retractable undercarriage for high speed flight. At take-off, landing and manoeuvers, a second wing would be extended to make the aircraft effectively a biplane. The Air Force was interested in such a novelty and allowed the two designers to build and test the aircraft under designation I-220. The designers themselves used the type designation IS-1 *(Istrebitel Skladnoi* = folding fighting).

Test flights began in May 1940. The aircraft stood at the airfield as a cantilever sesquiplane with an all-metal frame, partly clad with steel sheet, partly fabric-covered. Engine was a 900mhp M-63. Hollows in the side of the fuselage and underside of the upper wing allowed the lower wing to be lifted hydraulically after take-off and folded into the bays. Wing area was thereby reduced from 20.8sq.m to 13sq.m, together with all associated changes in characteristics. The aircraft had four fixed (but adjustable) ShKAS machine guns with 1,000 rounds of ammunition each.

It was found that the hydraulics worked well, and change-over of the wings in flight presented no serious difficulties. Characteristics, however, with both wing positions, showed little improvement. Maximum speed as a high-wing plane was 453kph at 4,900m and climb rate 8.5 mins. to 5000m, which was low. The IS-1 was viewed as an experimental aircraft and test flying continued throughout 1940 and until spring 1941.

The second prototype, IS-2 or I-220bis, was prepared in April 1941. It was a mighty aircraft with robust, yet clean lines, already a full scale

An interesting concept from designers Nikitin and Shevchenko was the 'folding fighter' which had a retractable lower wing. Above is the IS-1 (I-220) and, below, their second prototype, IS-2 (I-220bis), showing the upper wing bays which accommodated part of the lower wing. Conversion from biplane to monoplane was hydraulically operated.

Stalin gave his personal go-ahead to this variable geometry fighter project from Leningrad designer G I Bakshayev. Known as the RK-800 or RK-1, it featured two pairs of slim wings which could be covered by a broad wing telescopically extended from the fuselage sides. Completed by Autumn 1940, RK-800 never flew because the M-106 engine designated by Stalin was not available before the outbreak of war.

fighter with a modern M-87A engine of 950mhp. In view of the happenings of June 1941, the IS-2 was never flight-tested nor was the IS-1 further developed.

At around the same period, another variable-geometry aircraft was being developed, but along different lines. Designer was G I Bakshayev of the Leningrad Civil Aviation Institute, who had been working on a variable wing solution since 1937. That year he built an experimental monoplane under designation LIG-7. The purpose-designation was 'RK' (*Razdvizhnoye Krylo* = pull-out wing).

The LIG-7 was a two-seat, low-wing cantilever monoplane with a slim wing. From the fuselage sides an outer wing could be pulled out over the fixed wing. The new wing was broad, increasing wing area from 16.6sq.m to 23.4sq.m, and was constructed in 'strips', which could be telescopically extended or retracted.

With an experimental aircraft such as LIG-7 with a 100mhp, M-11 engine and a speed of 150kph, the characteristic changes were not easily recognised. It was really a case of testing the system and establishing that the change-over worked faultlessly during flight.

Results from LIG-7 led Bakshayev to the developement of a single-seat fighter with a big difference between maximum and minimum speed. Bakshayev's project was known as the RK-800 or RK-I. The fuselage was long with the engine situated in the nose and cooling behind the cabin.

It had two slim pairs of wings in tandem form on each side. The front wing was smooth with no ailerons or flaps, which were contained in the rear wing. Combined wing area was 11.9sq.m. On the fuselage the broad wing could be telescopically extended, which filled the area between the fixed wings and increased area to 28sq.m. Bakshayev expected a maximum speed of 720kph at 2,000m and intended to build-in two ShVAK cannon and two ShKAS machine guns.

Construction of such an interesting fighter received the personal go-ahead in early 1939 from Stalin, who was enthusiastic about the expected performance. In his enthusiasm he wanted to help the designer and decreed that the aircraft should receive the latest and mightiest powerplant of that time, the 1,600/1,800mhp Klimov M-106.

Bakshayev hastened work on RK-I which in autumn 1940 was ready to receive its engine. Sadly the same could not be said about the engine. Klimov had great difficulties in realising his project, and the M-106 was not ready by the outbreak of war in June 1941. The M-105 could have been used as a make-shift to test characteristics, but since Stalin had personally decided on the M-106 none had the courage to alter his instructions. The aircraft was rather left without an engine.

This episode illustrates very well the internal politics in the aircraft industry, and a promising and original design bit the dust.

This, then, reviews development of fighter air-craft in the months between the Munich agreement in 1938 and June 1941. Of the many prototypes and variants of that period only three of the technologically simpler aircraft were put into production: the Yak-1, LaGG-3 and MiG-3. In spite of this, production got going very slowly. In the year 1940 only 20 MiG-3 and 64 Yak-1 were built, and in the first half of 1941, 1,946 machines of the three types left assembly plants.

This production capacity was not enough to have these aircraft in service by summer 1941. Only 22% of fighters of the border protection squadrons were modern, and not all of these were ready to be put into action. New fighters needed better airfields, and those were still under construction. New fighters also needed re-trained pilots as characteristics were in most cases very different.

In May 1941, only 32% of pilots intended for the LaGG-3 had been schooled, and although figures for the MiG-3 at 80% was better, conversion for the Yak-1 had not even started.

The Soviet electronics industry was not able to provide all fighters with radio transmitters – only the squadron leaders were allowed such luxuries. Other pilots had to use coloured flares to communicate during manoeuvers, an antiquated technique. Fighters made up 56% of the full strength of the Red Air Fleet in summer 1941, but despite large numbers, the fighter forces were not effective nor ready for battle, when the German attack came.

CHAPTER 8

Interceptor Fighters

FIGHTER SQUADRONS for western border protection suffered particularly badly from the first wave of the German attack at dawn on June 22, 1941. Concentrated at a few airports, unprotected either by camouflage or a reliable information network, only a few aircraft managed to take off against the 4,000-strong German attack. Sixty-six airfields were attacked, especially those where German reconnaissance had detected new fighter aircraft. Of 1,200 Soviet machines destroyed that morning (including 800 on the ground) most were fighters.

This was a tragic setback for the Red Air Fleet. Although the Soviet fighter pilots tried everything and shot down 807 German aircraft between June 22 and July 5, they had no chance against the huge superiority of the Luftwaffe. But in spite of this, they won the decisive battle of 1941, that over Moscow.

The Defence Committee seconded all fighter aircraft from other parts of the country to defend the capital. The first sizeable attack took place on July 22, 1941. A 250-strong force of bombers and fighters approached the capital but were repelled. With the capture of advance airfields the German attacks became more frequent. Between July 22 and October 1, 4,212 German aircraft had carried out 36 attacks on Moscow.

The build-up of a strong fighter force became one of the priorities of the Defence Committee which met on June 30, 1941, under the chairmanship of Stalin. It was decided to evacuate all weapons and other industries further from the front line.

One aircraft manufacturing plant delivered the first MiG-3s ten days after transfer to the Volga area. By the end of December, 30 Migs had been produced. Output increased in the second half of 1941. In the first six months, 322 LaGG-3 and 335

Yak-1 were delivered compared to 2,141 LaGG-3 and 1,019 Yak-1 in the second half. In spite of large-scale evacuation, development of new aircraft continued unabated and in 1942 the Red Air Fleet took delivery of new models.

The development bureau of A S Yakovlev had a busy winter of 1941/42. In September the works were moved from Moscow to Kamensk in the Urals and three weeks later the first Yak-1 was completed. The monthly production of the Moscow works was exceeded after three months. Production of Yak-1s in other parts, particularly Siberia, was a lot slower which resulted in reduced delivery to the Front. As a stop-gap it was decided to convert the two-seater Yak-7V into a single-seat fighter. The Yak-7V was a trainer variant of the Yak-1, which earlier had the designation UTI-26. It had a VK-105PF engine and a fixed machine gun for practice shooting.

Conversion of the Yak-7V was complete by the winter, including full armament, i.e. one ShVAK cannon and two ShKAS machine guns, similar to the 1941 armament of Yak-1. The second seat was covered in metal sheeting and the relief-fighter was ready. Performances of Yak-1 and Yak-7A (as this

Three weeks after transfer of production from Moscow to Kamensk the first Yak-1 was ready. Yak-1s (top) became faster and more manoeuvrable, evolving into the Yak-1M (above) of which 8,721 were constructed.

Left: A line-up of Yak-7 fighters, heavier and more robust than the Yak-1 range. Many variants followed and production of all types totalled 6,399.

The Yak-7B was a faster variant featuring various design changes including a smaller wing area and new bubble canopy.

Above: A formation of Yak-9 which made their first appearance during fierce aerial battles around Leningrad.

Below: Prepared for use against tanks, the Yak-9K was armed with a 45mm cannon and entered service during 1944.

variant was designated) were identical.

Development of the lighter Yak-1 leaned towards faster and more manoeuvrable interceptor types, while the more robust Yak-7A was developed into heavier front-line and long-range fighters.

In 1942 the Yak-1 evolved into the Yak-1M with smaller wing area (14.9sq.m as against 17.2sq.m) with a new and lower rear fuselage. It also had the bubble cabin roof which became characteristic of all subsequent Yakovlev fighters. The Yak-1M was 12kph faster at 600kph and some 8,721 were constructed. Similar modifications to the Yak-7 led to the Yak-7B which now had a maximum speed of 610kph and a range 830km. The total production of all Yak-7 variants was 6,399.

Further development of the Yak-7 was dependent on the Soviet manufacturing industry producing new materials. In the summer of 1942, new alloys became available as well as the first Duralumin from aluminium works in the Urals. This enabled Yakovlev to replace the wooden wing spars, resulting in a lighter wing section and more room for fuel tanks. First model to have the new wing was the Yak-7DI. It was a long-range fighter *(Dalnyi Istrebitel)*, though the long-range was not to be taken too seriously since 900km was considered a success, being 80km more than that of the Yak-7B. Fuel capacity was increased from 415 to 450 litres and payload was 147kg up, though take-off weight was only 50kg higher. Armament consisted of a ShVAK cannon and UBS machine gun.

Between November 1942 and the beginning of February 1943 one of the biggest aerial battles took place around Stalingrad and it was during that period that the Red Air Fleet regained the initiative. Even then the Russians were numerically outnumbered with 1,115 aircraft against Germany's 1,216.

The battle of Stalingrad saw introduction of the Yak-9, a Yak-7DI with two ShKAS machine guns instead of the single UBS. The new fighter was 10-30kph faster at 4,000m than the Messerschmitt Bf-109G in level flight, though the Bf-109G became 40-60kph faster over 6,000m. The Yak-9 also had better climbing characteristics, reaching 5,000m in 4 minutes 54 seconds as against 5 minutes 18 seconds. Wing loading of the German aircraft was 33kg/sq.m. higher than the Yak-9 at only 167kg/sq.m.

The Yak-9 proved to be a versatile aircraft. In winter 1942/43 the Defence Committee asked Yakovlev to produce an anti-tank version with an 11-P-37 37mm cannon. Since not enough Ilyushin 11-2 low level strike aircraft were available, it was intended to use the robust Yak-9 for that purpose, the Yak-9T being put into series production from May 1943. The 11-P-37 was fixed as a motor cannon and had 32 shells. Since the weapon was very long, the cabin had to be moved 0.4m back. Later MPSh-20 or MP-23-VV were used, or a single UBS machine gun. In 1944, the 45mm OKB-16-45 anti-tank cannon were used, making it the Yak-9K (*Krupno-Kalibernyi* = heavy calibre). ShVAK cannon and two UBS machine guns. There was also a bomber-variant, the Yak-9B, which had a housing to the rear of the cabin for 400kg of bombs.

In the years 1942/43, bomber squadrons often had to advance into enemy territory without fighter protection, due mainly to the lack of a really long-range fighter. Yakovlev was therefore instructed to produce a long-distance fighter which he accomplished with the Yak-9D that before 1943 had achieved a range of 1,400km, similar to that of the Pe-2 bomber. The changes involved a lighter construction with fuel capacity increased from 450 to 640 litres. The Yak-9D had one cannon and one MG and its take-off weight was only 40kg higher than the normal front-line fighter.

In the Yak-9 the Red Air Fleet had a very versatile fighter and its strong construction enabled even heavily damaged aircraft to return home. Total production of all Yak-9 variants reached a record figure of 16,769 aircraft.

Apart from Yakovlev, one of the most important constructors of Soviet fighters was S A Lavochkin. Series production of the LaGG-3 was moved from Taganrog on the Black Sea to Tbilisi where he continued development of the fighter, which was by no means faultless. In the summer of 1942 he produced a so called lighter LaGG-3, reducing take-off weight from 3,150 to 2,865kg. The aircraft reached a speed of 564kph at 3,900m with a 1,180mph VK-105PF engine. Armament consisted of an MP-20 cannon and a UBS machine gun.

The Red Air Fleet, however, showed less and less interest in the LaGG-3 and it did not go into production. Lavochkin tried radical improvements in 1944 by producing the LaGG-3 Dubler with a VK-105PF-2 engine of 1,240mhp, VYa 23mm cannon and a UBS machine gun, which reached 618kph at 3,400m. The Dubler did not survive but Lavochkin cornered the market with radial engines.

Although he wanted to use the 1,700mhp VK-107, it never materialised. Production run of the LaGG-3 came to an end in 1942 after 6,528 had been built. Performance wise they were inferior to German fighters.

Airframe of the LaGG-3 was technologically sound, but it needed a lighter and more powerful engine. Such an engine would have been the double row radial 14-cylinder M-82, later known as ASh-82. LaGG-3 received the new engine in summer 1941 and performance increase was considerable – from 1,240mhp of the VK-105P to 1,330mhp of the ASh-82. This modification produced more horse power but the advantage was lost through greater frontal area. The LaGG-5 with the ASh-82 reached 554kph at 6,500m. A new variant, the LaG-5, was put into series production in 1942.

One 'G' was removed from the designation as M I Gudkov relinquished his position in the development group in summer 1941 and started on his own. In 1942, V P Gorbunov also left and from that time all aircraft were designated 'La'. The LaG-5 then became the La-5.

Before production started in July 1942, several modifications were made to the engine. A D Schvezov improved the ASh-82 into the ASh-82A with 1,510mhp which boosted speed to 603kph at 6,500m and the operating ceiling to 9,600m. Range was 655km.

Soon after production began yet another change was made to the power plant in the form of a new ASh-82F with 1,700mhp output, giving a speed of 613kph at 6,000m. These aircraft were designated La-5F and by the end of 1942, 1,129 had been built.

The arrival of La-5F at the front increased fighter strength. At around 6,000m it was slightly better than the Bf-109G-2, though its climb rate was slower.

Alas, the quality output from different factories was variable and in some cases very bad, which generally meant a lower battle performance of squadrons equipped with the La-5F. Only in March 1943 was it possible for the Commissioner of the aircraft industry, A I Shakhurin, to inform the Defence Committee that the quality of all La-machines was now the same.

Lavochkin also produced another variant with ASh-82FN engines of 1,525/1,850mhp and metal spars instead of wooden ones. Known as the La-5FN, the aircraft achieved 648kph at 6,400m and could reach 5,000m in 4.7 mins. This meant that the La-5FN was not only better than the Yak-9 but beat the enemy's best aircraft at that time, the Bf-109G-2 and Fw-190A-4.

The Fw-190A-4 got to 5,000m in 6.8 mins and its speed was 604kph at 6,000m. The La-5FN was superior in all aspects except for its armament. Range was in accordance with Soviet strategy for front-line fighters and was no more than 765km.

La-5FNs also saw service with the Czech fighter squadron of the 1st mixed Czech Fighter Regiment in the USSR. In 1944 two squadrons operated from an airfield near Zolna, in Slovakia behind German lines, to assist the Slovak uprising. After the war the La-5FN served with the Czech AF as S-95.

Production of the La-5FN, together with older variants, received full state assistance and 10,000 were built, being second only in numbers to the Yak-9 fighter.

The MiG-3 of Mikoyan/Gurevich's development group saw only limited front-line service. The Red Air Fleet considered these only for the protection of its cities. Out of necessity, the MiG-3 was sent to the front-line where it showed better performance than the German aircraft of early 1942 at heights of 5,000m, though its armament was weak. But at the usual altitude of air battles (i.e. below 4,000m) the MiG-3 was much inferior. Armament was improved in the field by attaching two gondolas under the wings which housed two fixed UBX-MG. This increased fire power, but reduced speed and range.

The Defence Committee viewed the MiG-3 as a hopeless case and stopped production of AM-35A engines in December 1941 in favour of the AM-38 for Ilyushin's Il-2. Production of the MiG-3 continued until spring 1942 when all AM-35As were used up and total aircraft stood at 3,222.

Mikoyan and Gurevich tried to save the MiG-3 somehow and installed the 1,330mhp M-82 engine in the winter of 1942/43. Thus originated the prototype I-211 (Ye) with two ShVAK cannon, being a mirror image of the LaG-5. During test flying the aircraft reached a maximum speed of 565kph at 6,150m with a service ceiling of 8,700m. The 1,550/1,700mhp ASh-82F engine was used later, which produced 670kph at 5,000m, reached in 4 mins. These were remarkable performances and it was decided to put the aircraft into series production as the MiG-9, though this idea was dropped at the last minute.

Mikoyan and Gurevich continued to concentrate on development of high-altitude fighters. In spring 1942 they built the prototype I-230(D), still with the AM-35A but with greatly improved aerodynamics and armament which consisted of two ShVAK and two ShKAS. The end of 1942 saw the I-220(A) which launched a whole family of high-altitude fighters. In spring 1943 the I-220(A) reached 700kph at 7,000m with the 1,700mhp AM-39 engine. Armament was four ShVAK cannon. The military series designation MiG-11 was allocated for this aircraft but never used.

High-altitude fighters were also fully developed in the bureau of P O Sukhoi. Prototype I-330 (or Su-1) was destroyed in Moscow prior to evacuation of the design bureau, but unfinished parts of the new fighter I-360 (or Su-3) were taken by train to Novosibirsk. The I-360 was derived from the I-330 but was somewhat smaller, with a reduction of the wing area from 19sq.m. to 17sq.m. The VK-195PF received the improved turbocharger TK-2, but new difficulties ensued. With the use of the TK-2, Su-3 reached 638kph at

Mikoyan and Gurevich's first attempts to save the MiG-3 resulted in I-211 (Ye), equipped with 1,330mhp M-82 engine which gave 565kph at 6,150m.

Featuring greatly improved aerodynamics, I-230(D) was offered by Mikoyan/Gurevich in the spring of 1942 in their quest for a successful high altitude fighter.

1-220(A) was the forerunner of a whole range of fighters capable of combat at altitude, achieving 700kph at 7,000m armed with four cannon.

10,000m but service ceiling of 11,900m was lower than Su-1 (12,500m). Turbocharging presented too many complications at that time and further development of the Su-3 was abandoned.

Despite general difficulties during the war years, and the evacuation, N N Polikarpov also continued to develop his I-185 range of fighters. In Autumn 1941, just before the evacuation, Polikarpov received a few examples of the new double-row radial engine ASh-71 from Shvetsov which he wanted to use in his new variants of the I-185. The 18-cylinder engine produced 1,700mhp and had 'stretchability' to over 2,000mhp, but there were teething troubles.

Not until early 1942 was Polikarpov able to begin testing I-185(R4) at his new works. The aircraft performed well, reaching 680kph at 6,100m with two UBS, two ShKAS machine guns and eight RS-82 rockets, but was let down by the engine.

In autumn 1942 a few airframes of the I-185 series of prototypes were ready but waiting for the delivery of new engines from Shvetsov. When the engine finally arrived, they were quickly installed, resulting in the I-185(R5). At the same time Polikarpov spent some time in Moscow where the Defence Industry agreed to provide more backing. It was considered that the airframe was of excellent construction and suitable for series production.

The new I-185(R5) with three ShVAK cannon made its maiden flight on November 20, 1942, with P M Stefanovsky at the controls. The test flight showed up deficiencies of the engine which often stalled without warning. This happened to one of the best test pilots, V A Stephanchenok, at low level over Moscow's Central Airport which cost him his life.

The I-185(R5) reached a speed of 685kph at 6,100m and its range was 1,130km. In these respects the aircraft was far superior to the 'La' or 'Yak' series. It was for this reason that work on the I-185 was continued. In winter 1942/43 it was tested on the front-line but returned with little success. It was unsuitable in difficult terrain and could not match its German counterparts at low altitudes. Thus ended its long and, in terms of human lives costly, development.

In 1942 Polikarpov prepared a new fighter with new concepts and heavier armament, October and November seeing the ITP(M-1) single-seat fighter debut. Designation ITP meant *Istrebitel Tyazhelyi Pushechnyi*, or heavy cannon-fighter, most appropriate as armament consisted of an engine mounted ShK 37mm cannon and two adjustable but fixed ShVAK cannon. Engine was the VK-107P of 1,300mhp

In addition, four 100kg bombs or eight RS-82 rockets could be fixed under the wings. With a take-off weight of 3,570kg, the aircraft was one of the heaviest single-seat fighters of its time. Speed was 645kph 8,700m and range 1,280km. Even though nothing adverse was said by the airworthiness authorities, the aircraft remained in prototype form.

It was one of the peculiarities of Soviet aircraft development that while work continued on a large scale, new types were generally only accepted from constructors who already had aircraft in series production. The question of fast production in large quantities was of paramount importance.

At the beginning of 1943 Polikarpov managed to alter the ITP fighter to take a new engine, the AM-39 of 1,700mhp. The prototype ITP(M-2) exhibited especially clean lines and good composite construction technology. Performance figures are not availale, though it is believed to have been better than the M-1. At that time, though, Polikarpov's types were no longer considered for series production.

Apart from those of larger development groups, numerous other fighters were designed and constructed. M I Gudkov, who resigned from Lavochkin's design bureau in summer of 1941 to set up his own development group took as a basis for development, the LaGG-3. So, in August 1941, he built three prototypes of his K-37 fighter. It was a slightly modified LaGG-3 with an ShK 37mm cannon in the propeller axis. The engine was the same (VK-105P) but test flying could not start as Gudkov's works were evacuated in September.

At the end of August 1941, shortly before evacuation, another prototype fighter was ready with a second nearing completion. This was the Gu-82 which used the LaGG-3 airframe with an M-82 engine, but Gudkov did not have the opportunity to test them. The Gu-82 was packed-up and by the time a suitable site for the new works was found it was already too late as series production of the La-5 was in full swing at Tbilisi.

In his new plant Gudkov first projected use of an AM-37 engine in the LaGG-3 airframe and then concentrated on the prototype Gu-1, which he already had on the drawing board in 1940. The Gu-1 was in many ways similar to the American Bell P-39 Airacobra. It had an AM-41 engine at the centre of gravity behind the pilot seat, and the airscrew was driven through a long shaft. A 37mm Taubin cannon was mounted to fire

Prototype I-330 (Su-1) was destroyed in Moscow prior to evacuation.

Unfinished parts of I-360 (Su-3) escaped from Moscow but the completed aircraft proved inferior to Su-1 and was abandoned after additional turbocharging difficulties.

Below: Polikarpov's ITP(M-2) featured the new 1,700mhp AM-39 engine.

Bottom: Heavy cannon fighter ITP(M-1) remained in prototype form.

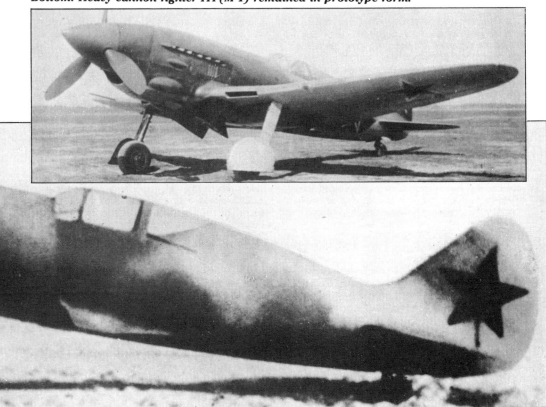

Tomashevich's I-110 fighter displayed a commendable number of features which made on-the-spot maintenance easier for ground crews. Unfortunately, they also gave the aircraft an unacceptably high empty weight.

through the airscrew boss.

Development of the Gu-1 proceeded slowly and it did not make a debut until July 12, 1943. The first flight was also the last as the aircraft was completely destroyed along with Gudkov's hopes of entry into aircraft manufacture.

Another machine was tested at the same time. D L Tomashevich, luckless design leader of the I-180, was now heading a group of internee constructors. In the autumn of 1942, a new fighter was prepared for test flying by this group, the I-110. It was a mighty, low-wing aircraft of composite construction with a VK-107 engine by Klimov which produced 1,700mhp at take-off. The aircraft had a ShVAK cannon and two UBS machine guns, was strongly armoured and could carry up to 500kg of bombs.

Its empty weight was relatively high at 3,285kg and take-off weight even higher at 3,980kg. P M Stefanovsky tested the machine and was satisfied with its characteristics. Performance was not very good – 610kph maximum speed at 6,250m and 5,000m was only attained in 7 mins. Tomashevich had exaggerated its easy, on-the-spot maintainability and had built in too many inspection panels and even an easily replaceable engine. All this resulted in an unacceptably high empty weight.

In Soviet books about aircraft development only the well-known and successful types are ever mentioned. Other, less successful types, are not talked about. These books, therefore, never give a complete picture of the endeavours of Soviet designers, even though development was carried out with all resources despite the prevailing industrial difficulties.

In the summer of 1943 the ratio of battle strength between Russia and Germany and its allies rapidly changed – at least over Soviet territory. In the summer 3,500 aircraft (2,000 German plus 1,500 allies) were pitched against 4,100 Soviet aircraft. This numerical superiority was not reflected in terms of absolute battle power, since the Soviets still used a great number of outdated designs such as 500 R-5 and U-2 biplanes. The fighter squadrons, however, were equipped with modern aircraft.

Between November 1942 and July 1943 the number of Soviet aircraft doubled and for the first time reserves and training units received more modern planes. Fighter command was strengthened from two squadrons to three and each flight consisted of two pairs of aircraft where before only three aircraft were used.

In Spring 1943 the American Bell P-39 Airacobra began operating from Soviet airfields. Over the whole period of the war, 4,924 aircraft were delivered to the USSR, of which 4,578 managed to reach their destination. Soviet fighter pilots were pleased with the P-39 as it was much like the Soviet front-fighters and had an optimum fighting altitude of under 5,000m. As early as 1942, 195 ageing Curtiss 81A-2 Tomahawk IIs were sent from Great Britain, which was part of an earlier US delivery to the RAF. In the USSR this aircraft was not considered as 'fighting-fit' and a better opinion was held over the P-40 series.

The first deliveries in winter 1942/43 were 100 Curtiss P-40F Warhawks from Great Britain (Kittyhawk II) and these were followed by P-40F direct from America as part of the lend/lease agreement. A total of 2,097 Curtiss aircraft were delivered, most of which were P-40N. In comparison to the Soviet aircraft, the P-40 was too delicate and not up to operations in difficult terrain. In battle the aircraft proved too sensitive.

From Britain the Soviets received in 1941/42, 143 Supermarine Spitfire II and VBs but mostly 2,952 Hawker Hurricane II and the Canadian Hurricane X. To complete the Anglo-American deliveries mention must be made of 2,421 Bell P-63 Kingcobras which, in the final phase of the war, were delivered direct to Siberia from Alaska.

The 12,200 fighters from Great Britain and America were certainly a great help. Not all were of like importance in battle. Soviet sources state that help came at a time when the Soviet industry was already in a position to help itself. It can be said that the P-39 was the best-liked, and three-times Hero of the Soviet Union, A I Pokryshkin, achieved the majority of his victories in this fighter.

CHAPTER 9

Fighter Strength 1943/1945

IN SPRING 1943 aerial battles raged over the Kuban front to an extent not previously seen in the war. The Soviet fighters were thrown into battle to finally gain air superiority over home skies. Equipped with new Yak-9 and La-5FN, the Soviets inflicted heavy losses on the Luftwaffe from which it never recovered. Between April and June 1943, the Luftwaffe apparently lost 3,700 aircraft over that area as the soviet pilots adopted new fighting formations which included a vertical grouping, the so-called 'Kubanskaya etazcherka' (Kuban bookstand).

A decisive blow was dealt during summer/autumn 1943 in the Soviet counter attack near Kursk. In 1,700 aerial battles, 2,100 German aircraft were shot down and 145 damaged, while flak brought down another 780. Losses were heavy on both sides, but the USSR at least achieved superiority in the air. Afterwards the Luftwaffe confined itself to defensive methods which consisted of occasional night attacks by bombers and attack aircraft.

For the first time since the beginning of the war, the USSR was now able to modernise its fleets in the Far East. Ageing I-16 and I-153 machines were transferred to training units. During the remainder of the war the Yak-3 became of importance, flying in convoy with the Lavochkin La-7.

The Yak-3 was developed from the Yak-1M. Through careful improvements to external contours and internal construction, an aircraft was produced which exhibited extremely good characteristics in level-flight speed, climbing rate and manoeuvrability. It was fitted with one ShVAK cannon, two UBS machine guns and occasionally with two ShKAS machine guns. Take-off weight at 2,600kg was a full 600kg less than the German Bf-109G-2, attaining a height of 5,000m in 4.1 minutes, while the Messerschmitt took 5.3mins The Soviet aircraft performed a roll at 1,000m in 18-19 seconds while the German machine re-

quired 22-23 secs.

With a range of only 670km, the Yak-3 remained a typical front-line fighter, powered by a 1,200mhp VK-105PF.

The aircraft saw limited front-line action at the end of 1943, but by spring 1944, several fighter groups were equipped with the type. The French squadron 'Normandie-Niemen', fighting in Russia, was originally equipped with Yak-1 and Yak-9 and was earmarked to receive new types in 1944. The pilots had a free choice between soviet aircraft and foreign ones – all decided in favour of the Yak-3. Those able to compare the Yak-3 with other types were particularly impressed by its ease of control and manoeuvrability, being able to turn in an unbelievably tight circle. The Red Air Fleet received a total of 4,848 Yak-3s.

Development of other Yak types also continued. In 1944 Yakovlev produced a true long-distance fighter, the Yak-9DD, whose 850 litre tanks enabled flights of up to 2,200km. A few Yak-9DDs were used in the summer of 1944 for a special

Produced in large quantities, the Yak-3 was a particular favourite with Soviet fighter pilots. It enjoyed good climb and exceptional turn performances.

task. At that time some heavy American day bombers were unable to return to their bases after an attack on Germany and landed on Russian airfields. Afer re-fuelling they then returned to their airfields in Italy. Yak-9DDs provided the Boeing B-17 and Consolidated B-24 with escort protection, staying at the airfield in Bari, Italy, where they assisted Yugoslav Partisans under Josip Broz-tito.

We have already met the 1,700mhp VK-107 engine in various prototypes. After ironing out teething troubles, the variant VK-107A was ready for series production. For this engine, Yakovlev constructed another Yak-9 variant, the Yak-9U, which began flying in December 1943. The Yak-9U was a development of the Yak-9T with a rear view cabin. Cannon was a 23mm MP-23-VV, and it also had two UBS machine guns. The works and government tests in January and February showed a maximum speed of 700kph at 5,500m, and a climb rate of 4 mins 36 secs. to 5,000m.

Production of the Yak-9U was delayed as a result of slow deliveries of the engine. The first machines did reach training schools in the second half of 1944, but they were seen at the front-line only in winter 1944 and spring 1945 in small numbers. They took little part in battles and were basically fighters for the post war period.

The development office of Lavochkin was fully occupied in the last months of 1943 and early 1944 on the new fighter designated La-120. In co-operation with TsAGI, Lavochkin refined the aerodynamics of the La-5FN, used more up-to-date technology and improved interior fittings and armament. At first glance the La-120 can be distinguished from the La-5NF by the oil-cooler under the cabin.

The La-120 had three ShVAK cannon, attached asymmetrically under the fuselage skin. With the same ASh-82FN engine, the La-120 had a speed of 680kph at 3,000m, as against 650kph of the La-5FN. Altitude of 5,000m was attained in 4 mins. 27 secs. which was not far behind the Yak-3's climb rate. Manoeuvrability was the same, but something had to be sacrificed – the range. The La-5FN could fly 765km, the new La-120 only 535 km. Again, a typical front-line fighter.

The Defence Committee decided to put the aircraft into series production as the La-7. since that time two type designations are typical of Lavochkin's work – low numbers for production aircraft, high numbers for prototypes. Other construction groups also adopted this method.

The La-7 was delivered to squadrons in large numbers only in the second half of 1944 but soon became popular. Performance of the production aircraft was slightly less than that of the prototypes (La-120) with a maximum speed of 665kph.

It was produced in two factories, at Moscow and Yaroslav. The aircraft from Yaroslav corresponded fully to the La-120 and were better finished. The La-7 built at Moscow had mostly only two ShVAK cannon and had a much rougher finish. In all respects they were better aircraft than those of the enemy, the Messerschmitt Bf-1096G-6 and

Focke-Wulf Fw 190A-8. A total of 5,753 were produced.

Lavochkin tried to develop the La-7 into a high-altitude fighter and in July and August 1944 his La-7TK, with an ASh-82FN and two TK-3 turbochargers, were tested. The La-7 TK reached 676kph at 8,000m, but armament had to be sacrificed to just one ShVAK cannon. At the same time, Lavochkin also tested an La-7 with a 2,000mhp 18-cylinder ASh-71TK engine, but this proved unsuitable.

In January 1945 yet another La-7 was test flown, this time with a new 2,000mhp ASh-82. The aircraft had two NS-23 cannon and attained 725kph at 7,400m. However, all these were only experimental.

Many experiments were carried out during the war years in respect to high-altitude fighters. Reports of German preparations for high-altitude bombers forced the Defence Committee to have high-altitude fighters in reserve and the Mikoyan/Gurevich development group was particularly strongly involved.

Mention has already been made of the high-altitude I-220(A) fighter, a low-wing aircraft with an AM-39 engine. In the summer of 1943 followed the I-221 (2A) with AM-39A engine and two 2TK-2B turbochargers. Then, in April 1944, came the I-222(3A) with AM-39B-1 of 1,630/1,900mhp. This engine had two TK-300B turbochargers which resulted in especially high performance. Speed at 13,100m was 690kph and service ceiling

Above: Il-224(4A) could operate at 14,100m with a pressurised cabin.
Below: Yak-9U entered production too late to see any significant wartime service.
Bottom: Lavochkin's La-7 was considered superior to its German equivalents in 1944.

Above: Polikarpov's project for a high-altitude fighter, VP(K).

Below: Development of Ilyushin's Il-1 ceased after failure of the Su-7.

was up to 14,500m. The aircraft had clean aerodynamic lines. The cooler was built into the wing leading edge, and under the fuselage the only projection was an air-intake to the turbochargers. The airscrew had four particularly broad blades.

In summer 1944, the I-222(3A) was accepted into the Red Air Fleet as the standard high-altitude fighter and its introduction into series production as the MiG-7 was in preparation. The rapid course of the war cut short those plans.

After the I-222(3A) came the I-224(4A) which reached a height of 14,100m. All these aircraft had pressurised cabins made of steel sheet, air for pressure regulation being taken from the turbochargers. The '220' series of high-altitude fighters was ended in March 1945 with the I-225(5A). Mikulin's AM-42FB engine produced 2,200mhp, and the aircraft attained a maximum speed of 726kph at 10,000m.

Mikoyan and Gurevich built another aircraft in the '230' series in 1943, the I-231(D). It was a development of the I-230(D) of 1942, with AM-39 engine of 1,700mhp and two ShVAK cannon. Its maximum speed of 707kph at 7,100m was fastest in the USSR by 1943.

Shortly before his death in August 1944, Polikarpov projected a high-altitude fighter, known as the VP(K). VP stands for *Vysotnyi Perekhvatchik* (high altitude interceptor). This machine also had the AM-39A engine with two TK-300B turbochargers. Polikarpov expected a speed in the region of 700kph and a service ceiling of 14,000m. Two NS-23 cannon were incorporated. Work on the prototype had already begun at the time of Polikarpov's death, but was then discontinued.

Apart from high-altitude fighters, the Defence Committee also demanded in Spring 1944 a heavy, low-level aircraft for the combined ground attack and pursuit role. They were to be heavily armed and armoured single-seat aircraft which could fulfil both roles. P O Sukhoi and S V Ilyushin were to look into these.

Sukhoi used the airframe of the earlier Su-6-1 attack aircraft made lighter by removing the heavy armour plating and used the 1,530/1,800mhp ASh-82FN (the Su-6-1 had the unreliable ASh-71). Two VYa-23mm cannon were built into the wings, each with 150 rounds of ammunition. Thus was developed the Su-7 fighter which, however, showed that it was not worth it to compromise. Its speed was only 590kph at 7,500m, which was slow for 1944. Its armour plating was far too light for battle, the aircraft's weight too heavy for a fighter.

Ilyushin at that time had not completed his Il-1 fighter. He wanted to use the 2,000mhp AM-42 engine and expected only 580kph. In April and May 1944 work on the Il-1 was stepped-up, but development was discontinued after failure of the Su-7 became known.

The Red Air Fleet had on strength 15,815 aircraft at the beginning of 1945; a year before it was only 8,818. When, at the battle of Stalingrad in November 1942, the Soviets had only 100 aircraft, this number had increased to 343 in spring 1945.

A total of 8,500 Soviet bombers, attack aircraft and fighters were concentrated on German positions in readiness for the final battle over Berlin. The Soviet fighter force, which on June 22, 1941, fought with only a few aircraft, completely destroyed the Luftwaffe. In 47 months of war between the Soviet Union and Germany 77,000 German aircraft were destroyed, according to Russian sources, the majority by Soviet fighters. By comparison, the Germans lost 8,000 aircraft over Western Europe, 9,000 over the Mediterranean and 7,500 over the Balkan area – again according to Soviet statements.

Before the war, fighters made up 56.2% of the Red Air Fleet. By the end this had reduced to 42%, especially as attack aircraft had to be produced in greater numbers. The total number of fighters was nevertheless large – 37,000 Yak and 22,000 La fighters were constructed.

Of three million operations of the Red Air Fleet, a considerable number goes to the credit of fighters. Over 20,000 pilots were decorated, 2,119 of them with the Star of Hero of the Soviet Union; 63 received this honour twice and two, A I Pokryshkin and I N Kozchedub, three times.

Below: Fastest aircraft in the USSR by 1943 was a development of Mikoyan and Gurevich's '230' series, the I-231(2D), which had a maximum speed of 707kph at 7,100m. Engine was a 1,700mhp AM-39.

THE FIRST post-war years saw a transition in aircraft technology from piston to jet-engined aircraft. In spite of this, development of military aircraft with piston engines continued in all countries, as it was still the easiest way to produce high performance aircraft. Pure jet propulsion required a lot of experimenting.

In the Soviet Union, piston-engined fighters were still built about three years after the war. In the first part of 1945 front line fighter squadrons received the first Yak-3U machines. These slowly replaced the older Yak types and, together with the Yak-9U, formed the backbone of squadrons.

Development of the Yak-3U started in spring 1944 along the same lines as the Yak-9U. Engine was a VK-107A, armament consisted of the ShVAK and two UBS, and metal replaced many wooden components. Between February and May 1944 the Yak-3U undertook its state testing, the airworthiness certificate and report naming it as best of the Russian and foreign fighters.

Maximum speed was 720kph at 5,750m and all performance and flight characteristics up to an altitude of 12,000m were better than the Yak-9U. The production run, however, suffered so badly from lack of VK-107A engines that it never reached the front line.

Yak-3U and Yak-9Us fought in 1949/50 in the North Korean War with Korean and Chinese pilots. The La-9 and La-11 also saw action in this war.

CHAPTER 10

Last Piston Engine Fighters

Lavochkin developed the new La-130 fighter in 1946. At first glance, relationship with the La-7 was evident, even the ASh-82FN engine was the same. The aircraft was nevertheless quite new and consisted of all-metal construction with laminar flow wing-profile. With the La-130,

Lavochkin's last single, piston engine fighters were the La-9 (La-130), pictured right, and the later La-11 (La-140) which sacrificed part of its armament for a greater range.

Lavochkin managed to reach a speed of 690kph at 6,250m with strong armament consisting of four fixed NS-23 cannon. It also had a relatively long range of 1,750km.

The La-130 was quickly put into production, and soon the all-metal La-9 appeared at airfields of the USSR and in occupied East Germany. The La-9 made it possible, for the first time, to provide escort for the medium-range horizontal and dive-bomber Tu-2 over its whole range.

At the beginning of 1947, Lavochkin built the La-140 prototype, again with the ASh-82FN. By removing one NS-23 cannon, fuel capacity was increased to 1,100 litres, as against 825 of the La-9. This machine was put into production as the La-11. It attained a maximum speed of 674kph at 6,200m, had a service ceiling of 10,000m and a range of 2,550km.

As ideas of future warfare changed, the Soviet Air Force demanded a long-range escort fighter similar to those employed by the Western powers.

As a makeshift, A N Tupolev took the airframe of the fast, medium Tu-2 bomber and altered it to the ANT-63P prototype. It was a two-seater with two AM-39F engines of 1,000mhp each, armed with four fixed NS-23 cannon and a moveable ShVAK cannon on top of the fuselage. The ANT-63P attained a speed of 680kph and had a range of 2,500km. It was put into limited production as the Tu-1.

The fast Pe-2 bomber was also converted into a fighter variant, the Pe-2I. ANT-63P was built in 1945, but the Pe-2I dated back to 1944 and was developed under the leadership of V M Mayasischev. The Pe-2I had two VK-107A engines and reached 657kph at an altitude of 5,700m with two NJS-23 cannon and a movable UBT machine gun. It is interesting to note that the Pe-2I succeeded not as a fighter but as a fast bomber with wider fuselage.

In the first months of 1946 test flying had already started with jet fighters. A new stage in the development of Soviet fighter aircraft had begun.

Rocket Aircraft

CHAPTER 11

SUCCESSES OF the USSR in rocket technology and space travel inspired quite a few authors to write numerous books on development, from the days of the old artillery rockets up to the present day cosmic marvels. It is not necessary to retell the early history of rockets on the territory of old Russia. Names like K E Tsiolkovsky are certainly well known and he may be regarded as the true father of space travel.

In the USSR, amateur rocket technologists, inspired by Tsiolkovsky's work, formed themselves into groups at the beginning of the twenties. There was even a small scientific centre, the cental study organisation for rocket technology, founded in 1924 under V P Verchinkin.

Among the amateurs of that time, F A Tsander

was particularly outstanding for his lectures and publications. In 1930 Tsander became a member of the Central Institute for aircraft engines, TsIAM, and there he was able to experiment on a larger scale. At TsIAM he built the first rocket engine, OR-1 with 5kg static thrust. It operated with fuel and compressed air. By 1932, the engine had completed 50 "fire tests" as Tsander called them.

Meanwhile, in the central committee of Osoaviakhim (the organisation of that time for defence and air sport) under Tsander's supervision, a section was formed for rocket engines. In 1932, it became the group for rocket propulsion research with the abbreviation GIRD, and built Tsander's OR-2 engine which had been designed in September/October 1931. OR-2 was an engine of 50kg thrust and burned fuel with liquid oxygen.

Left: A model of Korolyev's RP-318, the actual version of which was reconstructed from an SK-9 glider.

Below: The BICh-11 tail-less glider was selected for installation of GIRD's OR-2 rocket when it would take on designation RP-1. Both were tested independently in 1933 but no powered flights were made.

The GIRD group wanted to make their first flight with this engine in a glider. B I Cheranovskii was working on a tail-less glider, BICh-11, which after the incorporation of OR-2 was to be designated RP-1. (RP = *Raketny Planer* or rocket glider). On March 18, 1933, the engine was running in the test-house for the first time, and BICh-11 was being flown as a simple glider. No flights were made with the engine as it proved to be unreliable.

GIRD also designed and built a rocket, GIRD-X, of 2.2m length and 70kg thrust. With this the first flight was achieved on November 25, 1933, but Tsander had died seven months earlier.

Equally important was the work of another group under V P Glushko. This series of rocket engines began with the ORM-1 of 1930. ORM-1 burnt toluene methylbenzene with nitrogen peroxide and developed 20kg thrust. Three years later, ORM-50 was producing 150kg, and an ORM-52 of 300kg was also prepared.

The foundation of a Moscow-based research institute for jet propulsion in 1934 was of great importance for the further development of rocket technology. Glushko worked in the laboratory on the dynamics of gases, planning and partially building engines with the model designations ORM-53 to ORM-102. Especially successful was engine ORM-65 of 1936, with 155kg rated and 175kg maximum thrust.

For flight testing Glushko's rocket engines, designer S P Korolyev, later chief designer of the Soviet space rockets, reconstructed the glider SK-9. Engine was in the rear fuselage, under the tail. After numerous ground tests in 1937 and 1938, the glider and engine under model designation RP-318 was flown several times in 1940. QRM-65 had a combustion period of 230 seconds; when running intermittently there was enough fuel for 30 minutes.

A third group also worked in the sphere of rocket technology, the rocket section of the scientific-technological aviation company, AVIAvnito. At the beginning their activity ran parallel to GIRD and technical director of the section was L S Dushkin. This group's meteorological rocket was launched in December 1933. Then Dushkin devoted himself to the combustible combination of petroleum and nitric acid, and built several engines. One of them was tested on February 28, 1940, by V P Fedorov in the RP-318. The rocket glider was towed by an R-5 up to 2,300m, at which height the RP-318 disengaged. As Fedorov turned on the ignition, speed rose rapidly from 80 to 140kph. But as the RP-318 was only registered for 170kph he began to climb, reaching 2,900m in a few seconds. Dushkin's rocket engine had proved itself practicable.

Shortly before the war, Dushkin was commissioned to design a powerful engine for rocket fighters. Once again the engine was to burn petroleum and nitrid acid and have an adjustable thrust. The airframe designers also received their orders.

Above: In glider form, the BI made its first flight towed behind a Pe-2 bomber in 1941. The rocket powered BI-1 (below and left) had its engine mounted in the rear fuselage and was equipped with two ShVAK cannon, each holding 45 rounds of ammunition. First powered flight was on May 15, 1942.

Polikarpov's rocket fighter project 'Malyutka' died with its designer in 1944. This wooden model is all that survives.

IN JUNE 1939, the German rocket powered Heinkel He-176 was flown in secret. In 1940, they began designing the rocket fighter Messerschmitt Me 163 V-1. Its first powered flights took place in April 1941. At this time the design group of A Y Bereznyak and A I Isayev were working in the Zhukovsky military aviation academy under the direction of Professor V F Bolkhovitinov on the design of a rocket interceptor. Aircraft designation was BI from the names of the designers.

Dushkin, meanwhile, was working on the D-1A engine which was also to burn petroleum and nitric acid. Rated thrust was 1,100kp, the maximum 1,400kp and it was calculated that the fuel supply with adjustable thrust would allow up to fifteen minutes flying time. Bereznyak and Isayev had discussed the aerodynamic problems with Professor V S Pyshnov of TsAGI. It was decided that the speed had to be increased in stages. Final stage would be an estimated 1,000kph.

Towards the end of summer 1941, the first batch of five commissioned prototypes were ready. They had ballast in place of engines and towing hooks under the nose of the fuselage. On September 10, 1942, the BI-1 as a glider made its first towed flight behind a Pe-2 bomber, and tests proceeded up to evacuation of the test base. In Spring 1942, the towing tests could be resumed, pilots Bakhchivandzhi and Gruzdev being detailed by the fighter units of Moscow Defence.

G Ya Bakhchivandzhi was to be the first soviet rocket pilot. He practised taxying with the BI-1, adjustment of the engine and everything else that was necessary. On May 15, 1942, he took off on his first powered flight.

BI-1 was a low wing monoplane in all wood construction, a very small span of 6.48m (lifting surface 7 sq m) with retractable wheel or ski undercarriage and two small, round additional endplates on the horizontal tailplane. In the nose were two ShVAK cannon, each with 45 rounds of ammunition. Engine was in the rear of the fuselage with exhaust nozzle behind the tail surfaces.

After the first test flights the Red Air Force showed interest in a series of 40 to 50 rocket interceptors. But, meanwhile, they had run into a crisis with flight testing of the BI family. The manifestations of air compressibility at subsonic speeds were not yet explained.

Flight testing took longer as Bakhchivandzhi tried to shed light on these problems. On a flight in 1943, his machine fell to pieces in the air and he was killed. Testing continued with pilots M K Baikalov and B N Kudrin using the improved BI No.7. But the Air Force soon lost interest as they foresaw, with some justification, a delay in the design programme.

Seven BI machines were built and maximum speed in practice was only about 600kph. Only Bakhchivandzhi had flown faster, but the Mach number achieved on his fatal flight is unknown to this day.

A further rocket fighter aircraft was designed in 1942 by Professor M K Tikhonravov and given designation I-302. It was an all wood, mid wing monoplane, relatively large with about 12m span. The rocket engine NII-3 of 1500kg thrust was a joint design by Duskin and Stokolov. Under the wings were two ramjets by engineer Merkulov. These could be switched on or off as desired and prolonged the duration of flight. Armament consisted of four ShVAK cannon.

The I-302 was in flying condition in 1943, but after Bakhchivandzhi's accident, the state defence committee forbade rocket flights and I-302 was only to be tested as a glider behind a Pe-2. That was its only task! Unfortunately there is no known picture extant of the I-302.

In 1944, N N Polikarpov designed the rocket fighter 'Malyutka' with Dushkin's NII-1 engine of 1,200kp. The engine was already completed and tested, the airframe not far removed from the final stage of assembly when Polikarpov died in August 1944. As with his other models, there was no successor. Only a wooden model exists to show us what the machine looked like.

CHAPTER 12

Rocket Assisted Fighters

BY "AUXILIARY rocket power units" we don't mean, auxiliary take-off units. The inventors of these rockets, who had the task of helping overloaded aircraft into the air or of considerably reducing the take-off run were engineers V V Dudakov and V P Konstantionov. Their invention was developed in the gas dynamic laboratory in Leningrad in 1931. Fuel was gunpowder in solidified bars enclosed in a steel cylinder with an exhaust nozzle.

Two such rockets were tested for the first time in 1931 on the training biplane U-1. In 1932 and 1933 there were several tests, each time using four rockets on a TB-1 bomber. Results were good, the TB-1 for example could take about 33% more payload with the same take-off run. Nevertheless the rockets were soon forgotten.

When it became clear that rocket fighter aircraft would not be available as early as expected, attempts were made to achieve high speed by other means. Those concerned foresaw possible danger if Germany was able to use specially high horizontal and climbing speeds to be able to overtake the enemy or get out of critical situations. Simplest method was to incorporate rocket auxiliary power units in the fuselage tail.

In 1944, V P Glushko's rocket engine RD-1KhZ of 300kg thrust was built in the USSR. This burned petroleum and nitric acid and was distinguished by a strange turbine pump. From the combustion chamber a small quantity of hot gases was conducted to the turbine which with full thrust made up to 26,000 revolutions a minute. The turbine then drove, by gearing, the pumps for petroleum, nitric acid, oil and water. Water was necessary

Above: When tested with an RD-1KhZ auxiliary rocket unit, Sukhoi's Su-7 demonstrated an increase in speed from 590 to 700kph.

Left and below: Several flights of over 700kph were made with the La-7R which had Glushko's 300kg thrust RD-1KhZ in its tail. Damage to wooden airframes by acid vapours was a major problem, resulting in loss of the Yak-3RD.

because hot gases in front of the turbine were cooled by water injection, and the combustion chamber was also water cooled. The machinery had a total weight of 50kg.

RD-1KhZ was tested on several aircraft in the years 1944 to 1946, among them the Pe-2 bomber which made 110 flights. Between October 1944 and February 1945 an La-7R was test flown with the RD-1KhZ engine in the fuselage tail under a reconstructed tail fin. Pilots G M Shiyanov and A V Davydov went on several flights with the La-7R at speeds of over 700kph. But the engine installation was not reliable because the nitric acid tank and the circuit were not strong enough. Acid evaporated and vapours destroyed the plywood shell fuselage.

On the second test engine ZhRD-1 (*Zhidkostnyi Rekativnyi Dvigatel* = rocket engine with liquid fuel), in reality an improved RD-1KhZ, increase in speed was 85kph at 3,000m, the aircraft reaching 740kph.

In August 1946, spectators at the air parade in Tushino, near Moscow, were able to see the La-120R at the peak of its performance trailing a long tail of fire. The engine had a burning time of from 3 to 3.5 minutes.

Originally two models of fighters with auxiliary rockets were to be exhibited in Tushino. The second was Yakovlev's Yak-3RD. Before the air parade, V L Rastorguyev had reached as much as 780kph at 3,000m, an increase of speed of 140kph. At 7,800m the increase was 182, but this could not be maintained constantly as the airframe was not strong enough. The danger of damage from acid vapours showed up in a particularly drastic way on this aircraft and Rastorguyev lost his life shortly before the parade.

The heavy fighter, Sukhoi Su-7, was also tested, with RD-1KhZ, speed rising to 700kph from only 590kph.

Development of the auxiliary rocket units was continued for a little longer. The RD-2 engine was built with 600kg thrust, then the RD-3 with 900kg. They were primarily intended for bombers, but were no longer of use owing to rapid development of new jet aircraft.

CHAPTER 13

Post-War Development of Rocket Fighters

AFTER THE triumphal march of the Red Army to Germany, much booty was taken from German airfields, plants and test stations. In spite of the Germans' efforts to destroy or evacuate as much as possible, the booty was considerable. Among other things were several Messerschmitt Me-163 rocket fighters – various versions – also the new Me-263 which had not yet been put into use. Various documents were taken concerning the planned supersonic rocket aircraft DFS-346 which was to be built in the Siebel plants at Schkeuditz near Halle.

Soviet research and testing stations examined the German material carefully on the ground and in the air, and used the best ideas for their own design. The Americans, British and French did the same.

The USSR carefully examined the two-seat version of rocket fighter Me-163S, reconstructing it as a glider for research into flying qualities at high subsonic speeds. They were given the name 'Karas' and towed into the air by Tu-2

Rocket fighter I-270 (Sh) had a combat period of 4 minutes 15 seconds.

bombers. Pilots were M L Gallas, I I Vernikov, A A Yefimov.

Disregarding fantasy pictures which have been seen over the years, we are not yet fully acquainted with the Russians' home designing of rocket aircraft. Only one machine is well known, the I-270 (Sh) built by Mikoyan and Gurevich in 1946.

At first glance, similarity with the Messerschmitt Me-263 is obvious. The fuselage is familiar, but wings and controls, the most important parts of a high-speed aircraft, are quite different from the Messerschmitt design. The Me-263 had sweptback wings, 25 degrees on the leading edge; the I-270 (Sh) had short wings without sweep, trapezoidal and with a short aspect ratio. The Me 263 was tailess; the I-270 (Sh) had arrow type horizontal stabilisers on the tip of the vertical stabilisers. The aircraft had a retractable tricycle undercarriage and was armed with two NS-23 guns.

Engine was an RD-2M-3V of L S Dushkin, equipped with two combustion chambers. The combat chamber had 1,450kp thrust for a period of 4 minutes 15 seconds, and speed during this time reached 1,000kph. The smaller cruising chamber had only 400kp thrust but allowed a propelled flight of 9 minutes. Service ceiling was 18,000m, the first 10,000m could be reached in 2.37 minutes and 15,000m in 3.5 minutes. Of the 4,120kg take-off weight, 2,120kg was fuel.

In archives it was recorded that the Soviets tested the former German rocket aircraft DFS-346 in the form of Samolet-346 in 1951. The airframe had several modifications and engine was the German Walter HWK 509B-1 of 1,700-2,000kp thrust. Whether Soviet pilots managed to achieve the foreseen 2,270kph and 20,000m service ceiling after release from the mother 'plane at 10,000m is unfortunately not known.

Rocket fighters today belong to history. The experiences garnered by Soviet designers from the engines and airframes constituted quite a help in development of modern fighters and space rockets.

CHAPTER 14

First of the Jet Fighters

ON APRIL 24, 1946, test pilot A M Grinchik got into the cabin of the first jet fighter I-300(F), designed by the Mikoyan-Gurevich group, and made his first flight. When the I-300(F) had flown out of sight, M I Ivanov took off from the same runway in another jet, A S Yakovlev's Yak-15. On this day a new era began in the development of Soviet fighters.

Russian development was belated in comparison with other countries. The first German jet, Heinkel He178, had taken off in August 1939, while the Messerschmitt Me262 was flown for the first time in 1940 and in service by 1944. Britain launched the Gloster G.40 Squirt in May 1941, the first fighters, Gloster Meteor and de Havilland Vampire, reaching units in 1944 and 1945 respectively. In America, the Bell XP-59 Airacomet flew in October 1942 and the first production fighter, Lockheed P-80 Shooting Star, in 1945.

By Summer 1941 the construction in Leningrad of the first Soviet jet engine, VDR-1, was almost completed. The engine was designed by A M Lyulka featuring multi-stage axial compressor and developing 700kp thrust. But in September 1941 the design and research institutes had to be evacuated from Leningrad. The VRD-1 was not completed, neither was the VDR-2 which promised an estimated 2,000kp thrust.

Only after the return of the design group was Lyulka able to complete the VDR-3 engine, of 1,300kp thrust, in 1945. The engine had an eight stage axial compressor and a single-stage turbine. Its dry weight was 900kg. The bench test produced good results but the engine needed several modifications before it could be built into an airframe.

Lyulka had been busy since 1937 with the development of jet engines, but the idea was not new in the USSR. As early as 1912 engineer A Gorokhov had designed an aircraft with jet power. Its compressor was to be activated by a reciprocating engine, as were the later aircraft of Italy's Campini. In 1924 engineer V I Bazarov's patent for a jet engine with axial compressor appeared under the number 645. In 1929 the scientific assistant of TsAGI, B S Stechkin, published a work on the theory of jet engines. The rocket pioneer K E Tsiolkovskii also designed jet engines, among them a by-pass concept in 1932.

In spite of these designs and patents the USSR remained practically without any jet engines up to 1945. The ram jet auxiliary power unit was of temporary help. In 1944, the Yak 7PVRD (*Pryamototochnii Vozdushno-Reaktivnii Dvigatel* = ram jet) completed its flight test. It flew with two auxiliary ram jets suspended under the wings. Its test pilot, S N Anokhin, established that speed increased by 60 to 90kph.

After the war, S A Lavochkin's drawing office worked enthusistically on the problem of ram jet auxiliary power units for fighters. Between July and September 1946, test pilots made several flights with the machine La-126PVRD. It was a development of La-120 (La-7) with two PVRD-430

ram jet power units designed by I I Bondarjuk. These engines increased speed by 100kph. In 1947 they were also assembled on an La-138 prototype of the La-9 series and speed was boosted by about 110kph. The pulsating intermittent propulsive ducts RD-13 of V N Chelomej were tested under the wings of some La-9RD. Increase in speed on this model was 127kph, but the vibrations transmitted by the engine to the wings made flying more difficult.

Generally speaking it was established that while the ram jet power units certainly increased speed they also increased weight and consequently the drag. They were hardly used at all in standard operations.

The jet engine concept in which the compressor is activated by a reciprocating engine represents a simpler way, for in this case the theoretically and technologically complicated turbine is abandoned. But the speed of such engines is limited. Originator of such engines in the USSR was engineer Kholshchevnikov, a scientific worker at the TsIAM institute. The engine was built in 1943 and was given the name "Kholshchevnikov's Accelerator" (*Uskoritel Kholshchevnikova*). The accelerator was designed in such a way as to form part of the aircraft fuselage behind the cabin, so there was little or no drag.

Aircraft with the accelerator had a reciprocating engine with an ordinary propeller in the fuselage nose. The crank shaft was lengthened towards the rear and it activated the accelerator supercharger by means of a clutch coupling. The air inlet to the compressor was under the bottom of the fuselage nose and air was then conducted via the cabin to the fuselage tail. Here was the real combustion chamber of the accelerator, where fuel was injected and burned. The gases were discharged through a nozzle under the tail surfaces.

At the beginning of 1944 the drawing offices of Mikoyan-Gurevich and P O Sukhoi received from

Ram jet units fitted to the La-126PVRD, a development of the La-120 (La-7).

Combinations of jet and piston engined aircraft were Sukhoi's I-107 (Su-5) pictured above and the I-250(N) of Mikoyan and Gurevich (below). Both types were flown in March 1945 and featured Kholshchevnikov's accelerator.

the State Defence Committee a commission for the design of fighters with Kholshchevnikov's accelerator. The aircraft were to reach at least 800kph.

In March 1945 both model types were ready. Sukhoi introduced the I-107 or Su-5 fighter; Mikoyan and Gurevich built the I-250(N). Both machines were all-metal, low wing monoplanes with VK-107R engines of 1,700 metric horsepower in the fuselage nose; the I-107 had a four-blade propellor, the I-250(N) a three blade. Each had air inlets to the accelerator compressor under the spinner, but Mikoyan's machine had a frontal radiator whereas Sukhoi's I-107 had radiators in the centre wing section. The machines had identical armament – an NS-23 engine cannon with 100 rounds and two synchronised UBS machine guns, each with 400 rounds.

I-250(N) was test flown by A P Dejev on March 3, 1945. It had a speed of 825kph at 7,500m. Su-5 was a little slower at 810kph. Service ceilings were 11,900 and 11,950m respectively. Flight testing of the two models only continued up to June 1945. At that time the VK-107R engine of Su-5 was sent for repairs and never returned to the airframe. The Red Air Force quickly lost interest in such fighters for development of the "pure" jet aircraft promised better results.

On the occupied airfields of East Europe and in the German plants a lot of German Junkers Jumo 004 and BMW 003 were found, both model types with axial compressors and about 800kp thrust. The Soviet technical service decided that the number and qualities of the engines constituted a good basis for the development of Soviet jet aircraft until better models of home or foreign origin could be built.

The BMW 003 of 800kp thrust was taken on as RD-20. The RD-10, as the Jumo 004 was called, gave 850 to 900kp. Both engines had reached a stage of technical maturity and it was to be expected that performances would quickly increase when better raw materials were used and after further refinements. It was also expected that the life of "hot" parts would also be prolonged.

In Autumn 1945 four airframe drawing offices were given the task of designing aircraft for these engines. A S Yakovlev and S A Lavochkin were to design single-engine models with the RD-10; Mikoyan and Gurevich and Sukhoi were to prepare twin-engined machines with RD-20 engines. For the single-engine machines provision was made for two NS-23 cannon, while the twin-engined aircraft were to have additional 37mm N-37 cannon.

Yakovlev's drawing office chose a speedy way which was also simpler – reconstruction of the Yak-3 airframe, a fighter which had proved its worth. The machine had good streamlining and favourable flying qualities and Yakovlev thought, correctly, that pilots would like to transfer to the jet variant of a well known fighter. Nevertheless, the model director, J G Adler, had no easy task.

Reconstruction mainly involved removal of the reciprocating engine from the nose, where two NS-23 cannon were now put, and installation of the RD-10 engine under the front part of the fuselage with the axis of thrust slightly slanting upward. Incorporation of the engine caused considerable assembly and technology problems which were only solved by horseshoe-shaped cambering of the wing main spar.

The classic undercarriage was kept; only the tail wheel had to be made of steel as it was directly in the path of hot exhaust gases. Otherwise the composite construction was retained, that is wood wing with metal spar and fuselage of steel tube framework, sheet metal covering and fabric covering.

With a take-off weight of 2,640kg the Yak-15 was the lightest jet fighter of that time. Britain's de Havilland Vampire weighed 3,240kg and the American P-80 as much as 6,350kg.

Mikoyan and Gurevich had to choose a new design for their I-300(F) fighter. They built the two RD-20 engines close to one another in the underside of the fuselage with a common air inlet in the nose. The scoop separated into two channels, between which was the pilot's cockpit. Over the engines' exhaust nozzles the fuselage tapered into a slim tail boom. The aircraft had a tricycle undercarriage and, as the cockpit was quite far to the front, the pilot had an undisturbed field of front vision, a feature lacking in the Yak-15.

The armament of I-300(F) was positioned

Above: With a 2,604kg take-off weight, Yak-15 was the lightest jet fighter in the world when it first flew. Airframe was basically a reconstruction of the Yak-3.

First of the pure jet Soviet aircraft to fly was Mikoyan and Gurevich's I-300(F), later to be introduced as the MiG-9. It is shown below at about the time of its maiden flight on April 24, 1946, while illustrated left is the inlet-mounted armament.

around the air inlet. The two NS-23 cannon were underneath, the N-37 in the middle in the separating gap in the air inlet. I-300(F) was fairly heavy at 5,070kg take-off weight and with two additional tanks under the wing tips rose to 5,500kg.

Both models had successful first flights. For M I Ivanov the task was easier for the flying qualities of Yak-15 were really similar to those of Yak-3. A N Grinchik had first to accustom himself to a heavy aircraft with relatively high engine thrust.

Ivanov increased the speed of Yak-15 to 805kph at an altitude of 5,000m and soon discovered the inadequate stability of an airframe which was simply not built for such speeds. At 5,000m speed had to be reduced to Mach 0.68 (790kph). Further unpleasant characteristics showed up as hot gases burned the fabric covering of the underside of the fuselage and horizontal tail surfaces. The remedy was simple –the under part of the fuselage was covered with stainless steel sheets and the horizontal tail surfaces were given duralumin covering.

After such modifications the Yak-15 was a good fighter aircraft during that first period of transition from the reciprocating to the jet engine.

Grinchik soon mastered flying with the I-300(F) and was given permission to increase speed. Maximum for the I-300(F) was Mach 0.78 (910kph) at 5,000m. At speeds over 700kph heavy oscillations manifested themselves in the fuselage tail and these soon spread over the whole airframe. The aircraft vibrated and the pilot complained that after every flight his eyes "shivered in their sockets". They found out why after fairly lengthy investigations. The exhaust gases caused oscillation of the skin of the tail boom which was not stiff enough. These oscillations were then transmitted to the rest of the aircraft. The flaw was easily removed by internal stiffening.

The first I-300(F) only flew for a month. In May 1946, on a horizontal flight, the machine suddenly reared up when several hundred metres over the airfield, looped and fell in a dive to the ground. Grinchik was killed.

Test pilot M L Gallai was delegated to find the cause and he came close to a similar end when the second machine nearly did the same thing to him. It was discovered that the assembly man, shortly before take-off, had connected the current supply to the electric motors for the Flettner rudder the wrong way round. So the electric motors running in the opposite direction had caused the disaster.

Flight tests continued and Gallai reached Mach 0.8 but almost lost the tail unit in the process; he also completed firing tests at ground and aerial targets. G M Shipanov, another test pilot, accomplished the tests at low speeds. Some of the range tests were economy flights with only one engine running.

By Summer 1946 the I-300(F) could be regarded as a mature machine and the Air Force took it on as MiG-9.

The big air parade in Tushino near Moscow on August 18, 1946, culminated with the flying of various prototypes of new jet aircraft of Soviet design. On the following day the designers of Yak-15 and MiG-9 were invited to the Ministry for Aviation Industry. Here Stalin's wishes were made known to them. Fifteen machines of each type were to be ready by November 7, 1946, for a flight over the military parade in Red Square.

To ensure that Stalin's wishes were carried out, deputies of the minister went straight to the plants to hurry on production. They were given a piece of advice en route: "If the aircraft aren't ready, it would be preferable not to return to Moscow".

A S Yakovlev writes with humour in his memoirs about this situation, but in reality it was far from humorous. Nothing had been prepared for production; the designs had not even been copied. In spite of this the first Yak-15 machine was ready four weeks after the order and on October 21 the whole series were in flying condition.

Mikoyan's group had a far more difficult time, for Yakovlev had been able to take over most of the components available from his aircraft Yak-3. Nevertheless, the two groups of 15 aircraft were ready on the eve of parade day. The pilots were trained and there had been a practice fly-over.

But on November 7, 1946, twenty ninth anni-

Below: La-150 reached 850kph at 5,000m with its RD-10 engine in 1946.

Despite its external similarity to the Me 262, Sukhoi's Su-9 had many fundamental differences.

versary of the Revolution, there was such a thick fog over Moscow that no aircraft could leave the ground!

Muscovites first saw them on May 1, 1947, over Red Square. In this parade five further jet fighters with conspicuously thick fuselages and slim tail booms made an appearance. These machines were often redesigned in the Western technical press and people racked their brains to guess the identity of the designer. It was S A Lavochkin and the machine was designated La-150.

Test pilot A A Popov flew the first La-150 in September 1946. The forms of La-150 were singular; tadpole shaped fuselage in which were incorporated the cabin and RD-10 engine. The tricycle undercarriage was fully retractable into the fuselage and armament consisted of NS-23 guns. A speed of 850kph was reached at 5,000m, take-off weight was 2,961kg and duration of flight 50 minutes.

I E Fedorov and M I Gallai helped Popov test the five prototypes of La-150 and soon after the first flights the wing tips were cambered under to improve stability. The sixth machine was built as La-150M and was flown for the first time in Spring 1947. Later all previously constructed La-150s were modified to La-150M standards. Another modification was the La-150F. It was given an RD-10F engine that was quickly able to reach 1,110kp with the help of the first Soviet afterburner. Speed reached 950kph.

The La-150 was a counterpart to Yak-15. MiG-9 was also given a partner, O Sukhoi's twin-motored Su-9. Described as a copy of Me-262 this was not strictly true, for the only similarity was in the engine layout under the wings. The two RD-10 did create a little additional drag but they also left the fuselage free for fuel tanks and facilitated engine maintenance.

Su-9(K) was completed and test flown in 1946. In the nose were three cannon – two NS-23 and one N-37 with 2X200 and 30 shells. The tricycle undercarriage had a double nose wheel and take-off weight was fairly high at 5,890kg. The RD-10 engines certainly had more thrust than the RD-20 of the MiG-9, but they were heavily over-loaded at take-off with full armament. So two U-5 auxiliary rocket engines with solid fuel, each of 1,150kp thrust, had to be put under the fuselage as take-off assists.

On the wing trailing edge, between engine and fuselage, were dive brakes and in the fuselage tail a parachute brake. The speed of Su-9 was 847kph at low altitude and 900 at 5,000m altitude similar to those of MiG-9. But Su-9 had superior range at 1,140km with a normal volume of fuel as against the MiG-9's 800km or 1,110km with additional tanks. Service ceiling was lower than that of the MiG-9, 12,550m compared with 13,500m. Su-9 completed plant tests in 1946 and State tests in Spring 1947.

Models Yak-15 and MiG-9 were designed as standard jet fighters of the first stage. They were constantly improved, but even those drawing offices which had not been successful in the first stage did not stand still. During 1946-7 several further variants and new aircraft were built and tested.

Yakovlev tried, above all, to make thorough improvements in stability of the Yak-15 airframe. The new machine, Yak-17, was built in the Winter months of 1946 and tested in Spring 1947. More metal was used in the construction and, because pilots complained about limited vision when the aircraft was stationary, Yakovlev used a tricycle undercarriage. But the nose wheel could not be retracted into the fuselage because the engine was there. It was simply lifted and retracted into a small pod. Maximum speed was 751kph at 5,000m. Yak-17 soon replaced the older Yak-15 in order to give pilots experience on aircraft with tricycle gear.

MiG-9 fighters were given new engines in 1947, the RD-21 of 1,000kp thrust. Model designation was then MiG-9F (F=*Forsirovannii*, = reinforced). Changes in the RD-21 engine were principally brought about by the use of better raw materials which made possible increases in temperature in front of the turbine and therefore higher turbine rotation rate.

Soon after the MiG-9 the MiG-9FR made its appearance, featuring a pressurised cabin. The cabin was heavy and resulted in a displacement of the centre of gravity. The weapons had to be put further back to the sides of the fuselage. Two NS-23 cannon were mounted one over the other

Yak-17 soon replaced Yak-15 in Red Air Force service.

on the left side, an N-37 was on the right. MiG-9 were serially produced in this form up to the end of 1948.

Lavochkin's methods of construction on the La-150 were unsuccessful. The tail boom was not stiff enough and bent in flight, so Lavochkin quickly abandoned this line and between 1946 and 1947 built three prototypes of new fighters, the La-152, La-154 and La-156. They were all-metal, mid wing monoplanes, their forms reminiscent of the Yak-17 with RD-10 or RD-10F engines under the fuselage. The wings had especially slender laminar-flow airfoil so that the undercarriage had to be retracted into the fuselage. The last aircraft was more heavily armed with three NS-23 cannon.

The La-152 reached a maximum speed of 778kph at 5,000m. Take-off weight was 3,239kg, service ceiling 12,500m and range 500km. The La-154 had about the same performances but the La-150 reached 900kph.

Yet another jet fighter with the RD-10F was built at that time. In August 1947, during the Tushino parade, a new classic mid-wing monoplane with relatively big, spindle shaped fuselage and straight wings appeared. In the Western press this machine was called Red Thunderjet in recognition of similarity to the American F-84 Thunderjet. The Soviet machine was designated Yak-19 and was the result of experiments by Yakovlev to create a more modern and streamlined shape.

Yak-19 reached 904kph at 5,000m with afterburner but tests ended in August 1947 and it remained in prototype form only.

It was already clear when the first jet fighter prototypes were being test flown that Soviet aviation technology was still in its early stages. The first steps were being taken in the use of new aerodynamics and mechanics of high subsonic speeds. Speeds of up to 900kph could be reached by relatively conventional means, although there was much to be done in this department too.

It was not just a question of aerodynamics and airframe construction. Jet engines at the USSR's disposal at this time were adequate for this first step from reciprocating engines to jet engines. Doubling or further augmenting the engines certainly provided more thrust but the propulsive unit was too heavy, complicated and vulnerable. Development required money and time.

Money was soon obtained but time was short. The design groups of A M Lyulka, V J Klimov, V N Chelomej, A A Mikulin and others were in the early stage of their work. Soviet aviation urgently needed jet engines of more than 1,500kp thrust and, in the near future, engines of more than 2,000kp. Full use was made of the data in seized German documents and German technicians were sent to Soviet research and design

Below: La-152, first of a series of new prototypes built by Lavochkin between 1946 and 1947.

MiG-9FR with pressurised cabin quickly followed MiG-9 and was produced up to the end of 1948.

centres. Work proceeded fast and successfully but help had to be sought abroad.

In Spring 1947 the USSR received 30 Rolls-Royce Derwent jet engines and 25 of the most modern Rolls-Royce Nene from Britain. Both engines were robust, possessed centrifugal compressors and provided, respectively, 1,660kp and 2,270kp. They were particularly reliable engines, thanks to nimonic alloy of great durability. There were prospects of the Nene retaining its technological lead for many years, as well as further increasing its performances. Great Britain was later strongly criticised for this help accorded the USSR, but the engine business was profitable to both sides.

The British engines were assigned to Soviet research centres for study and preparations were to be made for serial production. Design groups of the airframe industry were also given the engines and the task of designing aircraft for them. Soviet designation given to the Derwent was RD-500, while the Nene was coded RD-45.

In 1947 aircraft for the RD-500 were built and examined in the drawing offices of Yakovlev and Lavochkin.

The Yakolev Yak-23 represented a further development of Yak-15 and Yak-17, that is, it had the engine under the fuselage. But on Yak-23 the engine was the larger RD-500, which also increased dimensions of the front fuselage. Yak-23 was in all metal construction and had a tricycle undercarriage which was retractable. Under the wing tips, two additional drop shaped tanks, each with 300 litres capacity, could be stowed. Yak-23 reached 920kph at 7,000m with 3,350kg take off weight and 950kph at 9,000m. Ceiling was 14,800m but as the cabin was not pressurised, the machine could normally only operate up to 13,000m. Armament consisted of twin fuselage-mounted 150P 23mm cannon; sometimes twin, wing-mounted NR-23K were added.

Yak-23 was serially produced on a fairly large scale and also delivered to the air forces of Poland, Bulgaria and Czechoslovakia. Czechoslovakian machines were given the designation S-101. The Polish test pilot, Ablamovicz, reached an international record for climb performance in 1957 with a Yak-23, reaching 6,000m in 3 minutes 17 seconds.

Lavochkin first used the RD-500 engine in his experimental La-174TK. "TK" meant *Tonkoye Krylo,* (Thin Wing). The La-174TK was used in tests on machines with extremely thin wing profile and at that time 6% profile thickness was already of extreme value. The machine was a continuation of the La-156 series with a stronger forward fuselage. It was finished in December 1947 and its flight tests continued until March 1948. Highest speed reached was 965kph at 3,000m.

Below: La-156 was more heavily armed than Lavochkin's other prototypes in this range.

Yak-19 received the nickname 'Red Thunderjet' due to its similarity to the American F-84 Thunderjet.

Above: Yak-23, a development of the Yak-15 and Yak-17 series but with a larger engine.

Below: Lavochkin's thin wing La-174TK which achieved a maximum of 965kph.

Su-11 was intended for long-range escort and combat sorties but did not reach production.

Sukhoi was the first Soviet designer to use the new Soviet engines within this time span. His aircraft was the Su-11, a further development of the twin-motored fighter, Su-9. The airframes of both machines were almost identical, but the second was bigger so that it might accommodate TR-1 engines, each of 1,300kp thrust. The engines were A M Lyulka's and a direct continuation of the experimental VDR-3.

Su-11 was not only intended for long-range fighter operations but also for combat sorties. The aircraft had, as its standard equipment, two NS-23 and a N-37 cannon; when used as a ground attack plane the N-37 cannon was exchanged for an automatic anti-tank gun of 45mm calibre. Under the wings were suspension devices for 500kg bombs. The pressurised cabin was a novelty.

Flight tests of Su-11 went on until April 1948. Maximum speed was not very great at 850kph at 8,000m, but on low level flights the machine could reach a creditable 740kph. Range of 900km made the Su-11 certainly not a long-range fighter, and the aircraft was never released for series production, because the department for aircraft construction always had reservations about Sukhoi's aeroplanes.

Lesser known is the work done by S M Alexeyev, formerly Lavochkin's deputy designer and co-author of La-5 and La-7 fighters. In 1946-1948 he had his own design bureau. His first type was the I-211 mid-wing monoplane powered by two Lyulka AL-1 engines of 1,000kp thrust. The I-211 had conventional lines with engine nacelles coming through the wing. Armament consisted of three NS-37 cannon. I-211 was tested in 1947 but results were poor because of the unproven engines.

In 1948 the I-212 appeared, having the same general lines as I-211 but with twin Nene engines. It had a trio of cannon in the nose – one NS-37 and twin NS-23. In the rear a remotely-controlled turret with twin G-20 cannon of 20mm could be operated by a gunner sitting behind the pilot. The machine was finished but not tested.

Third prototype by Alexeyev was the I-215 single seater of 1947, again similar to I-211. It had two Derwent engines and was conceived as a bomber-destroyer. Armament consisted of three N-37 or twin NS-57 cannon (35mm calibre) or, alternatively, twin 113P-57 of the same calibre. The I-215 had a radar scope in front of the fuselage. The first example had a conventional three-wheel undercarriage but the second was tested with a tandem system. In 1948 Alexeyev's work was suspended.

The aircraft mentioned so far represent the last Soviet jet fighter aircraft with straight wings and straight tail surfaces. At this stage the straight continuous surfaces reached their fullest potential for the times as regards profile, aspect ratios and span. Air compression now stood in the way of further speed increases. Only more powerful engines and, even more important, aerodynamic improvements in the airframe could make the conquest of sonic speed possible.

And it was not only a question of aerodynamics. The aircraft of sound particle velocity needed new methods of communication. Methods of navigation, especially methods of electronic navigation, had to be introduced or else improved on. The same went for the gunsight systems. In addition were difficulties like weight saving, miniaturising all equipment etc. Aviation, at the stage of conquering sonic speed, provided occupation for workers in varied technical fields and required close collaboration of numerous scientific spheres.

After many experiments at TsAGI the first sweptback surfaces in the USSR made their appearance in 1947. Yakovlev designed a one-seat test fighter, Yak-25, with RD-500 engine. The machine was a direct derivative of Yak-19, had straight wings but swept-back tail surfaces. Yakovlev made use of the discovery that the symptoms of air compression (i.e. laminar flow separation and ineffectiveness of control surfaces) manifest themselves on the tail surfaces sooner than on the straight wings. By using a swept-back tail, higher critical Mach numbers can be reached and the aircraft is able to fly faster, even with straight wings. Unfortunately, the difference is too slight, and flight testing of Yak-25 made this clear.

Flight tests began on October 31, 1947, and lasted until July 1948. The Yak-25, with S N

Anokhin at the controls, attained 982kph at sea level and 953kph at 5,000m. Armament consisted of a trio of NR-23 cannon. Yak-25 was a step forward but of limited importance in the fast development of jet fighters.

The combination of sweptback wings and tail surfaces represented a radical solution to the problem. Several constructional, aeronautical and practical problems cropped up in connection with these forms, and their solution took a lot of time and money. For instance, in the context of this explorative work, between 1946 and 1948, V P Tsybin designed and built several unmanned gliders with wings of various sweeps, including sweptforward construction. These were carried by bombers and released at height. They made landing flights at various speeds according to the volume of water ballast taken in fuselage tanks. The measuring and film apparatus on board then established results of the gliding flights.

Lavochkin's design group was first in the USSR to build an aircraft with sweptback wings – the La-160, test flown in June 1947. The wings had 35 degrees sweep-back, but otherwise the machine was strongly reminiscent of La-174TK. With a take-off weight of 4,060kg the aircraft reached 1,050kph at 5,700m, that is Mach 0.92 – a noteworthy achievement with an RD-10A engine of only 1,100kp thrust.

Although the La-160 was intended more as a test aircraft than a fighter, it had two N-37 cannon. With La-160 Lavochkin embarked on a whole series of experimental aircraft which were forerunners of technical advances and paved the way for other drawing offices.

Even at this stage of incomplete development the Soviets realised that the introduction of jet aircraft of even greater speeds would also make increasing demands on the airfields. True, all Soviet fighters were designed in such a way that they could operate without difficulties from grass fields, but for everyday service concrete strips were indispensable. Take-off and landing runways were also lengthened.

Soviet aircraft designers were inventive, shown by the fact that at the rudimentary stage of jet aircraft design they not only studied the problems of vertical take-off but also thought of conducting practical experiments.

In 1946 A J Shcherbakov designed a vertical take-off and landing fighter. His drawing office was dissolved in 1947 but the supreme command of the Air Force made it possible for him to continue his work. His aircraft had the designation VSI (*Vysotno-Skorostnii Istrebitel* = High Altitude and High Speed Pursuit Aircraft). It represented, once again, a compromise between the manoeuvrable and high speed fighter.

VSI had two rotatable engine nacelles on the tips of short wings. The jet engines in these nacelles (on VSI they were Rolls-Royce Nenes) enabled the aircraft to make a vertical take-off and also powered the aircraft in horizontal flight.

Design of the VSI was fairly advanced by 1947. An experimental model was built with a steel tube framework and two rotatable BMW 003 engines on the wing tips. The whole was fastened by ropes to four columns, so that the appliance could easily move up and down of its own accord. Before the designer could begin tests an order came to halt all work. The USSR might have achieved a notable advance in this field. But today there is nothing but a picture of the wind tunnel model.

Above: First Soviet fighter to have swept-back tail surfaces was Yak-25 which demonstrated the limited usefulness of this small step in the battle to achieve higher Mach numbers.

Below left: Swept-back wings first appeared in the USSR on Lavochkin's La-160, test flown in June 1947. It got to Mach 0.92 with a relatively weak RD-10A engine.

Right and below: These photographs of a wind tunnel model are all that remains of A J Shcherbakov's design for a VTOL fighter conceived in 1946. The engines rotated for forward or vertical flight.

CHAPTER 15

Jet Fighters of a new Generation

FIGHTERS WHICH reached speeds of over 1,000kph and nearly Mach 1 can safely be described as aircraft of the new generation, for they differed in all aspects from earlier models.

The year 1946 was significant for world aviation technology owing to the velocity jump of fighters. Prototypes appeared of the American XF-86 Sabre of the North-American firm and its counterpart the Soviet MiG-15, two aircraft closely connected with aviation history.

In March 1946 the leaders of some Soviet drawing offices were given the task of designing jet aircraft which could reach a speed of over 1,000kph on service with the troops. Other tactical-technical stipulations were rigorous and ambitious: service ceiling of over 14,000m, cannon armament, pressurised cabin with ejector seat, facilities for direct co-operation with the army on low level flights, provision for bombs and rockets etc., all this plus the ability to operate from grass runways in all weathers.

On December 30, 1947, A V Yuganov test flew the I-310 of design group Mikoyan-Gurevich. The machine was very robust in comparison to other Soviet fighters and possessed a thick, spindle-shaped fuselage. The wings, with 35 degrees sweep-back had a new TsAGI-S-10s airfoil with good high-velocity distribution, but the airfoil was not too thin to allow the incorporation of various pieces of equipment. The wing had an anhedral of 2 degrees. Tail surfaces were also well swept back, the vertical given an angle of 56 degrees on the leading edge. Horizontal fins were arranged in a typical fashion, high on the rudder. The point of this was to have them as far as possible from the centre of gravity so that they might be built small, that is, with low resistance and light weight.

The air intake in the fuselage was divided into two tunnels between which was the pilot's cockpit. Behind the cockpit were fuel tanks of 1,240 litres capacity and the Rolls-Royce Nene II engine which had a relatively short jet. On both sides of the fuselage, behind the wings, were two air brakes. The whole aircraft stood on a tricycle undercarriage.

Maintenance had been carefully thought out. The fuselage on the frame of the engine mounting could be separated into two parts. The back part could be pulled away and the whole engine cleared for maintenance. Armament consisted of two NS-23 cannon on the left side of the fuselage nose and an N-37 cannon on the right. The armament outfit consisted of a bathtub which was separable from the aircraft by means of a winch and steel rope for repairs, servicing of the ammunition etc. On the underside of the wing were two spare jettisonable ovoid tanks, each of 250 litres.

The original I-310 prototype needed some redesign and the occasion was used to include some new demands formulated by the Air Force in March 1947. Two new prototypes were built of I-310(S) in S-01 and S-02 forms. The first example (S-02) entered the Scientific and Test Institute of the Red Air Force on May 27, 1948, but in March it had already been decided to begin series production under designation MiG-15.

S-01 and S-02 prototypes were used for experiments with different engines, first with the Soviet-built Nenes known as RD-45 (2,270kpt) or RD-45F in an improved configuration. Later Klimov's VK-1 (2,700kpt) and its afterburner variant VK-1F (3,380kpt) were tested, too.

The speed of MiG-15 development is typified in the case of the I-300FN experimental prototype. This was a MiG-9 adapted for the installation of a single Rolls-Royce Nene in order to assess the engine for I-310(S). The I-300FN was built, but not tested, because I-310(S) could be flown earlier than expected.

Opening series production before the tests were concluded proved worthwhile. In 1949 the first units were equipped and the MiG-15 soon became the standard jet fighter of the USSR and its allies. Its performance lead was so great that the machine constituted the backbone of fighter units for ten or twelve years.

The MiG-15 reached 1,070kph maximum speed at 12,000m, that is Mach 0.92. Climbing speed at low

Above: Yak-30 was a late starter compared to its MiG-15 rival.

Below: S-101, prototype of the I-310 or MiG-15.

Bottom: MiG-15bis was designed in 1949 and equipped many friendly air forces.

altitude was 42m a second, the service ceiling 15,200m and range 1,450 to 1,960km. This was all achieved with 4,800kg take-off weight. American's XF-86 Sabre reached at that time 1,030kph with 6,220kg take-off weight, but its range was better, starting at 1,600km. Armament consisted of six M-3 machine guns of 12.7mm calibre.

The MiG-15 was superior to the models of other drawing offices. It was also ready much sooner for flight testing. On September 4, 1948, when the first rival, A S Yakovlev's Yak-30 took off, the MiG-15 had already been taken on. The two machines had, in many respects, an identical construction. But engine was the RD-500 of 1,590kpt and armament included only two cannon. On performance Yak-30 dropped behind, reaching only 1,025kph and a service ceiling of 15,000m.

A S Lavochkin's office was also very busy. Lavochkin tried to design fighter aeroplanes for both types of jet engines available, the Nene and Derwent. The La-168, tested by I E Fedorov on April 22, 1948, was like a MiG-15 converted to the shoulder-wing configuration favoured by Lavochkin at that time. It had the same engine and armament, but its wing had a sharper sweep-back of 37.3 degrees.

Tests lasted until February 1949 and the La-168 reached 1,084kph. During the trials one curious incident occurred when pilot V I Khomyakov fired all three cannon at 15,000m. The cabin roof cracked and Khomyakov lost consciousness in the decompression. The La-168 fell in an uncontrolled dive, attaining more than Mach 1. Some 4,000m later Khomyakov came round and was able to recover from the dive and land. Because of the ongoing MiG-15 production, La-168 was not accepted.

Lavochkin's La-174D (nothing like the La-174TK) was similar to a Yak-30 – the result of another philosophy of design. Lavochkin wanted to achieve the same performance with a lighter and smaller aircraft, using a less powerful engine. La-174D had a span of only 8.83m, but same

sweep-back as the La-168 and armament of three NS-23 cannon. With the Derwent engine it attained 1,040kph.

Tests lasted from August until September 1948 and the machine was recommended for series production as the La-15. Series machines had an RD-500 engine and only two NS-23 Cannon. Production was limited but the machines remained in service until 1954 and were well liked by their pilots.

So in 1948 the Soviet Air Force got two fighters – the heavy MiG-15 with its universal uses, and the lighter La-15. At this time the MiG-15 got its baptism of fire. In Korea a war was raging in which the air forces of America and Great Britain clearly showed their superiority. The American Lockheed F-80 Shooting Star, Republic F-84 Thunderjet and Grumman F9F Panther had no great difficulties with the reciprocating engine Yak-9 and La-9 fighters of the Koreans. B-29 Superfortresses were able to bombard their targets almost unhindered. In November 1950 the first MiG-15 of Chinese volunteer units made their appearance and the aerial advantage began to shift.

The Americans had to act fast. In the middle of December F-86A Sabres were flown to Korea, although the Americans had not originally wanted to use this model. So from December 1950 to summer 1953 the best jet fighters of the two big powers were in combat against one another. American sources gave the ratio shot down as 792:78 in Sabre's favour. But the Americans always expressed their respect for the combat performances and qualities of MiG-15. At heights of over 9,000m they were supposed to be better than F-86A in every respect, thanks to lighter weight and lower wing loading. They were more manoeuvrable, had better climbing speed and higher service ceiling.

Admittedly the MiG-15 guns could not fire as many projectiles per minute as the six-machine guns of the F-86A, but they could attack effectively from a greater distance. American sources esti-

Right: Lavochkin's La-168 suffered a curious incident when the cockpit canopy cracked on firing all three cannon at 15,000m. Testing continued for some ten months before the aircraft was shelved.

mated that 1,024 rounds on an average were necessary to shoot down a MiG-15.

America explains the great difference in the numbers shot down as being due to the inexperience of most Chinese and North Korean fighter pilots as compared to veterans of the Second World War. With a good Chinese or Russian fighter pilot the MiG-15 was an extremely dangerous weapon, though disadvantaged by not having the radar gunsights of F-86A. At any rate, the MiG-15 were as surprising for the Americans as the Japanese Mitsubishi A6M Zero fighter aircraft in 1941.

The USA tried to get hold of some MiG-15s in good condition in order to test them thoroughly. A few shot down machines were secured and in 1953 the first undamaged aircraft were obtained for a short time when two Polish pilots landed in Denmark seeking asylum. These machines had to be given back. Then, in summer 1953, a North Korean pilot, tempted by a 100,000 dollar reward, delivered one into American hands.

This was a new model, MiG-15bis, with several improvements to engine, equipment and outfit. The machine was propelled by a VK-1 engine – a development of V J Klimov's RD-45 of 2,700kp thrust. Earlier the improved RD-45F and FA had been incorporated.

The 15bis were designed in 1949 with prototype designation SD and soon replaced the MiG-15 on assembly lines. Climb performance was better at 46m a second, as was a speed of 1,114kph in some radiuses of flight. Combat power was also superior, for the new 23mm NR-23 guns had a faster rate of fire and higher muzzle velocity. Later two ARS-212 rocket projectiles of 116kg or four TRS-190, each of 46kg, were added. The detailed investigation of MiG-15bis in the USA was not without bearing on the development of military aviation.

There were other variants of the MiG-15 and MiG-15bis. The MiG-15P was a two-seater night fighter with radar in the nose. MiG-15SV was a standard 15 but with NR-23 cannon instead of the old NS-23. MiG-15SP-1 was again a night fighter with VK-1 engine, radar and only one NS-37 or NS-45 cannon. MiG-15S and -15BbisS were long-range escort fighters and MiG-15bis LSh were Shturmoviks with rockets.

MiG-15 and MiG-15bis fighters constituted the armament not only of the USSR and Korea, but also of other People's Democracies in East and Middle Europe. In Czechoslovakia the MiG-15 and MiG-15bis were produced under licence from 1951 onwards, being known respectively as S-102 and S-103. Poland and Hungary also built them; they were known in Poland as LiM-1 and LiM-2.

The MiG-15bis was an all-rounder. It could be used for photo reconnaissance and in combat operations with rocket missiles, bombs etc. Night interceptors were also built with only two NR-23

Left: Production of Lavochkin's La-15 (La-174) was limited, but this lightweight fighter was well-liked by pilots.

Below: MiG-15PF was a night interceptor variant with radar gun-laying equipment incorporated in a lip above the air intake.

La-200B was tested until September 1952 when the project was abandoned.

Above: Lavochkin's La-200A flew for the first time on September 9, 1949.
Below: The sole Su-15 broke up in the air while attempting to exceed Mach 1.

guns but featuring radar gun-laying equipment in the form of a broad lip on the upper side of the air inlet and an ovoid casing in the middle. This equipment, which had the name Isumrud, was first used on the SP-5 variant in 1950.

Aircraft were also given better drop tanks. Early ovoid ones did not fall clear but slid along to the wing tips and often damaged the ailerons. The new drop-shaped tanks had small auxiliary surfaces to facilitate separation.

It had become a certain tradition for the MiG-15 and MiG-15bis always to show up in those places where political crisis had arisen or even where open fighting had broken out. MiGs were used in the Middle East in 1956, operating along-side Egyptian aircraft. Unfortunately, Egyptian fighter pilots were not up to the standard of their machines. Several young states of South America and Asia were armed with MiGs, as was Cuba. If ever there was an aircraft with a political as well as military significance then this was certainly MiG-15.

In Summer 1948, immediately after the Air Force's design competition which had produced the MiG-15 and La-15 fighters, the drawing offices received further orders. The Air Force required heavy fighters for the systematic radar monitoring of Soviet sovereign territory under all climatic conditions. As Soviet radar equipment was still voluminous and heavy, requiring an operator, the aircraft had to be relatively heavy too, for they wanted an appropriate duration of flight and adequate armament.

The resulting models I-320(R) of Mikoyan and Guryevich and the La-200 of Lavochkin that appeared in 1949 were remarkably similar. Both were mid wing monoplanes with 35 degrees sweep of about 13m span and both had 10 tons take-off weight.

They were propelled by twin VK-1 engines, each of 2,740kp thrust. The first engine was in the nose, directly behind the air inlet, with an exhaust outlet under the fuselage. Behind came the cock-pit with two ejector seats next to one another,

followed by the second engine, exhaust nozzle being directly under the tail surfaces as on MiG-15. Air to the second engine was channelled from the nose through a duct.

There was a difference in the radar outfit. I-320(R) had a radar nose on the upper side of the air inlet, La-200's radar antenna was in a plastic egg in the main inlet. Armament consisted of three N-37 guns.

Mikoyan and Gurevich built their I-320(R) in three examples. The first, R-1, appeared at the end of 1949 and had twin RD-45F. A A Vernikov was its test pilot. In 1950 the R-2 and R-3 appeared, both flown by J A Antipov. They had VK-1 engines and many other changes. Whereas the R-1 attained 1,060kph the prototypes with VK-1 were 30kph faster. They could also take off and be cruise-flown with one engine stopped. All the tests ended in 1950.

Lavochkin's La-200 flew for the first time on September 9, 1949, with S F Moshkovskii as pilot and its test lasted until April 1951. It was recom-mended for series production, offering a speed of 1,062kph and the capability to reach Mach 1.01 in a shallow dive.

Another variant, La-200B, was built in 1951/52 and flight tested on July 3, 1952. Tests lasted until September when all work was abandoned due to appearance of the more conventional Yak-25. Engines were VK-1A of 3,100kp each.

Sukhoi also designed an all-weather fighter at that time, Su-15 or Samolet "P". The prototype had already been test flown on January 11, 1949. It had a single seat with two RD-45 engines one over the other. The upper engine was set slightly back and had its outlet under the controls; front engine had its outlet on the underside of the fuselage. Armament consisted of two N-37 guns each with 110 rounds.

On test flights in June 1949 the pilot tried to go over the Mach 1 speed at 4,550m, but there were heavy oscillations in the controls which caused the aircraft to break up in the air. The pilot was able to save himself by ejecting but the Su-15 was not developed further.

Meanwhile the war for speed continued to rage. Hardly had they reached 1,000kph than they aimed for sonic speed. This, too, was achieved by increasing surface sweep to 45 de-grees and improving thrust.

On December 26, 1948, Hero of the Soviet Union I V Fedorov reached Mach 1 for the first time in the USSR when he made a dive with full throttle from 10,000 to 7,000m. Aircraft was an experimental machine by Lavochkin, the La-176. It was a further development of the La-168 line with 45 degrees wing sweep and VK-1 engine.

Left: Mikoyan and Gurevich's I-320(R) competed with the La-200 for a heavy all-weather fighter contract.

A model of Sukhoi's Su-17. The full-scale aircraft was not completed.

By the end of January Federov and O V Sokolovskii had together made six supersonic level flights but the La-176 eventually crashed. After the findings had been analysed designers were able to develop new models for the series.

Before the end of 1949 two supersonic aircraft were completed and a third almost finished. Third aircraft was the Su-17 from Sukhoi's group, designed slightly to exceed Mach 1. Sukhoi counted on reaching M 1.02 (1,250kph) at low altitude and M 1.07 (1,150kph) at 11,000m. Wing sweep was 50 degrees and the Mikulin AM-3 engine of 4,600kp thrust with axial compressor was built in.

Sukhoi thought a lot about the rescue of the pilot. He imagined that at speeds of 1,150kph and at heights over 11,000m the ejector seat would not suffice, so he designed an ejector cabin for Su-17 which could be separated as a whole from the aircraft. This cabin increased the weight to 7,400kg, or so it is calculated. Two N-37 in the fuselage constituted the armament. By 1949 the airframe of Su-17 was almost completed when Sukhoi's drawing office was dissolved and the Su-17 destroyed.

The supersonic type finally introduced as the standard aircraft was much simpler than Su-17. Prototype I-330(S1) of the Mikoyan-Gurevich group was test flown in winter 1949-50. At first glance there was a close relationship with the MiG-15 family. But the wings had 45 degrees sweep and the VK-1 engine of 2,650kp thrust was in the fuselage which had a modified tail. Armament remained the same as on MiG-15 or MiG-15bis.

Pilots G A Sedov and I T Ivashchenko began the test programme in January 1950. With 5,200kg flying weight the SI-M prototype reached Mach 1 in horizontal flight. Maximum speed was 1,114kph at 2,200m; at 12,000m the speed was still 1,020kph. Rate of climb at low altitude was 50m a second and duration of flight was 110 minutes.

The SI-01 prototype crashed in March 1950 killing its pilot, Ivashchenko. The second prototype SI-2 (original designation MiG-15bis-45°) ended its tests in June 1951 and was put into production as the MiG-17. Normal armament consisted of one N-37 and twin NR-23 cannon.

A few years later the MiG-17 was also allocated to the air forces of some Eastern states. In Poland they were built under licence and designated LiM-5. The Poles also developed their own ground fighter, LiM-6, from MiG-17. The wing centre section was much extended so that it could take more fuel and there were twin wheels on the main undercarriage.

MiG-17s with VK-1 engine and Isumrud radar equipment were used in state defence units as interceptor MiG-17P. Shortly after introduction a new engine variant was designed and built, the VK-1F with an afterburner, which increased thrust from 2,650kp to 3,360kp. The -17 with afterburner was designated MiG-17F; as an interceptor it was designated MiG-17PF. The afterburner increased the maximum speed to 1,145kph at 3,000m and the service ceiling to 16,600m.

Above: First Soviet aircraft to exceed Mach 1, the experimental La-176.

Below: MiG-17P was an interceptor with VK-1 engine and Isumrud radar. Its ancestor was the MiG-17 prototype, SI (bottom).

Even at 15,600m the aircraft could execute complicated flying manoeuvres.

The combat F variant had the full armament of two NR-23 and one N-37 gun. P and PF models had only two NR-23 guns. At the beginning of the 1960s cannon armament was replaced by four air-to-air ARS-212 guided rockets. These machines were designated MiG-17PFU.

MiG-17s also constituted the armament of some forces in Africa and Asia as well as Cuba. During the Suez crisis in 1956, Egyptian MiG-17s fought with the Israeli Dassault Mystere-IVA, but success depended to a great extent on the quality of the pilots. Surprisingly successful were the MiG-17s at the beginning of the Vietnam conflict.

Parallel to MiG-17 another machine was developed, also intended to have Mach 1 speed, the Yak-50. Yakovlev also used wings with 45 degrees sweep and VK-1A engine, later introducing the VK-1F with afterburner. Yak-50 was regarded from the start as an interceptor, so it had Itsumrud radar equipment in the form of a nose over the air inlet and just two NR-23 guns. The aircraft had bicycle gear – a nose wheel and a double wheel under the fuselage. On the wing tips retracting struts were built in with small wheels. Yak-50 remained a mere prototype for it was easier to serially produce MiG-17. The speed of over 1,170kph was the best of its Soviet contemporaries.

In the first fifty years of this century machines were not yet available for a twenty-four hour monitoring system in the context of aerial defence of territory. During 1951 the USSR's electronics industry had designed new, effective radar equipment for target pick-up at longer ranges. But the equipment needed an operator and its antenna had a fairly large diameter requiring wide fuselages. The fighters for this role were to be designed in the drawing offices of Yakovlev and Lavochkin.

Yakovlev's machine was designated Yak-25, so it was his second model number 25. Yakovlev often used the model numbers of rejected machines again partly, perhaps, for reasons of camouflage. The Yak-25 was in every respect a more modern machine than La-200B – a midwing monoplane with 45 degrees wing sweep and thick, cylindrical fuselage as well as two slender AM-5 engines, each of 2,000kp, under the wing. The machine was a two seater, one behind the other, and had a bicycle gear with retractable struts under the wings. Armament consisted of two N-37 guns under the fuselage.

The whole nose was made of plastic material and formed the cover of the radar display. Yak-25 reached 1,140kph on test flights, service ceiling was 15,500m and range 2,500 to 3,000km.

In his book *"Tsel Shisni"* (Aim of Life) Yakovlev recalls a dramatic discussion in the Kremlin in 1952. A decision was to be made as to which of the two aircraft should be put into production. L P Berija backed Lavochkin's La-200B but Yakovlev tried to win Stalin over to his Yak-25 and succeeded.

Yak-25 was certainly more modern and had good potential for further development. By summer 1952 a few were introduced into the air parade in Tushino. Production machines had improved AM-5F engines of 3,600kp thrust with afterburner and remained the backbone of all-weather and night fighter units during the fifties.

Yak-25's plastic nose concealed an effective radar system which made it a cornerstone of Soviet defence during the 1950s.

Below left: Yak-50 was fastest Soviet aircraft of its day, but remained a prototype due to ongoing production of MiG-17.

Below: Yakovlev's second Yak-25 designation was allocated to this all-weather night fighter which won a taut battle for production in the Kremlin.

CHAPTER 16

Supersonic Fighters

AT THE beginning of the fifties, fighter speed rose higher and higher. But every step had to be won by complicated theoretical and experimental work in scientific institutions and the construction and testing of aircraft. Further aerodynamic improvements of the airframe, an increase in engine thrust, the use of afterburners, new methods for steering at high speeds; all these features combined to bring success.

As on all earlier occasions when there had been a leap ahead in fighter performance, Lavochkin again was the pioneer. Early in 1949 his design group had begun the study of a supersonic fighter, La-190. Development was slow and difficult, involving close collaboration with TsAGI. Lavochkin designed new variable camber flaps and slats, hydraulic servo-control, new bicycle gear and, above all, new wings with 55 degrees sweep back. All design details were first tested on prototypes before production machines could be built.

La-190 was completed in February 1951 and tested with Lyulka's AL-5 engine of 5,000kp thrust, achieving 1,190kph at 5,000m. Service ceiling was 15,600m and range 1,150km. These figures were not dramatic in comparison with production MiG-17s and flying qualities at maximum speed were not satisfactory. On the other hand, the La-190 was especially stable and simple to fly at lower speeds.

One peculiarity of La-190 was fuel tanks taking up the whole internal room of the wing, the first of their kind on Soviet fighters. La-190 well fulfilled its role – being the first step in the direction of supersonic speed. Unfortunately the AL-5 engine was far from reliable and there were only eight flights in all. The La-190 had twin N-37 cannon.

That the task was not at all easy is shown by Yakovlev's Yak-1000, again of 1951. It had the same AL-5 engine of 5,000kp but the wings and controls had a triangular form, the first on a Soviet fighter. The wing tips were angular, the low vertical fin was specially shaped and the aircraft had a bicycle gear with wing-tip struts. When the first ground tests were carried out Yak-1000 exhibited such serious defects that it had to be

sent back to the plant for revision, but never returned to the airfield.

Once again a machine of Mikoyan's, MiG-19, was the first Soviet supersonic fighter put into production. Mikoyan designed the machine himself, for Gurevich had to give up the active work for health reasons.

During a meeting in Stalin's office at the Kremlin in Summer 1951 development of this aircraft was approved. Mikoyan chose a twin engined design in order to achieve two goals – high thrust with high speed and flight of economical speed over long distances with only one engine running. This twin-engined project was called I-350(SM).

As insurance against possible failure of this concept Mikoyan projected a single-engined variant. The I-360 followed the lines of MiG-15 and MiG-17 family with high-set tailplane but wing sweep of 55 degrees. I-360 was built and flown but no detailed information has survived.

The I-350(SM) had new design features with a tailplane set low on the fuselage and two engines side-by-side behind the 55 degrees angle wing. The prototype I-350 (SM) was test flown for the first time on September 18, 1953, with twin Mikulin AM-5 engines of 2,000kp thrust. Originally it had three cannon – one N-37 in the fuselage and one NR-23 in each of the wing roots.

In the first test phase the prototype attained

Lavochkin's La-190, first flown in 1951, was a major advance in the quest for supersonic speed.

Mach 1.1 without difficulties. State acceptance tests began in the Spring of 1954 and in Autumn the machine was released for series production with two modified AM-5 of 2,250kp.

Machines of the first series batch suffered from poor tailplane effect and it was necessary to introduce an all-moving type with counter-balances against flutter. A gear was installed in the system called ARU (*Avtomaticheskii Regulator Upravlenia* = Automatic Rudder Regulator) that transmitted movements of the pilot's stick in relation to speed and altitude.

Series production machines were designated MiG-19, followed by MiG-19S after tailplane modification and MiG-19F when afterburners were added to the 3,150kp thrust AM-5F engines. Series MiG-19S and F had a trio of Nudelman-Richter NR-30 cannon – two in the wing roots and one in the fuselage. The fighters carried auxiliary tanks of 300, 400 or 800 litres capacity, two bombs of 250 or 500kg and unsteered rockets of 55mm calibre.

Left: Problems with Yak-1000 were such that it never returned for testing after preliminary ground tests.

Mikoyan came up with the USSR's first supersonic fighter in the form of MiG-19. His initial prototypes were twin-engined I-350 (SM), pictured below, and a single-engine variant, I-360 (above) which he produced as insurance against failure of his primary concept.

A MiG-19F, distinguished by the addition of afterburner and three Nudelman-Richter cannon.

MiG-19S and F were normally considered as day fighters. For bad weather service the MiG-19P interceptor was built with Izumrud radar in an upper lip and in a cone in the middle of the air intake.

Original MiG-19F attained 1,400kph and climbed 80 metres per second at sea level. Later MiG-19Fs from the second half of the 1950s attained 1,452kph at 10,000m and a climb rate of 115mps. They had AM-9B engines of 2,600kp (3,600kp with afterburner). An all-weather variant was the MiG-19PF and later came the MiG-19PM, lacking cannon but carrying four self-aiming rockets.

MiG-19s were of great importance to the Soviet Union and other socialist countries, as well as Indonesia, Afghanistan, Egypt, Cuba and Iraq. They were licence-built in Czechoslovakia (originally as the S-105) and in Poland (LiM-7) while non-licenced production was opened in China under the designation F-6. Others were delivered to Pakistan, Zambia and Tanzania. In China an assault version is in production with a pointed nose and twin air intakes called Q-5.

In the Soviet Union there were many experimental variants of MiG-19. The MiG-19SM-10 of 1955 was modified for in-flight refuelling and fitted with a long probe in the nose.

MiG-19SM-12PM of 1957 was powered by more powerful RS-26 engines of unknown thrust and had a long air intake with radar cone in the middle; speed was 1,720kph and ceiling 17,400m. In 1957 the MiG-19SM-12PMU appeared with twin RZM-26 engines and an under-fuselage pod containing a liquid fuel Dushkin RU-01Z auxiliary rocket engine. The machine attained 24,000m ceiling.

MiG-19SM-30 was used in 1956 for test launchings from a ramp on a lorry, using solid fuel auxiliary rockets. Last known variant was the MiG-19SM-50 of 1960, powered by twin AM-9BM of 3,300kp plus a U-19 liquid fuel auxiliary rocket engine of 3,200kp. The rocket was in a container under the fuselage and helped the machine attain 20,000m in 8 minutes, a ceiling of 24,000m and maximum speed of 1,800kph. It carried two NR-30 cannon.

Among fighters exhibited at the 1959 Tushino air parade, those with triangular wings and standard sweptback tail surfaces excited particular attention. The designs showed that they were intended for horizontal flights at Mach 2.

Aircraft with delta wings began to appear more and more frequently in newspapers. On October 31, 1959, it was announced that Hero of the USSR,

Below: MiG-19SM-10 were modified for in-flight refuelling.

MiG-19PF was an all-weather variant of the MiG-19 family.

Mosolov, had set a new speed record of 2,388kph with the Ye-66. It had Tumanskii R-37F engine of 3,900kp, or 6,000kp with afterburner. It soon became known that the Ye-66 was to be released as MiG-21.

They soon replaced the earlier MiG models in the Soviet Air Force and in units of Socialist states. Czechoslovakia produced them for some time under licence. In the earliest years MiG-21 was designated as a separate class among combat fighters of the world without comparable type anywhere.

In aerial combats over North Vietnam the Korean situation repeated itself. American sources rated the MiG-21 very highly, in some respects even superior to the McDonnell F-4 Phantom-II. But the quality of pilots again decreased operational efficiency. It was even worse at the time of the second Suez war in Summer 1967 when most Egyptian MiG-21 fell victim to a surprise attack before they could engage.

In comparision to other Mach 2 fighters, the MiG-21 is a light and refined machine with small engine thrust. Thanks to good airframe aerodynamics the aircraft could reach Mach 2 even with a weak engine.

Origins of MiG-21 began in 1955 when the Mikoyan group designed and built the I-1 prototype of a universal fighter destined to replace MiG-19. It had to be capable of intercept missions, engaging enemy fighters and attacking ground targets.

The I-1 had a wing of 60 degrees sweep and its single Klimov VK-3 engine of 8,400kp allowed 1,960kph maximum speed with 18,000m ceiling. Armament consisted of twin 30mm cannon and rockets.

From the same period came Mikoyan's Ye-50 with 55 degrees sweep, one TRD-9E turbojet of 3,800kp and an ShRD-S-155 rocket engine. The whole machine was relatively heavy at 8,500kg and attained 2,450kph on both engines. Ceiling was 25,600m and again there were twin NR-30 cannon.

In 1956 Mikoyan turned his attention to a lighter and more efficient concept. His Ye-2A, with one R-11-300 engine of 5,100kp reached 1,950kph, climbed to 10,000m in 1.3 minutes and its ceiling was 18,000m. It had a third NR-30 cannon. The lines were very similar to the later MiG-21 but the wing was swept-back to 55 degrees.

Mikoyan also began to use delta wings combined with swept-back tailplanes. Such a combination makes the aeroplane lighter and more manoeuvrable, enables the use of efficient

Below: MiG-19SM-12PM with radar cone in the centre of an extended nose.

Above: MiG-21 concluded a long period of exhaustive experimentation by Mikoyan.

Below: Ye-50 with additional ShRD-S-155 rocket engine in the tail.

Above: Lightweight Ye-2A with single R-11-300 engine.

Right: MiG-19SM-30 was tested in 1956 to assess the feasibility of launch from a motorised ramp. Rockets assisted take-off.

MiG-19 variants carrying liquid fuel auxiliary rocket engines in an under-fuselage pod were the MiG-19SM-50 (above) and MiG-19SM-12PMU (below). SM-50 was the last known version, appearing in 1960. It reached 20,000m in 8 minutes.

Mikoyan's final prototype in the build-up to MiG-21, the Ye-6 of 1958.

Ye-75F weighed 11,380kg at take-off but achieved remarkable performances.

A MiG-21F of Czechoslovakian origin, the only external constructors of this variant.

MiG-21PFM featured blown flaps and a broader back between cockpit and tail.

Fowler flaps and thus achieve relatively short take-off and landing distances without a high angle of attack necessary in plain triangular wings. Such benefits open up the possibility of operating from grass aerodromes when necessary, mostly with the use of auxiliary rocket engines and braking parachutes.

Triangular wings were used for the first time on Ye-4 and Ye-6 prototypes of 1956. Their leading edges had 57 degrees of sweep, engines were RD-11, speed 2,000kph and 15,000m was attained in 3.4 minutes. The Ye-75F of 1957 was again a much heavier type with 11,380kg take-off weight and one Lyulka AL-7F engine of 8,400kp. Its 2,300kph speed and 21,000m ceiling were remarkable, but Mikoyan returned to the lighter concept.

He debated between the Ye-2A and Ye-5 solution, built another swept-wing prototype, Ye-60, with an impressive speed of 2,460kph and 25,600m ceiling, but in the 1958 the long line of prototypes was terminated with the final solution – the Ye-6 prototype with triangular wing and single Tumanskii R-11F-300 engine of 5,100kp. The prototype was born and in 1959 its series production began with the name MiG-21.

First series version was the MiG-21F fitted with one R-11F-300 giving 3,900kp clean thrust and 5,750kp with afterburner. The machine climbed 140 metres per second and was armed with twin NR-30 cannon under the fuselage. Self-aiming rockets and unsteered rocket projectiles as well as bombs could be used.

The MiG-21PF with radar in the central cone had a better R-11F2-300 engine producing 6,200kp afterburning thrust. It climbed 150mps and attained 2,175kph. Only rockets were carried.

To improve landing/take-off characteristics and rate of turn Mikoyan began experiments with laminar-flow control on the MiG-21 family. The Ye-7 prototype of 1960 had blown flaps that lowered the landing speed by about 25 or 30kph and halved landing/take-off lengths. This equipment was named SPS (*Sduv Pogranichnogo Sloya* = Laminar-Flow Blow) and was used on series production MiG-21PFM. The PFM model had other modifications including better ejection seat, pods for auxiliary rocket engines etc.

Improved radar and other electronics and a broad back between the cabin and tail characterise the MiG-21PFMA.

Mainly for ground attack are the MiG-21MA and MF variants with a belly pod containing twin-barrel GSh-23 cannon of 23mm calibre. Newer variants are powered by the R-13-300 engine of 6,600kp thrust with afterburner.

Outside of the Soviet Union only Czechoslovakia produced the MiG-21F under licence for a short time. In January 1963 India received the first batch of six MiG-21F-13 and they were given the Indian designation Type 74. In 1964 another six MiG-21PF or Type 76 came and between 1966 and 1968 there followed the main shipment of export versions MiG-21FL (Type 77) and training two-seaters MiG-21U (Type 66).

Hindustan Aeronautics Ltd began to produce the MiG-21FL, originally from imported parts, in 1967 but since October 1970 has delivered the fully Indian-built Type 76. They use GSh-23 cannon and twin infra-red homed K-13A rockets, also built in India. The engine is of Indian origin and inner equipment is 60% domestic. Type 76 has the GSh-23 cannon in an under-belly pod while Type 88, also in production, has the same cannon built into the fuselage.

Without Soviet permission China opened production of a non-licence MiG-21 copy in 1964 under the designation J-7. But production was halted after about 100 had been constructed.

MiG-21s were famous fighters in their time. They were used by 33 air arms in almost all Socialist countries and other countries supported by the Soviet Union. In importance they can be compared only with the MiG-15.

America endeavoured to gain some undamaged examples and in 1966 an Iraqui deserter delivered one to Israel while others were captured during later struggles between Israel and Egypt. Some found their way to Edwards Air

Below: Ye-5 was one of the first testbeds for triangular wing form, appearing in 1956.

MiG-21 Type 92 used for testing vertical lift engines.

Interceptor Ye-150, a successor to the Ye-75F.

Above: One of many MiG-21FL types supplied to the Indian Air Force.
Right: Twin-engined version of the basic Ye-150 was Ye-152.
Below: Former speed record holder Ye-166 achieved 2,681kph during tests in 1961/62.

Base in the USA where they were tested.

In the USSR MiG-21s were used for vertical take-off and landing experiments with lifting jet engines mounted vertically in the fuselage between the cabin and the main engine. This variant, shown at the Domodedovo Air Show in 1967, was called MiG-21 Type 92.

The bigger member of the Mikoyan fighter family, the Ye-75F, also had its successors, first being the Ye-150 prototype of 1958. This was a relatively big aircraft with a cylindrical fuselage and fitted with a big afterburner. The common characteristics of this family were delta wings and swept tail surfaces. Almost all served as missile carriers for interception purposes.

A twin-engined arrangement of the basic Ye-150 was the Ye-152M with a speed of 3,000kph at 20,000m and a combat ceiling of 25,000m. In 1960 the Ye-152A appeared with twin R-11 engines of 5,100kp each. Final development was the Ye-166 prototype shown at Domodedovo in 1967. It was a very big machine with R-166 turbojet of 10,000kp. It bore on its fuselage a complete list of international records attained at the time of its tests in 1961-62 – speed over 15/25km base, G Mosolov, 2,681kph; speed over 100km circuit, A Fedotov, 2,401kph; ceiling in horizontal flight, P Ostapenko, 22,670m.

The records of Mosolov and Ostapenko were beaten by the American Lockheed YF-12A in 1965. But the two machines cannot be compared, for Ye-166 has a take-off weight of a little over 8,000kg and the YF-12A weighs a full 30 tons. Ye-166 has a classic duralumin construction while YF-12A is almost completely made of titanium and stainless steel.

After 1965 another Mikoyan-designed type appeared among the FAI records. It was a twin-engine type, Ye-266, and its engines were described in the protocols as R-266 of 11,000kp each. The first record flight was by A Fedotov on March 16, 1965, when a speed of 2,320kph was attained over a closed circuit of 1,000km with 2,000kg payload. The aircraft remained a secret until 1967 when it was shown at Domodedovo Airport, Moscow.

Mikoyan used a very new concept for the Ye-266, taking a broad wing of relatively modest sweep and low aspect ratio to ensure high performance at altitude together with acceptable characteristics for take-off, landing and low speed flight. Original were the vertical tail fins inclined outwards to avoid interference of airstream between them and to assure full effectiveness of the rudder. The great swept-back air intakes for the engines, with regulators for air entry in different flight patterns, were also original.

Technology was exceptionally simple with most parts built from duralumin. Areas more exposed to surface heating contained stainless steel but there was only modest use of titanium.

In October 1967 M Komarov and the Ye-266 recorded 2,981kph over 500km and Fedotov climbed to 29,977m with 2,000kg payload while further records fell in 1973, including an absolute ceiling of 36,240m.

Later a more refined variant appeared, the Ye-266M powered by a pair of 14,000kp engines and bettered some of the earlier records. Ceiling was pushed to 37,650m. A two-seater training variant was designated Ye-133 and served to achieve some feminine records.

Ye-266 was a prototype of the supersonic interceptor MiG-25. When one aircraft landed at Hakodate Airport, Japan, in September 1976, its relatively simple technology and the broad use of vacuum tube instead of solid-state electronics was often a source of unfavourable comments. But one fact remains: the MiG-25 is a very impressive machine with precision-made radar and high look-down ability.

A high-altitude reconnaissance type was evolved from the MiG-25, called MiG-25R, and from Ye-133 came the MiG-25U two-seat trainer.

During the often mentioned Soviet air show at Domodedovo in 1967 another machine designed by Mikoyan made its debut. It was a high-wing monoplane with variable geometry wing. Some years later its designation became known as MiG-23.

MiG-27 is adapted for close support work with the Army.

under the name J-8. The prototype is believed to have flown in 1980.

Another experimental fighter seen at Domodedovo had a MiG-23 type fuselage but fixed wings and vertical lift engines. Design number is still not known but NATO reporting name is 'Faithless.'

In 1953 Sukhoi was able to recommence design work as it became clear that the dissolution of his office in 1949 had been a great mistake. Sukhoi devoted his attentions to jet aircraft with delta wings and swept-back controls.

Sukhoi opened his new design office with projects for supersonic fighters of a new generation. For the first time in the USSR he projected all-moving tailplanes and regulation of air-stream in the intake by the use of a moveable cone. His first machine was called Su-1. Unfortunately no photographs are available but there were certainly some common characteristics with his later types.

During testing of the Su-1 in 1957 a speed of 2,170kph was attained.

Similar to the Su-1 but with a triangular wing was the T-3 built in 1956. It had a thick cylindrical fuselage and a radar nose over the air inlet.

T-3 became the basis for a range of experimental supersonic fighters between 1956 and 1959. They were called PT-7, PT-8, T-49 and T-5 and were, in fact, a further development of the T-3. Different shapes of air intakes were tested as well as air ducts inside the aircraft, different engines with new afterburners, new types of radar and their domes, auxiliary rocket engines, ejection seats etc. During experiments with new radars an asymmetrical air intake was tested with success on the PT-8.

The T-49 had twin side-mounted intakes which also showed up on the P-1 interceptor of 1957. It had a single engine of 10,000kp and its forward fuselage was full of 55m rockets. It attained 2,050kph and 19,500m ceiling but the tests were halted because of its unreliable engine.

When designing the T-37 Sukhoi used a very modern monocoque construction for the front and middle part of the fuselage whereas the tail part was welded from titanium and steel.

Besides the normal fighter an assault variant is known with a narrower nose, simpler air intake without regulators and heavier armament against ground targets. A special version for co-operation with the Army is designated MiG-27 and has more profound differences.

In 1979 a contract was signed with India for the licence production of MiG-23s at Hindustan Aeronautics and the first were delivered in 1982.

Some examples of MiG-23 delivered by the Soviet Union to Egypt are said to have been transported to China where a copy was built

Fitted with vertical lift engines, this aircraft is still only known by its NATO reporting name of 'Faithless'.

Ye-266 was a prototype of the supersonic interceptor MiG-25.

Above: MiG-23MF air combat fighter re-engined with R-29.

Below: A single seat variant developed for ground attack/strike is MiG-23BM.

Sukhoi's P-1 interceptor dating from 1957.

In 1959 two other prototypes appeared, the T-431 and T-405. The first of them was used by V Ilyushin (son of the designer) to set international records. On July 14, 1959, he attained 28,852m in dynamic ceiling and on September 4, 1962, in horizontal flight over a base of 15/25km, 21,170m ceiling with a speed of 2,100kph. On September 23 A Kozlov attained a speed of 2,337kph over a 500km closed circuit. In both cases the engine was described as TRD-31 of 10,000kp thrust.

The delta wing of the T-431 was the greatest difference when compared with the T-405 which had a sharp swept-back wing of about 55 degrees. The engine was the same TRD-31. On May 28, 1960, the T-405 with B Adrianov at the controls attained an international speed record over a closed circuit of 100km with 2,092kph.

It is very probable that the T-431 and T-405 were prototypes of pre-series machines of the two Sukhoi types we could identify some months later as the Su-9 and Su-7. A formation of 21 Su-7 was shown for the first time during the Tushino air parade in 1961.

It seems that the Su-7 was more successful in

Right: Su-7B taking off with the aid of auxiliary rocket engines.

Above: Su-78KL has low pressure tyres for operating on soft surfaces.

Su-7MK of the Egyptian Air Force.

the role of ground attack than as a pure fighter. For this purpose its Su-7B variant appeared and found widespread use in air arms of the Warsaw Pact states as well as Afghanistan, Egypt, India, Iraq, Syria, North Vietnam etc. The Egyptian, Syrian, Iraqui and Vietnamese Su-7s went through battle experience and proved to be excellent ground attack planes. The Indian Air Force encountered some difficulties with the required length of runway and relatively high fuel consumption of the Lyulka AL-7F-1-100 engine of 7,000/10,000kp.

The Su-7B has a pair of NR-30 cannon in the wing roots and under the fuselage are racks for two fuel tanks side-by-side. Under the wings are other racks for missiles, bombs, and /or external tanks.

After the Su-7B came the Su-7BM with a pair of braking parachutes in a cone over the jet exhaust. the Su-7BKL has low pressure tyres to aid take-off and landing on soft surfaces. Small skids on the main undercarriage legs support the main wheels and prevent subsidence into very soft ground. Su-7B can use a pair of rocket engines to shorten take-off runs.

The Su-9 differs from the Su-7 in its delta wing and very little is known through official sources. Sometimes the designation Su-11 is used in the press for a longer-nosed variant. A bigger twin-engined type is known as Su-15 and it has also been seen with lifting engines in the fuselage.

The need to shorten take-off and landing distances of Su-7 led to an experimental Su-71G with variable-geometry outer wing panels that can change the angle of sweep between 28 and 62 degrees. The Su-71G could later be seen in the air arms of Poland, Peru and Egypt. After the Su-71G, which was more or less an improvisation, the fully-designed Su-17 appeared along with larger and more efficient variants.

In conjuction with the design groups of Mikoyan and Sukhoi, S A Lavochkin also designed a supersonic fighter of the heavier class, intended primarily as a rocket carrier for air-to-air attacks. Lavochkin's machine was designated

113

Yak-28P, one of a family that covers a wide range of military tasks.

Above: Su-15 is a development of Su-9. It is larger and has two engines.
Right: The delta-winged Su-9, believed to have originated as prototype T-431.
Below: La-250, known as Anaconda among pilots, ended its life as a museum piece.

La-250, but among pilots it was known as Anaconda. The La-250, with delta wings and control surfaces, had twin AL-7 engines, each of 6,500kp thrust, next to each other in the fuselage tail.

On test flying there were accidents in July 1956 and November 1957. Design was halted, the machine repaired and put in the Academy Aviation Museum in Monino, near Moscow. It was Lavochkin's last design.

With these last more modern models we arrive at a period when Soviet instructions about secrecy mean that only a few concrete facts about new models are released.

Yakovlev continued the design of his all-weather fighter Yak-25 and also increased performances in the high supersonic sphere with Yak-28. This machine had a new wing shape, the leading edge had greater sweep between engines and fuselage, the engines had higher performance and an afterburner. Yak-28 is a universal aircraft delivered in day fighter, night fighter, ground attack, Front bomber attack and reconnaissance variants. Armament consists of air-to-air missiles.

To A N Tupolev's drawing office is usually ascribed a further air-to-air missile carrier, presumably designated Tu-28. This, too, is a twin-engined machine with engines lying next to each other in the fuselage tail and two air inlets on the sides of the fuselage in front of the wings. Rockets are carried under the fuselage and wings. NATO designated the aircraft 'Fiddler' on its first appearance at Tushino in 1961.

Variable geometry Su-17 replaced the improvised Su-71G as a prime combat aircraft.

Fighters

FOR ALMOST THREE decades the Mach 2 Mikoyan-Gurevich MiG-21 fighter has been among the best known Soviet aircraft in the world. It showed its qualities in combat over Vietnam, in the conflicts between India and Pakistan, and in the Middle-East. It is an unusually manoeuvrable, easily flown aircraft, undemanding as regards the length and surface of its airfields; it has good acceleration in the supersonic range and excellent qualities in low-level flight. Its limited range (a result of its lightness) is sufficient for its specific tasks – surprise attacks and interceptor work, air combat with fighters and close support work with ground forces on the fronts.

More information has come to light about the prototypes and experimental types which resulted in the final MiG-21 development.

During one test flight with the first MiG-21F prototype, registered Ye-6 by the design bureau, Nefedov's R-11F-300 engine flamed out at an altitude of 18,000m. Nefedov refused to eject and was fatally injured in the attempt to save his aircraft. The cause of the flame-out was found and this resulted in some adjustments to the engine intake. In 1959 the Ye-6T series prototype took to the air, and the MiG-21F was placed in series production.

During 1957 the MiG bureau also experimented with the more powerful Lyulka AL-7FI engine. Mounting of this engine meant a thorough modification of the tail section, which gave rise to prototype I-75F. With 8,400kp thrust a speed of 2,300kph was reached, ceiling was 21,000m and range 2,000km. I-75F was armed with two rockets.

Another AL-7 powered prototype was the swept-wing I-3U, which competed with Sukhoi's Su-7. The Ye-66, Ye-66A, Ye-76 and Ye-166 are also derivatives of the MiG-21 family.

The last generation of MiG-21 fighters is called MiG-21bis, which received the reporting-name 'Fishbed-N' in the West. This third generation version is considered to be the last variant of MiG-21 design and is powered by the 7,500kp thrust (with afterburner) Tumansky R-25 turbojet.

Like the preceding variants, MiG-21bis was high on the list of foreign air forces and the type is in full production at India's HAL plant in Nasik. India succeeded in integrating the short-range French Matra Magic missile by adding new nav-attack systems and other refinements to the standard avionics.

The MiG-21 is still one of the most attractive aircraft designed in the Soviet Union and, like the MiG-15 of Korea fame, will certainly retain its position in aviation history.

Also mentioned previously is 'Flogger', and since this type was first seen over Domodedovo in July 1967 much more information has been released. Following the reporting system used by

Right: Mikoyan's I-3U prototype.

Below: MiG-21bis of the Finnish Air Force.

NATO which allocates reporting names to Soviet material in order of appearance, it is possible to trace the development of this multi-role warplane, regarded as the most important Soviet tactical aircraft in the inventory of many nations.

The original experimental prototype, Ye-231, was allocated the name 'Flogger-A' and this variant was altered considerably, resulting in the production MiG-23MF or 'Flogger-B' version. Three main variants of this VG aircraft have been identified: the single-seat MiG-23MF, which has an air superiority task; the single-seat -23BM developed for ground attacks/strike; and the dual -23U and UM trainers. In all versions there are three wing-sweep positions, 16, 45 and 72 degrees.

The -23BM version differs by having a sloping tapered nose, which improves the view from the cockpit. The -23MF is armed with four air-to-air missiles and a twin-barrel 23mm GSh-23 cannon, -23BM having five external stores stations for bombs, rockets and air-to-ground missiles. The export-variant of MiG-23MF ('Flogger'E') features simpler avionics and the radar and armament of early MiGs.

During 1978 an air defence version, named 'Flogger-G' in the West, made a courtesy visit to Finland and France, and this gave Western experts a good opportunity to have a close look. It is also a variant of MiG-23MF, but has a more powerful engine and modest look-down/shoot-down capability.

India is preparing its production lines for a MiG-23BM version called MiG-27, or 'Flogger-D'. The Indian Air Force already flies the MiG-23BN version, which is similar to the ground attack -23BM variant. Indian pilots are extremely pleased with the handling qualities and ease of maintenance.

A dedicated tactical strike variant of -23BM, the -27, will be described in the ground-attack aircraft section.

The MiG bureau stunned spectators at the big 1967 Domodedovo air parade by showing several new aircraft, one of these being an 'Air Superiority Fighter' with Mach 3 plus capability. General aerodynamic and technical conception of this aircraft was highly original for the time, and its performance impressive – as demonstrated in a number of international FAI records.

Called 'Foxbat' by Western forces, and in FAI records known as type Ye-266, this aircraft has been a target of considerable speculation, fed by wild stories, when some 'Foxbats' flew over Israel at an altitude which, until then, had only been reached by Lockheed U-2s and stratospheric balloons. No small wonder that one American officer in the National Military Command Center, when hearing of the defection of one Viktor Belenko of the Soviet Air Force, exclaimed "Goddam, we've got a Foxbat".

Belenko flew his MiG-25, as this type is called by the MiG-bureau, to Japan where he landed on September 6, 1976. Japanese and American experts took this highly secret aircraft apart and studied every detail with trembling hands. Most of what they discovered is hidden in intelligence reports, but some of it reached Western technical magazines, which published both correct and speculative information.

On August 31, 1977, Fedotov took his Ye-266M (modified Ye-266) to an altitude of 37,650m. This variant was powered by two 14,000kg thrust jets, whereas the original Ye-266 has two 11,000kg engines. It took the same pilot 2 minutes and 34.2 seconds to reach an altitude of 25,000m in his Ye-266M on May 17, 1975, and on the very same day Ostapenko clocked 3 minutes 9.85 seconds when he reached 30km in a similar model. Fedotov, in the meantime, climbed to 35km, taking 4 minutes 11.7 seconds from take-off. Impressive figures, indeed!

The original MiG-25 highspeed, high-altitude interceptor was soon followed by a reconnaissance version with nose-mounted cameras,

Above: An Su-7B derivative is Su-20. Along with other members of the same family, this variable geometry aircraft carries a 'Fitter' reporting name.

Below: MiG-23MF has an air superiority task and carries reporting name 'Flogger-B'. It is normally armed with four missiles and a twin-barrel cannon.

the MiG-25R or 'Foxbat-B'. A second version of the -25R, with more extensive Elint (Electronic Intelligence) equipment but without cameras, is called 'Foxbat-D'. A two-seat training variant, which has also been exported to other MiG-25 users, is called 'Foxbat-C'. The MiG-25 is powered by two Tumansky R-15 afterburning turbojets and is armed with four air-to-air missiles.

Among a number of new generation aircraft which, according to Western sources, have been identified by intelligence satellites over the Soviet state trials centre at Ramenskoye (hence the Ram-registrations), is an updated version of the MiG-25 and was first called 'Super MiG-25'. According to the same sources this variant, the MiG-31, has a new look-down shoot-down radar, improved avionics and two seats. Recently the reporting name 'Foxhound' has been allotted, indicating that the type is ready for operational use. It is armed with eight air-to-air missiles.

Appearance of MiG-25 in 1967 signified that the Soviets had now gained a most unexpected lead over the USA. In former times it was usual to see western structural patterns on Soviet aircraft, but this time Mikoyan's aerodynamic concepts are evident in the design of modern American types, like the Grumman F-14 Tomcat and McDonnell-Douglas F-15 Eagle and F-18 Hornet. It might appear that tables are being turned, but similar design concepts often produce similar looking aircraft.

Another new type reported in the West, which seems to stem from the MiG-bureau, is called 'Fulcrum' (ex 'Ram-L') and this air-defence aircraft is thought to be the counterpart of the F-18 'Hornet'. The MiG-29 designation is, of course, highly premature and only based upon a logical line of thought, it being reported after the last known designation of the MiG bureau, MiG-27 'Flogger-D'. India is receiving 40 MiG-29s.

Artem Ivanovich Mikoyan, who died in 1970, was certainly the greatest designer of jet fighters in the Soviet Union, overshadowing P O Sukhoi in the public eye. Best known aircraft from the Sukhoi bureau was, and still is, the fighter-bomber Su-7B and its derivatives, the variable geometry Su-17, Su-20 and Su-22.

Examples of the Su-7B first made their appearance at Tushino in 1961. Since that time the aircraft has shown its value as a low-level attack aircraft, rocket launching platform and fighter-bomber in several conflicts, even though its role has not been universally hailed as outstanding. When Indian Su-7Bs were put into service during the Indian-Pakistan conflict they proved to have rather limited bombing and rocket ranges, and required escort fighters as protection against enemy fighters.

A variable geometry variant, Su-17, was shown to the public at Domodedovo in 1967. Bearing a close resemblance to the original Su-7 version, this new family of close air-support aircraft – Su-17, Su-20 and Su-22 – were all allocated 'Fitter' reporting names, Su-7B being 'Fitter-A', and the Su-17 prototype of 1967 being named 'Fitter-B'.

This is not in the least surprising when one studies the lines of the variable geometry version. Except for some minor external changes, main difference is found in the outer wing panels,

Below: Yak-36, a forerunner of the later Yak-36MP VTOL development.

Tu-28 is a long-range, twin-engined, all-weather interceptor.

which swivel at about half the wing span. Another external change is the dorsal spine, modest in the early versions but much more evident in later types, such as the 'Fitter-J' in Libyan service. Development of Su-17, and export -20 and -22, was closely followed in the West by allotting supplements to the 'Fitter' reporting name, 'Fitter-J' having been the last to be recognised.

'Fitter-C', 'D' and 'H' are powered by a 11,000kp thrust Lyulka AL-21F afterburning turbojet, giving a maximum speed of Mach 1.8 at 11km. 'Fitter-F' and 'J' have an 11,000kp Tumansky R.29B. Su-20 was the first of two export variants, the other one being called Su-22 by the Sukhoi bureau. One very surprising purchaser of the latter was Peru, which bought its first batch in 1977. Peru is reported to have 52 Su-22s ('Fitter-F') acting as strike aircraft.

Su-11, and the preceding Su-9, carry reporting name 'Fishpot', and both types are supersonic interceptors in the PVO-Strany inventory. Neither were exported outside the Soviet Union and both have limited all-weather capability.

What was believed to have been a development variant of the Sukhoi Su-9 air-defence fighter, the T-405 is also mentioned in FAI lists when B M Adrianov attained a speed of 2,092kph over a 100km closed course on May 28, 1960.

External contours of both Su-9 and Su-11 aircraft clearly indicate that they were developed alongside the Su-7 strike fighter, especially in front and side views. Both variants, which are powered by one Lyulka AL-7F afterburning turbojet, are still in service but due to be replaced in the near future.

To protect the lengthy border-areas of the

Below: Examples of the partial VTOL Yak-36MP.

Soviet Union large twin-engined interceptor fighters, featuring all-weather capability, were developed by the Tupolev, Lavochkin and Sukhoi bureaus. One of the most promising designs was Su-15, which is called 'Flagon'. This is a single-seat tailed-delta, powered by two 7,500kg thrust Tumansky R-13 turbojets (earlier variants had the R-11). It has a combat range of about 700km and carries two air-to-air missiles beneath the wing. Latest variant is called 'Flagon-F', with the Su-15U two-seat trainer having been allotted 'Flagon-C'.

A second long range, twin-engined, all-weather interceptor stems from the Tupolev bureau, the Tu-28P/-128 'Fiddler'. According to at least one Western source the bureau designation is Tu-102 and it was developed from the Tu-98 'Backfin' (note the difference in function, indicated by the first letter of the reporting name, 'B' meaning Bomber). The latter was shown in 1956 at Kubinka airfield, near Moscow, to a visiting delegation of the US Air Force.

'Fiddler' is powered by two 11,000kg Lyulka AL-21F turbojets, and although it is being replaced by more modern fighters, a small number are still operational for border-defence. The Tu-28P/-128 is a two-seater and is armed with four air-to-air missiles. Like the 'Flagon', no guns are carried.

With the introduction of new air-to-air missiles, coupled to modern look-down/shoot-down capability, the Sukhoi bureau is reported to have developed a single-seat, multi-role fighter called Su-27 ('Ram-K') prematurely in the West. According to some sources it is similar to the F-15 Eagle and carries the reporting name 'Flanker'.

As already mentioned, a number of STOL/VTOL aircraft were demonstrated during the Domodedovo airshow in July 1967. They were allotted reporting names, in some cases implying that they were developed from operational types, such as 'Flagon-B' and 'Fishbed-G', but also indicating that they were newly developed models, such as the MiG 'Faithless' and Yak 'Freehand'. Only the Yakovlev-bureau seems to have developed a true V/STOL prototype, although some Western sources would rather call it a VTOSL, indicating that it has vertical take-off capability only, due to its limited lift layout.

The Yak-36MP 'Forger' is often seen as an interim type, and is operational with the Soviet Navy. Western sources are not in agreement about the function of -36MP, some US sources implying that it has limited air-to-surface capability rather than air-to-air. Observers are impressed with its smooth VTO performance and suggest that electronic guidance is supplied by the mother ship. It is powered by an unidentified lift/cruise engine and two smaller lift engines. External stores may be supplied with air-to-ground missiles and/or unguided rockets, but air-to-air missiles have also been reported. A dual-trainer is called 'Forger-B', whereas the single seater is known as 'Forger-A'.

Ground Attack

MORE INFORMATION has come to light about Tupolev Tu-91, the experimental *'shturmovik'* (ground-attack) aircraft shown to a visiting US delegation at Kubinka airfield in 1956. The Tu-91, which was unofficially named 'Tarzan' and 'Bichok' ('Young Steer'), was designed to meet a specification for a specialised ground-attack aircraft, another design being the pure-jet Il-40. Although neither were developed further, due to Soviet policy of that time, reporting names were allotted, Tu-91 being called 'Boot' and the Il-40 'Brawny'.

Tu-91 was designed by a team led initially by Pavel Sukhoi, later succeeded by V A Chizhevsky. It was a two-seat monoplane with side-by-side arrangement, and was powered by a Kuznetsov NK-6 turboprop which drove contra-rotating, four-blade airscrews via a long extension shaft. A variety of armament could be mounted externally.

Test pilot K Zyuzin was rather pleased with the handling characteristics and stability when he carried out flight trials in 1956. View from the wide cockpit was excellent and a cruising speed of 650kph attained. Maximum range was 2,400km, maximum take-off weight 14,000kg and overall dimensions included a wing span of 17.17m and length of 16.35m.

A new tactical strike fighter with all-weather capability, the Su-24 (formerly reported as Su-19) was first reported in 1971 and has been the subject of much speculation in the West as to its capabilities. It is the first Soviet aircraft designed specifically for tactical air-to-ground operations since the Great Patriotic War, and possesses very modern avionics systems, such as terrain-following radar, doppler, laser, FLIR (Forward Looking Infra-Red) and other equipment. A wide cockpit seats two, the pilot on the left hand side being assisted by a weapons-system officer.

Su-24, which has been allotted the reporting name 'Fencer', is powered by two afterburning turbojets, possibly Tumansky R-29s, and has four fuselage and four wing-stations for tactical weaponry. The outer wing pylons are the first pivoting examples on a Soviet aircraft; the other two are attached to the wing gloves. 'Fencer-A' and 'C' have been reported.

As already briefly mentioned in the Fighter section, MiG-27 is a dedicated tactical strike derivative of the MiG-23BM/BN dual-role, air-ground/air-air version of the original MiG-23

design. It features the same nose as that of the MiG-23BM/BN version, with increased downward view. This nose probably houses a ranging radar, laser ranger and marked-target seeker. Other differences are simplified fixed-ramp air intakes, a shorter nozzle, and larger tyres of reduced pressure for operations from unpaved airstrips. The twin-barrel 23mm cannon has been replaced by a rotary six-barrel cannon of 23 or 30mm calibre. MiG-27s have been exported and are known in the West by their reporting names 'Flogger-D' and 'Flogger-J'.

Latest addition to the tactical air arm of the Soviet Air Force is the Sukhoi Su-25 'Frogfoot' (formerly known as 'Ram-J') ground-attack aircraft. It is similar in concept to the Fairchild A-10 tank-killer with two engines (possibly Tumansky R-13) on either side of the fuselage, under the shoulder mounted wing which has slight anhedral. The Su-25 has been deployed in Afghanistan as a close support aircraft and is also in service with the Czech Air Force.

The Yakovlev Yak-36MP, which may have air-to-surface capability rather than air-to-air, has been described in the Fighter section.

Above: Su-24, known as 'Fencer', is designed specifically for tactical air-to-ground operations and is powered by two afterburning turbojets.

Below: Similar in concept to the Fairchild A-10 Thunderbolt, Russia's Su-25 tank-killer has recently seen action in Afghanistan.

CHAPTER 17

Heavy Bombers

IN THE TWENTIES and thirties, heavy bombers of the TB class attracted particular attention throughout the world. They gave genuine proof of the ability of youthful Soviet aircraft technology to accomplish difficult tasks. No other state at this time could provide heavy bombers like these nor in such great numbers.

Russia had a long tradition of giant aircraft building. The designer I I Sikorsky was internationally known even before the First World War for he had designed the four-engined machines of the Russkii Vityaz class, above all, Ilya Muromets, five of which served up to 1921 in the Soviet Air Force and formed a bomber division. The machines were renamed, in accordance with the spirit of the times, Red Muromets.

At the beginning of the twenties, the Red Air Force was planning, in theory, on the use of heavy bombers in large units. The acquisition of such aircraft was another matter. It is not easy to visualise what a problem like this meant in a country which only a few months previously had been engaged in civil war, a country threatened by hunger and epidemics, a country where there was no developed aircraft industry and no wherewithal for the mining of non-ferrous metals.

Development of the heavy bomber is for ever linked in the USSR with the names of Andrei Nikolayevich Tupolev and his closest collaborators in the design centre, AGOS-TsAGI. Tupolev's choice of a design method similar to that of the Junkers was also decisive for future development. It was a particularly far-sighted method for its time which made possible the construction of cantilever wings with thick profile and fuselage with adequate internal room.

V M Petlyakov, who directed the wing brigade in AGOS-TsAGI and designed all ANT wings up to 1936, created a special type of wing different to the Junkers version.

The all-metal construction did not just require a design, but also duralumin. TsAGI and the technical university of Moscow promoted a large-scale search for this metal of the future which was to be speedily mined. Geological expeditions in 1918-1922 unearthed large and rich bauxite deposits in the Ural mountains and

near Tikhin. But great quantities of electrical energy are required to obtain pure aluminium and such were certainly not available.

By the way of a trial, the first Soviet duralumin had been obtained in the metallurgical plant of Kolchugino from December 1920 onwards under the direction of engineer I I Sidorin. It was called Kolchugaluminium and its tensile strength was 40-42 km/sq.mm. Kolchugino also produced the first moulded and extruded wing profiles.

But availability of Soviet duralumin was insufficient for series production of all-metal aircraft. So, in the twenties, the Soviet Union began to import duralumin from Germany and France. It can be said that during the thirties Soviet aircraft construction was completely dependent on the delivery of duralumin from abroad. Construction of power plants was held up, with the result that the bauxite deposits in Kamensk and Solikamsk in the Ural mountains could not be exploited on a very large scale. This led to economy measures in the construction of aircraft.

In order to make as quick a start as possible with all-metal aircraft and so that a fair number of specialists should be familiarised with the necessary technology, the Junkers company was encouraged to build a factory in the town quarter of Fili, Moscow, in 1923. Here the nucleus of aircraft construction in the USSR, Junkers F-13 and H-21, were assembled from parts produced in

ANT-4 Strana Sovietov which attempted an inter-continental flight in 1929.

Germany and up to about 150 H-21 and A-20 were built. The Junkers plant was in existence up to 1926 under German direction, then was taken over by the Soviet industry. It played a very decisive part in the development of Soviet aircraft construction.

Tupolev had already gathered experience in light metals with his first aircraft, the sporting two-seat ANT-1. This 1922 machine had some parts made out of aluminium and duralumin, but Tupolev's second aircraft, the commercial high-wing monoplane ANT-2, test flown in May 1924, was completely all-metal with corrugated sheet covering. ANT-2 was a milestone in Tupolev's work. There soon followed the first production reconnaissance aircraft, ANT-3 (R-3), which was test flown in Summer 1925, and the issue of Soviet all-metal aircraft was under way.

On Moscow's central airfield in November 1925 stood a large, twin-engined, low-wing monoplane ready for its first flight. Only a few initiated knew that it was the fourth design of Tupolev, the ANT-4, and only in the corrugated duralumin covering was any likeness to the Junkers models revealed. The inner design and external lines were quite different.

A I Tomashevskii test flew the aircraft on November 26 with virtually no difficulties. ANT-4, with its span of 28.76m and 6,500kg flying weight, was one of the biggest machines of that time.

The engines were twelve-cylinder, 450mhp British Napier Lions with French Lamblin coolers. ANT-4 reached 212kph with a service ceiling of 4,800m. It was used, above all, as a heavy bomber. In the fuselage and under the central wing section was provision for bombs of 1,000-3,000kg total weight. The aircraft could fly 1,400km with 1,000kg bombs or 400km with a load of 3,000kg. Crew consisted of six men and there were three turrets with twin machine guns in each of them.

The Red Air Force took ANT-4 as their first heavy bomber, TB-1. Because some pilots found the control forces too great, TsAGI later increased the size of the rudder balance areas.

Series production of the TB-1 was certainly justified, but initially the aircraft industry could only deliver a few. From 1928 onwards production reached a larger scale and up to 1932 a total of 218 TB-1 aircraft were dispatched, some as G-1 air freighters. Production machines had Soviet copies of the BMW-VI, the M-17, and performance dropped to 200kph with a service ceiling of 4,700m. Having a take-off weight of 6,500kg, the aircraft could only carry 730kg bombs, but could be overloaded up to 7,775kg.

ANT-4 was the first Soviet machine to accomplish an inter-continental flight. A long distance haul from Moscow to New York had been carefully prepared. V M Petlyakov was to ensure the technical side of individual legs over the mainland while R L Bartini was responsible for overwater flights, including the changing of undercarriage for floats.

ANT-4 *Strana Sovietov* (Land of the Soviets), flown by S A Shestakov and F J Bolotov, took off on August 8, 1929, from the central airfield in Moscow. But the machine had to make an emergency landing north of Chita in Siberia and was so heavily damaged that continuation could not be considered.

On August 23 the crew took off in a second ANT-4 with the same name. The route was via Omsk, Novosibirsk, Krasnoyarsk and Chita to Khabarovsk where the wheels were replaced by floats. As a float plane it continued via Petropavlovsk Kamchatskii to the Aleutian Islands, Steward, Sitka and Seattle. South of Sitka the machine had to make another emergency landing, but a damaged engine was quickly changed and the journey continued to Seattle where it was given wheels again. From Seattle ANT-4 then flew via San Francisco, Chicago and Detroit to New York where the aircraft landed on November 1.

At the time of this flight TB-1 were already serving in the Red Air Force. The machines proved their worth, both with wheeled undercarriage and with skis or floats. They performed well in the Arctic, an ANT-4 succeeding in landing on the Chukotsea ice-sheet to save the crew of the ice-bound steamer *Chelyuskin*. The TB-1 and G-1 remained in auxiliary units up to the outbreak of war in 1941.

ANT-4, prototype of the TB-1, first flew on November 26, 1925.

In 1926 a number of trimotor Junkers R-42 bombers were bought. They had been partially built in the Junkers plant in Moscow with L-5 engines of 300/310mhp. The Soviet Air Force had introduced the designation TB-2 for these aircraft, but they were better known in Russia as YuG-1. Several were also delivered as twin-float seaplanes.

Further help was provided in 1926 with the French Farman F-62 Goliath bombers which had twin Lorraine-Dietrich engines, each of 450mhp. These machines formed two squadrons and, although already antiquated, gave good service for training.

Individual aircraft designers also tried to provide machines which were simpler and could therefore be produced more quickly. Polikarpov designed the sesquiplane TB-2 in 1927 in classic wood construction. Design and construction took a fairly long time and when the prototype TB-2 was at last finished, in 1930, the TB-1 was already on the production line.

TB-2 had simple lines. Twin BMW-VI engines, each of 550mhp, were on the underwing. On the prototype the engine nacelles were standard; in the event of series production it was planned to lengthen the back of the nacelles and accommodate a crewman with twin machine guns.

Flying qualities of the new machine were fairly good. Maximum speed was 210kph and the range 1,800km. But to have two aircraft models for the same task was a luxury, even for the Soviet Air Force. TB-2 was not taken on and TB-1 remained the standard aircraft. The Red Air Force wanted to create a homogeneous line in heavy bombers, differing in size and bomb load but having the same basic construction.

On December 22, 1930, at TsAGI's test airfield, a new heavy giant bomber, ANT-6, was impelled off the snow surface by its four Curtiss V-1760 Conqueror engines. It rose majestically but slowly. Suddenly the machine slowed and spectators heard the engine revolutions dropping. Pilot M M Gromov was able to keep the machine in the air until they were running again at full strength and ANT-6 completed the prescribed round to land safely.

Only afterwards was Gromov able to say what the trouble had been. On take-off he had pushed the four throttle levers forward. As the aircraft took off the control forces mounted rapidly and Gromov had to hold the joy-stick with both hands. But the mounting support of the levers at full throttle position was not firm enough and vibration of the airframe caused them to slide backwards. Gromov noticed the changed position, pushed then forward again, and everything was all right. For the rest of the flight the air mechanic had to hold the throttle levers with his hand.

ANT-6 accomplished some test flying with V-1760 engines, then the native M-17, each of 500/730mhp were built in. With these the plant and state tests were completed from February 1931 onwards.

The Red Air Force demanded a rapid commissioning of the new machines which were to be designated TB-3. The industry did its utmost to fulfil this task. Up to April 1932 they managed to build and test fly nine aircraft and on May 1, 1932, an international audience was able to observe the giants above Red Square. It can be said that they attracted as much excitement and attention in the technical press as today's new rocket weapons.

Production of the TB-3 was accelerated to a fantastic degree. For some time in 1932 three TB-3s were delivered every two days. Up to 1937, when production was halted, 818 had been built.

In its original form the TB-3 was a cantilever low-wing monoplane with eight crew members and armed with three twin DA-2 machine guns. One was in the nose, above the bomb-aimer's position, the remaining two on the fuselage just above the wing trailing edge. In the wing, outside the outer engines, were two retractable gunner's positions with a single DA-1 machine gun. In later production machines the wing-mounted positions were deleted. In all the TB-3 carried 100 drums of ammunition with 63 rounds in each.

Despite a spacious fuselage it could only carry bombs on outer racks. There was normally 2,000kg in bombs but maximum was 4,000kg. All the performance data relates to a 1,000kg load.

The TB-3's undercarriage had distinctive,

ANT-6, the TB-3 prototype (below), almost came to grief on its maiden flight in 1930 when the throttle levers slipped back during take-off. Among subsequent TB-3 examples was the one pictured left which completed a European publicity tour.

small tandem wheels, two on every strut. Other features were also very distinctive and the aircraft was soon world famous. That does not mean that the aircraft was without problems from start to finish. There were many things to correct, above all the control forces were too high and had to be resolved by balance areas on the rudders. Service ceiling and range also constituted a great problem. The first prototype reached 4,660m but production machines with M-17 and without supercharger or reduction gear could not climb higher than 3,800m. Range of 2,200km with 1,000kg bomb load was a disappointment with a machine of 39.5m span. All TB-3s after 1934 were produced with a span of 41.85m and wing area 234.5sq.m instead of 230sq.m.

Tupolev and his assistants redesigned many details and completely revised the aerodynamics. In February 1933 Mikulin M-34 engines, each of 675/830mhp, were built in for the first time. But this proved a disappointment again. The ANT-6 with four M-34 was slower than the production model with M-17, reaching only 207kph compared to 215. At 3,000m the speed was better, 185 instead of 166kph, and 3,000m was reached in 32.8 minutes as opposed to 43.4. It was clear that a machine of this size needed geared engines and superchargers.

So in September 1933 the ANT-6 was given new geared M-34Rs. All performances were considerably improved. Speed at low altitude climbed to 231kph, at 3,000m it was still 211 and service ceiling was 4,600m despite increased dead weight. Comparing them: the prototype weighed 10,075kg when empty; production machines with M-17, 11,207kg; an experimental model with M-34, 11,900kg; and with M-34R, a full 12,230kg. Take off weight was now 18,607kg and this version was put on the production line in 1934.

Between March 1934 and October 1935 a thorough revision of TB-3's design was under way, the aim being to approximate performance to that of fighters. As early as 1932 a lightening commission was active under the direction of Petlyakov, its aim being to reduce the dead weight. Some elements of design which were oversize had been revised, the crew had been reduced to six and only three machine gun turrets had been built in. Thus they managed to reduce dead weight to 10,995kg on an experimental model and 6,300kg of fuel could now be taken instead of 5,000. Take-off weight climbed from 19,200 to 19,500kg and range, with a ton of bombs, was extended from 2,200 to 3,120km. In August 1934 this reconstructed TB-3 flew 2,470km with 2,000kg of bombs.

In 1936, TB-3 with M-34RN blower-fed engines were put on the assembly line. These engines produced 840/970mhp and, coupled with streamlining improvements, meant a significant heightening of the aircraft's performance. The TB-3 version of 1936 approached an international pinnacle. Maximum speed at low altitude was 245kph, at 3,000m it was 276 and the highest speed of all was 288 reached at a height of 4,200m. A service ceiling of 7,740m meant increased fighting efficiency where stronger fighter defence was used.

The version also had a new undercarriage with big single wheels which improved the taxiing qualities. Noteworthy, too, was the introduction of a machine gun turret in the tail behind the control surfaces. The wing-mounted guns were deleted.

It is interesting to note how various small improvements assisted performance. When the corrugated metal sheet over the wings and tail units was covered with fabric, the wing and head resistance were reduced, improving steering and making the machine 20 to 25kph faster; streamlined passages between fuselage and wings brought a further 8 to 10kph and 200 to 250m more ceiling.

TB-3 bombers could be seen in several European countries during the thirties. First, three TB-3 with M-34R engines flew to Italy in 1934 as a reply to the visit of Italian Savoia-Marchetti SM-55 flying boats to Odessa. TB-3 also visited Paris and were quite often in Prague.

Soviet TB-3 pilots were able to achieve several international records and A B Yumashev's crew were particularly successful. On September 11, 1936, Yumashev lifted 5,000kg load to 8,116m altitude. On October 28 he improved this to 8,980m. A load of ten tons was flown to a height of 6,605m on September 16 and 12,000kg to 2,700m by Yumashev in his TB-3 on September 20, 1937. All the performances were attained with the latest production machines powered by high-altitude AM-34FRN and AM-34FRNV engines of 900mhp.

The ANT-6 is also connected with the history of Soviet exploration bases in the Arctic. Aviaarktika, an independent department of the air traffic company Aeroflot, demanded in 1936 some ANT-6 from TsAGI which were specially reconstructed for service in the Arctic. Between May and October 1937 TsAGI test pilots tried out four ANT-6 with M-34RN engines, fully cased cabins with efficient heating, new and superior radio equipment, a lot of emergency equipment, and a new undercarriage with facilities for a quick change from wheels to skis. As it was foreseen that the aircraft would land on small fields, braking parachutes were incorporated.

On May 22, 1937, the first expedition was sent into the heart of the Arctic, Otto Shmidt's expedition leaving Moscow to set up the polar station *Severnii Polus-1* (North Pole-1). Four ANT-6 and an ANT-7 transported the whole expedition of 42 people, with their equipment, from Moscow via Kholmogori and Marjan-Mar to Rudolf's Island. They were still 900km away from their goal and on May 21 the last stage of the operation began.

Hero of the USSR M V Vodopyanov landed with ANT-6 SSSR-N-170 on a flat stretch of ice 20km away from the North Pole. Four days later the machines of Molokov and Alexeyev also landed here; the fourth machine (Masuruk's) came down 50km from the base and did not arrive until July 5. After one month all four machines took off on the return flight and only four men stayed behind in the SP-1 camp under the direction of Polar explorer, Papanin.

Such missions were quite often repeated. The four-engined ANT-6 displayed brilliant qualities on these occasions, even under the hardest conditions. An ANT-6 from the first Arctic expedition (registration SSR-N-169) was still in service in May 1941 transporting men on Ivan Cherevichnii's last pre-war expedition.

The TB-3 were certainly high class machines for their time, but their value rapidly diminished in the second half of the thirties. Feared antagonists in battles with the Japanese on the Khasan lake in summer 1938, a year later, on the Khalkhin-Gol river, Japanese fighter aircraft proved superior and only its all-metal construction protected the TB-3 from greater losses.

In the Finnish war of 1939, TB-3 were only used as transport aircraft and they retained this role during the 1941-45 war. Even before the war it was clear that the spacious aircraft was suitable for freight and was delivered in the cargo version, G-2, for Aeroflot.

TB-1 and TB-3 were the first two links in a whole chain of giant bombers of various sizes prepared by the drawing office of Tupolev and the Red Air Force. In the context of potentialities in aviation research and industry, it had been established in 1929 that Tupolev should be able to build machines of 70 tons take-off weight and 20 tons bomb load by increasing the dimensions and adding engines.

Next in line was the six-engined ANT-16, prototype of the giant TB-4 bomber. Its development lasted more than three years. Design began in March 1930 and the aircraft was test flown on July 3, 1933, by M M Gromov. With its 54m span it was the biggest machine in the world, but this was kept an official secret.

Outer lines were similar to ANT-6, but the wings had a thicker profile so that mechanics could crawl to the four M-34 engines in the leading edge of the wing during flight. Two further M-34 were in tandem arrangement on struts over the fuselage. The TB-4 stood on a gigantic undercarriage with twin wheels. The crew numbered twelve and armament consisted of twin moveable 20mm cannon and ten machine guns. Normal bomb load was 4,000kg, all stowed inside the aircraft; maximum load was 8,000kg, but overloaded it could take as much as 10,000kg.

Test flying proceeded slowly. Gromov reported that the control forces were almost insuperable and Tupolev had to build new balance areas. But the designers overdid it and now Gromov could not feel the aircraft at all. In the end everything was put right.

The TB-4 could take 5,000kg of bombs with 33,280kg take-off weight but only on a 775km route. With bigger tanks and with a take-off weight of 37,000kg, 2,000kg could be carried

2,200km which was, however, 120km less than the production TB-3. An overloaded TB-4 did transport 8,000kg bombs over 940km, but the aircraft could not climb higher than 2,000m and only reached a speed of 182kph. The TB-4 was no improvement on the TB-3 and was not pursued further.

Endeavours to show off the capacities of Soviet aviation technology led, in the first half of the thirties, to an unhealthy gargantuanism. 'The biggest and the heaviest' – these were the keywords of the time, even though such aircraft did not always serve their purpose. The civilian eight-engined giant, ANT-20 Maxim Gorkii, was a qualified success. It was a machine for propaganda flights and served its purpose, but would have been valueless as a means of combat.

Tupolev planned and designed another two aircraft of this mammoth class between 1929 and 1936. The bomber ANT-26, or TB-6, was to have a span of 95m and an estimated take-off weight of 70 tons. No less than twelve M-34FRN engines, each of 900mhp, were proposed – four on the leading edge of the wing with tractor propellers,

Below: A TB-3 with M-34FRN engines and ski undercarriage for use in the Arctic.

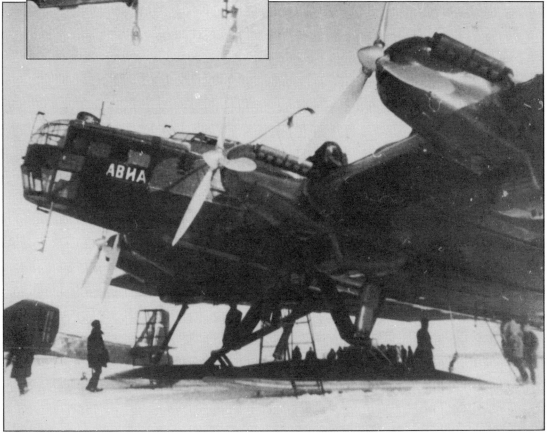

two on the trailing edge with pusher propellers, and two tandem groups on struts above the wings. The twenty-man crew were to have a 37mm cannon in the tail turret, a 20mm cannon was on top of the fuselage and the same in each of the elongated engine nacelles. A further four twin machine guns were in the fuselage.

Together with ANT-26 Tupolev also designed the transport ANT-28, which was to carry either a whole infantry company together with rations and ammunition, medium size combat vehicle or several field-pieces with traction engines etc. At the same time, professor of N J Shukovskii Military Aviation Academy, S G Koslov, designed a big bomber named Gigant. It was to be a machine with 60m span, twelve M-17 engines and twin tail booms. Its take-off weight was 40,000kg.

Failure of the TB-6 bomber convinced designers that they should no longer rely simply on increasing the geometrical dimensions of aircraft without applying a thoroughly new streamlined conception. Geometrical enlargement gave rise to giant aircraft with overlarge wings and low wing loading (in TB-3 81kg/sqm and in TB-4 only 79kg/sqm). They were slow, unwieldy and had a low ceiling. Money spent on the construction of TB-4 had to be written off and the designs for other giants abandoned. Tupolev did continue with occasional work on the ANT-26 and ANT-28 designs up to 1936, but the work was only academic.

The prototype TB-4 had an interesting end to its life. After flight tests it served as a showpiece in 1934-5 in a film *Bolshiye Kryla* (The Big Wings). Subject was the air disaster of a giant aircraft and the script was written after another Soviet giant had had a real accident. This was the K-7 of K A Kalinin.

Kalinin was chief designer in the design centre for civil aviation, GROS, in Kharkov, and a tireless champion of classical, pure elliptical wings, such as he himself used in his single-engined commercial 'planes. Kalinin designed K-7 in 1929 but

Above: The six-engined ANT-16 or TB-4 was the world's largest aircraft when it first appeared in July 1933. Four M-34 engines were set into the wings while a further two appeared in tandem on top of the giant bomber.

Below: A projected 12-engined bomber was ANT-26 or TB-6 with a proposed span of no less than 95m and 70 tons take-off weight. Design was ultimately abandoned.

it was two years before he received a construction licence and the first aircraft did not roll out of the assembly shop until July 1933.

Four years for design and construction proved disadvantageous as K-7 seemed relatively antiquated in comparison with Tupolev's machines. The wing had 53m span and its profile was 2.2m in the longitudinal axis of the aircraft. On the leading edge of the wing were six M-34F, each of 750mhp. Seventh engine was on the trailing edge with a pusher propeller, behind the fuselage nacelle. Twin booms with triangular cross-sections ran from the wings to the tail-unit. On the tips of these tail booms were turrets for 20mm cannon with a further cannon turret in the nose of the fuselage. Under the wing there were two long nacelles which incorporated the undercarriage, bombs, four machine guns and ladders for climbing onto the wings.

Kalinin also designed a commercial variant of K-7. In the wings it was planned to have cabins for

120 people, seated or lying down.

Construction was a steel tube framework with fabric covering. The tubes used orginated from the first delivery of chromemolybdenum steel from V I Lenin's plant in Dnepropetrovsk. The machine weighed 24,000kg when empty and was supposed to have a take-off weight of 38,000kg when fully equipped and armed. Overloaded with 19 tons of bombs it weighed as much as 42,400kg. Such features were all reckoned to be of value, coupled with a maximum speed of 225kph.

On its first flight on August 11, 1933, the K-7 had as yet no military equipment. The pilots were in general content, only complaining that the small diameter propellers depending on a gearless engine were less effective. K-7 went on eight flights in Autumn 1933 over the Kharkov area, always exciting great interest on the streets. A giant aircraft like this was visible proof of the progress of Soviet technology.

The ninth flight, on November 20, 1933, ended tragically. Heavy oscillations developed in the tail, apparently caused by the balance areas, and the right tail boom snapped. K-7 broke up in the air, fell to the ground and was burned.

After the catastrophe Kalinin was transferred to a new plant in Voronesh, where he was to build another two K-7 modernised bombers featuring stronger tail booms with rectangular cross-section. By 1935, with one machine two thirds finished, further work was banned. There were certainly no prospects for the K-7 at that time.

K-7 did not receive any military designation. So in the TB bomber series number 5 is missing. There was a heavy bomber TB-5 but it was D P Grigorovich's design, not Tupolev's.

TB-5 design originated in 1930 in the TsKB drawing office of interned designers *Vnutrennaja Tjurna*, and was coded TsKB No.8. The prototype was completed in spring 1931. It was a high-wing monoplane in composite construction with wooden wings and steel tube fuselage. Grigorovich originally wanted to use A A Bessonov's new FED 24 cylinder in-line X engines

The TB-5 design originated as TsKB No.8 in 1930 from a group of internees led by Grigorovich. A crash in 1932 ended its prospects.

(four in-line cylinders with X shape) of 800/1,000mhp. But as they were not ready at the right time (and eventually proved a failure) Grigorovich used two tandem pairs of Bristol Jupiter VI radials, each of 480mhp. They were secured low under the wings by means of struts, something like those on Farman and Dornier models of the period.

Pilot Bukhgolts test flew the TB-5 on May 1, 1931, but was not satisfied. The pusher propellers were inefficient, achieving only 2,600m altitude and 180kph. Steering was difficult too. In Spring 1932 M M Gromov had a serious accident with the TB-5 and that was the end of it.

In the mid thirties, V M Petlyakov's design group at TsAGI prepared the theoretical and technical conditions for design of a modern heavy bomber. It was clear that a large aircraft could only be successful in defending itself against fighters on a day attack if it could reach a high speed at great altitude. So together with bomb load and range, speed and service ceiling were the outstanding requirements.

To acquire these qualities the aircraft had to be more streamlined with better profiles, smooth lines and powerful high-altitude engines, if possible with superchargers. In 1934, when Petlyakov

completed the first studies, there were no engines with superchargers in the USSR. The engines' altitude power had to be achieved by different means.

The first prototype ANT-42, air force designated TB-7, took off on December 27, 1936, with Gromov at the controls. On the wing were four M-34FRN engines each of 930mhp, but their altitude performance was only 4,500m. This version had completed the first stage of testing by March 1937, unable to reach the required 400kph at 8,000m or over.

Not until June 1937 was the equipment ready to help achieve these performances. This was the power unit ATsN-2 *(Aggregat Tsentralnogo Nadduba = power unit of the central blower)* consisting of a single French Hispano-Suiza 12Ybrs engine of 850mhp driving a big supercharger with pressure pipes leading to individual engines of the aircraft. The whole ATsN-2 arrangement was incorporated inside the fuselage, so that TB-7 was a five-engined machine. The engines were later exchanged for superior M-34FRNs.

Flight testing with the ATsN-2 power unit lasted from August 11, 1937, until Summer 1938 and brought good results. The engines retained their full power at 8,000m and gave the ANT-42 a

First prototype of the TB-7 was ANT-42 which proved faster than most Western fighters at altitudes between 8,000 and 9,000m in 1938.

speed of 403kph. Service ceiling was 10,800m. Between 8,000 and 9,000m this bomber was faster than most production fighters of the Western powers.

ANT-42 was a mid-wing monoplane in duralumin with flat sheet covering monocoque fuselage and a lot of internal room. The eight-man crew had four turrets with twin machine-guns for defence. The two pilots sat one behind the other in a cockpit which was set assymmetrically to the left side of the fuselage. The M-34FRN had three-bladed propellers and each engine had its own cooler. Undercarriage could be retracted into the inner nacelles. Empty weight was relatively heavy at 18,000kg, aggravated by the ATsN-2 installation. Take-off weight with 2,000kg bombs was 23,860kg and with an overload of 4,000kg bombs it was as much as 32,000. In the first case the range was 3,000km and in the second only 1,000km.

The ANT-42 with ATsN-2 power unit was certainly a noteworthy machine. However, weight of the unit diminished bomb loading and fuel capacity, the fifth engine increased consumption and moreover the ATsN-2 was too complicated an installation for maintenance under field conditions, while in aerial combat it was very vulnerable.

Meanwhile the new high-altitude M-34FRNV engines were being produced which made the ATsN-2 superfluous. After the incorporation of these engines ANT-42's empty weight sank to 16,000kg, so too did maximum speed to 381kph at 3,000m. But service ceiling rose to 12,000m.

The M-34FRNV engines were nevertheless antiquated and their life was short, prolonging flight testing and causing difficulties. So the years 1937-39 were critical for the TB-7's existence. Shortage of duralumin, declining interest in heavy machines, an aircraft industry overburdened with other tasks, the difficult internal political situation – all hindered a solution to the problems of creating a modern heavy bomber.

In spite of everything, Petlyakov was able in 1939 to incorporate new twelve-cylinder AM-35A engines, each of 1,200mhp and good altitude performance. Thus the first step in development of TB-7 was concluded. Empty weight of the bomber was now 16,600kg and its normal take-off weight 27,000kg. Service ceiling was only 9,300m, but speed rose to 427kph at 6,000m and range with two tons of bombs to 4,700km. The highest bomb load was 4,000kg.

Petlyakov did not only alter the engines, he also changed the armament. There was a big 'glass house' on the underside of the nose of the first TB-7. It was the workroom of the bomber. In the new version the nose was slimmer and simpler with a spherical turret with twin ShKAS machine guns. A moveable ShVAK cannon was on the top of the fuselage and another in the tail turret. The interior engine nacelles were enlarged and in their rear parts was a turret with

Left: Another Soviet giant was Kalinin's K-7 which had an unusual grouping of seven engines, the odd one appearing as a pusher unit in the rear fuselage. K-7 broke up on its 9th flight and was totally destroyed.

a moveable UBT machine gun. The inner nacelles also contained the engine coolers.

Towards the end of 1939 state tests were brought to an end with bombing tests on the Crimean Peninsula, and TB-7 was put on the production line. But only 79 complete machines were constructed so TB-7 never matched in terms of importance the older TB-3.

In 1941 the name was changed to Pe-8 (Pe – after the designer, Petlyakov) and in 1940 A D Charomskii's new heavy-oil M-40 engines built in by way of experiment. They were 1,000mhp twelve-cylinder in-line engines with superchargers. It had been expected that these would extend the bomber's range considerably. So they did; range with 2,000kg bombs was 7,820km, but on the other hand maximum speed sank to 393kph at 5,600m and service ceiling to 9,200m.

Charomskii had been working in the TsIAM institute on heavy oil engines from 1931 onwards. In 1933 he tested his first, AN-1, which produced 850/900mhp, and later an improved variant, AN-1A, but with only small success. As home research and design produced nothing promising, the German heavy-oil engines, Junkers Jumo-4 and Jumo-5, were bought and tested in 1935. Jumo-4 was put in the reconnaissance biplane R-5 and flown uninterrupted by A I Shukov for just over 12 hours.

Results of the AN-1A, Jumo-4 and Jumo-5 testing were then utilised by Charomskii in design of the twelve-cylinder M-30 and M-40 prototypes, completed in 1939 (in 1941 they were renamed ACh-30 and ACh-40). After the failure of M-40, Charomskii concentrated on the simpler M-30 engine from which originated the 1941 variants ACh-30B, BF, -31 and -32. These engines were of 1,250-1,500mhp. In 1941 some Pe-8 were equipped with ACh-30B engines but the majority of airframes were given AM-35A engines. As they were preferentially assigned to MiG-3 fighters, Petlyakov sought alternatives and tried four new two-row radial ASh-82 engines in May 1941. With these the maximum speed was 405kph at 2,600m, service ceiling 8,000m and range 5,800km.

On the night of August 11, 1941, shortly after the first Soviet bomb attack on Berlin with long-range DB-3F bombers, Pe-8 with AM-35A and ACh-30B engines attacked the former German capital in order to show that the Red Air Force was by no means annihilated. The Pe-8s took off from Pushkino aerodrome near Leningrad under the command of M V Vodopyanov. In Summer 1942 the Pe-8 engaged on a whole series of night attacks. On July 19 Konigsberg in East Prussia (now Kaliningrad) was attacked, on August 26 Berlin, Danzig, Konigsberg and Stettin, and on September 4 Budapest. These assaults by small groups never attained the proportions nor destructive power of the Anglo-American attacks, but they were of psychological significance. Pe-8 were mostly used on the Front, making maximum use of the load bearing capacity of 4,000kg bombs. On the eve of the famous battle at Kursk in July 1943, Pe-8s were used to bomb German concentrations of tanks and other armoured vehicles.

It was also one of the few Soviet models flown into foreign countries during the war. In November 1941 a Pe-8 landed in Scotland carrying Soviet foreign minister V M Molotov. From Britain the machine flew to America and back. In 1942 the flight was repeated. The Pe-8 flew 17,800km, mostly at 8,000m altitude. Part of the flight took place over North Europe, where the German Air Force supervised the air space but had no idea about the Pe-8 being there, nor about its valuable load.

Use of Pe-8 was strongly limited due to a shortage of AM-35A engines. Not until 1943, when the situation had become critical, did I F Nezval redesign the Pe-8 for ASh-82FN two-row radial engines, each of 1,523/1,850mhp. This was after Petlyakov's death and the engines improved performance to 422kph with a range of 4,500km.

Production of single specimens of Pe-8 lasted until 1944. The life of the machine was amazingly long. Up to the fifties specimens could still be seen in operation as supply 'planes in the Arctic.

Heavy bombers of the TB class were especially noteworthy from a technical point of view. for various reasons they proved less successful than anticipated in their original military sphere.

Above: The TB-7 became Pe-8 in 1941 and most series production machines were given AM-35A engines, although a few had ACh-308 diesels.

Below: To overcome a shortage of AM-35A, preferentially allocated to MiG-3s, Petlyakov equipped some Pe-8 with two-row radial ASh-82 units.

CHAPTER 18

Long Range Bombers

IN THE DOCTRINE of Soviet bomber aviation elaborated in the period of transition between the twenties and thirties, long range bombers occupied an important place. These were seen as an effective means of taking strategic aerial war deep into the enemy hinter-land, where it was not expected. Mass attacks were not contemplated, but rather the use of single aircraft or small groups which could fly unnoticed to a target and drop a small bomb load.

Aircraft of the TB class were unsuited for such operations. The long-range bomber had to be more streamlined in order to reduce drag and save fuel. Engine speed was to be low, again to help fuel consumption. It was certainly difficult to design long-range aircraft, and the world marvelled when Soviet examples made an appearance to establish world records.

The Republic's Military Revolutionary Council, at that time the most highly placed organ for National Defence, decided in August 1931 to introduce such aircraft into the Air Force. A special commission composed design targets for A N Tupolev: with ungeared M-34 engines it was to be able to guarantee a range of at least 9,000km; with geared engines – 10,000km. The Soviet government approved proposals in December 1931 and formed a mixed commission to ensure continuation of the necessary work.

It was not just a question of the airframe and engine. New and better equipment had to be obtained, crews trained and new runways

The 1931 brief for a long range bomber produced ANT-25, Tupolev directing the design work which was executed by Sukhoi's bureau. Military designation was DB-1 while for record-breaking activities (bottom picture) it had the civilian coding RD.

constructed. It was further demanded that these long-range bombers should establish new international records, to afford proof to the rest of the world of the ability of the Soviet aviation industry.

Under Tupolev's direction P O Sukhoi's brigade in TsAGI worked out the design of ANT-25. For this aircraft the military designation DB-1 was chosen. Civilian coding wăs RD (*Rekord Dalnosti* = long distance record).

The project required a wing with slight induced drag and slight frictional resistance. Therefore, the gigantic wings of ANT-25, with their span of 34m and surface area of 88.2sq m, had a specially high aspect ratio of 13:1.Slenderness cut down the induced drag; varnished fabric covering over the original corrugated metal sheet reduced frictional resistance. Only a few months elapsed before they realised that wings like these have too big a head resistance, and that one could achieve improved streamlining by simpler means – for example, a smaller wing area, higher wing-load, a more efficient wing profile etc.

Otherwise the streamlining of ANT-25 was good. The crew sections were roofed over, the tail wheel cased and the landing wheels were half retractable backwards and up.

Construction of the first two aircraft began in June 1932 and a year later, on June 22, 1933, M M Gromov was able to test fly the first prototype, the second following on September 10. At first both machines had only corrugated sheet covering. The engines were specially prepared M-34 of 860mhp with 7:1 increased compression and a guaranteed undisturbed running time of 100 to 120 hours. The best materials available were used.

Some 6,100kg of fuel was distributed in small tanks over almost the whole span. Fuel supply lines began from tanks in the fuselage, so as to keep stress of the wing as uniform as possible and to lessen bending in the central section.

The engine was, of course, overloaded as it had to drive a machine of 11,500kg take-off weight. So everything depended on its undisturbed running. On first flights the propeller was two-bladed, later three-bladed. Exhaust gases were tranported to the heating plant of the cabin which contained pilot, radio navigator and air mechanic In the military version, 600kg bombs

and a moveable machine gun were to be taken.

During the flight testing of ANT-25, Frenchmen Codos and Rossi established a world distance record of 9,102km on a trip from New York to Syria in a Bleriot 110. This was a signal for the Soviets to begin their attacks on long-distance and flight duration records.

First attempt to beat the best flight duration took place in summer 1934. The machine, equipped as RD and with Gromov, A I Filin and I T Spirin as crew took off from a special runway in Shchelkovo, near Moscow. This concrete strip had an artificial slope so that the overloaded aircraft was able to attain speed more quickly. Twice the RD took off to fly the triangle Moscow-Tula-Ryazan, and twice it had to make premature landings owing to engine disturbance. Only the third try, on September 10, 1934, was successful.

Gromov flew a record 12,411km over the triangle in 75 hours 2 minutes. The average speed of 153kph was certainly not high, but it met requirements. However, as the USSR was not yet a member of the FAI, it could not be recognised. Nevertheless it excited much attention among the world public and all three pilots were decorated with the title 'Hero of the USSR'.

Gromov's crew were soon preparing for a new record flight, on which the possibilities of flying over the North Pole were to be investigated. Amid the preparations ,Gromov fell ill and a new crew had to be assembled and trained. In August 1935 S A Levanevskii's overloaded RD took off from Shchelkovo and flew via Leningrad to the North Pole. Over the Barents Sea, irregularities started to occur in the engines and Levanevskii received a radio instruction to turn back, landing on an airfield near Novgorod.

The lesson was clear: before a polar flight the aircraft should be thoroughly tested in Arctic conditions. The regions of North Siberia were excellent for such purposes so V P Chkalov, G F Bajdukov and A V Beljakov were given the task. The route, in accordance with the spirit of the times, was called *Stalinskii marshrut* (Stalin's marching route) and led from Shchelkovo via Franz Josef Land to Severnaya Zemla, Cape Tiksi and Petropavlovsk Kamchatskii. From there, depending on the fuel supply and weather, the aircraft was to fly to Nikolayevsk on the Amur or even to Chita.

Chkalov's RD took off on the night of July 19-20, 1936. It had wings painted red and bore the identification number SSR-N-25.First stage of the flight enjoyed favourable weather but further east conditions became more difficult. An Arctic depression forced the aircraft to fly through ice and fog, but the crew fought through.Over Cape Chelyuskin they steered southwards; Petropavlovsk Kamchatskii was flown over and they approached Nikolayevsk on the Amur. Over the Okhotsk Sea, ice pressed the aircraft lower and lower. The pilots reported their situation over the radio and received permission to land. On July 22, 1936, the RD touched down on a sand spit on the little island of Udd, not far from Mikolayevsk,

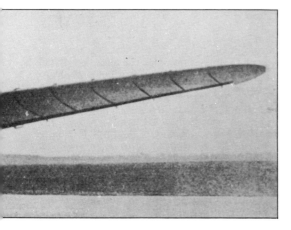

after 9,374km and 56 hours 20 minutes flying time. The island has been called Chkalov ever since.

One year later, Chkalov's crew flew from Moscow via the North Pole to the U S A under the most dramatic conditions. The aircraft took off on June 18, 1937, from Shchelkovo, and nature put on obstacle after another in their way. The oxygen system froze at 4,000-6,000m, the aircraft could not be flown at a lower altitude because of heavy thunderstorms and the risk of icing-up was great. Moreover, the aircraft had to overcome a strong head wind from the North Pole to America, and this reduced the fuel supplies faster than anticipated.

On June 20 Chkalov decided to land in Portland, near Vancouver, in the state of Washington. Route flown was 9,130km of which the FAI recognized 8,504km as slant range between take-off and landing runways. And that was too short for a new world record. Nevertheless, all three fliers were welcomed as heroes in America.

If Chkalov suffered from the weather, the flight of Gromov, A S Yumashev and S A Danilin was almost a like a pleasure flight - no thunderstorm and on several legs there was even a tail wind. Gromov's flight took place between July 12 and 14, 1937. Gromov's RD was heavily overloaded. Fuel alone weighed 6,230kg and a 1,650m run was required before the aircraft could get off the ground. An altitude of 500m was reached after 50km; 150km after take-off, the aircraft was still only 1,200m high. Gromov flew across Canada, and was prepared to continue as far as Mexico. But he was not given permission to land there and had to come down close to the Mexican border at San Jacinto in California.

The RD had covered 11,500km in 62 hours 17 minutes at an average speed of 185km. When they landed there was still enough fuel in the tanks for a further 1,500 to 1,700km. This time it was a clear world record. The FAI recognised 10,148km which stood for over a year until the English broke it in November 1938 with a Vickers Wellesley and 11,530km.

RD machines together with the TB-3 and little I-16 fighters, were among the most popular aircraft in the Soviet Union. There was no aviation newspaper in the world that did not give details of the flight and the aircraft. And enthusiasm in the Soviet Union was unbounded. Only to the initiated did jubilation ring hollow; for at this very time a wave of purges began and one of the most revered of men, A N Tupolev, was soon to be among the victims.

While civilian variants were successful, the same cannot be said for the military DB-1. The Red Air Force soon realised that this aircraft, with its 160-190kph cruising speed, 240kph maximum, low service ceiling, weak armament and unwieldy nature, was almost defenceless.

An improved version, ANT-36, had been planned, but in 1935 all work was halted. The 20 airframes built were used for tests with the high altitude aircraft BOK. Germany's Junkers Jumo-4

heavy oil engine was tested on a DB-1 in 1935. This also proved too low powered, the same as the AN-1 heavy oil engine designed by A D Charomshii.

Towards the end of 1933, the Soviet drawing offices received new orders for a long-range bomber of the next generation. Great distance was no longer expected and for the sake of reliability the machines were to be twin-engined with 350kph speed at 3,500m, capable of carrying 1,000kg of bombs at 3,000km range.

Sukhoi was to design the aircraft. He made use of experience from ANT-25 and constructed the prototype ANT-37 or DB-2. The wing was inherited but made a little smaller, spanning 31m with a lifting surface 84.9sqm. On the wing were twin French Gnome-Rhone 14K engines, each of 800mhp (Soviet designation M-85) into the nacelles of which the undercarriage retracted. A powerful spherical machine gun turret was built into the nose with a second on the top of the fuselage. N S Rybko tested the machine in June 1935, but soon ran into difficulties. It became clear that use of an antiquated airframe was a mistake. On speeds approaching 300kph tail unit oscillations were noticeable, and these were insupportable at 340kph. Gromov had an accident with the aircraft in July 1935 when the tail splintered to pieces in flight.

Only with the second improved prototype, ANT-37, were they able to test the long-distance flight qualities. On August 20, 1936, the 4,995km Moscow-Omsk-Moscow return trip was covered in 23 hours 20 minutes. Average speed was only 213kph, not much better than on the single-engined ANT-25, but altitude was better at about 4,200m. The Red Air Force needed such machines and ordered series production of DB-2.

The variant ANT-37bis was also built. It had more powerful M-86 engines, each of 800/900mhp developed by S K Tumanskii from the French Gnome-Rhone 14K. The new aircraft had 12,500kg take-off weight (previously 9,600kg) and 7,300km range (5,000km).

In September 1938, the aircraft appeared in the press under the name 'Rodina' (Fatherland) and it soon appeared in the FAI record lists too. Three female Soviet pilots, V S Grisobudov, P D Osipenkova and M M Raskova, set up an international women's long distance record on September 24/25, 1938, of 5,908.6km. The aircraft flew from

ANT-37 (DB-2) inherited a smaller version of the ANT-25's wing and took on two Gnome-Rhone 14K engines without any significant increase in speed.

Moscow to the Far East and landed with retracted undercarriage in the waterlogged valley of the Amur, near the village of Kerbi. The flight was actually 5,947km long, lasted 26 hours 29 minutes, and average speed was 224kph.

TsAGI had chosen too awkward a way to develop a long-range bomber. The ANT versions achieved noteworthy performances as record aircraft but their value for military purposes remained slight.

The Red Air force demanded long-range bombers from other design units too, in the hope that more modern methods would come to light. S V Ilyushin's TsKB drawing office devoted attention to the problem as did the design centres of N J Shukovskii's military aviation academy under the direction of V F Bolkhovitinov and J V Beljajev.

For the design of his bomber prototype TsKB-26, on which he had already been working since 1934, Ilyushin chose a more modern approach. The aircraft was relatively small with a wing span of 21.4m, lifting surface of 65.6sqm, clean lines flat sheet covering and monocoque fuselage. The twin high-altitude Gnome-Rhone 14K M-85 engines were the same as those built into ANT-37. At 4,200m, where the metric horse-power of each engine was 765, the TsKB-26 reached a full 390kph and cruising speed was a full 100kph better than the ANT-37bis. With 500kg bomb load TsKB-26 could fly 4,000km at 320kph at 4,600m.

This was great progress, but the prototype was only an experimental model, without gun turrets and with an open cockpit. Its wing and tail surfaces were of all metal construction, the fuselage a wooden monocoque.

In 1936 came prototype TsKB-30 into which the full armament and equipment were incorporated. In the nose was a ShKAS turret, a further machine gun was situated in a cylindrical turret on the upper side of the fuselage, and a third below towards the back. Crew consisted of four men. The construction was all-metal including the fuselage.

In the fuselage bay, ten 100kg bombs, three 500kg or one, 1,000kg bomb could be carried. On outer suspensions bomb load could be increased to 2,000kg and one 45-36-AN 940kg torpedo could also be attached. The fuel tanks held 3,600 litres and with smaller bomb loads up to 4,400 litres.

On flight tests, the aircraft showed outstanding qualities. V K Kokkinaki, who flew the whole test programme, looped the loop several times with TsKB-26 and TsKB-30, quite an achievement for a machine with up to 9,365kg take-off weight!

One of these loops was decisive for the future of the bomber, being performed over Red Square on May 1, 1936. Stalin was so enthusiastic that he ordered it to be put on the production line immediately. But the director of the factory refused,

TSKB-30, prototype of the DB-3, appeared in 1936. A loop performed over Red Square so impressed Stalin that he ordered it into immediate production.

his plant having just completed preparations for serial production of long-range bomber DB-2. Only after the personal intervention of Voroshilov, Ordshonikidse and General Alksnis, commander-in-chief of the Air Force, was TsKB-30 put on the production line. The military designation was DB-3.

The looping episode showed up some of the conditions under which Soviet aircraft design operated at that time. The Red Air Force, in particular, were sometimes not progressive enough, so heavy economic losses resulted when there was a change in production. Also, production plants defended themselves vigorously against all production changes, especially the change to new models. At that time finished machines were the most highly recognised criteria for a successful factory.

Finally, given Stalin's well-known penchant for aircraft technology and the infallibility of his decisions, those concerned could direct their thoughts skilfully in the direction desired. In this case a loop executed at the right time helped to introduce a new, more modern aircraft.

Kokkinaki was indefatigable. On July 17, 1936, he climbed in the TsKB-26 with 500kg load to 11,294m; on the 26th he carried 1,000kg to 11,402m. Both performances were recognised as FAI records. On August 3 TsKB-26 registered 12,816m with 500kg load; on August 21 the same aircraft and pilot transported 1,000kg to 12,101m and on September 7 the machine took 2,000kg to 11,005m. This last height beat the Italian record by 2,567m and was only superseded by a Boeing B-29 in 1946.

These altitude records clearly showed the superiority of the TsKBs to TsAGI designs. Long distance records still had to be established and were again achieved with Kokkinaki at the controls.

On August 26, 1937, Kokkinaki flew 5,000km between Moscow, Sebastopol, Sverdlovsk and Moscow with 1,000kg bomb load at an average speed of 325.275kph. This record did not last long, beaten a year later by the French with 400kph. A greater success was achieved on June 27/28, 1938, when Kokkinaki flew with navigator A M Bryandinskii from Moscow to Spassk, a distance of 7,589km. Time needed was 24 hours 36 minutes and the average speed 307kph.

For this record flight the aircraft was given civilian designation TsKB-30 and equipped accordingly. It had red wings with a large inscription 'Moskva'. It was the second 'Moskva' in Ilyushin's life. The first was a glider of 1925, when he was still a student at the military aviation academy in Moscow. We also know of a third 'Moskva', the four turboprop transport 'plane, Il-18.

Kokkinaki had prepared a further long flight for April 1939, this time to the USA. He was not going to fly over the North Pole, but westwards over the North Sea and northern Atlantic. It was a difficult route for those times because one always had to contend with a strong headwind in these parts.

When 'Moskva' took off on April 29 it seemed like a mere excursion to Kokkinaki and his navigator, M Kh. Gordiyenko. Weather was favourable, the machione had 5,480m altitude over Norway and the auto-pilot pointed the aircraft reliably in the direction of Iceland. But soon difficulties arose. The ice cold wind grew stronger and turned into a hurricane against which Kokkinaki had to fight hard, for now the auto-pilot failed too. Ground speed sank to 280kph.

DB-3F, later re-designated Il-4, was a totally revised variant with greatly improved performance.

Over Greenland everything changed and 'Moskva' was driven once again by a favourable tail wind, sometimes reaching up to 500kph. The route from Greenland to Labrador only took three hours. Over Labrador fog, snow and whirl-winds awaited the machine. Kokkinaki shunted into a height of 9,000m, but at this height several pieces of equipment froze. Moreover, a radio report was received prohibiting a landing in the area of New York because of fog. Kokkinaki decided on an emergency landing, bringing the aircraft down with undercarriage retracted near a lighthouse on the small island of Miscou in Canadian waters.

'Moskva' had covered 8,000km, the direct distance amounting to 6,505km. With a flight time of 22 hours 56 minutes, that gave an average speed of 348kph. Both fliers were slightly hurt in the emergency landing but their reception in the USA was marked by festivity – they were even received by President Roosevelt. But not so

much attention was afforded this flight as that of the previous year. The political situation in Europe in spring 1939 was already casting its shadow.

At the time of Kokkinaki's record flight, serial production of bomber DB-3b had already begun. The first machines were delivered with M-85 engines of 800mhp though the more powerful 950mhp M-87B were soon incorporated. Variants with these engines were introduced in 1938 as DB-3M. Construction of the aircraft was also simplified to make serial production easier.

In 1939 Kokkinaki tested a thoroughly revised variant designated DB-3F. It was given new M-88 engines of 1,100mhp and achieved an altitude performance of up to 4,700m. The fuselage nose was lengthened in the form of a cone and thickly glazed with a machine gun at the tip. The new engines allowed an increase in take-off weight to 10,055kg. Speed, too, was better, 445kph at 6,400m while 5,000m was reached in 13.6

The production version of DB-3 which carried a crew of four and 1,000kg internal bomb load.

minutes. Service ceiling rose to 9,000m and range with 1,000kg bombs was up to 3,500km at 340kph cruising speed. Such performances were above average for the times.

There were no impediments to the start of production of the DB-3F and in 1940 the army and naval aviation units received their first deliveries. All equipment made of duralumin was given freely, for advantage could be taken of Stalin's favourable feelings about the aircraft. Despite this, stocks of DB-3 and DB-3F were very low when one considers the tasks which strategic long-range bomber aviation had to accomplish. Even aircraft like these could not place any great obstacles in the path of advancing German troops nor destroy their transport bases behind the front.

At the beginning of 1941, when the designation system changed, the DB-3F was re-coded Il-4. An Il-4 of Baltic naval aviation was among the first aircraft to make an air raid on the Federal capital, Berlin. On the night of August 8, 1941, a group of Il-4 and Yer-2 under Colonel I N Preobashenskii took off from the island of Saaremaa on the Baltic Sea. The air raid was completely unexpected and there was no air alarm. It was repeated on September 4. At this time Estonia was already occupied by the Germans, so these long-range bombers actually operated from an airfield behind the front. Later the Il-4 were used more for tactical missions in the vicinity of the front.

Production of DB-3 or Il-4 lasted from 1936 to 1944 and reached 6,980 aircraft (other Soviet sources give 6,784). In the winter of 1941-2 designers had to change the construction so as to save as much duralumin as possible. So the spindle-shaped navigator's cabin was made of wood as were the passages between fuselage and controls, roofing of the pilots cockpit and finally, the curve of the edge of the wing. The use of wood reduced performance to some extent, speed falling by 6kph.

The Il-4 of that time was already flying M-88B engines of 1,100mhp attaining 410kph maximum speed at 6,500m, and spanning 3,800km with 1,000kg bombs at 320kph cruising speed. They even reached 4,260km at 263kph. In the turret on top of the fuselage was a UBT machine gun.

In 1943 Ilyushin tried to resume production of the Il-4 bomber, incorporating A D Charomskii's new heavy-oil ACh-30B engines. Il-6 was to carry a crew of six and be armed with five ShVAK cannon plus standard bomb load of 2,500kg. At a speed of 464kph range was to be 4,000km, but these are only estimations. Only four examples were built in 1943.

We have already mentioned how Yer-2 took part in the first bombardment of Berlin. They were aircraft of V G Yermolayev, built in small numbers and, compared to the Il-4 of small importance. The origins of Yer-2 ran contrary to normal development, i.e. first the transport 'plane was built and out of this the bomber was developed.

At first the low-wing transport monoplane, STAL-7, was assigned to Bartini's group and built in 1937. In August 1939 the STAL-7 became known through its Moscow-Sverdlovsk-Sebastopol flight and attracted the attention of Stalin who ordered the design of a long-range bomber version. As Bartini had been in prison since January 1938,

Yermolayev took over the reconstruction. The bomber prototype was called DB-240 and test flown by N P Shibanov in June 1940. As this machine was a desire of Stalin's it was on the production line by October 1940, although it had barely reached production stage.

Its general performances were good. With twin M-105 engines of 1,050mhp the DB-240 attained a maximum speed of 500kph at 6,000m and transported a ton of bombs over a distance of more than 4,100km. In contrast to the transport STAL-7, the DB-240 had twin rudders, glazed nose and glazed window in the belly of the fuselage behind the wing. The two pilot seats lay asymmetrically one behind the other on the left side of the aircraft. The strong W-shape wings were retained.

Serial production in Voronesh lasted not quite a year. In autumn 1941 the plant had to be evacuated after construction of 300 aircraft. Yermolayev experimented with further designs. In December 1940 he incorporated ACh-30B diesel engines of 1,250mhp and this increased range to 5,000km with 1,000kg bombs. At the beginning of 1941 the DB-240, or Yer-2 as it was already called, made a practice attack from Moscow at a target in the neighbourhood of Omsk in Siberia, dropped a ton of bombs and then returned.

In 1942 Yermolayev built a slightly enlarged machine, Yer-4, again with improved ACh-30B engines. Take off weight was 14,000kg which could be increased by overloading to 18,000kg. Maximum speed lowered to 420kph at 6,000m, but range with 1,000kg bombs and 320kph cruising speed was still 5,000km. Armament was stronger. In the nose and under the fuselage were UBT

machine guns instead of ShKAS and in the gun turret on the top of the fuselage was a moveable ShVAK. The prototype Yer-4 passed certification tests in December 1943 but was not put on the production line.

Long-range bombers were also designed in N J Shukovskii's Military Aviation Academy. Model DB-A had been worked out here in 1935, under the direction of Professor V F Bolkhovitnov, the 'A' standing for 'Akademiya' (academy). The real design work was then directed by M M Shishmarev.

Bolkhovitinov sought to combine the best qualities of the TB and DB class, that is load capacity with range and heavy armament. DB-A was an all-metal mid-wing monoplane with flat sheet covering and four M-34RN engines of 840/970mhp exhibiting superchargers and reduction gear.

In the nose, tail and inner engine nacelles were moveable ShKAS machine guns, while on top of the fuselage was a turret with ShVAK cannon. The crew consisted of eight men and 3,000kg of bombs were all stowed in the fuselage. Dead weight was an astonishing 15,400kg while take-off weight rose to 21,000kg.

First DB-A was ready in spring 1936, followed shortly afterwards by the second machine, designated DB-2A, which was to have an eleven-man crew and take-off weight of 24 tons. Nyukhtikov and Bajdukov test flew the 'planes with hardly any difficulties. The DB-A reached 330kph at 4,000m, the DB-2A reached 340kph at 6,000m. Service ceiling was respectively 7,220 and 8,000m. The DB-2A could carry three tons of bombs 2,000km, about twice as far as TB-3.

In 1936 and 1937, DB-2A set up some international records. On November 11, 1936, the pilots Nyukhtikov and Lipkin carried 10 tons payload to 7,032m and 13 tons to 2,000m. On May 14, 1937, Bajdukov and Kastanajev reached a speed of 280.246kph with 5,000kg load over 1,000 and 2,000km routes.

The DB-A is unfortunately also connected with one of the heaviest losses in aviation at the time. At daybreak on August 12, 1937, the first DB-A machine set off from Shchelkovo, near Moscow, on a flight over the North Pole to America. Commander-in-chief and first pilot was the polar flier S A Levanevskii; crew members were N G Kastanayev, V I Levchenko, G T Probeyimov, N N Godovikov and N J Galkovskii. The machine had civilian designation SSSR-N-209 and its task was to improve on Gromov's record reached a short time before with an RD-2.

The aircraft flew to Archangel and from there to the North Pole, The crew reported crossing the Pole and the flight towards Fairbanks in

Left: Yer-2 (DB-240) bombers were developed from the STAL-7 transport by Yermolayev. Only 300 aircraft were constructed before the Voronesh factory had to be evacuated.

Alaska. Then came a report that the right outboard engine had stopped owing to a disturbance in the pipeline, but flight was being continued. There followed two unintelligible wireless communications but from then on SSSR-N-209 gave no more reports.

Soviet and American military pilots joined in a large-scale search, especially between the Pole and 83 degrees north, where authorities suspected that the aircraft had crashed. There was some hope, for the crew had provisions and equipment for 100 days. Search operations lasted nine months – in vain. The Arctic never revealed the secret of this catastrophe.

In spite of this Bolkhovitinov's DB-A was pronounced a good aircraft. In 1938 a small issue was constructed of twelve DB-2A, equipped with M-34FRN engines. With a crew of eleven, the aircraft reached 346kph at 6,000m. Of the twelve aircraft, five actually served in a long-range bomber unit. The others were kept as reserves or were used in various tests. By this time it was apparent that the smaller, nimbler DB-3 was technically and tactically superior.

All the long-range bombers described up to now had more or less classical lines. But DB-LK, designed and built in 1939 by Professor J V Belyayev, was far from standard. Belyayev devoted long years to the unusual shaped "Bat's wings". The centre-section was broad and tapered into a sweepforward before the wing tips bent a little backwards again. A wing form like this displayed qualities of inherent stability and Belyayev used it successfully for tailless aircraft. In 1933 he built and tested a tailless glider TsAGI-BP-2, and in 1934 designed a transport aircraft with double fuselages and twin Wright Cyclone engines.

Long-range bomber DB-LK (LK stood for *Letajushchiye Krylo* – All wing) was a tailless, twin-boom aircraft. The fuselages originated in lengthened engine nacelles in the noses of which were twin M-87B engines, each of 950mhp. Behind the engines were cabins – in the left fuselage, the pilot's; in the right fuselage, the navigator's. Pilot and navigator had a very limited view forwards and backwards, especially on approach flights, which caused difficulties.

The fuselage tails were strongly glazed and in each sat a machine gunner with a twin ShKAS. Each fuselage also accommodated a bay for 1,000kg bombs and room for the retracted wheel. Over each fuselage tail projected a high rudder unit topped by a horizontal tail unit.

Test pilots approached the DB-LK with distrust. Flaws in the undercarriage shock absorption caused unpleasant taxiing characteristics and M A Nyukhtikov only made short jumps over a long period. Pilots called the aircraft 'Hen' as it would not fly!

Not until summer 1939 did Nyukhtikov manage to lengthen a jump to a real flight – and he was astonished how easily and stably the aircraft flew. Gone was the distrust and further flight

testing proceeded without difficulties. DB-LK reached 395kph at low altitude, 488kph at 5,100m, and could achieve 3,000km range with a ton of bombs. These were good performances, but the aircraft remained a prototype.

These then, were the long-range bombers of the thirties. They were primarily used as a means of political propaganda to show what a country, about whose technical capabilites the world showed considerable doubt, could do. Militarily and technically these aircraft were not always promising, but they were talked about!

Above: The substantial DB-A bomber weighed in at 15,400kg empty and 21,000kg at take-off. The first example was lost without trace during a distance record attempt.

Belayev's fascination for bat-wing form manifested itself in his DB-LK, a reluctant flier at first but competent once in the air. It remained a prototype.

CHAPTER 19

High Speed Bombers

IN 1934 A N TUPOLEV was engaged in the study of a high-speed tactical bomber. Working with him at TsAGI was the design brigade of A A Arkhangelskii.

The Red Air Force possessed no aircraft of this class. Between the twin-engined heavy TB-1 bomber and the multi-purpose biplane R-5 there was too great a gap and Tupolev was working to fill it with a machine which, with further development, would be adequate until the end of the thirties. Technical Office of the air force specified 330kph, 8,00m service ceiling and the ability to carry 500kg bombs 800km distance. Moreover, the aircraft was to be able to take off and land on normal combat airfields.

Tupolev considered the requirements inadequate and not sufficiently ambitious for an aircraft which was to have long years of use. In his opinion, performances should have been much better. So he built two prototypes according to the conceptions of the air force and a third according to his own ideas. All three aircraft were almost indentical, cantilever, mid-wing monoplanes with light metal monocoque fuselage, flat sheet covering, glazed cabins for three crew members and a retractable undercarriage.

First prototype of the SB (*Skorostnoy Bombardirovshchik*) had twin American Wright Cyclone F5 nine-cylinder radial engines, each of 730mhp. Later they were replaced by twin M-87 fourteen-cylinder double-row radials of 900mhp. This prototype had a span of 19m and wing area of 47.6sq.m and was flight tested by I S Shurov and K K Popov on April 25, 1934.

Unsatisfactory results prompted a new wing with the same span but 46.3sq.m area. A new series of flight tests lasted from February 5, 1935, until June 31 when it was decided to use in-line engines, the Hispano Suiza 12Ybrs of 760mhp. The heavier engines and their coolers brought about another increase in wing area to 51.92sq.m, but in general this SB-1, or ANT-40, did not satisfy.

Better was the ANT-40-1 prototype with HS 12Ybrs engines and some modifications, tested between February and and July 1935.

All the experience with both prototypes was amalgamated into the third, really Tupolevian prototype, ANT-40-2. Its tests took place between September 1935 and February 1936 and were without problems. ANT-40-2 had a span of 19m, but the wings of series production machines were enlarged to 20.33m span and 56.7sq.m area. The Red Air Force gave it designation SB-2.

In April 1934, months before the first flight of the prototypes, arrangements were being made for large-scale serial production – so great was the need for such aircraft and so great the trust accorded Tupolev's work. Time between construction of the prototype and serial production was to be as short as possible.

ANT-40 only reached 325kph at 4,000m whereas ANT-40-2 was incomparably better – 404kph at 5,000m. Service ceiling, too, rose from 6,800 to

First prototype of the SB (ANT-40) had its Wright Cyclone engines replaced by M-87 14-cylinder, double-row radials (above) and made its maiden flight on April 25, 1934.

9,400m. The first ANT-40 had only 940 litres fuel supply, restricting range to 700km. ANT-40-2 could carry 1,760 litres and fly 1,250km. These qualities represented a high-speed bomber capable of evading most fighters of that time.

With the beginning of series production, some combat aviation units were able to receive aircraft in the first quarter of 1936. Production proceeded in several aircraft plants, together with manufacture of M-100 engines, licensed version of Hispano-Suiza 12Ybrs. At their peak in 1937-38 the plants delivered up to 13 machines a day. Owing to technical improvements the production of the machine in 1938 only required 47% of the time taken in 1937.

First machines were given 750mph M-100 engines which reduced speed to 395kph. But designer V J Klimov quickly built an M-100A variant of 860mhp which corresponded to performance of the French HS-12Ybrs. This brought the speed up to 423kph at 4,000m, making it possible to increase bomb load to 600kg. Bombs were stowed in a vertical bay with six box shaped receptacles. Armament consisted of twin ShKAS in the nose and in a mount on top of the fuselage.

In October 1936, Soviet freighter Bolshevik docked in the Spanish harbour of Cartagena with military equipment for the revolutionary army in the Spanish Civil War. Among the items were several specimens of the SB-2 bomber, first in an issue of 210 machines delivered to Spain.

The use of SB-2 marked a turning point in the aerial war over Spain. Nicknamed 'Katushka',

they were considered invulnerable, faster than most early fighters. Only the Messerschmitt Bf 109 could offer dangerous resistance.

After the Spanish Civil War, 18 airworthy SB-2 machines were retained in Spain. They mostly had French 12Ybrs engines, a substitute for the susceptible M-100A. Franco's air force used the first in the combat units, then for training purposes. Spanish airmen called them 'Sofia'

SB-2 were built in Czechoslovakia from 1937 to 1939. The Czechoslovakian Skoda plant sold the U S S R licence rights for an excellent mountain gun, C-5, and in return Czechoslovakia received the rights for SB-2 as well as one complete specimen. The contract was signed in March 1937. In April, the first sample copy made its appearance. Avia aircraft plants, a branch of the Skoda combine, were the licensees and first machine appeared in Winter 1938 known as B-71.

In April and May 1938, Czechlovakian crews flew 60 completed machines from Kiev to Czechoslovakia. In Kiev, Czech Avia HS 12Ybrs engines were assembled into Soviet airframes. Equipment and armament was Czech too. Meanwhile Avia and its sub-suppliers, Aero and Letov, had made preparations for production. The order was for 101 bombers and 60 long-range reconnaissance aircraft. But no licensed aircraft were ready to fly by Autumn 1938, time of the Munich crisis. Not until Winter 1938 did the first machines arrive from Avia and Aero; Letov had not done any more work on the machines. Most of the aircraft were still delivered to the German air force which

Left: SB-2 variants with M-103 engines and the new VISh-22 variable pitch propellors were designated SB-2bis and achieved 450kph.

Below: SB-2 were used in Czechoslovakia as the Avia B-71.

used them for training and target towing while others were delivered to Bulgaria.

Soviet SB-2 bombers were also supplied to forces of Chiang Kai-shek in China and proved their worth. Foreign users of SB-2 were on the whole content, but they did complain about the noisy airframe, constricted crew compartments, hard undercarriage suspension and the dangerous seating of the nose gunner. As this gunner could only reach his cabin from underneath there was no possibility of escape in the event of an emergency landing with retracted undercarriage.

Arkhangelskii continued design of the SB series and in 1936 Klimov's plant built the first M-103 engines, a Soviet development of the Hispano-Suiza. These engines developed 860/960mhp and had the new VISh-22 controllable pitch propellers. In order to make full use of performance, a new engine cowl was built without frontal radiators. The radiators were given a tunnel shape and placed under the nacelle.

Aircraft with these engines were designated SB-2bis. Their maximum speed was 450kph at 4,100m and with slight overloading they could carry 500kg bombs 2,300km. Armament was increased by a ShKAS machine gun on the floor of the back turret that was used instead of the original mount. Performances of the SB-2bis were certainly good, especially at higher altitudes. M J Alexeyev even managed to create an international FAI record on September 2, 1937, when he reached 12,246.5m altitude with 1,000kg payload. So Kokkinaki's record with the DB-3 was beaten.

Alexeyev had reached 12,695m with the same payload on November 1, 1936 but as the USSR was not, at that time, a member of the FAI, this performance could not be registered.

In 1937 a further improvement was shown with the model SB-3. Arkhangelskii used two new M-103A engines with 950/1,000mhp which gave the aircraft a speed of 455kph and justified inclusion on the production line.

SB-3s had an enlarged turret under the fuselage to give more free movement to the machine gun. For the training of pilots a dual-control variant was produced, designated USB (*Uchebnii Skorostnoy Bombardirovshchik*) with a longer front fuselage and an open cockpit for the instructor in front of the normal cabin windscreen. During the War, USB were widely used for towing Antonov A-7 gliders.

Other aerodynamical refinements led to the SB-3bis variant of 1938 with 486kph speed, but this did not enter production. Also not producd was the MMN variant of 1939 which had a new-shape cabin, enclosed together with the front gunner/bomb aimer's room. MMN reached 458kph with twin M-105 engines of 1,050mhp. The prototype was used by Aeroflot for post routes and named 'Shchuka' (Pike).

In 1939 a lot of experience garnered from aerial combats in the Spanish Civil War had been turned to account, not only in the U S S R. Especially impressive were successes of the German Junkers Ju 87 dive bombers. In an air-space

in which German and Italian fighters could be assured of absolute dominance towards the end of the war, the Stukas suffered virtually no interference and became models of precise bombing.

In the U S S R, where dive bombers had already been designed and delivered, there was a demand for similar aircraft, and even the SB high-speed bombers were reconstructed for dive bombing.

In 1939 Arkhangelskii built the first prototype of the horizontal and dive-bomber SB-RK. All module units were changed, especially the wing. According to Arkhangelskii's original plans the aircraft was to have a system of slotted, variable camber flaps which were to curb the diving speed and help with landing. Hence the designation RK '*Rasresnoye Krylo*' (slotted wing). This system proved too complicated and time consuming and was given up, but designation of the aircraft was kept.

Instead of the slot system, Arkhangelskii built a wing with stronger internal design, 8sqm less wing surface and electrically operated vertical-dive suppressor grids under the wing leading edge. The aircraft was given new M-105R engines, each of 1,110mhp, which were cowled with smooth nacelles. Radiators were built into the tips of the nacelles with air intake holes in the wing leading edge.

Lines of the fuselage were also improved. A moveable ShKAS machine gun was in the nose, the same in the fuselage top turret, and another underneath. SB-RK reached 480kph at 4,700m, its service ceiling was – thanks to the two-step supercharger – 10,500m and it could carry 1,000kg bombs 1,000km.

SB-RK was quickly put on the production line, but only 200 specimens could be delivered. It was for this reason that the powerful Ar-2 bomber, as it was called after January 1941, was so seldom seen. Of the 6,656 specimens of all SB variants built between 1934 and 1941, the Ar-2 formed the smallest part. SB bombers fought in the first months of the war without fighter escort and in the teeth of Germany's absolute aerial supremacy.

By this time most SB were antiquated. Some airmen, as for example, N F Gastello, preferred to engage in suicide missions in order to be sure of destroying the enemy. In a suicide diving attack on June 26, 1941, Gastello destroyed a mechanised unit by the explosion of his bombs and tanks.

As far as possible, SB machines were commandeered for auxiliary tasks, especially supplying partisan units by the depositing of tanks or towing A-7 cargo gliders. SB models were in service before the war for several design and research tasks. Designer I P Tolstych reconstructed an SB-2bis in 1940 to test a tricycle undercarriage. The fixed undercarriage was filmed at take-off and on landing in order to collect data concerning the problem of 'shimmy' on the nose-wheel. The aircraft was called 'Pterodactyl' by the pilots.

Tupolev and Arkhangelskii also made use of the basic concept in further design work, but the planned machines were not built. In 1935 Arkhangelskii designed the long-range recon-

*Above: SB-3 had more powerful M-103A engines
and an enlarged gun turret under the fuselage.*

*Below: SB-RK was the prototype for a horizontal
and dive bomber variant in the SB range, produced
by Arkhangelskii in 1939. Service designation was
Ar-2.*

naissance aircraft ANT-49, a derivative of SB-2 with photographic apparatus in the fuselage bomb bay and larger fuel tanks. The designs ANT-38 and ANT-48 of 1936, were also SB inspired.

Only a little later, K A Kaliin was working on the design of a high-speed tactical combat bomber. In 1934, immediately after his arrival in Voronesh, he conceived a high-speed bomber in the form of a tailless flying wing. Compartments for the crew and engines were fully buried in the wing.

To test the potential, Kalinin planned three stages of design – a glider with 9m span, a test plane with 18m span, and then the real aircraft.

A tailless glider with trapezoidal wing completed 100 flights in 1934 and 1935, demonstrating good stability. The test plane had a trapezoidal wing with slotted flaps over the whole span of the trailing edge. The inner served as plain flaps, the outer as ailerons. In the centre of the wing was a short fuselage nacelle for three crew together with ShKAS machine gun turrets in the nose and tail. On the underside of the fuselage was a bay for 500kg bomb load while on the wing leading edge were twin M-22 engines, each of 480mhp.

The undercarriage was retractable whereas fins and rudders were on the wing tips.

Kalinin designated the aircraft K-12, the Air-Force called it BS-2 'Shar-Ptitsa'. 'BS' stands for *'Beshvostii Samolet'* (tailless aircraft) and 'Shar Ptitsa' means Phoenix. P M Stefanovskii began test flying in December 1936 and he was very surprised by the queer characteristics, aggravated by a flaw in the controls. Only slowly were they brought into line with those of other aircraft.

K-12 was never an up-to -standard bomber. Its twin 480mhp engines provided only 240kph at 3,000m and range of 700km. On account of these poor performances the aircraft was not considered for military purposes and final construction of the flying wing was dropped. Brightly painted like a real phoenix and flown in the 1937 Tushino air parade, the aircraft excited much attention among foreign observers, thus fulfilling its purpose.

At this time a further design of Kalinin's was nearing conclusion – the K-13 bomber, a classic monoplane with steel tube framework and fabric covering. Only the horizontal tail unit was unusual because of its double-decker form, the fixed lower surface served as a stabiliser and the upper

Above: Two perspectives of Samolet 103 or ANT-58, first prototype of the Tu-2, produced by Tupolev while under arrest and working in poor conditions.

Right: Eye-catcher at the 1937 Tushino air parade was the Kalinin K-12 or BS-2 in paintwork to represent its 'Phoenix' label.

Right: A model of Ilyushin's all-metal TsKB-56 horizontal and dive bomber which was never assembled due to the designer's commitment to existing aircraft development.

surface as an elevator. It was planned to have twin 750mhp M-34 and a three-man crew.

Kalinin was not able to finish the K-13. In Spring 1938 he was arrested on a trumped-up charge and later executed, the first in a long line of leading personalities in aviation technology.

In 1938 the Red Air Force demanded new types of high-speed bombers. SB variants were approaching the peak of their potential, so Tupolev and Ilyushin were commissioned to design new aircraft of this class. Dive capacity was one of the stipulations.

Ilyushin proposed an all-metal, mid-wing monoplane with twin 1,200mhp AM-35A engines, three-man crew, twin rudders and retractable tricycle undercarriage. But this TsKB-56 was never assembled as the designer was fully employed in further development of the long-range bomber DB-3 and combat aircraft BSh-2 (later Il-2).

Tupolev was already under arrest and working in a special drawing office under scarcely tolerable conditions. He designed an aircraft under the camouflage name Samolet 103 but in the ANT's model sequence it was ANT-58. It was an all-metal mid-wing monoplane for a crew of three, powered by twin, new in-line AM-37 engines of 1,400mhp designed by A A Mikulin. The machine gunner in the turret on top of the fuselage could shoot with twin ShKAS in a backwards direction while the pilot could fire two fixed ShVAK cannon situated in the wing roots. Bomb load lay between 1,000 and 3,000kg according to required range.

The prototype was test flown on January 29, 1941, by M A Nyukhtikov. Everything indicated that another aircraft with outstanding prospects had made its appearance as all performance requirements were surpassed. Maximum speed was 635kph at 8,000m, range 2,500km and service ceiling 10,600m.

But all performances were dependent on one thing – the engines. These were not yet sufficiently developed, were afflicted with numerous growing pains and had not yet reached production stage. Moreover, people were too busy with the series production of AM-35A engines and time could not be devoted to others. Also the airframe was too ambitious, given limited duralumin supply at

that particular time. So up to Summer 1941, preparations were made for production, but nothing materialised.

Meanwhile Tupolev continued development of the aircraft on the basis of test findings and his own ideas. On May 18, 1941, the second machine, ANT-59, was flown. It had camouflage designation Samolet 103U and the same AM-37 engines, but allowed for a four-man crew. Beneath the tail was a turret with moveable ShKAS, so the aircraft was protected in an area where, up to now, it had been vulnerable. Because of the non-availability of AM-37 engines, the ANT-59 changed to twin ASh-82 engines of 1,330/1,700mhp. Its maximum speed dropped to 530kph.

The ANT-60 or Samolet 103V of December 1941 had the same crew and armament. On this machine Tupolev also replaced the in-line engines by the ASh-82 two-row radial engines, each of 1,330mhp, and redesigned the airframe for series production. The performances were lower: 525kph at 3,250m, service ceiling 9,000m and range 2,000km. But these were good enough, and since the engines were now reliable and had reached production stage, there were good prospects for improvement.

Not until the beginning of 1942 could limited production be started. The serial version differed in some constructional details from ANT-60 and was designated ANT-61 while the Red Air Force introduced it as Tu-2. Three machines of the pilot series were tested in September 1942 in a front line bomb unit near Kalinin, proving fast, easily controlled, with comfortable cabins, strong armament and with quite a long range.

Combat fliers demanded quick delivery of this aircraft, but the aviation industry thought otherwise as introduction of such an aircraft was too complicated given the circumstances of the time. So Tupolev had to simplify construction and equipment, managing to reduce the work expenditure by 29 per cent. In spite of this, series production was not started until 1943 and combat units first received their Tu-2s in Spring 1944.

These machines could be given 1,520-1,850mhp ASh-82FN engines providing maximum speed and 2,100km normal range. The flexible machine guns were 12.7mm UBT and the standard bomb load 1,000kg. But production was inadequate. Up to the end only 1,111 were delivered, about one tenth the number of the lighter Pe-2.

By the end it had become clear how promising Tupolev's Tu-2 design was. As late as 1945 it still had design potential and constituted the armament not only of the Soviet Air Force but also of several satellite states. There were also numerous variants.

The Tu-2 was also used as a carrier for the cross-country vehicle GAZ-67B in parachute units. The automobile was half retracted into the bomb bay and landed by parachute. On December 3, 1946, the ground attack and armoured fighter plane Tu-2Sh was tested with a 57mm RShR anti-tank gun in its sheet covered nose.

Other Tu-2Sh variants had twin fixed N5-45, NS-37 and ShVAK 20 cannon (the numbers are for the calibre) and one moveable UBT for rear defence. One other experimental Tu-2Sh, tested

Below: A Tu-2 modified as the ANT-62 prototype in October 1944.

An ANT-59 prototype with experimental higher cabin roofing.

The Tu-2S in series form.

A GAZ-67B vehicle half retracted into the bomb bay of a Tu-2.

Termed 'Paravan', this Tu-2 variant was created to sever the cables of barrage balloons.

in 1944, had 48 7.62mm sub machine guns of the PPSh type, directed to shoot downwards against unarmoured personal targets. The tests were not successful. Another carried one 75mm cannon to be used against railway traffic. Only one example was tested in 1944.

An interesting variant had the name 'Paravan' and was equipped to cut the cables of barrage balloons. In front of the nose was a six metre long cone from which two steel wires stretched to the tips of the wings. The balloon cables were to be pushed to the tips where they were severed by a cutting arrangement.

Three more examples of the numerous Tu-2 variants. ANT-65 (below) was a high altitude version operating at 11,000m; ANT-68 (Tu-10) was fastest of all at 635kph and built in a small series (centre); ANT-67 (bottom) had ACh-30BF diesel engines and was capable of a 4,100km range.

Tu-2 were also employed for various experimental tasks. For example, they tried out the first Soviet radar bombsights and were used for flight tests of jet engines like RD-500 and RD-45 which were suspended under the fuselage.

The greatest number of Tu-2 variants built after the war were equipped with ASh-82FN engines.

In October 1944 a long distance ANT-62 or Tu-2D was produced. Span was increased from 18.86m to 22.2m and the nose given a better shape. Maximum speed for this five-seater was 517kph at 5,200m. It could carry 1,000kg bombs 3,000km or 4,000kg 1,400km. After the war Tu-2 was put on the production line.

A torpedo variant, ANT-62T or Tu-2T, was tested as a prototype between January and March 1945 and then introduced into the naval aviation sector. There was also a long range reconnaissance variant, Tu-2R or Tu-6, which had several automatic cameras in the bomb bay.

High-altitude ASh-82FN engines were used in one of the last variants, ANT-69 or Tu-8, of 1940. General lines were the same but four-bladed propellers were used and stronger armament incorporated. The fixed wing cannon were now 23mm NS-23 and the flexible UBT machine guns were replaced by 20mm B-20 cannon. Wing area was 61.26sq.m. Other variants included the Tu-8B with twin AM-42 and Tu-8S with twin ACh-39BF diesels.

Tupolev had been experimenting since 1945 with a whole series of engines on the Tu-2. Mikulin's twelve cylinder AM-42 of 2,000mhp was tested on the ANT-64 prototype of 1945, lines ot the aeroplane being much improved. ANT-65, built in 1946, was definitely a high-altitude aircraft

with twin AM-44 engines, each equipped with two TK-300 superchargers. These increased service ceiling to 11,000m, speed was 578kph and range 2,570km.

But the best performances of any Tu-2 variant were exhibited by ANT-68 as early as Summer 1945. This, too, was a high altitude version with twin Mikulin AM-39FNV twelve-cylinder in line engines, each of 1,185mhp. Maximum speed was 635kph but range had to be shortened to 1,660km. After several modifications in 1946, ANT-68 was built in a small series as Tu-10.

Between January 1946 and January 1947 a small pilot series of ANT-67 were tested. These were developments of Tu-2 with the new heavy-oil engines of A D Charomskii, the ACh-30BF of 1,900mhp. ANT-67 had lower speed than the production Tu-2S, that is 509kph, but range reached a full 4,100km. Despite this, ANT-67 was not put into production, again because of engine difficulties. ANT-67 was also the heaviest of all Tu-2 variants. Its take-off weight was 17,170kg.

Over 2,500 Tu-2 machines of all types were built, including the Tu-6, Tu-8 and Tu-10. Series production was halted in 1948, but the aircraft was still in operation well into the fifties.

We have already mentioned a further Soviet high-speed horizontal and dive bomber, the Pe-2, a design of V M Petlyakov. This machine was contructed in about the same conditions as Tu-2 but won more recognition as it was used throughout the war and was practically the only bomber available in large numbers.

Petlyakov's machine was designed from 1938 onwards, almost parallel with Tupolev's machine. But it had complicated beginnings and initially was not intended to be a bomber at all. The marked uncertainty of the highest commanders-in-chief of the Red Air Force was reflected in the initial design and in the forties further uncertainty was caused by, among other things, the internal political situation and purges at all levels of the armed forces and industry.

The Pe-2 story has its beginnings in Petlyakov's 1938 design of high altitude fighter VI-100. Provision was made for twin M-105R engines and a high-pressure cabin designed by M N Petrov. In the middle of preparations the air force changed its mind, demanding a high altitude bomber, still with high-pressure cabin and twin M-105R engines, in both cases equipped with TK-3 superchargers. There was to be a crew of two in the VI-100 with the machine gunner behind the wing at the end of a long cabin roofing. For the final bomber version Petlyakov was to make the cabin three-seat with remote-controlled machine gun armament above and below the fuselage.

Before Petlyakov could begin changing the airframe another complete change of design was introduced. The air force, aware of the inadequacy of their bomb sights and impressed by successes of German dive bombers in Spain, pronounced the high altitude bomber superfluous. They demanded of Petlyakov a high-speed horizontal and dive bomber for close collaborative work with the Army on the Front.

Thus the VI-100 became the PB-100 (*Pikiruyush-chii Bombardirovshchik* = dive-bomber). Super-chargers were left out, the cabin, still with long roofing, was no longer equipped for high pressure, and under the wings dive-brakes were incorporated as in the bomber Ar-2. M-105R engines of 1,050/1,100mhp were kept, fitted with three-blade propellors and buried radiators. Cool air was conducted through openings in the leading edge of the wings.

P M Stefanovskii started flight testing of the first prototype PB-100, still under the old desig-nation V1-100, in April 1940. In the air, the right engine suddenly stopped, forcing the pilot to make a quick landing. At touch-down the under-carriage suspension bounced the machine back into the air but Stefanovskii was able to recover.

There were flaws of varying importance to be removed. In particular, a bigger horizontal tail-unit was necessary and there always remained room for improvement in the undercarriage. The aircraft was also very susceptible if it stalled, and went into a flat spin almost without warning. Landing speed of 150 to 170kph was an unpleasant surprise for the pilots too.

Preparation for series production began in 1940, the second prototype and production ma-chines varying in several details from the first PB-100. The pilot's cockpit was now short and terminated with a mount containing a ShKAS ma-chine gun which was to provide protection from behind. The nose was glazed on the underside and another twin fixed ShKAS incorporated. The third crew member sat in a small cabin on the trailing edge of the wing and was able to lower his ShKAS on a flexible gun carriage and operate it by a periscopic sight. Another machine gun could be fired alternatively from small portholes in the side windows of this cabin. Standard bomb load in the bay was 600kg, while a further 400kg could be stored under the wings.

Interesting was the electro-hydraulic opera-tion of various parts, such as the dive brakes, undercarriage, bomb bay cover, variable camber flaps etc. Eighteen electric motors operated the hydraulic pumps for their individual operations. A half automatic arrangement was also incor-porated, which took over the pilot's duties in the critical phase of diving,

In conjunction with the dive bomber variant, a ground support aircraft was also built and presen-ted in prototype form. In the bomb bay were two ShVAK cannon and two UBK machine guns, all firing diagonally forwards. It was not put into production.

The performance of PB-100 was unusually high – better than U S S R production fighters of that time. Maximum speed at 5,000m was 540kph while at low altitude 460kph could be achieved. Range with 600kg bombs amounted to 1,200km and service ceiling was 9,000m. Accuracy was good on diving attacks thanks to the efficient brakes which limited diving speeds to 600kph. Limit of the airframe on such occasions was 725kph.

In 1940 only two PB-100 production machines were completed and in January 1941 designation was changed to Pe-2. By the middle of 1941, 462 specimens of Pe-2 had been delivered, but they were seldom used on the Front as crews were not yet trained. The few Pe-2 there proved their worth, even at a time of absolute German air supremacy.

By the second half of 1941 the Front had received as many as 1,405 Pe-2 aircraft. The ma-chines had noteworthy speed and were even able to evade the Messerschmitt Bf 109E. British fighter pilots watching over Murmansk in Winter 1941-2 with their Hawker Hurricanes were surprised to find that the Pe-2 could easily give them the slip.

The situation changed in Spring 1942 with introduction of the German Bf 109F. These fighters were 50kph faster at 3,000-4,000m, the most favourable altitude for Pe-2. When the Pe-2

pushed their combat altitude up to 5,000-7,000m, the superiority of Bf 109F certainly diminished, but so did the accuracy of horizontal bomb attacks.

The Front demanded a rapid and effective means to change this unfavourable situation. When Petlyakov was killed in an aircraft accident in January 1942, Putilov took over the drawing office and a year later V M Myasishchev was appointed director.

The design unit could not improve perfomance of the bomber quickly, so they first strengthened the armament. A turret with UBT machine gun replaced the flexible ShKAS in the back of the pilot's cockpit. From June 1942 all Pe-2 were delivered with these turrets and all older Pe-2

versions were similarly modified. Moreover, the armour plating protecting the crew was strengthened.

At some airfields the ground mechanics themselves incorporated another two flexible ShKAS machine guns into the sides of the fuselage at the rear gunner's cabin.

The aircraft with UBT machine gun turret was designated Pe-2FT ('*Frontovoye Trebovanie*' = 'Demand of the Front'). Through the improvement to armament and armour, vulnerability was diminished, but the usual vicious circle occurred – the armament was improved, the weight increased and performances deteriorated. This was felt particularly clearly towards the end of 1942 when the new Messerschmitt Bf 109G

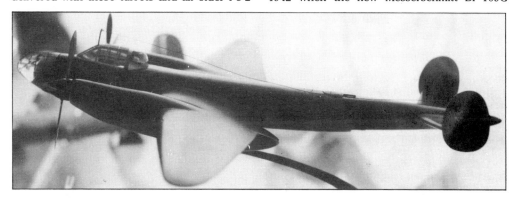

VI-100 was an advanced concept by Petlyakov. It is shown (top) as originally conceived in model form and (above) as actually built.

Left: ANT-69 was the last Tu-2 development.

157

The Pe-2 in original series form. Their speed proved a surprise to both friend and foe during early days at the Front!

fighters intervened.

Towards the end of 1943 the first Pe-2FT left assembly lines with new VK-105PF engines. They were the same as delivered for Yak-3 and Yak-9, but without cannon. Their maximum performance was 1,260mhp and at 2,700m still a full 1,180mhp.

This certainly helped to lift performances again but it did not rest at that. Designers built new wings with better profile and better slots on the flaps and ailerons; they introduced better cowlings and bomb gear under the wings. All that, together with the increase in horse power, gave the Pe-2FT an increase in speed of 40kph, so the situation was saved.

During the relatively long production life of the Pe-2 there were many variants and modifications – some of them hurriedly made in field workshops to cover a certain new situation at the Front, some prepared in the production factories and some only as experiments in the prototype factory.

Pe-2M was a prototype built in October 1941, just before the evacuation from Moscow. It had VK-105 engines and an enlarged belly to take the big 500kg FAB-500 bomb. After the evacuation there was no time to test it. One Pe-2 was tested with retractable skis and another with a new MB-3 turret for the UBT gun.

The Pe-2FZ of 1943 was an improved variant of the Pe-2FT with better cabin facilities for the navigator and his UBT machine gun. It appeared in series production.

In 1943 the ASh-82 double-row radials were tested with good results – maximum speed being 547kph at 6,000m. A small series production appeared but it was difficult to change the shape of the nacelles in a full-scale production.

Pe-2B of 1943 had twin VK-105PF, three UBT guns, one ShKAS and a longer range – 1,400km with 600kg bomb load. Some of the refinements of the Pe-2B were incorporated into the series production Pe-2FT and no special Pe-2B were produced.

Like the Tu-2, the Pe-2 was used for 'Paravan' experiments with a long cone in front of the fuselage, this time in the form of a girder construction made from duralumin profiles and tubes.

The good performance of the Pe-2 inspired their use as a heavy fighter. In 1941 a small series of the Pe-3 appeared with twin VK-105P and heavy fixed armament – twin ShKAS, twin UBS and twin ShVAK. They were used in the defence of Moscow together with some later Pe-3bis powered by VK-107A of 1,650mhp. Some had twin ShVAK and three UBS as fixed armament.

Pe-2VI was a prototype high-altitude fighter with VK-105PF. This single-seater with hermetic cabin was tested in 1943. Another fighter variant, Pe-3M, remained in the prototype stage.

Under the leadership of V M Myasishchev the Pe-2 was reworked to a new Pe-2I line with VK-107A engines of 1,675mhp. Tested between May and June 1944, the Pe-2I was changed to mid-wing configuration. It could accommodate up to 1,000kg internally and another 1,000kg on external bomb racks. Speed was 100kph better.

Only two UB guns were used, one fixed for the pilot and the other remotely controlled by the navigator and situated in the tail. With a speed of 656kph, 11,000m ceiling and 2,275km range, the Pe-2I entered series production after the war.

The Pe-2K was an experiment to combine some parts of the Pe-2I with engines and parts of the series production Pe-2s. VK-107As were used to power the Pe-2D, a bomber with 1,500kg load and 600kph speed, but only one example was built.

A Pe-2RD prototype with twin VK-105RA of 1,100mhp was tested with an auxiliary RD-1 rocket engine of 300kpt in the tail. During tests in 1944 the engine exploded. No encouraging results were obtained!

By the time hostilities ended 11,426 Pe-2 aircraft of all variants had been delivered, forming the main contingent of Front bomber units. Unfortunately, their number was still not great enough, especially in the middle stage of the war. At that time many machines were delivered to the Red Air Force from England and America. Under the 'Lend and Lease' agreement, 2,900 Douglas DB-7 bombers, which were very popular, were received, besides 870 North American NA-42 (B-25 Mitchell). Futher models, such as the British Armstrong-Whitworth Albemarle, were only available in insignificant numbers.

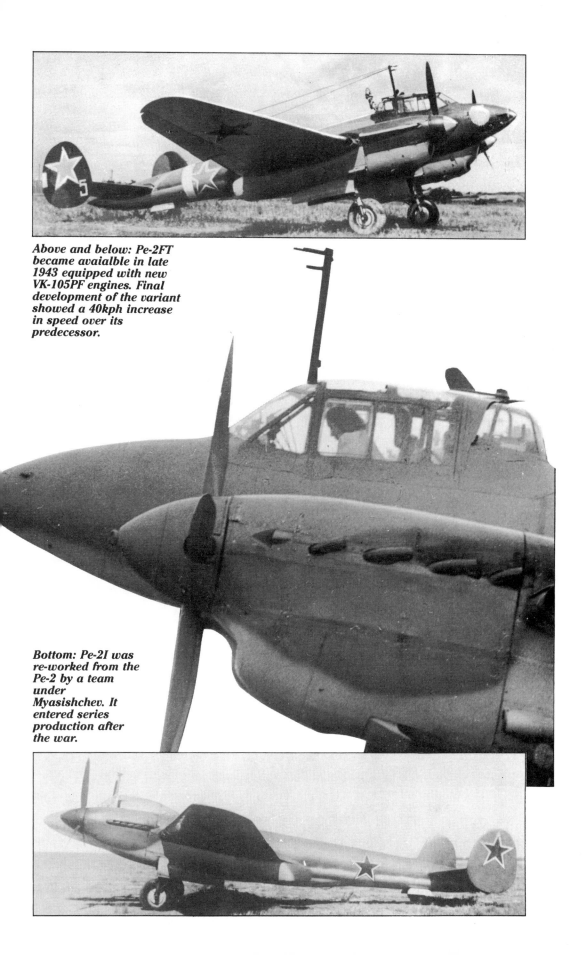

Above and below: Pe-2FT became avaialble in late 1943 equipped with new VK-105PF engines. Final development of the variant showed a 40kph increase in speed over its predecessor.

Bottom: Pe-2I was re-worked from the Pe-2 by a team under Myasishchev. It entered series production after the war.

CHAPTER 20

Night Bombers

IN 1943 THERE appeared among Soviet prototypes a machine with the unusual name 'Nochnoi Bombovos' (literally 'night bomb conductor') designation NB(T). It was a design of N N Polikarpov and a rarity in the Second World War, for no special night bombers were being built in any country. NB(T) was a mid-wing monoplane with wooden wings, duralumin fuselage and twin ASh-82A engines each of 1,430mhp. For the production machines there was provision for 2,000mhp ASh-71.

Construction of the first NB(T) was started in autumn 1943. Fuselage was built for a five-man crew and armament was distributed in three turrets – there was a flexible UBT 12.7mm machine gun in the nose and the same behind the wing on both top and underside of the fuselage. In addition, the pilot had another fixed machine gun. The bomb bay could take 3,000-5,000kg bombs, predominantly larger calibre.

In May 1944, NB(T) completed its first flight and in August began official testing. The aircraft revealed good performances: maximum speed 515kph at 6,250m, service ceiling 8,800m and range 3,000km. But after Polikarpov's death, flights were halted and the aircraft destroyed.

So night bomb attacks of the Red Air Force were made with normal bombers. One model is especially interesting, namely the two-seat biplane, LNB (*Legkii Nochnoi Bombardirovshchik* = light night bomber). It was originally an emergency reconstruction of the liaison biplane U-2VS with 115mhp M-11D engine. As the Red Air Force lacked bombers in 1941/2, these machines were also used for night harassing raids against German positions. The attacks proved effective and so the aircraft was used throughout the war.

LNB machines had silencers on the engines, were painted black and were often able to evade German observation posts. They were in evidence in quite large numbers in Stalingrad and were mostly used to block German airfields. They flew in pairs – one aircraft lit up the target area with the spotlight and the second dropped its 200kg of bombs. These night engagements were very effective at the time and made it more difficult for the trapped 6th Army to receive air supplies. LNB also attacked German headquarters, concentrations of transport, artillery batteries etc., and was very popular with the Soviet pilots.

A S Yakovlev tried to introduce a specially designed light night bomber and the prototype was test flown in 1942 as NBB. It was a simple low-wing monoplane in composite construction with twin 140mhp M-11F engines and retractable undercarriage. The machine could carry up to 500kg load in the shape of 50 to 250kg bombs. A flexible ShKAS machine gun served the two-man crew for defence or low-level shooting.

NBB aircraft were manufactured in 1943, but proved their worth more in the second role as light transport to the Front. They are to be found in the chapter about commercial aircraft under the designation Yak-6.

Polikarpov's purpose-built night bomber, NB(T), began flight testing in 1944 but was destroyed after the designer's death.

CHAPTER 21

Dive Bombers

ACCURATE BOMBING of targets in dives was an important combat method, constantly supported – indeed also demanded – by the Red Air Force as there was only one machine capable of such specialised flights – the all-metal biplane R-3. The R-3 could drop its bombs on a flight closely approaching the vertical, but stability of the machine did not permit true dive bombing. Only fighters could drop small bombs on nose dives, but the effect was slight.

Not until 1936 was a real dive bomber produced, by reconstruction of a fighter. N N Polikarpov designed prototype TsKB-29 out of the well known 1-16 fighter. Its airframe was strengthened to withstand the loads and to reduce diving speed, hydraulically operated flight brakes were built into the trailing edge of the wing, placed vertically in the direction of flight. Under the wing were attachments for two 250kg FAB bombs whose trajectory lay outside the plane of propellor rotation.

The first prototype was tested in 1936 with a 710mhp American Wright Cyclone engine and attained 460kph at 3,000m without bombs. The designation given by the Red Air Force was therefore justified. It was SPB (*Skorostnii Pikiruy-ushcii Bombardirovshchik* = high speed dive bomber). SPB were built and delivered with Soviet M-25A and later M25-W engines and were especially used by naval aviators. Their final engagement was in the parasite mode under bomber TB-3.

D P Grigorovich was also working on a dive bomber at this time. Polikarpov made the SPB from fighter 1-16 whereas Grigorovich wanted to produce his PB-1 from the reconnaissance low-wing monoplane DG-58, which he had recently designed. PB-1 was to reach 450kph at 4,000m with an M-85 engine. But Grigorovich was unable to complete work on either the reconnaissance aircraft DG-58 or the dive bomber PB-1. He fell ill in 1937 and died in 1938.

Dive capacity was a stipulation for new bombers in 1938 and 1939, and designs of the later models Pe-2 and Tu-2 originated at this time. Also at that time there were plans for several models specially intended for dive attacks. Only one model was built – Polikarpov's SPB/D. The initial 'D' stood for *'Dvukhmotornii''* ('Twin-engined').

SPB/D was derived from the heavy fighter TIS/A and B N Kudrin test flew the prototype in 1940 with twin AM-37 engines reaching 620kph with 600kg of bombs. Testing SPD/D prototypes unfortunately cost lives as two machines crashed, in one case due to tail unit vibration. SPB/D was not taken on, being superceded by the PB-100.

Among new projects and prototypes of 1942, produced after stabilisation of the Soviet aviation industry, we also find the one-seat dive bomber OPB by S A Kocherigin and Z I Ickovich. It was to be a robust, mid-wing monoplane with two-row radial M-90 engines of 1,500mhp. The large bay was to carry up to 1000kg bombs and calculated maximum speed was 600kph at 6,500m.

The state defence committee did not want to introduce any specialised machines for dive attacks and so OPB was not put into production. In Spring 1942, Kocherigin's drawing office was dissolved.

Below: OPB was a single-seat dive bomber design offered by Kocherigin shortly before his department was disbanded.

CHAPTER 22

High Altitude Bombers

HIGH ALTITUDE bombers which operate in the lower limit of the stratosphere, often undisturbed by enemy combat pilots and above the normal atmospheric disturbances, were the ideal of aircraft designers and commanders-in-chief of Air Forces throughout the world. But the creation of such aircraft was a difficult problem demanding a broad basis of research in aeronautical technology.

In the thirties, Soviet designers and scientists devoted a lot of effort to the high-altitude aircraft which operated at 10,000m or over. Not all these endeavours were exclusively concerned with bombers, but they contributed a lot to the solution of high-altitude bomber design.

When an aircraft stayed for a long time at great altitudes, protection was necessary for the crew against low pressure, cold and lack of oxygen. Some particularly resilient people, like the Soviet test pilot V K Kokkinaki, could already reach a very great altitude. Kokkinaki had achieved 14,575m in an I-15 equipped only with oxygen. But if one were in these altitudes for a longish time precautions were indispensable.

From experience with diving suits it was not a big step to the high pressure suits of the first high-altitude pilots. A certain amount of success was achieved by them (British aircraft Bristol-138A and Italian biplane Caproni Ca 161) but it was not the right way. The pilot was too constricted in the cumbersome suit and could only with difficulty make the simplest movements.

A better solution was presented by the pressurised cabin in which the crew had more freedom of movement. Design ranged from the German Junkers Ju 49 with separable pressurised cabin to the completely pressurised fuselage cabin as used in the American Lockheed XC-35 and the production-built Boeing Stratoliner.

Until recently only a little was known about Soviet experiments in this sphere. A lot had actually been done about the problem but the direct results could not be immediately established.

Soviet aviation only experimented with high-altitude cabins. The designer A J Shcherbakov had dedicated himself since 1934 to the semi rigid pressurised cabin. The first one had a steel tube framework with walls of thick rubber. The pilot received air and oxygen from a pressure cylinder and termed the invention "rubber stocking". Shcherbakov developed his cabin and made test flights with a high-altitude glider of Gribovskii in 1935 followed a year later with the fighter I-15.

Rigid pressurised cabins had better prospects on account of their greater stability, longer life expectancy and greater reliability. In the thirties, the design of both cabins and the aircraft were concentrated in a special drawing-office of TsAGI called BOK. Director of the office was V A Chishevskii.

In BOK the spherical cabin of the stratosphere balloon SSSR-1 was designed. This reached an altitude of 18,000m in 1933. The cabin was equipped for regeneration, harmful products of breathing being eliminated and the air regularly enriched with oxygen.

The pressurised cabin of the Soviet Union's first stratosphere aircraft, BOK-1 built in 1926, was fitted out in a similar way. Its other designation or purpose designation was SS (*Stratosfernii Samolet* = stratosphere aircraft). For the construction of BOK-1 Chishevskii used the airframe of the long-range bomber ANT-25, ideally suited with long, slim wings. The airframe was lightened, the span was a little shortened, the undercarriage was made fixed and cowled (because no value was placed upon high speed) and only one wheel was built in. Engine was the twelve cylinder 725mhp M-34RN with reduction gear and super-

A diagram of BOK-1 showing installation of a pressurised cabin in what is basically an ANT-25 airframe. Air tests began in 1936.

charger. It could, according ot its manufacturers, maintain its performance up to 10,000m.

The cabin was an independent unit which fitted into the fuselage or could be taken out again, according to requirements. It was a cylinder with two cubic metres of inner space, a wall thickness of 1.8 to 2mm and concave front walls. The two seats were one behind the other, with five windows for the pilot and six for the observation pilot/navigator/radioman. Entry was from above, an emergency exit leading backwards into the fuselage space. Oxygen was conducted from the pressure cylinders which also balanced loss of pressure originating from the exits. Air warmed by the engine cooling fluid kept the temperature, between 15 and 18 degrees C.

In summer 1936, test pilot I F Petrov began the first flights in Smolensk. He felt unsure of himself when confined in the submarine-like cabin so P M Stefanovskii took over flight testing in June 1936. The aircraft was stable, without oscillations, and could fly for a fairly long time with released controls. Maximum speed was 230kph but we know that the aircraft was not built for speed.

During the first stage in Smolensk, Stefanovskii reached 10,700m altitude. Later, after transfer to Moscow and drastic lightening of the airframe, the aircraft managed to reach 14,100m.

In June 1937, BOK-1 was given the new M-34RNV engine with better high-altitude performances (the maker had greatly exaggerated the high-altitude qualities of the M-34RN). M-34RNV had two superchargers, the machine was 118kg heavier and yet reached altitudes of over 12,000m.

Such performances did not escape the notice of the Red Air Force. They wanted a series of international altitude records, using the BOK-1 with 5,000kg payload. But in October 1937 a supercharger went to pieces in the air, damaging the engine and airframe to such an extent that the aircraft could not be flown again.

In 1938 a second machine, the BOK-7, was completed. The airframe was also taken over from an ANT-25 with the full span of 34m (in BOK-1 it was only 30m). But the cabin was different; it was no longer detachable, now forming an integral part of the fuselage. The fuselage was lower and the two crewmen sat with their heads in half-spherical domes which projected from the contour of the fuselage. In each dome were small windows with double glazing. The engine was also modified; it was an M-34FRN of 860mhp with two superchargers.

Flight testing in spring 1939 produced satisfactory results, but more interesting is the ground testing of BOK-7. These appear to us today as forerunning present day tests of cosmic rocket cabins. The purpose designation of BOK-7 was K-17, the initial "K" stood for *"Krugosvetnii"* that is, "round the world" and Soviet pilots really wanted to make such a flight with this aircraft.

The exact details are no longer known but the

Left: BOK-11, a strategic reconnaissance aircraft, was never fully tested due to the voltatile political situation in Russia at the time of its apearance in early 1939.

Above: Non-availability of suitable engines brought about an early demise for Myasischev's DVB-102 which was not able to meet the required criteria of distance and altitude.

route was to be from Moscow via Siberia, North America, the Atlantic and North Europe and back to Moscow, scheduled for 1939/40. Exact particulars were worked out by the Scientific-Technical Institute of the Red Air Force. A I Filin, a member of Chkalov's crew on the U S A flight with the ANT-25, was director of the Institute. He was arrested and executed in 1940 and with him disappeared details of the prepared flight.

It was believed that the installation for cabin air regeneration would operate for 100 flying hours. The authorities wanted to determine, before flight, how the crew would tolerate four days in a narrow compartment, and how effective the installations for air regeneration and removal of excrement etc. would be. In the course of 1939 several two-man crews were confined for a period of days in the cabin of BOK-7 and the long distance flight was simulated on

Below: VB-108 represented another failure for Myasischev. Only the first of two projected prototypes was built and testing was incomplete.

the ground. Thus the pilots, Gromov, Yumashev, Danilin, Spirin, Bajdukov, Beljakov etc, received their baptism of fire. The cabin proved satisfactory. But for the real flight another axial supercharger was built in, powered by the engine. This was to compensate for the drop in pressure caused by deformation of the cabin in flight.

The prepared flight around the world did not take place because of the complicated internal political situation. In any case, war had broken out in West Europe and there was no call for, nor attention given to, such performances at that particular moment.

Shortly after BOK-7 the BOK office designed a strategic reconnaissance aircraft BOK-11. It was to penetrate enemy territory at a great altitude and collect information of strategic importance.

The BOK-11 was BOK-7 double, but its crew was to comprise three men to allow for machine gun armament – a remote-control installation designed by V S Kostyshkin and K V Shbanov. The gunner was to sit in the pressurised cabin and be able, with a system described as "electro-auto-synchroniser", to aim and fire the weapons housed in a swivel gun-carriage.

The installation was in the test plant by December 1939, but unfortunately BOK-11 never flew with it. Work at BOK was seriously affected by events in the U S S R. In 1938 Chishevskii and some of his collaborators were arrested and in the consequent state of uncertainty nobody felt like undertaking anything complicated or risky. For that reason the two BOK-11 prototypes were not fully tested. The first of them was delivered from the plant at the beginning of 1939.

During 1940 the situation improved and design

of high-altitude aircraft continued for a time. Two BOK-15s were built, derivations of the BOK-11s. Both were without armament but with three-man crew and Charomskii's M-40 heavy-oil engines. Flight testing went off very satisfactorily and inspired thoughts once again of making a long distance flight and establishing some records. Enthusiasm was short-lived for at the beginning of 1941 the BOK drawing office was dissolved.

V M Petlyakov's group also devoted their attentions to high-altitude aircraft. In 1936 Petlaykov designed in TsAGI the high-altitude bomber ANT-53 with twin high-altitude M-34FRNV engines. But the design was not carried out. We already know that Petlyakov then designed the high-altitude fighter VI-100 with pressurised cabin, and from this he developed the high-altitude bomber from which the horizontal and dive bomber Pe-2 originated.

Petlyakov's drawing office gathered a certain amount of experience from this work. After Petlyakov's death his successor, V M Myasishchev, was able to turn this experience to account when he designed the high-altitude and long-range bomber DVB-102 in 1942. The DVB-102 was an all-metal, high-wing monoplane with long fuselage. In this fuselage were two pressurised cabins, separated by a 7m long bay for 3,000kg bombs. In the front pressurised compartment sat the pilot, navigator and radioman. The pilot was able to shoot with a fixed ShVAK. In the back cabin was the machine gunner under a big dome. From there he was able to operate, by remote control, a flexible ShVAK machine gun coupled with the UBT machine gun. A further flexible ShVAK was under the fuselage. The aircraft had a tricycle undercarriage and twin rudder.

According to the design, DVB-102 was to be given twin two-row radial engines, the eighteen-cylinder M-120, each of 2,500mhp. As these were at no time available, Myasishchev had to be content with the less powerful ASh-71F of 2,200mhp. On tests the first prototype reached 460kph at low altitude in 1943, and 543kph at 6,250m. That was not bad, but the service ceiling did not exceed 8,300m and the range of 2,200km did not match up to conceptions about what a high-altitude and long-distance bomber should be. In 1944 they would have incorporated ASh-73 engines, each of 2,300mhp, but these were not available and so the design of DVB-102 was abandoned.

At this time Myasishchev's prototype plant built a further high-altitude bomber, the VB-108. This three-seat mid-wing monoplane with twin in-line VK-108 engines, each of 1,920mhp, had a lot in common with the Pe-2 bomber as regards its outer lines, but was more robust with pressurised cabin and four-bladed propellers. Three ShVak cannon and one BS machine gun were built in (one fixed cannon in the fuselage, and a flexible, remotely controlled weapon on top.

Only the first of the two prototypes built was flight-tested in the second half of 1944. The tests were not completed.

After the failures with DVB-102 and VB-108, the Air Force concentrated attention on the work of A N Tupolev. His drawing office focussed on a new weapon – the strategic bomber. This was one of the landmarks of this office and was called Tu-4.

The design of Tu-4 is characteristic of the political situation at that time and the condition of the Soviet aviation industry. The regrouping of world powers at the end of the war and the first signs of dissent between the allies forced commanders in chief of the Soviet fighting forces to create a thoroughly modern and far-sighted conception of the Air Force for post-war years. The creation of a strategic bomber force was indispensable. Nuclear weapons demanded more effective methods and existing Soviet bomber units were not good enough.

It was almost impossible to catch up with the lead of other countries, especially the U S A, within an acceptable period. To plan and design from scratch would mean a great loss of time and it was very probable that such an aircraft would already be out of date at the moment of its take off. The USSR needed an aircraft which was almost complete, possessed a proficient design and promising technical performance over several years.

Such aircraft were in existence at that time – the American Boeing B-29 Superfortress had been conducting attacks against Japan since the summer of 1944. They were machines designed with rare foresight and a technical and military advance of several years had been built into them. Pressurised cabins, powerful engines, remote-controlled armament with automatic connection of individual turrets, sophisticated bomb

sights, radar equipment and electronic means of navigation – in short everything on these machines could serve as a pattern for a new stage of production in the USSR.

This particular phase in the history of Soviet aviation technology is still glossed over in official Soviet works. But truth is not to be hidden, nor is there reason to be ashamed. In the years when Soviet aviation technology was being built, foreign specimens often had to be taken as models. The engines were mostly licensed constructions or copies of foreign specimens. Soviet aircraft technology, still in its early stages, could not begin at an empty table and the situation was similar in 1944. With fighters, ground attack bombers and fighter bombers the Soviet aviation industry was extremely successful. With heavy bombers the USSR lost continuity and now needed help. A N Tupolev prepared a design named Tu-64 for a heavy, high-altitude, long-range bomber with four AM-44TK engines of 2,200mhp each. He worked in 1945 and 1946 on the Tu-64, but it was eventually abandoned.

B-29 bombers damaged in attacks against Japan were sometimes able to save themselves by making an emergency landing in East Siberia. The crews received a friendly welcome and soon returned to the USA. Their machines remained in the USSR and were studied in detail. These studies produced a clear result – B-29s were the best models for reverse engineering.

Copying a specimen, that is dismembering

Above: Tu-4s engaged in wing-to-wing refuelling.

Below: Unmistakably a Boeing B-29, the Soviet Tu-4 equivalent was an essential unlicenced copy aircraft to fill a technology gap.

piece by piece, measuring, testing the technical value of materials and then designing, is no simple task with a simple aircraft, even less with the B-29 which had 43.1m span and 34 tons dead weight. The work was assigned to Tupolev and Myasishchev. A D Shvetsov's office was to imitate the engines, other groups were then to design the various systems of interior equipment and prepare for construction.

In spring the first in a series of twenty Tu-4 prototypes was ready. N S Rybko test flew the first machine in July 1947, followed by M L Gallaj with the second and A G Vasilchenko with the third. All three formed one of the highlights of the Tushino air parade in summer 1948.

Tu-4 combined speed of up to 570kph with an excellent range of 4,900km with 5,000kg bomb load. It operated without difficulty in altitudes of 11,000 to 12,500m and was perfectly armed. A non-stop transit flight from Moscow to the Crimea and back was a mere trifle. A complete test programme of the twenty prototypes proceeded quickly and without any great difficultites. By 1949 the Soviet Air Force was in possession of its first strategic bomber units.

It might seem as if the Tu-4 and B-29, whose prototype had taken off in 1942, were unlikely to be up-to-date in 1949. But they were considered first-class models of their type and at that time Britain also took on B-29s under the name Washington B.Mk.1 as equipment of the RAF.

Exterior lines of the Tu-4 were identical to those of B-29. The engines, a reconstruction of the American Wright R-335D Duplex Cyclone, had designation ASh-73TK and with superchargers boasted 2,300mhp take-off performance. The eleven-strong crew sat in pressurised compartments in the nose, behind the wings and in the fuselage tail. Above and below the fuselage were four remote-controlled turrets, each containing two NS-23 cannon. A fifth turret was in the tail. These weapons could be electronically

Above: Tupolev's first attempt to improve the Tu-4 resulted in Tu-80. Though lighter and aerodynamically refined it remained a prototype.

Below: The last Soviet bomber with reciprocating engines was Tu-85 featuring four 24-cylinder VD-4K units of 4,300mhp each. But the jet era had already made its impact and Tu-85 was no more than an interesting prototype.

aimed and fired from the machine gunners' cabins. Individual gunners could transfer the control of individual turrets, or a single gunner could take control of several. Radar equipment made possible accurate dropping of bombs at an altitude of 12,000m, even under bad weather conditions and at night.

All these installations on Tu-4 were very important for several branches of industry in the USSR. Some plants had to learn new methods of production – more refined and more precise. They got to know how to miniaturise equipment and meet the highest demands of quality and materials etc. The Tu-4 was therefore a good school for a great part of the industry.

Tu-4 remained the backbone of the Soviet strategic bomber force well into the fifties. For example, there were some Tu-4s on the photographs taken by the American Lockheed U-2 espionage plane in May 1960. At that time Tu-4 was already in the strategic reserve. They were, of course, developed further, among other things being given an installation for in-flight refuelling

and serving as long-distance maritime reconnaissance aircraft.

Myasishchev's group did not want to content themselves with a simple copy of the B-29. In 1946 Myasishchev designed the DVB-202 bomber. He wanted to build a mid-wing monoplane using module units of the B-29, but the Soviet Air Force preferred the direct imitation.

Tupolev then set to work on improvement of Tu-4. In 1949 he built the prototype Tu-80 with new wings and lightweight spars. The airframe was also lightened to assist a greater range. The whole airframe had been aerodynamically refined and about 15% more fuel could be carried. Maximum speed with the same ASh-73TK engines was now 640kph.

During the revolutionary period of the forties and fifties Tupolev tried to prolong the period of bombers with reciprocating engines by using V A Dobrynin's new air-cooled in-line engine with 24 cylinders, the VD-4K, which gave 4,300mhp at take-off with supercharger.

The bomber with these four motors was called Tu-85 and several prototypes were built in 1950. With a span of 56m the machine had 107 tons take-off weight, of which 44 tons were fuel and oil. This was necessary to achieve a range of 12,000km with 5,000kg bombs. The long fuselage, with its elegant lines, carried a sixteen-man crew who could relieve each other in two shifts during long-distance flights. Armament consisted of five turrets, each with two NR-23 cannon, remote-controlled like the Tu-4's.

Tu-85 could reach 665kph and its cruising speed on long, non-stop transit flights was 450kph. But that was meagre in the era of jet fighters of over 1,000kph and as new turboprops and more powerful jet engines promised very good results the Soviet Air Force preferred to use these. The Tu-85 remained only a prototype, the last Soviet bomber with reciprocating engines.

An engine with similar power (4,300mhp) was at the same time developed by the A D Shvetsov team. It was the ASh-2, a four-row radial of 28 cylinders, but remained unused.

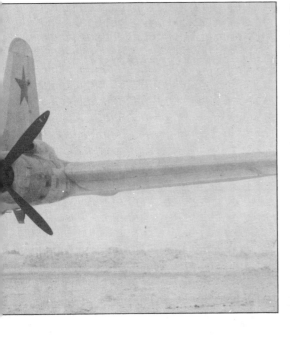

CHAPTER 23

Jet Bombers

THE DISPLAY of modern aircraft at Tushino on August 3, 1947, brought some surprises. For the first time people were able to see the Soviet-designed jet bombers. Over the heads of spectators thundered two-engined and four engined machines. The outlines did at least allow observers to determine which drawing office was responsible for each of the two models. The two-engined aircraft definitely showed characteristics of Tupolev's work, while the four-engined machine was just as certainly a product of Ilyushin.

Tupolev's model had been the first jet bomber in the USSR as prototype Tu-77. Tupolev used the same philosophy in the design as did Yakovlev on Yak-15. He wanted to create a machine for the transition period between reciprocating-engine and jet bombers. The Tu-77 shows a clear kinship to bomber Tu-2. The lines, of course, were improved on and adapted to higher performances but even the twin tail fins were kept, apparently the only ones on a two-engined jet aircraft of that time. One great novelty was the tricycle undercarriage.

A D Pereljot test flew the first Tu-77 on June 27, 1947. The machine had two Rolls-Royce Derwent engines under the wing in nacelles which also accepted the landing wheels.

On flight tests a maximum speed of 783kph could be reached. Range was 2,200km and service ceiling 11,300m – good performances for a transition period machine which was intended more for retraining the crew in the handling of a different type of aircraft than for use in combat. Tu-77 was taken over by the Air Force and, as Tu-12, built in a small series. But the Tu-12s did not enter regular service and remained as test specimens.

Ilyushin's four-engined bomber had the designation Il-22. It was no transition machine but an attempt at an up-to-standard bomber. Ilyushin used four TR-1 Lyulka engines, each of 1,300kp thrust, mounted in individual nacelles under the wing. The great fuselage provided enough room for a five-man crew and their armament. In the turret on top of the fuselage was a twin B-20 cannon while turrets in the tail and nose each brandished two NS-23. The bomb bay took 2,000 to 3,000kg load.

Brothers V K Kokkinaki and K K Kokkinaki test flew the first Il-22 on July 24, 1947, only a few days before displaying the new bomber at Tushino. Its performances were not that high for 1947. Maximum speed was only 718kph, altitude 11,100m and range 1,850km, although fuel supply was as much as 11,250 litres. The test programme continued until September 22, 1947, when all work was halted.

Ilyushin designed another jet bomber, the Il-24 with four Derwents coupled in two pairs under the wing similar to that of the 12-22. The Il-24 remained on paper only.

At least the Il-22 had been built and tested; although they had begun building the four-engined Su-10 of P O Sukhoi a few months later, it was not completed. Sukhoi followed the same stipulation in his design as Ilyushin, but used more powerful TR-1A engines, each of 1,500kp, built in two groups of two. Once again there were remote controlled automatic cannon turrets, this time with B-20 guns, the pilot having an additional fixed weapon. Bomb load was to reach four tons, the overloaded aircraft possessing four disposable solid propellant U-5 rockets giving 1,150kp thrust for 8 seconds on take-off.

By the beginning of 1948 the prototype airframe was almost completed when an order came to halt work. Estimated performances were 925kph at 4,000m, with a range of 2,000km.

For a long time after the war Soviet work in the jet bomber field was primarily centred on tactical machines, for the Tu-4 was regarded as an efficient heavy bomber, British Rolls-Royce engines

Above: Projected but not constructed was Sukhoi's Su-10, using 1,500kp TR-1A engines one above the other in two groups.

Above: First jet bomber in the USSR was prototype Tu-77 from Tupolev. It is believed to have been unique in retaining twin tail fins.

Below: Il-22 was a bold attempt by Ilyushin to produce a modern jet bomber. It was first flown on July 24, 1947, but abandoned two months later.

bought at the beginning of 1947 were an especial help.

Noteworthy among the first users' of these engines in tactical bombers was Tupolev's group. Tupolev conceived his machines for service in the naval combat forces. They were to have adequate flight duration, a spacious bomb bay with room for torpedos and mines, and radar devices for finding water targets including submarines. About the same time as the transition model Tu-77, the new model Tu-72 was designed. It was intended as a pure naval bomber with the possibility of use as a tactical bomber for the combat force.

Tu-72 was a classic mid-wing monoplane with Rolls-Royce Nene-1 engines mounted under the wing. Tail unit surfaces were standard but the vertical fin was broad and had a long keel while the elevator had a strong sweepback in order to raise the critical Mach number of the tail as high as possible.

The four-man crew were accomodated in two separate pressurised cabins. Pilot, navigator and radio operator/machine gunner sat in the front part of the fuselage. In the nose were two fixed B-20 guns and a twin B-20 was in a top turret, remotely controlled by the radio operator/machine gunner By the trailing edge of the wing was a further cabin for a machine gunner defending the rear from underneath. Its remote controlled gun turret, with two B-20, was under the fuselage and sighting apparatus was incorporated in two transparent domes.

It was decided not to build the twin-engined Tu-72 as the Air Force and Tupolev's drawing office were concentrating on a second version, the Tu-73. During design work on Tu-72 there had been concern that two Nene engines were insufficient for an aircraft with about 20 tons take-off weight. So Tupolev designed a trimotor variant, the Tu-73, which was then built instead of Tu-72.

F F Opadchic flew the Tu-73 on December 29, 1947, and tests lasted until June 1948. External lines were the same as those of Tu-72, but span was 21.7m instead of 19.7 and there was a third engine in the fuselage tail – a Rolls-Royce Derwent with air inlet in the root of the keel fin. Measured performances were 870kph maximum speed, service ceiling 11,500m and range 2,800km. There was also a photographic reconnaissance variant named Tu-73R or Tu-74.

Everyone of importance was convinced of the necessity of the trimotor version. But Tupolev designed both concurrently in order to collect data for final decision.

On April 17, 1948, the prototype Tu-78 took off. This was a development of the Tu-73 with Soviet copies of the British engines, two RD-45 and one RD-500. The Tu-78 was tested up to December 1948 and then pronounced ready for serial production under Air Force designation Tu-20.

A long range reconnaissance variant was also prepared, the bomb area being reserved for fuel and photographic apparatus. First variant was called Tu-78R and corresponded to Tu-73R, but Tu-79 was intended for production. This aircraft had two new VK-1 engines and one RD-500. Military designation was Tu-22, but this was never used. There were plans to use NS-23 23mm guns for all serial productions of the bomber and long range reconnaissance variant.

The final prototype, Tu-81, was developed from the twin-motored Tu-72 and tested in 1948

Above: The three-engined Tu-73 prototype, designed in reaction to concern that two engines were insufficient for a 20-ton aircraft.

Tu-14 (Tu-81) in its standard form (below) and as the Tu-14T torpedo carrying variant (right).

and 1949. In contrast to the complicated trimotor machines, Tu-81 was quite simple. Under the wing were two VK-1 engines and armament comprised two fixed NR-23 plus two flexible weapons. It was released for production in 1949 designated Tu-14 and first specimens reached naval aviation units in 1951.

The Tu-14 had a maximum speed of 845kph at 5,000m, a range of up to 3,000km, service ceiling of 11,200m and the ability to carry a bomb load of 1,000 – 3,000kg. Several special variants were built, like torpedo carrying Tu-14T, the long range reconnaissance Tu-14R (development designation Tu-89) and aircraft with several blister antennae under the fuselage.

Tu-14 reached production stage despite a difficult and expensive development. The machines were robust and reliable but were always more unweildy than the tactical bomber of combat aviation, the Ilyushin Il-28. When V K Kokkinaki test flew the first prototype of Il-28 on July 8, 1948, an uninitiated observer could have mistaken it for a variant of the Tu machines, for Il-28 had the same lines with straight wing, two engine nacelles and sweptback tailplane. But Ilyushin's aircraft was smaller, carried only three and was easily recognisable by a conspicuous sweepback of the fin.

Kokkinaki reached 913kph with the Il-28 prototype which possessed two Nene engines. Later, when full armament had been built in, this sank to 848kph at 5,000m. Service ceiling was 12,300m under test conditions and 11,130m on production machines. Range was 2,600km, maximum bomb load 3,000kg and armament consisted of two fixed and two flexible NS-23 (later NR-23), one in the tail.

After completion of state tests in spring 1949 the aircraft was immediately put on the production line. By the end of 1949 a few pre-production specimens were ready with RD-45, and in May 1950 the first Il-28 formation could be seen over Red Square. But the main deliveries with VK-1 engines did not begin till 1951. There were also Il-28R reconnaissance and Il-28T torpedo carrying variants.

Il-28 became the standard bombers of tactical units. A few Socialist states also took on Il-28, for example, China, East Germany, Indonesia, Egypt, Cuba, Poland and Czechoslovakia where the machines were originally designated B-228. The Il-28s have been considered antiquated for some years but they are still flown for training and experimental purposes in places like the GDR.

So both Soviet aerial combat forces were given efficient machines in the form of Il-28 and Tu-14.

Il-28 (above) became the Red Air Force's standard bomber in the early 1950s and also equipped other Socialist countries such as Czechoslovakia where they were originally known as B-228 (below).

Both models could be flown at high subsonic speeds and fulfil a whole range of combat tasks. But at the same time a big step forward had been taken by fighters. Sweptback wings enabled them to exceed 1,000kph and approach nearer and nearer an important threshold – sonic speed. The bombers could not lag far behind. Lavochkin did a lot to increase the speed of Soviet fighters – Tupolev and Ilyushin did the same for bombers.

Tupolev was first in the USSR to design a bomber with sweptback surfaces. In Febuary 1949, A D Pereljot test flew the prototype Tu-82, reminiscent of Tu-14 but with sweptback wings and controls. Under the wing there were two VK-1 engines in separate nacelles. The Tu-82 was a relatively small machine with 18.6m span and only 13,000kg take off weight.

It was not designed as a record breaker but as an experimental machine for determining the flying qualities required of large swept wing aircraft. The Tu-82 reached 934kph and its range

was 2,750km. Noteworthy was the service ceiling of 14,000m with 13,000kg take-off weight. When overloaded to 18,000kg, ceiling was still 12,000m. Tupolev planned a slightly enlarged combat version, the Tu-86, to be powered by two AM-2 or TR-3 engines with axial compressor, but this machine was not built.

Two years later Ilyushin once again led the field with the first Soviet bomber to achieve

Above: First Soviet jet bomber with swept wings, Tu-82 made its maiden flight in February 1949.

Soviet bombers first achieved 1,000kph in the form of Il-30 (above) powered by two 4,600kp thrust TR-3 engines.

Below: Il-46 was to all intents and purposes an enlarged Il-28. It achieved 930kph.

Above: Victory over other bomber rivals went to Tupolev's Tu-88. It was produced on a large scale under designation Tu-16.

A pair of Tu-16s at large (left) and an example equipped with anti-shipping missiles (below).

Above: Tu-98 was test flown in 1955, representing a refinement of Tu-88 (Tu-16). It remained at prototype stage.

1,000kph – the Il-30. The prototype, test flown in spring 1951, had two TR-3 engines, each of 4,600kp thrust, mounted under the wing. The bicycle gear was an important novelty. It consisted of two tandem pairs of wheels under the fuselage which were retractable in front of and behind the bomb bay. The bay could take 2,000 – 3,000kg load and strut wheels under the engine nacelles were also dual and retractable.

Il-30's armament did not deviate from the norm: a pair of NR-23 guns in the fuselage tail, a pair each on the upper and under side of the fuselage. Speed reached 1,000kph, range 3,500km and service ceiling 13,000m. But the aircraft remained a prototype.

In 1951 Soviet engine designers took a great step forward and were at last freed from dependance on British models. A M Lyulka's AL-5 engine achieved 5,000kp and A A Milkulin reached 8,200kp with his powerful AM-3. Mikulin's engine, in particular, provided a real impetus to the development of bombers of a larger category and also permitted the design of long range jet bombers.

Soviet designers had not only managed to catch up with the engine performance lead of Western states but even to overtake it. On the other hand, the most important parts of the engine still had a far shorter life than those on American and British models – the British engines being farthest advanced in this respect. Even so, the high thrust performance made it possible to reduce the number of engines compared with Western bombers of comparable weight.

So in 1951 Tupolev and Ilyushin embarked on design of the first jet bombers to totally replace Tu-4 reciprocating-engine aircraft.

Ilyushin saw the easiest way to success in extensive use of experience garnered with Il-28. The prototype of his heavy bomber Il-46 can actually be described as an enlargement of Il-28. The machine had the same fuselage contours; wings were straight, without sweepback and with a relatively small area; tail unit surfaces were kept sweptback and made it possible to

reach a relatively high critical Mach number.

The Il-46 had a take-off weight of 42 tons, almost twice as high as Il-28, and AL-5 engines each of 5,000kp were incorporated in slender nacelles under the wing. The crew consisted of three men and armament was the same as on Il-28. A distinctive feature was that all under-carriage wheels had double tyres and on the tip of the rudder unit was a radar early warning system.

V K Kokkinaki test flew the Il-46 on August 15, 1952. Subsequent plant and state tests demonstra-ted good performances and flying qualities; speed was 930kph at 3,000m, service ceiling 12,300m and range with 3,000kg of bombs 5,000km. The maximum bomb load was doubly effective on shorter distances. In spite of these qualities Il-46 did not become a standard heavy bomber of the Soviet Air Force.

On comparitive flights Tupolev's new aircraft, Tu-88 or Samolet N, emerged victorious over Il-46. Tu-88's development had been on more fruitful lines. The great wing of 34.54m span had 40.5 degrees sweepback between fuselage and the first boundary layer fence and 37.5 degrees on the wing tips, measured on the leading edge. A long fuselage had pressurised cabins for a seven

man crew. In the nose were the navigator and bombardier, behind them the pilot with the radio operator and finally the three gunners. Two of them operated remote controlled NR-23 gun domes on top and under the fuselage. A third gunner sat in the rear cabin with this twin NR-23 and a further fixed NR-23 projected from the side of the nose for the pilot's use. Fuselage took 3,000-6,000kg of bombs or other missiles.

Accomodation of two AM-3 engines in the wing roots close to the fuselage was typical of Tu-88. Typical, too, was the undercarriage, a multiple-wheel type used for the first time in the U S S R. The four wheels on every main strut were retractable into the spindle shaped nacelles on the wing trailing edge. These nacelles not only took the undercarriage, they also helped to satisfy the important area-rule concept.

When test flown in 1952 the Tu-88 weighed a full 72 tons, reached 945kph, had a service ceiling between 11,000 and 12,000m and standard range with 6,000kg bomb load was 4,800km. With 3,000kg it was as much as 6,400km. These were impressive achievements for that time, and it is not surprising that Tu-88 was given preference over Il-46. Tu-88 were serially produced on a large scale and the strategic bomber aviation department was given this model under designation Tu-16.

During its long years of service Tu-16 was developed further.Most important technical modification was the incorporation of new AM-3 engines, each of 8,700kp thrust, which brought maximum speed up to 1,000kph. All Tu-16 bombers were equipped for re-fuelling in flight and Tupolev even developed a special flying tanker variant with a cross section several times larger than that of the standard machine.

Not only the Tu-16 of Soviet naval aviation, but also machines delivered to Egypt and Indonesia were equipped with two remote controlled missiles for attacks on ships. These missiles (NATO designation 'Kennel') look like small unmanned aircraft similar to MiG-15. Independent radar systems guided them to their targets.

Other Tu-16 carried under their fuselage a large remote controlled ram jet bomb for direction against ground targets. Shape of the aircraft nose was modified, with a broad casing around the bomb's radar guidance system. Tu-16 with various attachments under the fuselage were also photographed over the Pacific. These attachments were apparently casings to radar equipment.

Hardly had the bombers reached 1,000kph than they were already deemed too slow and it was required that they should approach or even exceed Mach 1. A breakthrough into the transonic sphere came later, of course, for bombers than for fighters. The years 1954 and 1955 brought the first experiments in this field, thanks above all to a new engine from A M Lyulka, the Al-7F of 9,000kp static thrust. Once again a duel took place between the designs of Ilyushin and Tupolev. Both prototypes were test flown in 1955.

Ilyushin's prototype Il-54 looked like a sequel to Il-30, though its lines were adapted to the higher speeds. Wings had a 55 degrees sweep on the leading edge and the long fuselage was conspicuously pointed. Engines were in relatively short nacelles under the wings, bicycle undercarriage was kept, but the small strut wheels retracted into spindle shaped bodies on the wing tips. Crew consisted of three men; armament of two flexible NR-23 in the tail and two fixed NR-23 in the nose.

The Il-54 reached 1,150kph on test flights at an unspecified altitude, range was 2,400km and service ceiling 13,000m. So the Il-54 fitted rather into the category of tactical bombers, something like Il-28 or Tu-14.

This machine was relatively well known in the West. In summer 1956, Premier Krushchov invited commanders-in-chief of the American Air Force to see new aircraft models at the Kubinka test station near Moscow. Among machines seen by the American delegation, under the leadership of General Nathan P Twining, was the Il-54. The Americans did not know at the time what the aircraft was called, nor was further information

Below: Among military aircraft viewed by an American delegation to Moscow in 1956 was the prototype Il-54. Like the Tu-98 it appeared at a time when opinion was shifting against the classic bomber concept.

Above and left: The first and only production bomber with turboprops was Tupolev's Tu-95, a giant aircraft with up to 170 tons take-off weight and contra-rotating propellors 5.6m in diameter.

Below: Worthy transonic tactical bomber was the Yak-28, shown here in its R form.

available. After their return to the USA the machine was dubbed 'Blowlamp' and only much later was the real designation and data revealed.

The second aircraft, Tupolev's Tu-98, was also often featured in Western technical press. It was displayed during air parades and photographed in the vicinity of test airfields. The aircraft was given NATO designation 'Backfin' but its origins remained obscure for a long time.

The Tu-98 was test flown in 1955. It had two AL-7F engines with afterburners and represented a refinement of Tu-88 in the sense that it had a 'pure' wing without nacelles etc. Engines were incorporated into the rear part of the fuselage, next to one another with air inlet holes in front of the wing. So the lines of the aircraft were particularly clean.

With its size and weight Tu-98 was roughly in the class of Tu-88 but reached 1,060kph at 6,000m altitude and at 12,000m with afterburners as much as 1,240kph. But both Tu-98 and Il-54 originated at a time when commanders-in-chief of the Soviet Air Force had many varying views about the future of the classic bomber. Some opined that they were altogether useless and bomber assignments should be undertaken with rockets alone. Because of these opinions the aircraft remained at prototype stage.

As a transonic tactical bomber, the two-engined Yakovlev Yak-28 in particular showed its worth. This aircraft was a sequel to the night fighter Yak-25, but only the general construction of the aircraft was reminiscent. Yak-28 had a sharply pointed nose with glazing, enlarged wing sweepback between engine nacelles and fuselage and a broken leading edge to the outboard wings; all these were aerodynamic devices which with the help of more powerful engines allowed high operational speeds while take off and landing speeds remained good for tactical aircraft.

There is still one area left to talk about – giant bombers. They date from the beginning of the fifties when engine technology was sufficiently developed and aerodynamic findings made it possible to achieve high speeds even on such big machines.

Tupolev – who else? – the creator of the biggest aircraft of the reciprocating-engine period, also built the biggest bomber of the jet period. In 1952 design work was begun on the giant Tu-95. This aircraft has remained a singularity in aviation technology, being the first and only production bomber with turboprops.

N D Kusnetsov completed development of the huge NK-12 engines in 1953. These were six metre long power units with two, four-bladed, contra-rotating propellors of 5.6m diameter. Take-off engine performance began at 12,000mhp and on the NK-12M variant was increased to 15,000. The incredible engine performance and surprising effectiveness of the propellers allowed Tupolev to use the NK-12 in an aircraft with a calculated speed of 900-950kph, a technical performance that had never before been anticipated.

In 1954 the first Tu-95 was completed and test

Above: The massive M-52 bomber with MiG-21 fighter escort. There was speculation before the aircraft's debut that it might be nuclear powered.

flown. With a span of 51m it was one of the biggest bombers of its time. The slender fuselage was adapted for a six-man crew and its armament corresponded to that of the Tu-16 – gun turrets containing two NR-23 remotely controlled from the pressurised cabins. The tail turret was also kept as were the two drop shaped side windows under the controls. The mighty wing had a sweepback of 35 degrees, two fences on each side, and a set of take-off and landing auxillary surfaces on the trailing edge. Multiple wheel landing gear was retractable into the lengthened internal engine nacelles.

This aircraft was designed to carry 150-170 tons take-off weight. Without military equipment it reached 950kph, with complete outfit and equipment a noteworthy 870kph, and the operational speed never fell below 800. Most economic cruising speed on long distance flights was 750kph. Service ceiling was 12,500m and the range between 12,000-17,500km, bomb load normally being 10,000kg.

Production machines based on the prototype were given military designation Tu-20 and put into service in 1955. At the beginning of the 1960s most were withdrawn from bomber service and fitted out as long range reconnaissance aircraft, especially for maritime work. Photographs of these aircraft over the Pacific are often shown. Various blister antennae and other special outfits

show up clearly, as does equipment for refuelling in flight. Special variants to Tu-16 and also the four-engined M-4 are mostly in service as tankers.

The airframe and engines of Tu-20 were a help to Tupolev's drawing office in design of the large commercial aircraft, Tu-114 'Rossija'.

Jet counterpart of the Tu-20 is the four engined M-4 of V M Myasishchev. M-4 is certainly more elegant than Tu-20. It has four AM-3 engines incorporated in the wing near the fuselage. The wing itself is swept back and bears on the tips spindle-shaped bodies into which the strut wheels of the undercarriage are retracted. The M-4 has a bicycle undercarriage with two large pairs of wheels on the tips of a long bomb bay. They are retractable into the fuselage.

We have no further information about the M-4 bombers, or rather about their standard military bomber or long range reconnaissance version. Speed is estimated at 1,000kph at 3,000m and range with 5,000kg bombs about 11,000-12,000km. The flying world has learned more about M-4's

Myasischev's M-4 in original bomber form (above) and the 201-M maritime reconnaissance version (below). The aircraft made many record-breaking flights in 1959 under camouflage designations but was not accurately identified until 1967.

capacities on its numerous record flights. These were flown in 1959 and the aircraft received two different camouflage designations, 103-M and 201-M.

On October 30, 1959, Anatolii Lipko reached 1,028.664kph with 103-M over a distance of 1,000km and with 27,000kg payload. With this flight seven international records were simultaneously broken : the records for payloads of 1,000, 2,000, 5,000, 10,000, 15,000, 20,000 and 25,000kg. The day before Boris Stepanov's crew reached 13,121m with 201-M and thus five records were broken for payloads of 35, 40, 45, 50 and 55 tons. The biggest load (55,220kg) was lifted by Stepanov's machine up to the internationally established height of 2,000m.

These performances clearly showed the capacities of the machine which had already set up a record on September 16, 1959, when Nikolaj Gorjanov and five crew members brought a load of 10 tons up to 15,317m altitude. On the occasion of these record flights, the USSR revealed the names of the engines – apparently four D-15 each of 13,000kp. The 201-M was displayed at a big show on Domodedovo airfield in summer 1967, when it was confirmed that 201-M and M-4 were one and the same aircraft.

In the Tushino air parade of 1967 several bomber models were shown. The giant M-52 was perhaps one of the greatest surprises. This was also one of Myasishchev's designs and the surprise was not merely that a new aircraft had been shown but that at last more light could be shed on the machine. The existence of this aircraft was known about in the West and there was often speculation as to whether it was nuclear propelled!

People were now able to see that, despite the machine's imposing dimensions, it was still a classic jet. The M-52's fuselage was about 55m long, calculated by comparison with the MiG-21 fighter escorts. The delta wing had 45 degrees sweepback in its centre section, easing at the outer sections. Two powerful engines are mounted under the wing, with two more on the wing tips. Weight of the giant is calculated at 140 tons.

Another bomber also made an impressive appearance. The long, spindle-shaped fuselage with characteristic blister antennae on the nose, sharply swept wing, neat undercarriage nacelles on the trailing edge, engine nacelles of both engines close to the root of the tail fin all gave an

Tu-22 in the air and on the ground. Speed is calculated at between Mach 1.5 and 2.

overall impression of singular technical beauty. The aircraft originated in 1958 in Tupolev's office, prototype being designated Tu-105, but it was also called Samolet-Yu. It's engines are of about 12,000kp thrust with afterburners and they give the aircraft a speed of Mach 1.5 – Mach 2.

They are now in operation in quite large numbers under the military designation Tu-22, and form a supersonic substitute for the subsonic Tu-16 bombers. Press pictures from the USSR show various versions of Tu-22 with and without refuelling outfit, with and without rocket missiles and remote controlled bodies etc. It would seem that Tu-22 was a worthy conclusion to the design work of that Master of Soviet aeronautics, A N Tupolev.

CHAPTER 24

Reconnaissance Aircraft and Light Bombers

AT THE BEGINNING of the first Soviet Five-Year Plan in 1929, reconnaissance aircraft constituted 80% of the total number of aircraft belonging to the Red Air Force. The percentage was high, not only because aircraft of this type were specifically needed, but also because of the situation prevailing in the aviation industry at that time. Simple reconnaissance biplanes were relatively easy to produce and could be used instead of specialised aircraft which the industry was not yet able to produce on any great scale.

Reconnaissance and bomber biplanes had also been major components of the Czar's air force, and several were taken over or captured by the revolutionaries. Further machines had been captured from intervening foreign troops, among them DH-9 from the last months of the First World War. The modern DH-9 made excellent reconnaissance aircraft and light bombers; Soviet pilots were extremely happy with the De Havillands and demanded more. As it was not possible to capture sufficient numbers in combat, imitations were begun at Moscow's 'Dux' plant in 1920-1921. This plant had held plans of the DH-4 since 1917, when licence production had been intended but never actually started.

Under the direction of N N Polikarpov, the plant produced twenty copies of the DH-4 with the Italian 240mhp Fiat A-12 engines and delivered them to the air force. Maximum speed was 150kph, service ceiling 4,000m and range 400km. Armament consisted of a fixed machine gun and a moveable twin machine gun.

After the twentieth aircraft Dux switched to the DH-9. By 1923, 100 specimens had been constructed with 260mhp Mercedes engines, partly using airframes bought in Britain, while a further 130 were given British Siddeley Puma engines of 220mhp. Speed with the Mercedes was 170kph and range 600km. DH-9s with Mercedes were named R-1 and those with Puma R-2.

Both machines were the embryo of aircraft construction in the USSR, which was not without its difficulties: there was delay owing to lack of material or fittings which slowed down the supply of new aircraft to the units. The Soviet government gave assistance by buying about 300 complete aircraft abroad. Between 1922 and 1924, the Italian Ansaldo ASV and, more important, the Dutch Fokker C-IV came on the scene. But dependence of the new republic on deliveries from abroad was already unacceptable for political reasons, and soon ways and means were being sought to design and mass produce on home ground.

After the October Revolution in 1917, political emigrant and engineer D D Fedorov returned to Russia. While abroad he had designed a reconnaissance aircraft which he wished to dedicate to his country. This aircraft, the DF-1, was a biplane with interesting lines, especially the wings. Construction began in November 1920 in the aircraft repair plant of the 4th Red Army under very unfavourable supply conditions. Then work was transferred to the hinterland where the aircraft was finished in Spring 1922. Pilot P P

Uspasskii was very content with the machine and recommended its mass production. But in the military repair plants there were no opportunities for such construction and so the DF-1 remained a mere prototype. The designer himself never saw the aircraft in flight – he fell ill and died while work was under way on the prototype.

The Moscow Dux plant had better opportunities for mass production. In 1923 Polikarpov, who worked here as chief designer, prepared a constructive 'mixture' of the two British DH machines. In his design he counted on the aircraft being equipped with an American 400mhp Liberty engine, the purchase of which was already under discussion. From the beginning it was designed for territorial and meteorological conditions of the USSR.

In Autumn 1923, Dux delivered the first two machines with military designation R-I (R meant *Rasvedchik* or reconnaissance aircraft). The R-I had a wooden framework with fabric covering; it was a two-seater armed with a moveable twin machine gun and one fixed weapon plus provision for up to 400kg of bombs. Maximum speed was 204kph, range 750km and ceiling 5,500m.

That Winter the plant was prepared for more extensive output and in 1924 Dux delivered the first hundred aircraft. Series production in this plant continued until 1931 when the 2,800th aircraft had been produced. Although in the last years it was used more in training than in combat activity, the R-I stayed for a long, long time on the programme of construction. The first 2,000 were built up to 1927, mostly given Liberty engines, or later, 400mhp Soviet M-5 imitations. Twenty R-I with 240mhp BMW-1Va motors were used for training.

The important role played by R-I machines in building up the Red Air Force in the twenties is undeniable. Production of such simple aircraft was possible even in those difficult times and adequate to meet the requirements of national defence. Thousands of pilots and observers made their maiden flights in the R-I, thousands of mechanics and other ground personnel gathered experience. And the aircraft had an ideological advantage too. The large numbers made it possible to show the R-1 in every part of the country, where appearance of a 'steel bird' brought about

R-I was a reconnaissance aircraft designed by Polikarpov from a mixture of De Havilland DH-4 and DH-9 machines. Production ran to 2,800 examples.

Above and below: In 1925 A A Krylov designed and built the R-II as a potential replacement for R-I which was considered a reconstructed machine. Despite good flying qualities and an efficient German Maybach MB-IVa engine it was not accepted.

a significant strengthening of the authority of the new Soviet power.

Some R-I were even flown into foreign countries. One of the longest flights, involving a number of aircraft, was from Moscow to Peking. The group took off on June 10, 1925, and landed in Peking after a 6,476km staged flight on July 13. M M Gromov and M A Volkovoynov then continued from Peking to Tokyo in their R-I aircraft. In 1926 pilot Moiseyev completed a 6,200km Moscow – Teheran – Moscow flight in stages, between July 14 and 25. Another, P Kh Meshraup, flew 1,940km from Moscow to Ankara in Turkey, via Kharkov and Sebastopol in July 1926.

In spite of successes, Soviet designers regarded the R-I as a reconstructed foreign machine and often tried to create their own. However, no design constituted enough of an improvement to justify a change in production. In 1925, for example, A A Krylov designed and constructed a reconnaissance biplane R-II. It was a robust machine powered by the German 260mhp Maybach MB-IVa engine and flew well but was not accepted. M M Shishmarev's R-III had a similar end. Here the designer had adopted most structural parts of R-1 but assembled his biplane the 'wrong' way about, that is the fuselage hung on the upper wing and the under wing stretched straight under the fuselage. Shishmarev wanted to use a bigger propellor for a better rate of climb.

Reconnaissance aircraft took over the role of light bombers for the Front, just as they did in the air forces of other countries. However, from time to time there also appeared designs for specialised light bombers which were intended for short attacks on the Front or in the vicinity. In 1925 such an aircraft was built in the USSR – L D Kolpakov-Miroshnichenko's three-seat biplane LB-2LD. The designer had worked during the war with Lebed and created some twin-engined aircraft for them.

The abbreviation LB stood for *Legkii Bombardirovshchik* (light bomber). Provision was made for the use of two Lorraine-Dietrich engines, each of 400mhp, but the finished aircraft had to make do with two 260mhp Fiat A-12 engines. LB-2LD was successfully test flown, achieving 150kph with 500kg bomb load, but remained a prototype for the R-I was able to accomplish identical work by simpler means.

R-II, R-III and LB-2LD were of little importance in the further development of reconnaissance aircraft and light bombers. In the drawing-office AGOS-TsAGI, an aircraft with better prospects was designed, in all-metal construction of duralumin sheet – A N Tupolev's ANT-3.

As has already been learned, Tupolev was able with his test-monoplane ANT-2 to convince air force chiefs of duralumin construction potential. Now, with ANT-3, he was to create the first Soviet all-metal military type. Tupolev worked in accordance with the tactical-technical conditions of 1924, design consisting of sesquiplane with corrugated duralumin outer casing. The fuselage in oval cross-section showed the underside very much contracted, as was the case with ANT-2. There were two open seats, one fixed machine gun and one moveable twin.

In TsAGI's prototype plant two aircraft with

Above: R-5 first flew in 1928 and went on to a production run of almost 5,000 in various forms, one of the greatest achievements of Russia's developing aviation industry.

Below: Tupolev created the first Soviet all-metal military type with R-3 (ANT-3). Limited capacity for manufacturing in metal restricted production to just 101 aircraft.

the 450mhp British Napier Lion engine were constructed and equipped with characteristic Lamblin radiators. Plant tests under V N Filipov lasted from August to October 1925, and state tests were concluded in May 1926 with a very favourable rating by the chief pilot, M M Gromov. On the strength of this the Red Air Force ordered it in quite large numbers under designation R-3.

R-3 was certainly a good aircraft and its technology matched the period. However, the Soviet aircraft industry was very limited in its capacity for serial production of all-metal aircraft, and so the R-3 was not so much in circulation as it might have been. Production lasted from 1926 to 1929; 101 aircraft were produced, 79 of which had French 450mhp Lorraine-Dietrich engines and the rest built in 1928 had Soviet M-5. All production aircraft had front radiators behind the propeller.

The design and construction of all-metal aircraft was certainly a source of pride so the Soviet government set up a special commission to make preparations for propaganda flights into foreign countries.

In the early hours of August 31, 1926, a Napier Lion powered ANT-3 took off from Moscow, piloted by Gromov and accompanied by flight engineer Rodsevich, on a Moscow-Konigsberg – Berlin – Paris – Rome – Vienna – Warsaw – Moscow tour. The aircraft, named *'Proletarii'*, completed the 7,150km route in 34 hours 15 minutes of actual flying time. Progress was interrupted by an accident over Czechoslovakia and could only be continued after repair in the Letov aircraft plant.

A year later another ANT-3 left Moscow bearing the name *'Nash Otvet'* (Our Answer). The crew consisted of pilot S A Shestakov and mechanic D V Fufayev. This time they flew in an easterly direction to Sarapul, Omsk, Novosibirsk, Krasnoyarsk, Irkutsk, Chita, Blagoveshchensk and Spassk and from there via Nanyang and Okayama to Tokyo. The Japanese capital was reached on September 1, 1927, and the aircraft then retraced its route back to Moscow. The whole flight was 22,000km long and required 153 hours of flying time.

Tupolev continued efforts to improve his R-3 by using a 500mhp M-17 engine, but the R-4 remained only a prototype. Production capacity of the Soviet industry was really exhausted. Nevertheless at this time the air force got a few more all-metal reconnaissance aircraft.

Between 1923 and 1925 the Junkers branch in Fili, near Moscow, constructed 80 reconnaissance high-wing monoplanes. Originally designated H-21 in Germany, the Ju-21 had a BMW – IIIa of 185mhp. They were by no means exceptional and had to be reconstructed because of insufficient stability of the airframe. Ju-21 were used in Turkestan up to 1931.

Besides these, five low-wing German Ju-20 monoplanes were delivered with wheeled undercarriages and BMW-111A engines. They were mostly produced in the USSR as twin float seaplanes; wheels were not a normal feature.

The USSR certainly supported the design of all-metal reconnaissance aircraft and, as far as possible, introduced their series production. However, they knew that in the time allotted only classical aircraft of composite construction could be built and delivered in sufficient numbers, hence the design of a new, more modern reconnaissance aircraft in 1925. German 500/680mhp in-line BMW-VI engines were to be used whenever possible since their series production as M-17 was projected.

Who else could construct an aircraft like this except N N Polikarpov? He was working as chief designer at Moscow's No. 25 plant, concentrating on the new R-5. High performance, good stability, simple flying, unassuming wood technology and long life were the desired qualities. Test flight of the prototype in 1928 showed that Polikarpov was able to harmonise all these heterogenous requirements into a many sided, multi-purpose aircraft such as had been requested!

Caterpillar tracks replaced wheels on this experimental R-5.

The prototype with BMW-VI had a fixed PV-1 machine gun and a moveable DG-1 or DG-2 for the observer. Maximum speed was 260kph at 3,000m, 230kph at low altitude and service ceiling reached 6,400m. Under the wings were racks for 250kg of bombs but as a light bomber it had provision for 300-400kg.

Before the R-5 was put into production, it had to stand comparison with a further prototype. This was the R-7 or ANT-10 sesquiplane of Tupolev, also produced in all-metal construction and with BMW-VI engine. Design dated from 1928, when the R-5 was already being flown, and first take-off did not take place until January 30. No great advantages could be established and preference was given to the simpler R-5.

R-5 was put on the production line in 1931 and remained for a full six years in different forms. A total of 4,995 were built, one of the greatest accomplishments of pre-war Soviet aviation industry. The design allowed simple reconstruc-

Below: R-6 (ANT-7) was a heavy reconnaissance aircraft of 1929 modelled on the TB-1 bomber but much smaller. Some were still operating in 1941.

tion and R-5 could easily be adapted to different purposes.

In 1931, came a twin float seaplane variant, R-5a or MR-5bis, and in 1932 a one-seat torpedo aircraft, R-5T, of which fifty specimens were constructed. In 1933 the combat R-5Sh made its appearance. This aircraft had additional armour-plating and four fixed PV-1 machine guns built in obliquely for anti-infantry fire. There was provision for 500kg of bombs and some hundred examples were built.

In 1934 an improved R-5SSS appeared with the more powerful M-17F engine of 650mhp. Stream-lining improvements to the wheel-casings struts and cockpit helped increase speed by about 16kph.

Designers D S Markov and A A Skarbov re-constructed the R-5SSS and in 1935 put R-Z on the line. The R-Z displayed all improvements in streamlining and technology of the R-5SSS plus the new 820mhp M-34RN engine. Series production switched to the new model and in two years 1,031 R-Z were made.

Performance was considerably better: maximum speed 316kph, service ceiling 8,700m and range 1,000km. These were not records for the period but the R-Z still constituted the majority of reconnaissance aircraft of the Red Air Force at the beginning of the forties.

One R-Z was fitted experimentally with a high-altitude M-34RNV engine and in May 1937, V V Shevchenko reached a height of 11,000m with this aircraft. An outside temperature of -63 degrees was measured.

The robust airframe of R-5 and R-Z made them suitable for various experiments. In 1935 an R-5 served as a flying test-bed for the heavy-oil engine Jumo 4; another machine flew with Vee-controls; a further was used to test the new caterpillar undercarriage of inventor Chechubalin. This undercarriage consisted of two small caterpillar units instead of wheels, but they proved too

awkward.

R-5 and R-Z biplanes were therefore the standard aircraft for Red Air Force reconnaissance units. In spite of the great number built, reconnaissance aircraft decreased in the first half of the thirties, only constituting 26.2% of total stock in 1934. Soviet industry was now able to produce specialised aircraft and reconnaissance aircraft were kept purely for reconnaissance purposes.

But the design of new models was not halted as specialisation applied to this category of aircraft too. A first attempt was the design of a heavy reconnsaissance aircraft with two engines.

On September 11, 1929, M M Gromov test flew the twin-engined ANT-7. It was a cantilever, all duralumin, low-wing monoplane on the lines of the TB-1 but smaller and lighter. Dimensions were drastically reduced: the span was 5.5m less than TB-1's and the wings were only 80 square metres compared to 115.8. Speed of ANT-7 climbed to 240kph using the same M-17 engines with which TB-1 only reached 200. Service ceiling was also better – 6,000m instead of 4,700.

State tests were concluded in the Summer of 1930 by P M Stefanovskii and the aircraft released for production. Altogether 400 were constructed, most of them as heavy reconnaissance aircraft R-6. The machines were three-seat, had two DA-2 twin machine guns and could fly 1,000km. There was provision for up to 500kg of bombs.

The R-6 was a more modern design of aircraft, of the type that had been aimed at some years previously with the biplane LB-2LD: well armed, self-sufficient and equipped for engagement in an effective bombing mission. They were very popular and their life was almost eternal. Quite a lot were still operating from Soviet border airfields in Summer of 1941 – unfortunately they were hopelessly antiquated.

In contrast to the heavy R-6 were the light reconnaissance aircraft LR-1 (*Legkii Rasvedchik* = light reconnaissance aircraft) created under the direction of Kocherigin and Ickovich. This was designed as prototype TsKB-1 and tested in July 1933. LR-1 was an attempt to construct a more modern reconnaissance biplane than R-5. The designers reduced dimensions and wing area came down from 50.2 to 36.2 square metres. Everything was carefully smoothed and covered; even the machine gunner received a glazed turret though the pilot's seat remained exposed.

The first TsKB-1 prototype reached only 270kph at low altitude with a 650/750mhp M-34 engine. The second machine, test flown with ski under-carriage in the first weeks of 1934, had a more powerful 750/815mhp M-34 engine and did better. Speed rose to 314kph, range was 800km and service ceiling 9,100m, but this LR-1 was not put on the production line. In 1934 Kocherigin and Ickovich planned to build yet another LR-2 biplane with M-34RN engine, fully glazed flight-crew's cabin and cantilever undercarriage – but they did not get permission.

The position of R-5 and R-Z biplanes thus remained unshaken. Both aircraft were easy to construct, had favourable qualities and were popular – so popular that the combat efficiency of reconnaissance flights began to be imperilled. The USSR had constructed reconnaissance biplanes for too long. Meanwhile, fighter aircraft had become fast monoplanes and against them the R-Z were practically defenceless. Soviet reconnaissance aircraft had to be quickly modernised too.

The aviation industry's design bureau in Kharkov surprised everyone in 1932 with a revolutionary single-engined commercial monoplane, KhAI-1, designed by Nieman. This aircraft, with retractable undercarriage and M-22 engine, reached 325kph – 38kph faster than production I-5 fighters, which had the same engine.

In 1935 Nieman built two military machines KhAI-1V (*Voiskovii Variant* = military variant) which were intended as light bombers, reconnaissance aircraft or for the training of bomber crews. He also built an aircraft for purely reconnaissance purposes with the lines of KhAI-1V but called KhAI-6. It was an all-metal, low-wing monoplane with rectractable undercarriage and an American Wright Cyclone SGR-1820F-3 engine of 710mhp.

Through revision of the design of KhAI-6 a further reconnaissance and light bomber was produced in 1936. This was the KhAI-5 (model numbers did not always follow in strict sequence in the USSR) which also had a Cyclone engine and was two-seat. In order to give the pilot as good a vision as possible his cockpit had been built right in the front, immediately behind the engine. The observer/machine gunner sat a considerable distance away in a rotary machine gun turret with a ShKAS almost directly in front of the controls. Two fixed ShKAS were under the engine casing. KhAI-5 attained 388kph at 2,500m, could fly 950km and climbed to 7,700m.

Contemporary with KhAI-5 was another monoplane, this time designed by Kocherigin. An all-metal, mid-wing aircraft, it had design number TsKB-27 and military designation SR (*Skorotsnii Rasvedchik* = fast reconnaissance aircraft). The machine was supposed to be fast and it was. When tested with a Gnome-Rhone 14K Mistral Major of 670/780mhp in 1936, a speed of 460kph was measured. It had retractable undercarriage and was armed with two machine guns. There was also provision for 60kg of bombs, yet bomb attacks were only regarded as of secondary importance.

The SR displayed difficulties in flying qualities, in the undercarriage mechanism and in the possibilities for co-operation between the two widely separated crew members – also a disadvantage of the KhAI-5.

Kocherigin resolved some problems with prototype R-9 in 1936. The machine was a mid-wing monoplane with Gnome-Rhone 14K and had fixed, spatted undercarriage. Limited vision and shooting possibilities for the second crew member which appeared in the SR were solved by a glazed machine gun turret and two fixed ShKAS were also built in. There was provision for 60kg of bombs in the bay.

The fixed undercarriage certainly simplified design, but performance was reduced. Maximum speed sank to 447kph at 4,200m, range was 1,300km and service ceiling 8,350m. The R-9 did not get a favourable assessment from the air force. Kocherigin tried introducing a variant which could be used as a light bomber and assault aircraft, or one for purely assault purposes (Sh), but he had no success.

Commanding officers preferred heavier aircraft which could also be used for other purposes and thought they had found the answer in KhAI-5. Even so it was not immediately taken over for series production. Before this, the air force launched a competition in order to have as many machines as possible for comparison and eventual decision. The competition began in 1936, code-named Ivanov. From the first batch, models KhAI-5 by Nieman, DG-58bis by Grigorovich, Ivanov by Polikarpov and ANT-51 by Tupolev were selected.

Winner of the competition was unequivocally KhAI-5. Not without reason – for the stipulations were all based around this aircraft and KhAI-5 was the only one ready at the right time for flight testing. And its qualities and performance more than satisfied the commission.

KhAI-5 received military designation R-10 and series production proceeded quickly. By 1938 first specimens of the batch of 490 aircraft were delivered, equipped with 730mhp M-25V engine and larger fuel tanks to allow a range of 1,300km. On the other hand, take-off weight rose to 2,875kg and maximum speed sank to a disappointing 370kph.

It became evident that the design of R-10 had been insufficiently thought out. Their performance was very faulty and tactically the aircraft fell below expectations. Especially difficult was the co-operative work between pilot and observer. As a result, in the first months of war R-10 were hardly used, for they were almost defenceless.

Let us now turn to other participants in the Ivanov competition. The DG-58bis, or rather DG-58R, by Grigorovich was a reconnaissance variant of dive-bomber DG-58 or PB-1. The machine was an all-metal, low-wing monoplane with Gnome-Rhone 14K (Soviet designation M-85) and an estimated speed of 450kph. DG-58bis was not constructed for Grigorovich fell ill while the aircraft was being designed and died in 1938.

Polikarpov called his competition aircraft simply Ivanov. Not until 1938 did he manage to construct two prototypes, by which time the R-10 were already in production. Ivanov was an all-metal low-wing monoplane with rectractable undercarriage and the nine-cylinder 830mhp M-62. On the wing were four fixed ShKAS machine guns, a further moveable UBT weapon was in a turret at the end of the glazed area on top of the fuselage and a ShKAS could shoot downwards through a gap in the floor of the rear cabin.

The first Ivanov was tested between February and August 1938, attaining 410kph. It was relatively heavy with a take-off weight of 3,929kg and there was considerable room for improvement in

The second TsKB-1 (LR-1) prototype had ski undercarriage and M-34 engine.

KhAI-5 (R-10) was equipped with a rotary machine gun turret.

Above: Kocherigin's fast reconnaissance model SR reached 460kph in 1936.
Below: R-9 was an attempt to improve on the SR, but performance levels came down.

Polikarpov's entry in the 1936 'Ivanov' competition was simply named 'Ivanov'.

ANT-51 was Tupolev's 'Ivanov' offering and had a nine-cylinder M-62 engine.

Above: Su-2 (BB-1) was a reconstruction on ANT-51 by Sukhoi. This example is fitted with the M-82.
Below: ShB, a close-support fighter variant of Su-2, remained a prototype.

flying qualities. Because R-10 was already in production only the first Ivanov was completed. Work on the second was abandoned before final assembly.

Last aircraft of the competition was Tupolev's ANT-51 or S-3, the design of which dated from 1936. This, again, was an all-metal, low-wing monoplane with a long cabin and nine-cylinder M-62. The engine casing had small, drop-shaped cowls over the cylinders. On the wing were four fixed ShKAS machine guns and in the turret a twin machine gun. There was provision for 200kg of bombs in the bay while a further 200kg could be stored under the wings.

Tupolev's ANT-51 was test flown on August 25, 1937, by Gromov, still with its stable, spatted undercarriage as the retractable version was not yet available. ANT-51 reached a speed of 403kph at 4,700m, 360kph at low altitude, and the flying qualities were good. Some improvements were still needed but Tupolev was not able to conduct the work and at the beginning of 1938 he was arrested.

At the end of 1938 P O Sukhoi began to reconstruct ANT-51 according to new requirements. Sukhoi adapted to the lack of aluminium, building the fuselage as wooden shell and used the powerful and newer M-87 engine which allowed him to increase the bomb load to 600kg.

Towards the end of 1939 two prototypes of Sukhoi's new Ivanov were ready and the air force had taken them on as BB-1 (*Blishnii Bombardiovshchik* or short distance bomber). Only differences were in the A and B variants of the M-87 engine, in each case producing 950mhp. The third prototype, appearing at the beginning of 1940 with an M-88 engine of 950mhp, was the one put into production.

So competition Ivanov had brought two winners – an official winner, the R-10 whose antiquated design became obvious at the very first sortie: and an unofficial winner, the BB-1. Nieman still tried to save the R-10 and in 1939 constructed an improved variant, KhAI-52. It had an M-62 engine but 358kph at 3,000m remained very low.

The mass produced BB-1 had four ShKAS machine guns, each with 650 rounds of ammunition. In the bay was provision for up to 600kg of bombs and up to six RS-82 rocket missiles could be carried under the wings. Detachable armour plating protected the crew from underneath, behind and in front. Maximum speed at 5,200m was 468kph, at low altitude 375kph and the range reached 1,200km.

At the beginning of 1941 BB-1 received the new designation Su-2. While aircrew were satisfied with their machines, the commanders-in-chief were less enthusiastic. Su-2 were too slow, especially at the rather low altitude at which most sorties would be carried out.

Sukhoi responded and in Spring 1941 the 1,000mhp M-88B engine was built into a lighter version of Su-2. At the same time, two fixed machine guns were discarded, the bomb load limited to 400kg and fuel tanks reduced in size.

Take-off weight of this variant sank from 4,435 to 4,150kg and speed at low altitude climbed to 410kph. At 7,100m it was 512kph but range dropped to 1,000km. The Red Air Force considered this limited amount of armament inadequate and demanded more on all the aircraft. The new issue with M-88B got six fixed machine guns and ten RS-82 rocket missiles. Result – speed at low altitude was again 378kph.

Up to the outbreak of war in Summer 1941 the Red Air Force received about 100 Su-2 aircraft with M-88 and M-88B. Most machines were destroyed on the ground and those remaining were defenceless without their fighter escort. Sukhoi tried once again to save the situation. Aircraft still being built at the beginning of Autumn got the new 1,330mhp Ash-82 and performance roughly corresponded to that of the lighter version of Su-2 with a low altitude speed of 430kph.

After resettlement of the production plant following evacuation of the aircraft industry, Su-2 was dropped and remaining aircraft sent to the Far East or used for various auxiliary purposes such as target-towing. Sukhoi designed and constructed further variants of the Su-2 but they were all turned down.

In 1940, for example, a close-support fighter variant came out with stronger armour-plating, altered casing of the M-88 and a new retractable undercarriage whereby the wheels lay flat in the wings. ShB remained a prototype and its performance was 460kph with a range of 1,200km.

In 1941 Sukhoi constructed the prototype Su-4, a more powerful variant of Su-2 with the new 2,100mhp M-90 engine. This machine had two-fixed UBK machine guns in the wings and two turret-mounted guns. It could carry 400kg of bombs and ten RS-82 rocket missiles. Su-4 reached a speed of 450kph at low altitude and 515kph at 5,800m. But the engine had such growing pains that a test flight was impossible until the period of evacuation arrived, and then design was postponed until 1942. With an ASh-82 engine it was then produced in limited numbers.

After Sukhoi's BB-1 there appeared BB-2, designed in the Moscow Aviation Institute under P D Grushin and constructed in 1939. With tandem wings and M-105 engine, BB-2 may be regarded as a continuation of the assault aircraft Sh-Tandem, which is described in the chapter about ground attack types. BB-2 had a tricycle undercarriage, one of the first on a military aircraft of the U S S R, but after the failure of Sh-Tandem, testing of BB-2 was also dropped. Photographs and data are totally lacking.

Greatest mistake up to now in the design of R- and BB- machines was low speed and consequent vulnerability. Two Soviet design groups tried another solution with reconnaissance or light bomber aircraft, believing that such machines should rely more on speed than armament. The same belief manifested itself in other countries too and led to the British de Havilland Mosquito.

A S Yakovlev designed the first Soviet machine with these qualites. In 1938 he proposed the fast combat aircraft Ya-22, a low-wing monoplane of

Professor V F Bolkhovitinov's Type S was tested in two forms – with twin M-103 engines in tandem driving contra-rotating propellers (above) and with a single M-103 (below). Neither version produced satisfactory results.

Below: Yak-2 version of the BB-22 with twin M-103 engines. Yak-4 differed in having M-105 units and token armament of one ShKAS machine gun in a modified cabin. The extra weight also necessitated double wheels.

composite construction with a two-seat cockpit, 960mhp M-103 engines and twin rudder. Undercarriage could be retracted into the engine nacelles. Originally there was no armament, but a small bay took 200kg of bombs while two 100kg bombs could be stored under the wing between fuselage and engines.

A demonstration given by the prototype Ya-22 before Stalin in May 1939 was very impressive. With its speed of 567kph the machine could escape from the production fighters of the time without difficulty. There was capacity for 400kg of bombs on a distance of 800km, and 1,600km was achievable with just photographic equipment.

That was the machine they had been waiting for, the ideal combat aircraft! Yakovlev received great recognition and Ya-22 was taken into the inventory as BB-22. Series production under the name Yak-2 with M-103 and Yak-4 with M-105 engines was under way very quickly. Unfortunately the military people were wary of an unarmed aircraft and insisted on the installation of guns. The Yak-4 therefore had one moveable ShKAS in a modified cabin and that spoiled the aircraft's excellent aerodynamic lines. The higher weight had to be compensated for by double wheels on the undercarriage.

Yak-4 was one of the greatest hopes – unfortunately it was also one of the greatest disappointments. High performance was attained at the expense of stability and durability and the machines showed themselves to be ill-adapted to the hard conditions of war when conducted from operational bases. Production was halted and those machines already constructed were used to transport weapons, ammunition etc. A sad fate for a fast combat aircraft.

Experiments were made to use Ya-22 in its original form for other purposes. There were prototypes of the R-12 fast reconnaissance aircraft and the I-29 escort fighter, the latter with

two ShVAK. Neither was produced in any quantity.

In 1936-1941 another candidate was put on the testing ground, this time a design of Professor V F Bolkhovitinov. It was known under the designation 'S' or *'Skorostniii'* – 'The fast one'. 'S' was a well-formed aircraft. The undercarriage was retractable and there were twin rudders. What was really special about the machine was its power plant. Two M-103 engines, each of 960mhp, were in tandem and powered two contra-rotating three-bladed propellers. There was provision for up to 400kg of bombs and one moveable ShKAS, situated right on the tip of the fuselage where it had an absolutely unhindered field of fire.

The power plant proved a source of endless difficulties. The back engine did not transmit its performance directly to the crankshaft of the front engine but through an elongated shaft to the gear of the two propellers. The shaft was too long, not firmly enough bedded, was distorted and caused almost insurmountable difficulties. Manoeuvrability of the aircraft was not exactly excellent either. On test flights that began in Summer of 1939 a speed of only 570kph was measured at a height of 4,600m and range was a modest 700km. Perpetual disturbances of the power plant compelled Bolkhovitinov to simplify his design drastically. 'S' was reconstructed with a single M-103 engine, but performance sank so low that the machine was written off.

On the whole, aircraft of the Ivanov category or BB were a failure. It was not only the fault of designers but also the weakness of aerial war theoreticians. Other world powers also found that single-engined light bombers were inferior when the fighter plane branch was unable to protect them. And such was always the case.

Reconnaissance aircraft in 1938 constituted only 9.5% of stock. In spite of every effort the Red Air Force was very weakly and one-sidedly equipped in this branch. Strategic long-distance and high-altitude reconnaissance aircraft, such as the incompleted BOK-11, were lacking. The design of 1935 for the ANT-49 was not used. This was a long-distance reconnaissance aircraft, well equipped with photographic apparatus, and with the airframe and engines of the SB-2 bomber.

Perhaps the lack of effective strategic reconnaissance aircraft and neglect of strategic reconnaissance as a whole combined to bring about the heavy military defeat in the first months of the war, when the U S S R was totally taken aback by Germany's attack.

During the war, fighters and combat bombers took over the reconnaissance role. For example, Petlyakov created the variant Pe-2R which was equipped for long night flights and possessed three cameras for vertical and panoramic aerial photography. Its two additional tanks of 145 litres each brought the range up to 1,700km. A Tu-2R was similarly constructed, equipped with wings

of greater span and lifting surface. These aircraft served long after the war.

The practice continued with jet aircraft. In every MiG fighter series there were reconnaissance versions and even the Il-28 were fitted out for this purpose. Il-28R were distinguishable from the Il-28 bombers by cigar-shaped bodies on the tips of the wings. Into these various electronic fittings were incorporated.

So far as is known, only one special reconnaissance aircraft was constructed in the U S S R after the war. Sukhoi started to design Su-12 in 1946 and in 1948 the first prototype was test flown by M L Gallai and S N Anokhin.

Sukhoi used the twin fuselage construction which had proved its worth in the German Focke-Wulf Fw 189. Su-12 was bigger and heavier. Its take-off weight reached 8,839kg and it was powered by two ASh-82M of 2,100mhp each. Armament was considerable: a fixed NS-23 cannon on the left side of the fuselage, a remote controlled cannon dome with two NS-23 on top and a tail turret with the same weapons. At 6,000 metres speed was only 550kph, not much for the post-war period. In low altitude it reached 450kph and range was 1,000km. Such performances did not justify series production and therefore only a few specimens of Su-12 existed. These aircraft were spotted by a few foreign observers, sometimes in the region of Leningrad, sometimes even in the Far East, and hence arose the story that the Soviet Air Force built them in quantity.

In more recent years the Force introduced A S Yakovlev's tactical reconnaissance aircraft in greater numbers. These are developments of the former Yak-25 all-weather fighters, reconstructed for other engagements. In 1953/4 there appeared the Yak-25R, first low level attack variant of the fighter aircraft. The machine was distinguished in particular by a greater sweepback of the wings between fuselage and engine nacelles. Yak-25R served for general co-operative work with the army, not only as a reconnaissance aircraft but also as a tactical and fighter bomber, capable of speeds up to Mach 0.9.

In the period 1956/9 Yak-26 was constructed – another remodelled Yak-25. The fuselage nose was glazed and there was a pitot tube on the edge of the wing. Only one N-37 cannon was fitted but several storage spaces for rocket missiles were built in.

The Yak-28, in use since 1959 and 1960, arose

from improvements in streamlining and more powerful engines of 6,000kp. They operate at about Mach 1.3, that is 1.460kph, are a little larger and have provision for 3,000kg of bombs. A variant purely for reconnaissance purposes, Yak-28R, was exhibited in 1967 at Domodedovo, near Moscow, featuring a yet more pointed nose.

It is interesting to see how easily the basic construction of Yak-25 could be modified, not only as a tactical aircraft for co-operation with the army, but also as a high-altitude reconnaissance aircraft.

In 1959 Yakovlev designed from Yak-25 a high-altitude reconnaissance aircraft, Yak-RV (*Rekord Visoti* or altitude record). The machine had straight wings of about 20m span (in Yak-25 11.2m) and tanks on the tips. On July 13, 1959, Major Smirnov reached 20,465m with an RV carrying 1,000kg pay-load and on July 29 achieved 20,174m with 2,000kg. Both performances were recognised as altitude records. With the same aircraft, Marina Popovich set a woman's record speed of 735.038kph at 12,000m over a distance of 200km on August 11, 1965. Yak-RV was used as a high-altitude photo reconnaissance aircraft and in NATO acquired the name 'Mandrake'.

Strategic reconnaissance units of the Soviet Air Force are at present equipped with special variants of the Tu-16, Tu-20 or M-4 with numerous electronic additions and domes. For early warning, modified Tu-114 commercial aircraft are also used, carrying a gigantic lentiform dome above the fuselage.

Among reconnaissance work a special place is occupied by light aircraft for directing artillery

Right: Yet another variant of the versatile An-2 was An-2NAK or An-2F, specially prepared by Antonov for artillery observation. It was armed with one NR-23 machine gun.

Su-12 is believed to have been the only post-war, purpose-built reconnaissance aircraft.

Yakovlev's high-altitude Yak-RV developed from the Yak-25.

fire. This task is one of the oldest in military aviation, practised since the first days of the First World War. Originally it was the task of the captive balloon, but owing to the rapid development of fighters the balloon became more and more vulnerable until its use had to be abandoned. Light aircraft proved to be better, especially since they often went unobserved amid the fray.

Polikarpov's light biplanes, U-2, were in use long before the war. Development of the U-2 will be discussed in the chapters about training and sporting aircraft, but in 1943 a special version was introduced for artillery observation at night. The variant was called U-2NAK (*Nochnoi Artillerii-skii Korrektirovshchik* = Night artillery correcting aircraft). It was equipped with an effective silencer and had the same task before, during and a long time after the war. Several attempts at a substitute failed.

In Germany there was a particularly successful aircraft for this task, the Fieseler Fi 156 Storch (Stork). It was a strutbraced, high-wing monoplane with effective slats, variable camber flaps and well-sprung undercarriage. The Fi 156 could take off and land at very small runways and was still reliable at a minimum speed of 55kph.

After signing of the German-Soviet pact of friendship and non-aggression in Summer 1939, Fi 156 was one of the first aircraft to be delivered by the Germans. The Storch excited much attention in the U S S R as an ideal machine not only for artillery observation but also for liaison, ambulance work etc. O K Antonov was quickly given the job of designing an aircraft as quickly as he could, and if design took too long he was to construct a copy.

In 1940 some prototypes were test flown. The variant ShS (*Shtabnoy-Sviasnoy* = staff and liaison aircraft) was three-seated and intended for liaison work and artillery observation. Variant N2 was an ambulance aircraft for two wounded men on stretchers The Soviet imitation corresponded exactly to the German pattern. Only the engine was different, an air-cooled, six-cylinder MV-6 of

Antonov's copy of the Fieseler Fi 156 Storch was designated ShS when used for liaison and artillery observation. Only prototypes were flown, the factory being destroyed before production machines could be delivered.

220mhp being used.

Series production of the ShS and N2 was started at the beginning of 1941 in Estonia. The production plant was near the frontier and was immediately destroyed by German attack before it could deliver a single aircraft.

After the war, Antonov designed An-2NAK or An-2F, an artillery variant of his well-known multipurpose biplane An-2 (see chapter about general purpose aircraft). Rear of the fuselage was built as an observation dome and equipped with an NR-23. The controls had to be redesigned and possessed twin vertical surfaces.

Today, helicopters have taken over most of the tasks of this type of aircraft. In the chapters about gyroplanes and helicopters we will discover the attempts of Soviet designers in this field.

Bombers

A NUMBER OF NEW developments have been reported, but most reports are vague and, once again, come from Western sources.

In 1969 the US aviation press issued the first information about a Soviet jet bomber with variable geometry wing. Source was the Pentagon. The aircraft was reported to have been discovered by espionage satellites and NATO promptly allocated the reporting name 'Backfire'. This information came at the right time: the US senate were planning to vote an astronomic sum of dollars for development of the North American-Rockwell B-1. Whether it was mere chance that the information was issued at such an opportune moment, or whether the affair was cleverly staged we shall not try to determine here.

Soon the new bomber was known in the West as Tupolev Tu-26, but during the Strategic Arms Limitation Talks (SALT) negotiations, Soviets quoted designation Tu-22M, implying that the new bomber was nothing but an improvement of the ageing Tu-22, reporting name 'Blinder', which stems from the 1950s.

We shall not go into the arguments, which kept the Americans and Soviets occupied in the SALT negotiations, about whether the Tu-26 or Tu-22M has a strategic capability or if it is intended for maritime and strike missions only. The fact is that the 'Backfire' is operational with the DA (*Dal'nyaya Aviatsiya* = Long Range Aviation) and with AV-MF (*Aviatsiya Voyenno-Morskoyo Flota* = Air Element of the Navy). Three versions have been identified, the prototype and development batch, called 'Backfire-A' in the West, the further improved 'Backfire-B' version, which seems to be the only production variant so far, and the 'C' model.

Tu-26 (-22M) is powered by two 20,500kg thrust Kuznetsov NK-144 afterburning turbofans, believed to be of the same type as those used in the Tu-144 supersonic airliner. It is armed with two remotely controlled 23mm cannon in a tail barbette for defence, and with one or two stand-off missiles or bombs. Total stores capacity is estimated at 8,000kg. 'Backfire' has been seen with an FR (Flight-Refuelling) probe, but also as many times without it.

The reporting name 'Blackjack' has been allotted to what is believed to be an intercontinental strategic bomber, originally identified as the 'Ram-P'. It is reported to have variable-geometry wings, similar to the Rockwell International B-1 bomber and Tu-26.

No reporting name has been allotted to an experimental bomber derivative of the supersonic Tu-144 airliner, which has been known for some time as 'Ram-H'. Another four-engined compound delta supersonic bomber was developed by the Sukhoi bureau, but not put into production.

Variable geometry Tu-22M (Tu-26) is believed to have the same type of engines that powered Russia's Tu-144 supersonic airliner.

Reconnaissance Aircraft

ONLY A FEW ADDITIONS need to be made to this section. Two reconnaissance versions of the MiG-21 fighter have been identified, both carrying a detachable pod with photographic apparatus beneath the fuselage. General design of these versions is similar to that of the standard MiG-21. they have been identified as MiG-21R, which stems from the -21FMA, and MiG-21RF, developed from the -21MF.

High-altitude reconnaissance is supplied by the MiG-25R 'Foxbat B' with nose-mounted cameras, and 'Foxbat-D' without cameras but with extensive Elint equipment.

Designation 'Ram-M' has been mentioned in the West as being an SR-71 style high-altitude reconnaissance aircraft, featuring a twin-tail unit. There is no further information.

The Yakovlev Yak-28 bomber, described earlier, is now probably mainly used in the recon-

naissance and ECM (Electronic Counter-Measures) roles. Reporting names 'Brewer-D' and 'E' have been allotted to these variants, and the latter is reported to carry active jamming equipment for the support of strike aircraft.

Two ageing aircraft, the Antonov An-12 'Cub' and Ilyushin Il-18 'Coot', are used as electronic intelligence gatherers. The 'Cub-B' variant features a number of ventral bulges, whereas 'Cub-C' is used in the ECM-role having the tail-turret replaced by a rear radome and canoe type aerial fairings beneath the fuselage. Similar canoe fairings have been seen on Il-18s, reporting name 'Coot-A', which are operational with Naval Aviation (AV-MF).

Other older types, the Tupolev Tu-16 'Badger', Tu-20 'Bear', Tu-22 'Blinder' and Myasishchev Mya-4 'Bison', have already been described. They are used for a variety of tasks, including electronic warfare. Reporting names have been adapted accordingly, but will not be repeated here. Bureau designation of the Tu-16 was Tu-88, Tu-20 was Tu-95, with the AV-MF versions apparently being designated Tu-142 and the Tu-22 named Tu-105 by the Tupolev bureau. Versions of the Mya-4 have been reported in FAI record lists as Type 103-M and 201-M. Tu-16 and Mya-4 are also used in the tanker role.

To counter the growing threat of NATO's Polaris and Poseidon armed submarines the Soviets developed Ilyushin Il-38 ASW (Anti-

A pair of MiG-25R 'Foxbat B' high-altitude reconnaissance aircraft with nose-mounted cameras. 'Foxbat D' is the same except that Elint equipment replaces cameras.

Above: Tu-16 'Badger' equipped with Elint for maritime reconnaissance.

Left: Yak-28P, an ageing bomber type now thought to operate mainly in the reconnaissance and ECM roles.

Below: An Elint stocked Tu-20 'Bear' on maritime reconnaissance patrol.

Submarine Warfare) aircraft. It is developed from the Il-18 airliner and carries reporting name 'May'. The main radar is mounted beneath the nose, slightly aft of the cockpit, and a MAD (Magnetic Anomaly Detector) boom is sticking out at the rear end of the fuselage, indicating its ASW capability.

The Il-38, a number of which have been exported to the Indian Navy, is powered by four 5,200shp Ivchenko AI-20M turboprops, variants of which were also used to power the An-8, An-10, An-12, Be-12 and Il-18. Il-38 corresponds roughly to the Lockheed P-3 Orion and gives the Soviet Navy a supplement to the heli-borne ASW-fleet and Be-12 amphibian.

Although not a reconnaissance aircraft, mention must be made in this section of the Soviet AWACS aircraft, the Tupolev-designed Tu-126, reporting name 'Moss'. Tu-126 airframe is based on that of the Tu-114 airliner and, like the Boeing E-3A Sentry, features a large saucer-shaped radome on top of the rear part of the fuselage, just in front of the fin. Tu-126 is used in connection with air-defence fighters, enabling it, through a number of aerials, to guide fighter aircraft to their targets. Both Middle East and Falklands crises have demonstrated the importance of AWACS in modern air fighting.

According to at least one US source a number of Ilyushin Il-76 'Candid' transport aircraft are being modified for the AWACS role, and an improved radar in a so called 'parasol' rotodome has been observed. Reporting name is 'Mainstay'.

 # UPDATE

Another Tu-20 version is this model fitted with missile guidance equipment.

Above: Anti-submarine Il-38 watched by a US Navy A-6E Intruder.

Below: Tu-126 AWACS aircraft is based on the Tu-114 airliner.

AT THE BEGINNING of the thirties, the first five-year plan for the industrialisation of Russia went into action. As it took effect the design and construction of a whole series of special types of aircraft became possible for the first time. Close co-operation between aircraft and army was the theme of numerous works by Soviet military theoreticians and as early as 1924 the scientific-technical committee of the Red Air Force had established the principles for low-level attack.

On the basis of these works it was possible to begin tests in which reconstructed R-1, R-3 and later R-5 aircraft were used. These trials never assumed great importance, for the aircraft had simply not been designed for such demanding service.

In the USSR much money and effort were devoted to the design of ground attack fighters. Nevertheless, one has to admit that this problem remained unsolved in the thirties. Although several prototypes and many test planes were constructed, results were only indirect – in the gathering of precious knowledge and experience. From this, S V Ilyushin was able to develop his Shturmovik Il-2.

The Red Air Force took an interest in three basic categories of ground fighters at the beginning of the thirties: LSh (*Legkii Shturmovik*), TSh (*Tiashelii Shturmovik*) and TShB (*Tiashelii Shturmovik Bronirovanii*). LSh were light models to undertake short surprise attacks against enemy troops. The heavy Shturmovik (TSh) were intended for more prolonged attacks in co-operation with the attacking infantry and cavalry. And the TShB (heavy armoured ground fighters) were to form a sort of flying artillery which would hit targets otherwise unattainable, such as concentrations of enemy strength behind the Front.

The TsKB office was given responsibility for design of the first two types of aircraft while TShB was to be designed by TsAGI.

The technical committee of TsKB commissioned D P Grigorovich to design the proposed model as quickly as possible. To this end Grigorovich used to a large extent ready-made parts of the production reconnaissance biplane R-5. The parts had to be reinforced as greater dead weight and take-off weight of the armoured ground fighters had to be reckoned with. Shturmovik LSh-1 was designed under the industrial name TsKB-5, utilising reinforced wings of the R-5 but a new fuselage with armoured engine and cockpit. M-17 was established as the engine while armament was to consist of four fixed, obliquely slanting machine guns and a moveable twin machine gun.

The design was not carried out as the air force decided in summer 1930 not to use this too light category of ground fighter but devote their engines to the TSh-1.

In the construction of TSh-1 or TsKB-6, the reconstructed wings of R-5 were also used. In the winter of 1930-1, J I Piontkovski and B L Bukhgolts tested three prototypes. The individual machines were distinguishable from one another by the armour plating for crews and engines. On one aircraft the armour plating was welded, on the second rivetted and on the third bolted together. Engine cooling also varied between water and glycol. At the final stage, bolted armour and water cooling were chosen.

Armament was impressive. Under the lower wing were four weapon containers each with two fixed, obliquely slanting, PV-1 7.62mm machine guns. The observer had a twin DA-2 machine gun and there was provision for up to 100kg of bombs.

The air force had taken on TSh-1 as a prototype, but for the production line they demanded more changes. Thus there was to be reinforcement of the lower wings which were to be constructed with duralumin airframe so that the fixed machine guns could be built in. TsKB accordingly altered the aircraft and called it TSh-2 or TsKB-21.

In 1932 ten TSh-2 were constructed. The lower wings were about double thickness where the weapons were incorporated but the new aircraft was more streamlined. This was shown by a speed of 215kph compared to 200kph in the TSh-1. But the design took too long and the ten machines still did not have a high enough performance. In 1933 the TSh-2 were withdrawn.

In this year prototype of the third heavy Shturmovik, TSh-3 or TsKB-24, appeared on the testing ground. Designers Kocherigin and Gurevich tried the low-wing monoplane layout. The wing, with a thick profile, was entirely made of wood and supported to the fuselage by two Vee struts. On the wing, ten fixed ShKAS machine guns were built in and engine was an AM-34F of 750/830mhp. Tanks and cockpit were protected by 5-8mm armour plating and under the wings was provision for up to 500kg bombs. Test flights in 1934 certainly confirmed that performance was quite high but the overall evaluation was negative.

Meanwhile A N Tupolev's group in TsAGI were working on the heavy armoured Shturmovik TShB. Tupolev gave the design his initials

ANT-17. It was to be almost a flying armoured car: an all-metal monoplane with twin AM-34 engines on the wing, one fixed cannon of 75mm calibre plus four fixed machine guns, one moveable twin machine gun and up to 1,500kg of bombs.

From the total weight of 1,000kg of the armour-plating, about 380kg contributed to the airframe structure. Thus they sought to use part of the armour constructively in order to reduce the dead weight. ANT-17 looked very promising but it was not built because the air force now had other ideas. ANT-18, a reconstruction of ANT-7 for the TShB assignment, also remained on paper.

Besides the TSh and TShB, another ground attack aircraft was also designed at that time. In Soviet Turkestan were the rebel Basmachi, well-equipped and organised, who wrought havoc among the population. The Soviet government decided to eliminate this danger. Powerful punitive units were sent to Turkestan with the mission of destroying the Basmachi by any means available. Among the means conceived was the light assault aircraft ShON *(Shturmovik Osobogo Nasnacheniya* or assault aircraft for special purposes).

The aircraft was designed in 1931 in TsKB as TsKB-23, again using parts of R-5. The aircraft was not armoured because it was thought that the small arms of the Basmachi could not harm the aircraft. Engine was an M-17 and there were four fixed and two moveable machine guns. The wings had to be made so that they could be folded back for transport by train. Grigorvich quickly designed and constructed the aircraft, but ShON was not used because the Basmachi were eliminated by ground forces.

So none of the prepared models met the demands of the air force, neither did they contribute to the close-support units planned. A further machine, the prototype TsKB-18 of 1934, was no help either. It was a reconstruction of Polikarpov's I-16 low-level attack fighter.

The aircraft had six fixed machine guns on the wing, provision for two 100kg bombs and the pilot was protected by three sheets of armour plating. The aircraft had a speed of 350kph and was therefore fastest of all assault aircraft designed up to this time. On the other hand, its armour did not protect the engine or fuel tanks and additional protection was restricted by the load capacity. Moreover the aircraft was very unstable around the longitudinal axis and so made a bad basis for shooting at ground targets.

In 1936 designers Kocherigin and Ickovich tried to develop a combat variant from their reconnaissance aircraft R-9. The R-9 was a mid-wing monoplane with M-85 engine, fixed undercarriage, and a flying weight of 2,730kg. As a ground attack fighter, armoured and with five machine guns instead of the three weapons of R-9, the aircraft weighed 3,450kg and was now called Sh or LBSh *(Legkii Bombardirovshchik-Shturmovik* = light bomber and ground fighter). Speed was 439kph at 5,200m, but flying qualities

were not pleasant at low-level owing to the excessive weight. Sh and LBSh were also rejected.

A unique Shturmovik by P D Grushin of the Moscow Aviation Institute suffered the same fate. This was the Sh-Tandem, an aircraft with two tandem wings, the back wing possessing 45 per cent of the lifting surface of the front wing. The machine had a 930mhp M-85 engine, retractable undercarriage and two lateral surfaces on both sides of the fuselage. Armament consisted of four fixed ShKAS machine guns and a fifth moveable weapon in a turret on the end of the fuselage. Bomb load was 200kg.

Test flying began on October 5, 1937, under P M Stefanovskii and lasted until 1939. The aircraft had its difficulties; for example, the directional stability was initially poor because the fixed vertical fin area was inadequate. But its qualities in general were good, and after a little refinement the TSh Tandem could have become a good combat aircraft. Also, the all-wood construction was useful for the period. But the air force found it too complicated, unreliable and did not take it on.

Soviet designers found help abroad in many instances when they were not capable of solving a problem themselves. In 1936 a Soviet technical expedition under Tupolev stayed in the USA. Among models bought by the expedition, together with the construction rights, was a light bomber

especially efficient for its time, the Vultee V-11GB. It was a low-wing monoplane with Wright Cyclone SR-1820-G2 engine of 750mhp, retractable undercarriage, four fixed and one moveable machine gun and a bomb load of 250kg. Between 1937 and 1938 thirty-six aircraft of this type were built in the USSR with only slightly altered airframe and provision for the Soviet M-62IR engine.

Designation of this machine was BSh-1 *(Bronirovanii Shturmovik =* armoured ground attack fighter), being given more armour and weapons than the American model. Consequently the weight increased. Maximum speed at low level was only 318kph rising to 339kph at 1,800m. The air force thought that BSh-1's performance was insufficient and machines already built were given to the civilian air traffic company Aeroflot for use as mail planes.

In the first round the Red Air Force acquired none of its desired ground attack fighters. Reconstructed two-seat DI-6 fighter biplanes were used in emergency in the second half of the thirties for low-level attack training missions. The variants were called DI-6Sh and their serial production lasted from 1936 to 1939. Engines were the same 630/700mhp M-25s as used in the fighter aircraft, but armour plating and two additional machine guns increased the empty weight from 1,360 to 1,434kg and take-off weight from 1,955 to 2,115kg. Performance was weak but there was nothing better available!

Below: ShON (TsKB-23) produced to fight rebel Basmachi tribesmen.

Bottom: Armament on the TsKB-6 was impressive, comprising a total of eight 7.62mm machine guns.

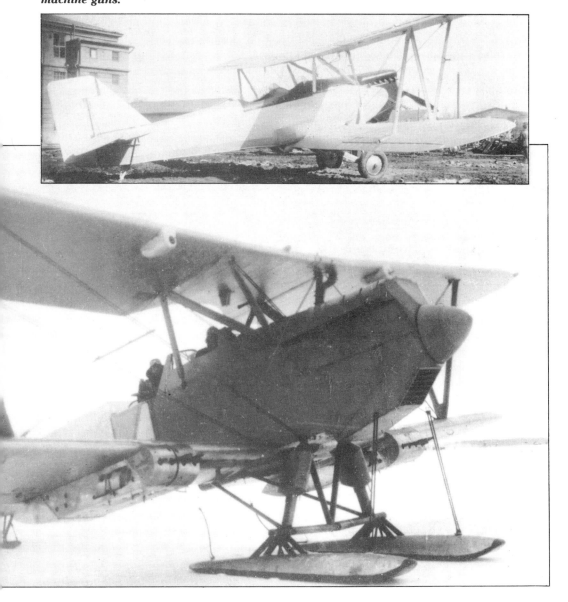

ONE OF THE arguments brought against all ground attack aircraft was their almost total ineffectiveness against armoured units. Against armoured cars, these aircraft could only fight with bombs, and since they were not designed for vertical dives, they were by no means guaranteed direct hits.

In a final effort to combat armour the Air Force commissioned Polikarpov's group to design an appropriate aircraft in May 1935. The new models were to be designed for use against tanks, armoured trains, fortifications and other small but important targets. These targets were to be destroyed either by concentrated artillery fire from the aircraft or by bombs released on vertical dives.

Polikarpov's brief was to design a model which, with only a few alterations and with the same airframe, could fulfil both tasks. Military designation of the aircraft for the first type of mission was VIT (*Vosdushnii Istrebitel Tankov* = aerial tank fighter) and for the second SVB (*Samolet Vosdushnogo Boya* = aircraft for aerial combat).

First to appear was the TsKB-44 which could be used for both purposes. It was a three-seat, all-metal, low wing monoplane with retractable undercarriage and two M-103 engines of 950mhp. The variant VIT-1 carried four 37mm ShK anti-tank defence cannon in the central part of the wing near the fuselage while in the glazed nose was a moveable ShVAK cannon operated by the observer. The radio operator, behind the pilot, could shoot with a ShKAS machine gun and in the fuselage was a bay with provision for 600kg of bombs.

Variant SVB-1 for tactical bomb attacks on vertical dives, had no anti-tank cannon but a further 600kg of bombs could be stored under the wings. Disc-like dive brakes were built in on either side of the fuselage between wings and controls, opening hydraulically in the opposite direction to flight.

Polikarpov went even further than expected. He built yet a third variant, a heavy fighter, MPI-1 (*Mnogomestnii Pushechnii Istrebitel* = multi-seat artillery fighter) which was armed with two 37mm and three 20mm cannon. All three prototypes were built in 1937 and tested by summer 1938.

Flying qualities and performance were particularly good, maximum speed reaching 450kph. But for those times, when aircraft had to operate from relatively small bases, the take-off and landing runs were too long.

In 1938 more highly-powered engines were coming into operation, including the first specimens of the 1,050mhp M-105. Polikarpov was able to use these engines for the new VIT-2 (TsKB-48) test flown in May, 1938, under V P Chkalov. The new aircraft was streamlined and even better adapted to sorties than VIT-1. The fuselage had a longer fully glazed cockpit, twin rudder and new controllable-pitch VISh propellers. VIT-2 was one of the first aircraft which could be examined in TsAGI's new, big wind-tunnel in its finished life-size form.

Armament was, among the heaviest for aircraft of this weight class. The four ShK 37mm cannon were kept as well as the nose ShVAK. Rear machine gun was replaced by a moveable ShVAK and transferred to the ventral position. VIT-2's performance was good. At low altitude the aircraft attained 486kph and at 4,500m as much as 513kph. Higher vertical dive speeds produced vibrations in the controls, but these were easily eliminated by strengthening the back fuselage dive-brakes.

The Red Air Force ordered five VIT-2 and tested them thoroughly. Why these aircraft, so much ahead of their time, were not then released for production remains a mystery. Stefanovski's assessment was favourable, performance high and the armament incomparable. It is likely that rocket missiles RS-82 and RS-132, successfully developed in the meantime and also designed for aiming at armoured targets, spelt the death sentence of VIT-2 because it was realised that simpler aircraft could be used.

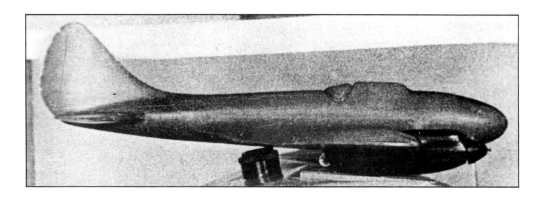

Above: Model of an early specialised tank fighter, VIT-1. Below: SPB(D), a variant of the VIT-2, undergoing tests in TsAGI's large wind tunnel. Bottom: Polikarpov's VIT-2. Five machines were favourably tested but no production run was ordered.

CHAPTER 27

World War 2 Ground Attack Aircraft

THE ARMOURED Il-2 ground fighter by S V Ilyushin became a real symbol of Red Air Force fighting efficiency during the war. And the name 'Shturmovik' became a household word in the history of aerial combat throughout the world.

The route to such a successful aircraft was not short nor simple. We have already seen how much effort was expended in the vain attempt to create a good ground attack fighter. The attempts remained unsuccessful although designers were often quite near to their goal.

In the tense days of Autumn 1938, Air Force commanders were working on a new conception of aerial combat which was mainly influenced by findings from the Spanish Civil War. The aerial war in Spain revealed some weak points in equipment and as a result there was a greater effort to design new aircraft of all sorts in the years 1938-40. Among the military aircraft commissioned an important place was accorded to ground fighters. The BSh model was especially favoured, developed from the American Vultee V-11GB.

In Autumn 1938, Ilyushin's team was commissioned to design a BSh type ground fighter. Shortly afterwards, at the beginning of 1940, Sukhoi's group received the same order as security in case of failure by Ilyushin. It was not an easy task for either designer. The aircraft were to operate at under 500m, within the range of infantry fire, which meant effective armour plating for the vital parts. Armour could not increase the empty weight too much since there had to be ample room for weapons, ammunition, bombs and fuel.

Ilyushin and Sukhoi solved this problem simply by making the sheet steel armour plating, varying in thickness between 4-7mm, into a fuselage shell extending from the airscrew-spinner to behind the cockpit. Though this armour weighed 700kg it was no dead weight as it constituted a structural part of the fuselage.

In Spring 1939, the first prototype TsKB-55 was ready. Rather than a prototype it was a life-size showpiece which was to help solve the problems of armour-plating, construction, seating and vision for the aircrew. Only the second prototype was built for test flight, taken up on December 30 1939, by V K Kokkinaki.

The prototype was designated as ground fighter BSh-2. It was a cantilever, low-wing monoplane of mixed construction. Front fuselage was the armour-plated shell, the back section was made of plywood, wings and tail surfaces were built in duralumin. Engine was the 1,350mhp twelve-cylinder AM-35. The pilot could fire four ShKAS fixed machine guns in the wings and machine gunner or radioman operated a moveable weapon. Bomb bays in the central part of the wing between fuselage and undercarriage nacelles could carry up to 500kg.

The state commission which was to take over BSh-2 in April 1940 made a series of criticisms. Engine performance was too low; take-off weight of 4,735kg left no reserve; take-off run was too long; the climb rate too slow; armament was not considered to be very effective, and longitudinal instability made it difficult to shoot at targets. First step of the Shturmovik was therefore unsuccessful.

On October 12, 1940, Kokkinaki was able to take off with the new prototype TsKB-57, reconstructed in accordance with the findings. This time, the new 1,600mhp twelve-cylinder AM-38 was installed. Its rated height sank from 4,500 to 3,000m and armament dropped to two fixed 20mm ShVAK cannon and two 7.62mm ShKAS machine guns. Armoured wall behind the pilot was now 7mm thick instead of the previous 4mm, and last but not least, new tail surfaces gave good longitudinal stability. But the state commission was still against a range of only 576km.

In the end, they had to look for a compromise. As the load capacity of the aircraft was exhausted, the Air Force had to give up plans for active self-defence in the BSh-2. The second crew member and his armament were eliminated

One of Ilyushin's experiments with the Il-2 was to fit an ASh-82FN radial engine as a safeguard against any delivery problems with the regular AM-38F.

Above: The first production Il-2s had no rear protection, the assumption being that they would always operate under fighter cover.

Below: Birth of the Shturmovik: BSh-2 was the first flying prototype, beginning its tests on December 30, 1939. It was reconstructed to form the TsKB-57 prototype.

Overshadowed by the Il-2 range were Sukhoi's Su-6-1 or SA (above) and S-2A (below). Performances were good but they suffered from temperamental engines, first the ASh-71 and then the fuel injected ASh-71F.

Left: Il-2M appeared in 1942, answering criticisms about the Il-2's lack of defensive armament and ineffectiveness against new German tanks.

and the weight used for increasing fuel supply from 315 to 470 litres. The fuel tanks had an interesting novelty – cooled gas from the exhaust was transported over the fuel, lessening the danger of fire in the case of a hit for the gas was now incombustible.

Thus the Shturmovik was born. It had a speed of 450kph at low altitude and 470kph at 2,500m. There was provision for 400kg of bombs and eight RS-82 or four RS-132 rocket missiles under the wings. An unprotected rear was accepted on condition that the Shturmoviks should always operate under effective cover from fighters. That this was an unrealistic policy was shown in the first months of the war.

TsKB-57's state tests were successfully concluded in March 1941, and the aircraft was put into production. In accordance with the new style of designation, using designers' names, the aircraft was called Il-2. Up to June 1941, 249 were produced, of which the greater part were used only in training units. A small combat unit of Il-2s flew in the first days of the war, showing effective resistance against ground fire, good take-off and landing qualities even on bad operational bases, and strong fire power.

The only fault was that there were too few of such aircraft, a situation which got even more difficult in the second half of 1941 and in winter. Evacuation of plants to the east delayed production, yet it was only two months on average before production began again in new, mostly improvised, factories. That was an achievement unparalleled in aeronautical history.

How vital the Il-2 was for the Front was underlined by Stalin in his teleprint to factory workers in December 1941: "The Red Army needs the Il-2, like air, like bread..." In the second half of 1941, 1,293 were produced, but that was still too few.

Sukhoi and his men began design of the BSh

type in 1940, by which time Ilyushin's BSh-2 had already taken shape. Sukhoi had, from the beginning, chosen to construct a single-seater with heavy armament. His machine, the Su-6-1 or SA, was a robust low-wing monoplane with completely retractable undercarriage. In the wings were two long 23mm cannon and four ShKAS machine guns. Sukhoi chose as his engine the new two-row radial, eighteen cylinder ASh-71 of 2,000mhp, development of which was supposed to be completed.

The airframe of Su-6-1 was certainly good; unfortunately the same could not be said for the engine. ASh-71 was a source of endless difficulties. Test flights had to be postponed again and again and it was January 1942 before they could begin. The Su-6-1 had a better performance than the Il-2, reaching 478kph at low altitude and 527kph at 2,500m. Armament was heavier and there was provision for up to ten rocket missiles and 400kg of bombs.

In spite of this, Su-6-1 was not granted production because the engine was unreliable. Moreover, Il-2 was already being mass produced and during the war no less than 36,163 specimens of the Il-2 range were produced. A genuine record!

With the large number of Il-2 in operation much experience could be gathered and imperfections revealed. At the beginning of 1942, a conference was held in Moscow involving Il-2 combat pilots, designer Ilyushin, and commanders-in-chief of the Air Force. The pilots certainly praised their Shturmoviks but also enumerated the faults which they had to contend with.

Lack of defence to the rear was condemned as a basic error; Soviet fighter units were very weak in 1941-2 and could not protect ground attack aircraft in action. In the beginning German fighters treated the Il-2 with respect for they believed them to be invulnerable. But they soon realised that the "flying tanks" were easily assailable from behind and exploited the fact successfully. A further complaint was made about the armament, as ShVAK cannon were ineffective against new German tanks.

The state defence committee took quick and effective steps to improve the situation. Ilyushin, Sukhoi and the group under A I Mikoyan and M I Gurevich were requested to design new machines without these faults.

Ilyushin's position was certainly the surest and it was clear that a modified Il-2 would be kept on the production line. The new variant was called Il-2M. It passed state tests in July 1942 and soon afterwards the first aircraft went into action. They were used in quite large numbers in January and February 1943 in the battles round Stalingrad.

Defence to the rear was provided by a gunner who sat behind the pilot and operated a 12.7mm UBT machine gun. His position was not particularly secure as usually there was little or no armour plating for him. Weight of the gunner and armament had to be initially compensated for by removal of the two wing machine guns.

Cannon in the Il-2M were no longer ShVAK but the new VYa of 23mm calibre which had been designed by Volkov and Yartsev. These weapons distinguished themselves by higher muzzle velocity and greater penetrating power. From May 1943 onwards, new Il-2 type 3M also got the new automatic 37mm Il-P-37 cannon of Nudelman and Suranov. These proved to be especially effective when used in July 1943 in the battles at Kursk.

Take-off weight rose from 5,340 to 5,873kg which demanded a more powerful engine. A A Mikulin reconstructed his AM-38 as the AM-38F which attained a take-off performance of 1,750mhp and was only intended for Shturmovik aircraft. Compression was reduced from 6.8:1 to 6:1 so that car petrol could be used and nominal height was reduced to 7.5m. The AM-38F made it possible once again to build ShKAS machine guns into the wings.

Ilyushin also realised a series of improvements in streamlining which had been recommended to him by TsAGI, especially refinements to cooling intakes, to the passage between wing and fuselage, etc. Thus the maximum speed could be raised by 35kph when the machine gun cowling was closed, though when the cowling was opened for firing speed diminished again.

So the Shturmovik Il-2M and 3M became an aircraft beloved by its crew, feared by opponents. It caused heavy damage to German tanks. According to the Soviets, Model 3s destroyed seventy tanks in twenty minutes in a concentrated attack at Kursk. Only thirty of an original three hundred tanks of the 3rd German Armoured Division were left after the battle.

From the Summer of 1943 onwards, Il-2 also used small 2.5kg bombs with hollow charge against tanks, railway traffic and concentrations of weapons. They were called PTAB and in a DAG-10 container was provision for 200 such bombs which were 'sown' from the air. Il-2 also proved their worth in naval aviation units, especially against torpedo boats.

Production was stepped up and up, and the committee for state defence put every means at the disposal of factories. Of 35,000 military aircraft constructed in 1943 the Il-2 constituted about 25% and during the heaviest fighting of 1943, 1,000 machines were delivered a month. Production was well prepared, technologically speaking, and there were even reserves. For example, in 1943, only 37.9% of the time needed in 1942 was required for the production of an Il-2. Also, small improvements and economies were very successful. In plant No.18 four extra aircraft monthly could be produced owing to a 1% saving

Above: One of three aircraft designed to replace Il-2M and 3M, Ilyushin's Il-8 was quick but proved difficult to fly and was certainly not precise enough at low level.

Right: Eliminated along with Il-8 was Sukhoi's Su-6 with Mikulin's new twelve cylinder AM-42 engine.

of duralumin plating.

Ilyushin also made a few experiments in the period 1942-43 with the Il-2M trying the two-row radial ASh-82FN engine of 1,523/1,850mhp as a safeguard against difficulties with AM-38F. The Shturmovik with ASh-82FN certainly flew very well but as no problems arose in the production of AM-38F, there was no reason why radial engines should be used in any greater number.

The competing models by Sukhoi and Mikoyan-Gurevich were overshadowed by the success of Il-2M and 3M. A few prototypes of Sukhoi's S-2A or Su-6-11 were built in the Winter of 1942-3. He changed his machine as Ilyushin had done, building a longer cabin with room for rear gunner and UBT machine gun. The long barrels of two anti-tank 11-P-37 cannon in the wings gave the aircraft a particularly militant look.

Sukhoi acquired a new engine, the Shvetsov ASh-71F with fuel injection and 2,200mhp take-off performance. With this, speed at low altitude rose to 480kph and to 514kph at 2,500m, higher performances than those of Il-2M and 3M. But the Su-6-11 was not used; firstly the authorities did not want to interrupt serial production of Il-2 and secondly the ASh-71F were still very temperamental and very far removed from production.

Mikoyan and Gurevich proposed a Shturmovik of the TSh or MiG-6 model, according to technical requirements, but it remained at design stage. The position of Il-2M and 3M remained unshaken.

In 1943 the State Defence Committee decided to create new, more modern ground attack aircraft for the final stage of the war with enough de-velopment potential to continue in operation afterwards. Technical and tactical conditions for design of the new Shturmovik were to be handed over once again to groups of designers under Ilyushin and Sukhoi and both were to deliver prototypes for comparative flights.

For the third time, Sukhoi had an opportunity to prevail with his Su-6. His new Su-6III corresponded to the Su-6-II but had Mikulin's new in-line engine, the 2,000mhp, twelve-cylinder AM-42. In summer 1944, comparative flights of Su-6-III and two Ilyushin models, the Il-8 and Il-10, took place. Again the Su-6-III had to withdraw.

Ilyushin's Il-8 was designed along the lines of Il-2. The engine was an AM-42, the undercarriage was no longer retracted into the nacelles but directly into the wings, and there were several improvements in streamlining. It was described as a heavy assault plane. Armament comprised two 23mm VYa fixed cannon, two ShKAS machine guns and a moveable UBT for the machine gunner. Bomb load was 1,000kg and the range up to 1,140km. Maximum speed at low altitude was a very high 509kph but flying of the aircraft was very troublesome and it was not capable of precise manoeuvring at low altitude.

The Il-8 brought no success to Ilyushin's drawing office but the Il-10 did. This was a steamlined, aesthetic aircraft that was also, technologically speaking, very well balanced for fighting purposes. With an AM-42 engine, the Il-10 was superior to Su-6-II in low-level flights, could achieve 500kph against 485, and had better handling qualities. In Autumn 1944, the first production Il-10 left the plants for training units and from March 1945 till the end of the war about 100

were used in combat units. They were in operation over the Reich but could not be used more extensively. So it can be said that the Il-2M and 3M were the aircraft which helped to win the war.

Proportions of Il-10 were better. For example, the openings for cool air in the roots of the wings were improved, the cockpit was made shorter and completely closed. In the first models two VYa cannon, two ShKAS machine guns and a UBT machine gun were once again built in. In 1951 Il-10M could be found with first two and then as many as four NS-23 cannon of 23mm calibre. These displayed a greater penetrating power than the VYa. In the turret a 20mm UB-20 cannon was built in while there was provision for 400-600kg of bombs and up to eight rocket missiles.

Il-10M were withdrawn from service in 1956. Some used a small rocket engine for assisted take-off on short airstrips.

In all 14,966 Il-10 were produced in the USSR. Approximately half that number were constructed in Czechoslovakia at the Avia plants in Let-

Below: An Il-10M with rocket motor in the tail for assisted take-off at small airfields.

Il-16 represented the peak of Ilyushin's Shturmovik activity but production ceased early as hostilities came to an end.

nany, near Prague, after the war under designation Avia B-33. Training variants of the two most widely used Ilyushin Shturmoviks were also constructed. These had dual controls and differed by the addition UT (*Uchebnii Trenirovochnii* = training aircraft) so they were Il-2UT and Il-10UT.

Il-10 made its last battle flights in Korea. Some were captured and tested by the USA.

Ilyushin's activity in the sphere of ground attack fighters reached its height in 1944-45 with the Il-16. It was a lighter variant of Il-10 without a turret but having a hand-held mount for the UBT machine gun. The first prototype and some specimens received Mikulin's new 2,200 mhp AM-43 engine, which suffered from heavy vibrations of the crankshaft owing to a false equilibrium, and was soon replaced by the good old AM-42.

When test flying the prototype in August 1945, an even more serious fault came to light. Owing to an error in design, the centre of gravity only amounted to 15% of the mid chord. By lengthening the rear of the fuselage, they managed to push this figure up to 22% and subsequent flights were without difficulties. Series production commenced but as the war in Japan came to an end the Il-16 was dropped after completion of the 53rd aircraft.

The Il-2 and Il-10 overshadowed one small but especially effective fighter – Polikarpov's well-known U-2 biplane. Successful bomb attacks by this aircraft led, in 1941, to development of a close-support fighter variant, LSh (*Legkii Shturmovik*) or U-2VOM-1. These machines were reconstructed, provisionally, in repair plants for the Front. They were armed with four RS-82 rocket missiles, 120kg of bombs and the observer could shoot with a moveable ShKAS. From 1942 until the war ended, the LSh proved successful against trenches, shooting through trees at camouflaged positions and, in fact, everywhere that heavy aircraft could not attack. The M-11D engine had reached its limit of performance, for the LSh with its 1,400kg flying weight, was one of the heaviest U-2 variants.

Successes of the light fighter-bomber variant of U-2 led D M Tomasevich's group of designers to construct a light but heavily armed fighter-bomber 'Pegas'. It was a simple low-wing monoplane of all-wood construction but the one-seat cockpit had armoured walls. In the nose were two fixed 23mm VYa cannon and a UBK machine gun. For surprise bomb attacks the 'Pegas' was to carry up to 500kg of explosives but in this version the cannon were removed. Engines were twin 140mhp M.11F with wooden propellers, taken over from the U-2 and maximum speed was 172kph.

V F Bolotinikov and P M Stefanovskii tested the 'Pegas' in February 1943. Flying qualities were in

Effective against many awkward targets was Polikarpov's close-support fighter variant of the U-2, the LSh or U-2VOM-1.

Above: Heavyweight Shturmovik Su-8 had massive offensive and defensive capability but came too late for series production.

An all-wood fighter-bomber was offered by the Tomasevich design group. 'Pegas' in its original form (below) was first tested in February 1943 and subsequently flew with a modified, shortened nose (left). The aircraft was underpowered and did not progress further.

general good, but the aircraft was not recommended for series production as its engines were too loaded. Stronger engines could perhaps have helped, had they been available.

In contrast was the particularly heavy Shturmovik Su-8 designed by Sukhoi. This machine was tested in 1944 but its history goes back to 1943. At that time the State Defence Committee demanded design of a heavy armoured fighter with great range, under the designation DDBSh (*Dvukhmotornii Dalnii Bronirovanii Shturmovik* = twin-engined armoured long-distance fighter-bomber).

The new aircraft was to unite two qualities: especially high efficiency against heavily armoured targets and great range. The short endurance of all Il-2 models began to cause difficulties in the second half of the war. In quick attacks, the Soviet tank corps often went beyond the range of ground attack fighters, whose operational bases were often far behind the Front and could not be transferred easily.

The Su-8 was an isolated design, a slim low-wing monoplane with twin 2,200mhp ASh-71F engines and all-metal construction. The fuselage from nose to wing trailing edge and engine casings were armoured, making up 1,680kg of the whole empty weight of 9,180kg. The crew consisted of two, second man being observer, radioman and machine gunner. He also saw to loading of the four 45mm anti-tank cannon which were built into a bathtub gunner's pit. For every weapon, fifty shells were taken. In the wings, outside the propellers' range, were four ShKAS fixed machine guns. And for rear defence were two moveable machine guns, a UBT of 12.7mm and underneath a ShKAS. All machine guns together had 5,900 rounds at their disposal and the whole supply of ammunition weighed 652kg.

This flying arsenal was, surprisingly enough, especially easy to fly and manoeuvre. Maximum speed at low altitude was 485kph and the 1,100km range about twice that of Il-2-Model-3. But Su-8 was never introduced to combat units. By the Winter of 1944-1945 the State Defence Committee had concluded that the war could be won with existing means and the aircraft had come too late for series production.

CHAPTER 28

Post-War Ground Attack Aircraft

THE DISTINGUISHED role played by ground attack aircraft in the war was naturally continued in the post-war period. Experience gathered from the use of these machines was carefully evaluated and theoretical preparations made as it was clear that the close co-operation of combat pilots with the Army would play a significant part in the future conduct of war. The Il-10 had enough performance reserve for several years, but it was necessary to look even further and to design new models.

Who else should design the new ground attackers but S V Ilyushin? In 1948 his new model Il-20 made its appearance. The test pilots called it 'Gorbach' (Hunchback). Everything was unusual about this aircraft and there was nothing to remind one of the slender lines of Il-10. The pilot sat in an armoured cockpit above the 3,000mhp MF-47 engine enjoying something which he missed in the older Ilyushin models – an excellent vision frontwards which is particularly important when searching for targets in undulating country. The second crew member sat behind, facing backwards, and operated twin NA-23 23mm cannon in a remote-controlled turret. Offensive armament consisted of four NS-23 cannon in the wings, 1,000kg of bombs and eight rocket missiles.

The 'Gorbach' was certainly an unusual aircraft, but its performance was not high enough to qualify for production. Maximum speed at low altitude was 515kph and range 1,680km.

A contemporary to the Il-20 was the designed but never built I-218 projected by the design bureau of S M Alexeyev in 1948. It was a twin-boom pusher with a large armoured pilot cabin and powered by the Dobrynin VD-251 piston engine of 2,000mhp. Behind the front cabin there was an extremely powerful battery of four NR-23, twin N-37 or twin N-57 cannon firing downwards under 25 degrees depression. The second crew member aimed remotely controlled cannon in two side barbettes on the booms.

Ilyushin also tried with his ground fighters to break into the class of jets at a time when there was a general feeling that jet aircraft were not suitable for such missions. In 1953 he constructed the Il-40, last member of the historic Shturmoviks. It was a two-seater with swept back wings and tailplane. The crew and engines were again surrounded by armour plating and cockpit was positioned between twin 2,700kp thrust AM-5F jet engines sharing a common air intake in the nose. The gunner could fire twin remote-controlled NS-23 tail cannon and in the relatively thick wings were four 37mm cannon. A fuselage bay housed 1,500kg of bombs and under the wings was space for rocket missiles or further bombs. In test flights a maximum speed of 964kph was measured and range was 1,000km.

Prototypes of Il-40 were carefully compared with MiG-15 jet fighters. They wanted to establish if it were worthwhile serially producing an aircraft with only one use or whether the MiG-15 was as suitable for ground fighting as aerial combat. The second prognosis was fulfilled. MiG-15 emerged clearly as a victor from comparative flights and the Il-40 was rejected because of its limited possibilities of use.

With the Il-40 Ilyushin's activity in this sphere came to an end. But the aircraft retained a place in aviation history as the only armoured jet assault aeroplane in the world until the American Fairchild A-9 appeared.

Even the Mikoyan design bureau tried to develop a Shturmovik version of its famous jet fighters. In 1953 the MiG-17SN appeared, powered by one VK-1 jet engine. The whole front part of the fuselage was redesigned in order to gain space for coupled twin NR-23 cannon that could fire in the range between 40 degrees elevation and 40 degrees depression. The cannon were in the nose and the air intakes moved aft to the sides of the fuselage. MiG-17SN was tested but not used.

The last known Soviet attack aircraft was the Tupolev Tu-91 Bychok of 1956.

Last of the Shturmoviks – Ilyushin's Il-40, shown here in model form, bowed out when it was shown that MiG-15s could perform both fighter and ground attack roles.

Above: Despite the fate of the Il-40, Mikoyan and Gurevich attempted a Shturmovik with MiG-17SN featuring a completely redesigned nose to accommodate twin moveable cannon.

Below: Known as the 'Hunchback', Ilyushin's unusual Il-20 could delivery 1,000kg of bombs and eight rockets plus a barrage from four wing-mounted cannon.

CHAPTER 29

Military Training Aircraft

TRAINING activities are always overshadowed and yet are of vital importance in the fields of both civilian and military aviation.

When it came to reconstruction of the Red Air Force after the Revolution, training of new pilots and crews was one of the main preoccupations. Only a few pilots – officers and non-commissioned officers – remained from the days of the Tzar. New ones were selected, in particular from ground staff, mechanics, motor vehicle drivers etc.

In the basic trainer units there were many different aircraft, including the two-seat Farman biplane, Russian aircraft, Khioni, Porokhov-shchikov-IV etc, which complicated training and the pilot's work in combat units. There was no suitable Soviet design of a basic trainer and therefore help had to be sought abroad. In 1919 Red Units shot down an Avro 504 of the White Army near Petrosavodsk. The machine was only slightly damaged and it was immediately brought to Moscow. Here tests established that it could make a good basic trainer.

In the Dux plant in Moscow the Avro 504 was copied and a reconstruction prepared. From 1922 onwards, the aircraft was in production under designation U-1 (*Uchebnii* = basic trainer) with a 120mhp Gnome rotary engine that was also produced under licence and introduced as the M-2. A total of 737 U-1 were built.

The Avro 504 was certainly one of the best basic trainers of the First World War and remained so during the early post-war period. It proved its worth within and outside the Soviet Union. But it was a 1914 design and during the twenties its value diminished very rapidly. Moreover, the rotary engine vested this machine with special characteristics which the pilots did not find on other models; conversion to aircraft with fixed engines was then difficult.

In 1926 N N Polikarpov started to design a new standard aircraft for the aviation schools which was easy to fly, stable and reliable. The engine already existed – it was the 100mhp five-cylinder radial M-11, one of the best and most used engines of the USSR. Polikarpov had to bear in mind the very ambitious requirements of the Scientific-Technical Institute of the Red Air Force which demanded really simple production technology with maximum interchangeability of parts.

Polikarpov built the first U-2 with straight wings and 14% wing profile. The upper and lower wings were interchangeable, so too were the elevators and rudders. Technologically the machine was certainly well thought out, but it flew very badly because it was too heavy and not sufficiently streamlined.

After this failure, Polikarpov redesigned the U-2 from scratch, using his own ideas. The new machine had rounded wing tips and the lower wing was a little smaller than the upper. The two-seat basic trainer version with dual control had a take-off weight of 890kg, reached 156kph, 4,000m ceiling and had a range of 400km. Landing speed was 65kph, requiring a 100m run, whereas take-off distance was only 65m. The U-2 was a very stable machine – perhaps too stable for basic training purposes – it had no tendency to spin, and had surprising load capacity. Because of these qualities, U-2 was soon introduced to other tasks besides basic training.

M M Gromov test flew the prototype on January 7, 1928, and the first production machines were delivered in 1930, continuing until 1953. During this time some 33,000 'planes were produced, a record number in international aviation. Up to the outbreak of war, 13,500 U-2 were built, not all, by any means, basic trainers. All sorts of very diverse variants of U-2 appeared and during

Above: Polikarpov's U-2, or Po-2, in Yugoslavian colours.
Below: U-2 under test fitted experimentally with a GAZ-Avia car engine.
Bottom: One of 737 U-1 copies of the Avro 504 basic trainer.

Mikhelson's U-3 was an unsuccessful rival to the mass-produced U-2.

the course of their history performed almost every task open to aircraft apart from fighter operations. In agricultural aviation, the U-2 was given the name by which it became known world-wide – 'Kurkurusnik'.

The two-seat basic trainer version was not modified until 1941 when variant U-2UT was given the 115mhp M-11D engine. In 1941 new designations using the first few letters of the designer's name had yet to be introduced, but in 1944, after Polikarpov's death, the U-2 was renamed Po-2. The engine was improved in 1946 and became M-11K, still producing the same power.

The USSR tried to export the Po-2 in 1948, showing it at fairs in Budapest, Poznan and Prague. But the aircraft already seemed very antiquated. Polikarpov's U-2 was very widely used in military and civilian aviation units of the USSR but in the later thirties more and more critical voices were raised. Particularly it was protested that the U-2 were not fit for aerobatic flying.

A few 'Anti-U-2' models were constructed without much success. For example, designer N G Mikhelson built the U-3 biplane in 1935 with a 200mhp M-48 engine. But the qualities were no better and so the U-3 never became a substitute. In 1936 the U-4, a smaller version of the U-2, was built and abandoned.

More encouraging was V V Nikitin's smaller two-seat basic training biplane U-5 of 1939. It originally had a 100mhp M-11 but after being test flown for a few months was given a 165mhp M-11F and called U-5bis. The Red Air Force took an interest and demanded series production but the commissariat of the Aviation Industry promoted the production of Yakovlev's UT-2 monoplanes (Yakovlev was deputy to the commissioner). In 1942 Nikitin rebuilt one of the prototypes as a staff plane, U-5-MG-31, with military designation LSh (*Legkii Shtabnii* = light staff plane). LSh, with its enclosed three-seat cockpit and MG-31F seven-cylinder engine of 330mhp reached 272kph as compared to 200kph of the U-5bis. However, it remained the only one.

In the mid-thirties, I-16 single-seat fighters were being serially produced on a large scale. This served to highlight what was already apparent – fighter pilots needed a good machine to prepare them for the unstable I-16 after training on the too stable U-2. Fighter biplanes were some help at this transitional stage, but their flying qualities were diametrically opposed to those of the I-16.

Yakovlev had designed a trainer in 1934 with two tandem seats under a canopy. The machine was a low-wing monoplane in composite construction with fixed, well-faired undercarriage and an M-11 cowled with a Townend ring. It was designated AIR-9. In a short time the AIR-9 was joined by another version, the AIR-9bis, only difference being a backwards sloping windscreen whereas the AIR-9's sloped forward.

Both 'Niners' had the same engine as U-2, but what a difference in performance! Maximum speed was 215kph compared with U-2's 156, ceiling was 6,500m and the range 750km. The sport aviation organization 'Osoaviakhim' favoured the AIR-9 and -9bis rather than two other sport and training low-wing monoplanes built at the same time and with the same engine – the G-20 of V K Gribovskii and K-10 of K A Kalinin. Yakovlev's machines were declared victorious in the design

Staff version of the U-5 with enclosed three-seat cockpit.

competition and also won some sport events in the USSR.

Yakovlev modified the Air-9bis in 1936 for series production, in particular removing the cockpit roofing for fliers at that time preferred open seats. This alteration, to make model AIR-10, reduced speed to 200kph. In order to increase speed again, Yakovlev used the 150mhp M-11E engine on the AIR-20 variant in 1937, this time without a Townend ring. AIR-20 reached 230kph, ceiling was 6,500m and the normal range 450km. AIR-20 was a production model and by 1938 the machine was in training units under the designation UT-2 (*Uchebnii Trenirovochnii* = aircraft for basic and other training).

In the course of 1938, the more powerful M-11E engines were replaced by the standard M-11 and speed of the production UT-2 fell to 205kph. As the fuel tanks were a little bigger, the range was extended to 500km. From 1938 to 1946 7,243 examples were produced with hardly a modification. In 1943 a smaller number of UT-2MV were built. The UT-2MV was a more modern variant with enclosed cabin, faired undercarriage and individual cowl-like fairings of the cylinger heads. This may be regarded as a forerunner of the post-war Yak-18.

With the exception of the MV variant, all UT-2 were very simple in construction, serving either as basic trainers or intermediate training aircraft for apprentice pilots who had received their basic tuition on U-2 biplanes.

After the UT-2, future fighter pilots graduated to aerobatic training on the single-seat UT-1. This was also designed in Yakovlev's bureau and its prototype, AIR-14, was test flown in 1936. UT-1 may be regarded as a smaller UT-2, span being only 7.3m compared with 10.2. The first UT-1 had 100mhp M-11 engines, some the 120mhp M-11G, but most had the M-11E of 150mhp. On prototype AIR-18 was mounted the 140mhp in-line MV-4 engine, a licensed construction of the French Renault 'Bengali' 4Pei. Besides this, there existed another variant with two wooden floats, the UT-IV.

The UT-1 was generally a good aerobatic aeroplane for its time, but control was very difficult in certain manoeuvres. This aircraft was under construction until 1942 and, in all, 1,241 were built.

The aircraft mentioned so far were used principally for pilot training. The other crew members were at first trained on slightly modified versions of standard combat aircraft, but this proved too costly. Polikarpov's simple P-2 biplane may be regarded as the first instructor

Above: Yakovlev's AIR-10, a modified version of his AIR-9bis (left) seen at the Milan Air Show in 1935.

AIR-20 entered service in 1938 under designation UT-2. This particular example was flown with a Renault Bengali 4 engine.

UT-1 (AIR-24) was the next step up for trainee pilots after mastering the basics on UT-2. It was small and reasonably aerobatic.

P-2 was the first specialised aircraft for training navigators, gunner and bombardiers. Fifty-five were built between 1928 and 1930.

A transitional aircraft for bomber pilots was the G-27 offered by Gribovskii in 1939. It did not go into production.

for navigators, machine gunners and bombardiers, the 'P' standing for *Perekhodnii* or 'aircraft for intermediate training'. P-2 looked like a smaller version of the reconnaissance R-5 and had the 300mhp M-6, a licensed construction of the eight cylinder French Hispano-Suiza 8Fb which dated from the last months of the 1914-1918 war. Between 1928 and 1930 fifty-five P-2 were built, but they were seldom seen in the schools as flying qualities and stability were unsatisfactory. The training variant of R-1 with 240mhp BMW-1Va engine was, in fact, more used for transitional training than the P-2.

Introduction of modern, high-speed, two-motored bombers highlighted the need for an economic transitional machine and initiative for design was taken by the Aviation Engineering Institute KAI in Kasan. Under the direction of T I Ickovich, KAI-3 was developed here from the two-engined touring aircraft KAI-1 and test flown in May 1935.

It was an unwieldy, low-wing monoplane in composite construction with two M-11 engines and fixed, faired undercarriage. The crew consisted of three and a spacious cabin made it particularly suitable for training. KAI-3 was given the military designation UPB (*Uchebnii Perekhodnii Bombardirovshchik* = bomber for transitional training). It was intended that 25 should be built for bomber schools, but the overloaded Soviet aviation industry could not produce them.

In 1937 Yakovlev built a transitional low-wing monoplane AIR-17 of composite construction with two 220mhp MV-6 engines. The machine had interesting lines, retractable undercarriage, variable camber flaps, bomb bay, fixed and flexible armament and other bomber equipment. The Red Air Force took on the prototype as UT-3, intending serial produced on a large scale, but it never materialised. Only 20 machines were built.

V K Gribovskii designed and built another transitional aircraft in 1939, the low-wing monoplane G-27, again a three-seater with fine lines, retractable undercarriage or fixed snow skids, flaps and two M-11 five-cylinder motors. The G-27 reached 240kph and its qualities were good. Verdict on the plane was favourable but, once again, it was not put into production.

In most cases the crews of modern two-engined combat aircraft were trained on variants of the operational machines. These were distinguished by an added instructor's cockpit and had the same designation as the combat aircraft with the additional initials UT.

SB-2UT, for example, was the training variant of the high-speed medium bomber with an open seat in front of the real pilot's cockpit. The second controls were in this additional space and only in cases of necessity did the instructor thrust his head out and steer the machine himself. During the war Pe-2UT variants were built from the level and dive bomber Pe-2, the second pilot being enclosed and located behind the normal cockpit.

After the war, Tu-2 bombers were assigned to units in quite large numbers but were too expensive for training purposes. So P O Sukhoi was

Touring monoplane KAI-1 (left) formed the basis for a bomber trainer in 1935. Designated KAI-3, the re-worked machine fell foul of an overloaded aviation industry.

227

commissioned to design a lighter trainer for Tu-2 crews. Sukhoi developed UTB from the drastically lightened airframe of Tu-2 and equipped it with two 700mhp ASh-21 seven-cylinder engines. This *Uchebnii-Trenirovochnii Bombardirovshchik* was in service for a long time after the war.

With the enhanced performances of fighters and increasing demands made on their pilots, a need was felt for two-seat transitional variants of modern single-seat fighters. In particular, the introduction of I-16s made transitional training with instructors indispensable, for the aircraft had unusual flight characteristics and the first examples resulted in heavy losses of men and materials.

In 1935, A A Borovkov designed the two-seat I-16UTI or UTI-4. These were standard I-16, either with only one machine gun or completely unarmed. They had the M-25A engine of 650/730mhp and usually a fixed undercarriage. The speed of 389kph increased to 473kph when the undercarriage was retracted. In series production of I-16 every fourth aircraft was a two-seater. UTI-4 were popular and were used not only as transitional trainers but also for liaison and reconnaissance.

After the I-16 almost all fighters had their two-seat transitional variant. For example, the DIT (*Dvukhmestnii Istrebitel Trenirovochnii* = two-seat training fighter) was developed from I-152 and UTI-26 was developed from I-26 (Yak-1). Later, during the war, the La-5UTI, La-7UTI and, after the war, La-9UTI were often to be seen, also serving for mail, reconnaissance and transport of the higher commanders in chief.

Efforts were also made to design a cheap trainer for fighter pilots. The aircraft was to be simple to build and small, with less powerful engine and yet fast enough and with qualities to match the real fighters. V V Nikitin, in particular, did a lot of work in this direction and V P Chkalov had test flown his wire-braced low-wing monoplane NV-1 in September 1933. This single-seater of only 6.4m span with an M-11 engine and wooden propeller from the U-2, reached 210kph and with a new propeller as much as 232kph. Flying qualities matched those of the new I-16.

NV-1 was built in plants of the aerial sport organisation, Osoaviakhim. There, too, in 1935 the cantilever monoplane NV-2 was developed. This aircraft had the 100mhp M-11 engine, was equipped with semi-retractable undercarriage, enclosed cockpit and could achieve 230kph. In 1938 Nikitin was able to mount the 165mhp MG-11 into a modified airframe and thus increase speed to 260kph.

This reconstructed aircraft, NV-2bis, excited the attention of the Air Force and it was ordered as military training fighter UTI-5. The first UTI-5 and small number of subsequent production aeroplanes were given yet more powerful 300mhp MG-31 engines to produce 350kph, not much lower than the real fighters. They could also be flown with two fixed machine guns.

Nikitin built a miniature aerobatic biplane, NV-4, in 1939. With its span of 7m it looked more like a toy than a real aircraft, but the 165mhp MG-11F engine allowed execution of the most complicated aerobatic manoeuvres. The Red Air Force took on a few NV-4 aircraft as UTI-6, but they could not put up much competition against the Yakovlev UT-1.

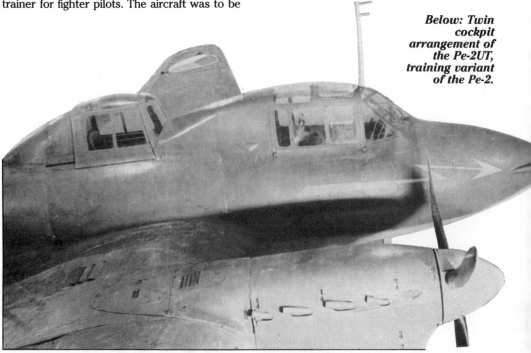

Below: Twin cockpit arrangement of the Pe-2UT, training variant of the Pe-2.

Above: Sukhoi's UTB, a radically lightened training version of the Tu-2.

Right- Two-seat UTI-4 or I-16UTI, a trainer which also served in the liaison and reconnaissance roles.

Below: One of many fighter trainers to follow I-16's example, the La-7UTI.

Chkalov's NV-1 was first flown in September 1933 and later reached 232kph.

NV-2 appeared in 1935, featuring semi-retractable undercarriage.

Nikitin's dimunitive UTI-6 had a span of only 7m and was fully aerobatic.

The standard UT-2 were somewhat under-equipped by the standards of the time. During the war a retractable undercarriage, variable camber flaps, radio devices etc, were common features of all military aircraft. None of the Soviet basic trainers were able to provide such equipment for students starting from scratch. The students only learned how to use it in the second stage of their training, and that was already too late.

Yakovlev had decided on a modernisation of the UT-2 in 1945, and this was to be taken even further than the updating of UT-2MV. Thus arose the basic trainer Yak-18, a machine which is typical of post-war Soviet basic trainers and sports planes. Yak-18 was a cantilever, low-wing monoplane in all-metal, partly dural sheet and partly fabric covered. Its undercarriage was semi-retractable while under the trailing edge of the wing centre section and below the fuselage was a split, variable camber flap.

Engine was a 160mhp M-11FR, not very large for an aircraft of 1,120kg take-off weight and 17sq m lifting surface. Yak-18 was, moreover, not one of those aircraft with which one could take liberties. Even its aerobatic potential was very limited. Yak-18 was a robust machine for reliable basic training with a maximum speed of 250kph, 4,000m service ceiling and 1,000km range.

Soon after its introduction to the training units and aviation clubs, Soviet sport fliers launched a real attack on FAI records. On September 16, 1949, a speed of 262.77kph was reached over a 100km course; on the same day 223.560kph was attained over 1,000km and 209.664kph over 2,000km.

On October 11, 1951, 251.823kph was reached over 500km; on May 8, 1954, an altitude record of 5,521m was set; by June 18, 1954, altitude had been raised to 6,511m; on September 11, 1954, a record for rectilinear distance over a closed circuit was set at 1,245.33km and this increased to 2,004.618km fourteen days later.

That was a noteworthy series in which not only the quality of the aircraft played a great part, but also the initiative of the fliers.

Yak-18 was built without significant change up to the middle of the fifties, yet right at the beginning of production, in 1946, a variant made its appearance. This was the single-seat Yak-5. The prototype suffered an accident during flight testing and work was discontinued.

In 1954 Yakovlev's design bureau responded to demands of the flying schools for a new basic trainer with retractable tricycle undercarriage. At a time when almost all Soviet aircraft already had tricycle gear there were none with this arrangement for training in take-off and landing techniques. Yakovlev put his Yak-18U in producition.

Yak-18U had a rather long nose with an M-11FR-1 engine beneath a modified cowling. On the firewall, the nose-wheel leg was installed. In flight it could be retracted rearwards and upwards, but leg and wheel remained outside the contour of the fuselage. Legs of the landing

Below: Yak-18 was the first of a new generation of post-war trainers, continuing in production up to the mid-1950s.

Below: An early variant of Yak-18 was Yak-5 which appeared in 1946. An accident during testing brought an abrupt end to the type.

Above: Yak-18U emerged in 1954 as a result of demands for a trainer with tricycle under-carriage. The legs were partially retractable.

Above: Yak-18PM variants occupied the first four places in the fourth FAI aerobatic championships held in Moscow.

Left: Yak-18A was an almost completely new machine and first variant to be fitted with Ivchenko's new nine-cylinder AI-14R engine.

Below: First of the single seat variants for aerobatic competitions, Yak-18P was developed from the -18A.

wheels were attached not in front, but behind the main spar and could be retracted forwards and up, once again remaining outside the wing surface.

So this was an emergency solution, intention being to use the tricycle undercarriage without greatly modifying the airframe. Empty weight increased from 816 to 970kg, speed sank to 235kph and the range was shortened to 900km. But at least transitional training on aircraft with tricycle undercarriage could begin.

As increasing demands were made on basic trainers, the Yak-18 had to improve its performances. Demands were also made for better aircraft equipment and in consequence a higher payload was required. The airframe of Yak-18 was able to meet new requirements, but the M-11 engine was at the limit of its potential. Luckily a new one was available – A G Ivchenko's nine-cylinder AI-14R with an output at take-off of 260mhp.

First Yak-18 variants with AI-14R were the Yak-20 of 1957, but on introduction Yakovlev resumed the family designation, calling it Yak-18A to demonstrate continuation of the series. Actually the Yak-18A could almost be described as a completely new machine. But in spite of all the modernisation, they kept the previous undercarriage on prototypes and first production models. Only machines of the main series were given an improved undercarriage where the main wheels and legs were retractable into the wings; the nose-wheel remained semi-buried.

Weight of the new aircraft increased a little (empty weight was now 1,025kg and take-off weight 1,316kg) but all flying performanaces and qualities were markedly better, thanks to increased engine performance. Yak-18A was now almost ready for aerobatic flying. Its maximum speed rose to 260kph, climbing speed at low altitude was 5.4m a second compared with the first Yak-18's 3.5m, and service ceiling was now 5,060m. Range was less at only 750km, though this was not particularly important for a trainer. After a few months the Yak-18A replaced older Yak-18 in training units and sporting DOSAAF organisations.

In the big international aerobatic championships, special single-seat variants of Yak-18 became increasingly important. First variant to be produced was the Yak-18P, developed from the -18A but with a short, single-seat cockpit. There was much experimentation on this aircraft with location of the centre of gravity, the cockpit being moved backwards and forwards until the satisfactory place was decided to be in front.

In the first FAI international aerobatic championships in Bratislava, Czechoslovakia, in 1960 one Yak-18P had a cockpit in the rear and B N Vasyakin flew it into fifth place. This was the

heaviest aircraft of the championships, not so manoeuvrable nor aerobatic as the Czechoslovakian Zlin, but with sufficient engine performance to carry out precisely the obligatory aerobatic manoeuvres. In free style the machine was weaker, but nevertheless excellent in vertical manoeuvres.

Two years later four Soviet Yak-18P featured in the championships at Budapest. This time they had front located seats and improved, completely retractable undercarriage. Lojchikov finished second while the other Soviet machines were placed seventh, ninth and tenth.

Soviet fliers and their Yaks participated on a larger scale in the third international championships in Bilbao, Spain. Piskunov, Ovsyakin, Pochernin and Martemyanov took fourth, fifth, sixth and seventh places respectively. As for the women, they were in the first three places with Sanosina heading the list.

In the fourth championships in Moscow, the Soviet pilots were able to make full use of the improved variant Yak-18PM, occupying the first four places led by V Martemyanov. Best woman was Gina Korchuganova.

Yak-18PM had improved aerodynamics and structural engineering plus the new 300mhp AI-14FR engine with V-530-D-25 propeller. Cockpit of the Yak-18PM is in the rear and wing dihedral is only 2 degrees instead of the 7.3 of its

Yak-11 was an advanced trainer built in 1946. Its existence remained unknown to the West until 1948 when one made an emergency landing in Turkey.

predecessors. All this enabled the pilot to fly the set aerobatic manoeuvres more precisely and win necessary points in the free style. The older Yak-18P reached 275kph and climbed 8.6m per second at low altitude. The PM variant flies at 315kph and climb performance is 10m per second. The Yak-18A needed 215m for take-off, 163m were enough for Yak-18P and only 142m for the PM. These aerobatic machines were only allotted to outstanding fliers in the Soviet sport aviation organisation; most used the Czech trainer and aerobatic aircraft, Zlin, usually models Z-326 and Z-226.

The commercial company, Aeroflot, ordered an aircraft for pilot training from Yakovlev's design bureau in 1966. Aeroflot required a machine with spacious cabin for an instructor and three students who could also be taught radio liaison and navigation. Yakovlev handed over the job to his son, Sergei, who decided to use the wings, undercarriage, controls and also the AI-14FR engine of Yak-18PM. Fuselage was spacious, containing a broad, four-seat cabin. The new aircraft carried designation Yak-18T and was first shown at the 27th Aero-Salon in Paris in 1967. The exhibited machine was a variant for tourism but with its technical lines and equipment was obviously intended for export.

Yak-18T reached 300kph and range was between 600 and 1,000km. About 500 Yak-18Ts were produced.

Only specialised variants of Yak-18 are still built, but the designer can take pleasure in reflecting that the aircraft was serially produced for more than 20 years, a total of 6,786 aircraft being issued, 950 of them the Yak-18A variant.

After the first Yak-20 had been renamed Yak-18A, the model name Yak-20 was brought into use again in 1961, being given to a new sport and basic training aircraft. The new Yak-20 was an all-metal machine with fixed undercarriage and AI-14R engine. The broad cockpit had three seats, two for the students side-by-side and one for the instructor, behind and in a central position. Yak-20 apparently remained in prototype form. We have no further details about this aircraft.

With the Yak-18, pilot basic training was assured for the post-war period. But it was even more important to have an effective aircraft for advanced training. Such a machine was to bring students up to the stage of handling trainer variants of normal combat aircraft, also to allow them practice in bombing, machine gunning of air and ground targets, radio navigation etc.

Yakovlev designed such a trainer in 1946, designated Yak-11. The uneven model number indicates that it could almost be described as a two-seat fighter. The lines were similar to those of Yak single-seat fighters of the end of war period, airframe being mostly covered with dural sheet with the exception of rudder and tail section. Yakovlev used the 615/700mhp seven-cylinder ASh-21 engine which A D Shvetsov had designed from parts of the double-row radial ASh-82.

Thanks to its good aerodynamics and small lifting surface (15.4sq m), Yak-11 reached 424kph at low altitude and as much as 460kph at 2,250m. Service ceiling was 7,100m and range 1,280km. A fixed UBS machine gun could be mounted on the left side, above the engine, and sometimes the aircraft could be seen with a photographic machine gun in a cowling on the upper side of the frame of the protective dome. Under the wing were pylons for practice bombs, rocket missiles etc.

The existence of Yak-11 remained unknown until 1948 when a Soviet pilot made an emergency landing in Turkey. Its real designation was revealed in 1951 when the first of several FAI records were broken. On July 11, 1951, a speed record of 471.348kph was set over a 500km closed circuit; August 26. 1951, saw a speed of 442.289kph over 1,000km; on October 21, 1952, speed over 2,000km was 360.032kph and on September 11, 1954, a record for rectilinear distance was established at 1,990.183km. Numerous national records were also broken.

The Yak-11 was of great significance for training in the Soviet Air Force and in air forces of East Europe. In the USSR, 3,859 Yak-11 were produced and a further 700 appeared between 1952 and 1956 from the Czechoslovakian LET aircraft plant, in Kunovice. Czechoslovakian designation was C-11. In Kunovice the nose-wheel variant

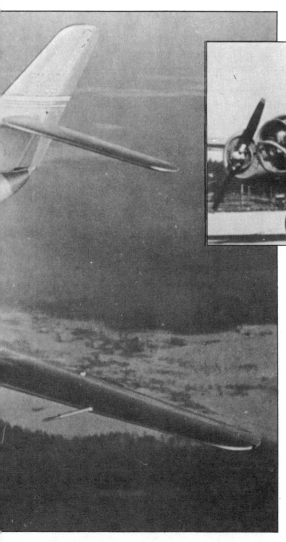

Above: Yak-200 had all the appearances of a small bomber and was fully equipped for training but remained a prototype only.

Soviet entries in a Warsaw Pact design competition for a new jet trainer were the Yak-30 or Yak-104 (left) and its single seat version, the Yak-32 (above).

C-11U was also designed (the aircraft known in the USSR as Yak-11U) but it was not put into production. Numerous Yak-11 were supplied to Egypt, Austria and the Yemen.

Yakovlev tried to produce other two-engined training aircraft after the war. A few examples of Yak-16, a light commercial 'plane which had not been taken on, were fitted out as flying training halls for radio operators or navigators. Besides this, in 1953 Yakovlev built a specialised trainer Yak-200 with two ASh-21. This all-metal, mid-wing monoplane had the lines of a small bomber with glazed nose, a bomb bay and other appurtenances of a military trainer. The Yak-200 was not, however, put into production.

After the war, training in the USSR was carried out in three stages. First was the elementary stage, carried out on Yak-18. There then followed more advanced training on Yak-11 and for the third stage, flights were undertaken on variants of machines actually in service, including jets.

First training jet aircraft in the USSR was Yak-17UTI, a two-seat variant of the 1947 Yak-17 fighter, equipped with two tandem seats in a lengthened cockpit. There followed two-seat training variants of all the single-seat jet fighters, like MiG-15UTI etc. La-15UTI was also built, factory designated La-180, and even the two-engined jet bomber Il-28 had its training double. This was Il-28UT with instructor's cabin in the nose in front of the actual cockpit.

More modern jet fighters also have training versions like MiG-21UTI and Su-7UTI. There was one variant of the MiG-21UTI, a single-seater called Ye-33, in which Soviet women pilots set up a few records. N Prokhanova climbed on the peak of a ballistic curve to 24,300m on May 22, 1965, and L Sajtseva made a level flight at 19,020m on June 26, 1965.

Target training for pilots of modern jet fighters demands more sophisticated methods. The earlier, towed target gliders were far from sufficient and the aim was small, free flying, remote-controlled target planes with jet propulsion. Lavochkin's bureau designed a small target plane, La-17, between 1950 and 1953. This was really a model-size aircraft with rectangular surface and an inverted jet engine mounted under the fuselage. Unfortunately we have no details about this machine, but several models were built.

Towards the end of the fifties, the value of three-stage training began to be questioned. New jet trainers were to cater for students from their first forays in the air up to the point of simulated combat. The trainers were to be able to take adequate equipment and outfit, their performances and qualities well developed, and their operation

A selection of early Soviet jet trainers – MiG-9UTI or I-301T (above); MiG-15UTI or ST-7 (above left); Yak-17UTI (left); Yak-23UTI (below) and La-15UTI or La-180 (below left).

Below: MiG-21UTI trainer, a special version of which enabled two women pilots to establish altitude records in 1965.

Right: The end of another training sortie for Su-7UTI crew.

Above: Training version of the Il-28 jet bomber was Il-28UT with instructor's cabin in the nose.

was to be very economic – unlike combat aircraft previously used for second-stage training.

In the middle of the fifties, design bureaux in the USSR, Poland and Czechoslovakia began work on this type. Among states of the Warsaw Pact it was agreed that these three countries should deliver aircraft for comparative flights, and the best machine would then be chosen as standard trainer for the Pact.

Yakovlev was the Soviet designer in this competition. His jet trainer was the all-metal low-wing monoplane Yak-104 which had an RU-19 engine of 850 to 1,050kp static thrust designed by S K Tumanskii. The fuselage had either a cockpit with two seats in tandem arrangement or a single-seat cockpit, designated Yak-30 and Yak-32. Both variants appeared with straight wings, tricycle undercarriage and a fuselage which tapered sharply upwards behind the engine. In August 1961 the two machines were shown at Tushino, and during the aerobatic world championships in Moscow in 1966, were statically displayed.

Comparative flights of the three competing machines were made in August 1961 in Moscow. Yakovlev represented the USSR, from Poland came the mid-wing monoplane TS-11 'Iskra' of Diploma Engineer Tadeusz Soltyk, and from Czechoslovakia the L-29 'Delfin' designed by Rublic and Tomas. Only the L-29 fulfilled all demands of the competition, especially in the sphere of reliability. The L-29 was not so fast as its competitors but proved especially suited to the ambitious form of flight training. So the Czechoslovakian aircraft was declared the victor and since that date the L-29 has been produced for countries of the Warsaw Pact; only Poland has stuck to her TS-11.

As for the Soviet planes, only six prototypes in all were constructed of Yak-30 and Yak-32. Both models, however, set up a few FAI records. Yak-32 climbed to an altitude of 14,238m on February 22, 1961, to establish a record for Class C-2-d. This was soon beaten by the Italians with an Aermacchi MB-326, but a new standard was set by the USSR when the two-seat Yak-30 reached an altitude of 16,128m on August 25, 1961. Three days previously, the Yak-30 had also set up a speed record when V V Smirnov, pilot of the earlier record flights, flew over the 15/25km circuit at 767.308kph.

Soviet machines certainly set up records, but the Czechoslovakian L-29 became the standard trainer. In summer 1966 a celebration took place on the occasion of delivery of the thousandth machine of this type.

At the present time the new Czechoslovak jet trainer L-39 Albatros has taken over in Soviet and other Warsaw Pact flying schools.

CHAPTER 30

Sports Aircraft

AT THE BEGINNING of the twenties, a real fever broke out among young Soviets who, seeing aviation as representing progress and a promising future for their country, were anxious to promote it by all means.

In schools, factories, organisations, military units etc, circles of enthusiasts were formed, lectures arranged, and models and gliders built. In 1923 these individual groups were combined to form a single organisation ODVF (*Obshchestvo Drusjej Vosdushnogo Flota* = Association of the Friends of the Air Force). After a year, ODVF counted 963,000 members!

At that time public collections for the ODVF were being held over a very wide area and some funds were used to buy military aircraft for the youthful Red Air Force. It was not long before the ODVF found itself increasingly fulfilling the role of providing pre-military training for young people.

ODVF was combined in March 1925 with the organisation for voluntary chemical defence, Dobrokhim, to form a new Aviakhim. In January 1927 there arose a body which combined all branches of military training-Osoaviakhim. Towards the end of the twenties, parachuting as a sport was added.

Soviet sports fliers achieved noteworthy performances, but could not make their presence felt on an international scale as the USSR did not join the FAI until March 1935. The USSR was represented by the Central Aeroclub in Moscow, named in honour of A V Kosarev. In 1939 his name was replaced by V P Chkalov who had just lost his life in a I-180 crash. From 1935 onwards the names of Soviet fliers and aircraft were found in increasing numbers in the FAI record lists. By spring 1938, a quarter of the world records had been set by the USSR and out of 27 of the then Class C (landplanes) records eleven were held by Soviet fliers. In light aircraft classes they were less successful.

Soviet sports aviation encountered great difficulties at the outset in a country that had just concluded a civil war and was threatened by need and hunger. Nevertheless, enthusiasm helped to overcome many a difficulty, including the absolute lack of sports planes. Since the aviation industry could not deliver any, sports fliers designed and built their own.

This was a golden period for amateur aircraft construction. Light planes were built in the Osoaviakhim clubs, by fliers in the factories, schools, workshops and even by individuals. Financial backing was obtained from Osoaviakhim but the builders had to make use of whatever skills they could muster. Some noteworthy talents were displayed and many amateur designers embarked on a career which was to lead them to the big design bureaus, factories and universities.

The aircraft were built in small workshops, storerooms and even in apartments. For example, A N Tupolev built his first low-wing sports monoplane, ANT-1, in his apartment. When the time came to bring out the assembled airframe he had

Early Soviet sports aircraft were often produced under primitive conditions. Tupolev built ANT-1 (below) in his apartment and incorporated dural components in anticipation of an all-metal aeroplane.

to take off the door. The test for strength was simple – Tupolev and his friends sat on the aircraft's wing.

The greatest problem was getting hold of an engine. Tupolev's ANT-1 flew with an Anzani six-cylinder of 45/60mhp. Others usually had to make do with reconstructed motorcycle engines such as the 8mhp JAP or Harley-Davidson and Indian of 7 to 18mhp. Some engines were imported, like the British 18mhp Blackburn Tomtit, 30/35mhp Bristol Cherub, 40/60mhp ADC -Cirrus and the Czechoslovakian Walter NZ-60 and NZ-85.

There were a very great number of individual small sports aircraft (*Avietka*) built from 1924 and Tupolev's ANT-1 was one of the first. Already Tupolev was using dural for the wing and tail ribs and even the cantilever wing was a preparation for his future all-metal monoplane.

Between 1924 and 1929, V P Nevdachin's low-wing monoplane *'Burevestnik'* ('Storm Bird') was very popular. Nevdachin had built a sailplane, P-5, of the same name and design in 1922, which

Jungmeister used to reach a distance record of 532km in November 1923 at Koktebel in the Crimea. In 1924 Nevdachin motorised the P-5 glider with a 7mhp Harley-Davidson to create the S-2, but tests in August showed it to be underpowered. Nevdachin next tried a 12mhp Harley-Davidson in the S-3 which reached 75kph and a ceiling of 300m in 1926.

A complete success was not achieved until 1927 on the S-4 which had a Blackburn Tomtit and was test flown in July by A I Shukov. The S-4 flew at 140kph and became well known because of its flight from Moscow to Odessa and Shukov's altitude record of 5,500m. In 1928 another model made its appearance, the S-5 with a 35mhp Bristol Cherub. This aircraft was displayed at the 1929 ILA aircraft show in Berlin and shortly afterwards was given to the aviation club of the Siberian town of Irkutsk.

Together with the S-5, a two-seat high-wing monoplane *'Tri Druga'* (Three Friends) was also shown. The name was symbolical and had two meanings. Firstly, it was part of the sentence,

Right: A popular aircraft between 1924 and 1929 was Nevdachin's S-4 Burevestnik or 'Storm Bird.'

"Strength, Simplicity and Cheapness, three friends of Aviation". This was the motto of the ODVF design competition in 1924. Secondly, three friends had designed and built the aircraft – L I Sutugin, A A Semenov and S N Gorelov. 'Tri Druga' was a good aircraft. With Cherub engine it reached 127kph while ceiling was 3,200m in the two-seat version and 4,300m in a single-seater.

Out of 27 projects in the design competition of 1924, five were recommended for construction, but more than five were actually built and flown with a varying amount of success. A new light engine was also produced at this time, the 'Bolshevik' of L J Palmen, a two-cylinder engine of 20mhp.

A S Yakovlev's work in the sports sector was decisive. As a boy he had built models and, later on, sailplanes. In order to become better acquainted with aviation technology, he took a post in the N J Shukovskii Military Aviation Academy and became active in the Osoaviakhim organisation.

On May 12, 1927, Yakovlev's friend, J I Piontkovskii, test flew the first Yakovlev plane, the VVA-3 (*Vojenno-Vozdushnaja-Akademija* = Military Aviation Academy). Shortly afterwards Yakovlev changed the designation to AIR-1, in honour of the president of Osoaviakhim, A I Rykov, who was also president of the Council of the People's Commissary. After Rykov's arrest in 1937 he changed the designation into a Yakovlev number. His pre-war designs were given the abbreviation Ya, in contrast to Yak which was used after 1941.

Yakovlev built the biplane with funds and a British 60mhp ADC Cirrus engine obtained from the Moscow Osoaviakhim organisation. Directors of the Academy were opposed to the design of this aircraft, but Yakovlev knew how to vindicate himself. The aircraft was constructed in the hall of the Academy club, mostly after regular working time and mostly made of wood. Piontkovskii rated the flying qualities as "Excellent". He also made an overland flight in June 1927, from Sevastopol to Moscow without any intermediate landing, covering 1,240km in 15½ hours. The speed of AIR-1 was 140kph.

In 1928 Yakovlev built a development with the designation AIR-2. Between 1928 and 1931 six aircraft of this type were produced, all with five-cylinder radial engines, either 60mhp Walter NZ-60, 85mhp Siemens or 65mhp NAMI M-23. The aircraft with the Siemens was given the designation AIR-2S and test flown in May 1931 with two of V B Shavrov's wooden floats, creating a great sensation among Muscovites.

On the strength of AIR-2, Yakovlev was taken

on as a student of the Academy. In summer 1929 he built a strut-braced high-wing monoplane AIR-3, also called *Pionerskaya Pravda* after the newspaper of the young Communists. It was driven by the Czech five-cylinder Walter NZ-60. In 1929 Filin and Kovalkov flew an AIR-3, without any intermediate landings, the 1,835km from Moscow to Mineralnyje Vodi at an average speed of 166.8kph. This was an international record, but the USSR was not at that time a member of the FAI. Like all Yakovlev's aircraft, the AIR-3 had good aerodynamics and under normal conditions reached 146kph. Landing speed was 66kph.

In 1930 Yakovlev introduced further refinements in the design. He built a new undercarriage with split axle and thus AIR-4 was born. The aircraft was used in 1933 in tests with slats and variable camber flaps, when a landing speed of 35kph was achieved. Building line of the strut-braced, high-wing monoplane was repeated again in 1934 on Yakovlev's AIR-8, which also had an 85mhp Siemens.

In 1937-8, Professor S G Kozlov of the Military Aviation Academy in Moscow used AIR-3 in interesting experiments to create an 'invisible' aircraft. The whole airframe was covered with a transparent material from France called 'Rhodoid', which was treated on the inner side with silver amalgam. The design was a success, for shortly after take-off the aircraft was indeed out of sight. Unfortunately the material was impaired by abrasions and after a short time became dull, so that the effect of 'invisibility' was lost.

While still at the Academy, Yakovlev built a very effective aircraft in the low-wing racing monoplane AIR-7. It was strut and wire-braced with fixed 'trouser-leg' undercarriage, two-seat cockpit and 420mhp M-22 engine. Piontkovskii test flew the aircraft in summer 1932, and after a few weeks it had reached 325kph which rose in the spring of 1933 to 332kph. AIR-7 became the fastest aircraft in the USSR and it was nominated for the transport of printing stencils of daily newspapers from Moscow to other towns. Unfortunately there was an accident in 1934 when an aileron flew off and Piontkovskii seriously damaged the aircraft in an emergency landing.

After the opening of his own plant in 1934, Yakovlev devoted himself in particular to the design of basic and other trainers. There were only very slight differences at that time between such aircraft and sports planes, but the low-wing monoplane AIR-11 of 1936 can be described as purely a sports aircraft. It had an enclosed three-seat cockpit, a 120mhp de Havilland Gipsy Major engine and reached 206kph.

Above: AIR-1 (VVA-3) was one of Yakovlev's first machines, appearing in 1927.
Left: AIR-2S was test flown with floats in May 1931.
Below: AIR-3 achieved a non-stop flight of 1,835km in 1929.

Yakovlev's high-wing, strut-braced AIR-8 monoplane.

Gribovskii's first powered aircraft was the G-5 with Blackburn Tomtit engine.

G-8 followed G-5 in 1931, making a 4,500km flight during October 1932.

Of the same period was another low-wing monoplane, AIR-12, constructed for a long distance record attempt by women fliers V S Grizodubova and M M Raskova. Interior of the fuselage over the wing was taken up by fuel tanks, behind was a cockpit for the navigator, Raskova, and just in front of the control unit was the pilot's cockpit. Engine was a 100mhp M-11 and the aircraft had a retractable undercarriage. The two women set up their record in 1938 when they flew 1,444km from Moscow to Aktyubinsk, in the Kazakhian Republic. But the FAI did not recognise it.

In 1937 Yakovlev built another two elegantly shaped, low-wing monoplanes – the four-seat touring aircraft AIR-16 with 220mhp MV-6 engine and the light single-seater AIR-18 with 140mhp MV-4.

V K Gribovskii had been known among sports plane designers since 1926 when he worked on an unfinished aircraft, the G-4. Gribovskii was a military flier and gifted designer who, among other things, created 17 sailplane models. The low-wing monoplane G-5, designed in 1928 with a Blackburn Tomtit engine, was Gribovskii's first real flying plane, capable of 60kph. Then, in 1931, he produced the successful G-8 monoplane powered by a Walter NZ-60 with which D A Koshits made a tour from Moscow – Riazan – Kazan – Samara – Saratov – Stalingrad – Rostov – Zaporoshi – Feodosiya – Poltava – Kharkov and back to Moscow, altogether 4,500km, in October 1932.

Gribovskii's tiny high-wing monoplane G-10 dated from 1934. This was a single-seater with M-23 and later a M-11 engine. The low wing monoplane G-15 with M-11 was a touring aircraft with two seats side-by-side and fixed faired undercarriage. Built in 1934, it was considered one of the best Soviet sports planes of its time.

With a top speed of 332kph, Yakovlev's racing monoplane AIR-7 became the USSR's fastest aircraft in Spring 1933. Power came from a 420mhp M-22 engine.

The G-21, another low-wing tourer of 1936, was more modern. This had a 150mhp M-11E and a speed of 220kph in comparison with the 185kph of G-15.

All Gribovskii machines had wooden construction with monocoque fuselage, like the little low-wing monoplane G-22, a single-seater with 50mhp Walter Mikron-I and cantilever undercarriage. Female pilot, Mednikova, set up an international speed record of 164.94kph with a G-22 in July 1938. In 1939, an English 80mhp Pobjoy Niagara was mounted, and later the Soviet M-23 of 63mhp. The G-26, with a four-cylinder, in-line MG-40 engine of 140mhp, was a sequel to G-22.

Low-wing monoplane G-23 was built in 1936 with a 56mhp GAZ-M-1 car engine and successfully tested by the Scientific-Technical Institute of the Red Air Force. It reached 150kph but climb performances were bad. I Grodsyanskii made a 2,584km flight with the G-23 from Moscow to Kharkov, Zaporoshi and back to Moscow, in 21 hours of actual flying time, at an average speed of 123kph. The second aircraft was given an M-11E radial engine and called G-23bis. Compared with the G-23, the G-23bis had excellent climb performances and also set up two international records. In summer 1938, Grodsyanskii climbed to 7,266m and, a few weeks later, H D Fedoseyev reached 7,985m.

Gribovskii showed a preference for monoplanes, but an exception was the G-25 biplane, constructed in 1937 with 85mhp Pobjoy Niagara. This engine was replaced in 1938 by an 85mhp automobile engine, GAZ-Avia, which adversely affected performance.

All the aircraft mentioned so far were only available in very small numbers, and were of little importance in the mass training of sports pilots in Osoaviakhim air clubs, where the U-2 was used. U-2's qualities were excellent, but they excited the same aversion in the civilian as in the military flying schools.

Several designers worked on the construction of a pure sports and touring aircraft, particularly in 1934 when the scientific technical society AVIAnvito published a design competition for the 'Votsdushnii Ford,' that is, a 'Flying Ford'. The AT-1 emerged victorious. This was a cantilever low-wing monoplane in composite construction, three seats, an M-11 and fixed undercarriage designed by I N Vinogradov and A A Krylov from the Moscow Trade School for Aeronautical Technology.

Professor V S Pyshnov designed a cabin biplane, VVA-1, with an M-11, but this was difficult to build owing to its specially streamlined shape, and it was therefore rejected. Other contributions to the competition were the tailless aircraft LK-1 and KhAI-4, which will be described elsewhere, and V B Shavrov's light water/land plane, Sh-2.

Too many sports planes were designed and built at that time for us to be able to describe them all in greater detail, but Kalinin's high-wing monoplane K-9 of 1932 was interesting, especially its elliptical wing which proved too big for the 60mhp Walter NZ-60. Foreign technicians of Aeroflot built a strut-braced, low-wing monoplane E-1 in 1932, in their spare time. This was also given a designation based on the name of the designer, GF-1 from Friedrich Gup.

Most sports planes were powered by the M-11, but foreign engines were not lacking. Attempts were made to counteract the dearth of light engines by using reconstructed automobile motors but performance and qualities of the aircraft were always lower. To improve matters the deputy chief designer in Automobile Gorkii, J V Agitov, introduced in 1935 a flying variant of the 56mhp GAZ-M-1 car engine. This was characterised by the extensive replacement of cast steel by aluminium.

Interesting, too, is A A Solin's low-wing monoplane KSM-1 of 1935, first aircraft to be built specially for the automobile engine. Motor and airframe were both too heavy and the aircraft could scarcely fly. Gribovskii tried to lighten the airframe but did not succeed in making a good aircraft out of the KSM-1 until 1939. There were several other cases of an automobile engine being mounted in an aircraft by way of experiment, but results were always the same – the engines were too heavy, too weak and therefore unsuitable.

In the thirties, attempts were made to design and build ultra-light, single-seat sports planes. Design of the 'SkyFlea' ('Pou du Ciel') by Frenchman Henri Mignet, inspired several designers in the USSR. Hence the appellation 'Blokha' became something of a general designation for ultra-lights in Soviet aviation.

In 1936, Osoaviakhim and AVIAvnito published a competition for a light sports plane, receiving 35 designs or already constructed machines for assessment. Not all of these were good and not all designs were carried out. We will therefore describe the most important projects briefly.

P D Grushin, of the MAI, built a single-seater 'Oktyabrynonok' (Son of the October Revolution'). It had tandem wings and a variety of engines – originally a 22mhp Aubier-Dunne then a fairly old 30mhp Bristol Cherub and finally a 45mhp Salmson Ad-9. The aircraft was too heavy at 400kg flying weight instead of the expected 230kg, and therefore stability and manoevrability left a lot to be desired.

Sailplane designer B N Sheremetyev built a 'Blokha' in 1935. The wing stagger was like Mignet's 'Flea' but there were standard ailerons and elevators with an 18mhp Aubier-Dunne it reached 115kph, had a landing speed of only 48kph, flew well and was stable.

Another single-seat 'Oktyabryonok' had more conventional lines. It was built in 1936/37 by students of the Military Aviation Academy in Moscow – A I Mikoyan, K A Samarin and N A Pavlov – as their certificate piece. The high-wing monoplane had a slender tail boom and a 25mhp engine with pusher propeller which allowed

126kph top speed.

In Kharkov a two-seat, high-wing monoplane KhAI-2 was built in the KhAI institute under the direction of P I Shishov. It was really a powered sailplane of 13m span with an elastic cable launch. Driven during flight by P Labur's two-cylinder 11/14mhp engine, KhAI-2 reached 80kph in level flight.

Aircraft were also built for specific sporting purposes, especially record flights and races. B N Sheremetyev designed a cantilever, low-wing monoplane, Sh-13, which was test flown in 1939 by P D Golovin. Sh-13 had wings of 13m span and high aspect ratio. It was driven by a 40mhp engine of unknown origin and classified as an aircraft for long distance flights in the lightest category. According to calculations it would have been capable of flying 24 hours and of covering 3,300km. But in these stirring times it did not accomplish any record flights.

D P Grigorovich's two-engined, low-wing monoplane DG-55 or E-2 was also intended for long distance flights. This machine was designed and built in the MAI Institute in 1935 where Grigorovich was working as a professor. The aircraft was also dubbed 'Girls' Plane' for in the MAI group of student designers there were eight girls – an absolute majority. For DG-55 the designers took over, more or less, the lines of Britain's de Havilland D H 88 'Comet' which had become known through its long distance flights from England to Australia.

DG-55 was in all-wood construction, a two-seater, had a retractable undercarriage and two British Cirrus Hermes engines each of 120mhp. The aircraft reached 296kph with a range of 2,200km. After test flying, the machine was handed over to Osoaviakhim and used for various administrative and mail flights.

For August 1941 Osoaviakhim had prepared a race for light sports planes, and three design groups built aircraft for the occasion. Gribovskii produced his G-28 'Krechet' (Falcon or Hawk), a fine, low-wing monoplane with 240mhp MV-6 engine, something on the lines of G-22 but with retractable undercarriage. Unfortunately, because of the German attack, tests could not be finished. M M Gromov and A B Yumashev flew it and were highly satisfied. The G-28 was the only conventional aircraft built for the race.

Second aircraft was A S Moskalev's SAM-13, featured in the fighters section, while the third was a tailles, low-wing monoplane, BICh-21, designed by B I Cheranovskii. The other designation of this aircraft was SG-1 (Samolet Gonochnij = Racing Plane).

BICh-21 had narrow, tapered wings and a flat fuselage with MV-6 engine in the nose. To the rear of the cockpit, the fuselage formed an integral part of the vertical fin. There was no horizontal fin. On test, BICh-21 reached as much as 417kph and was very stable. It appeared to have great race prospects for the faster SAM-13, from which 607kph was expected, had difficulties. Unfortunately the German invasion of June 22

Dating from 1934, Gribovskii's G-10 was a single-seat touring model.

G-21 appeared in 1936, featuring a 150mhp M-11E engine.

Above: Prof. V S Pyshnov designed the ambitious VVA-1 cabin biplane.
Below: The eliptical wing was a notable point on Kalinin's K-9.

Right: Women student designers played a
great part in Grigorovich's DG-55 or E-2
which was largely based on De
Havilland's DH 88 Comet. It achieved
296kph with a range of 2,200km.

Sh-13, a 1939 design, was calculated to be capable of staying aloft for 24 hours.

Smolin KSM-1 of 1936 with a 56hp GAZ M-1 automobile engine.

GF-1 or Guep 1, a strut-braced monoplane by German engineer Fridrich Guep.

meant the race could not be held.

This was not the only event arranged by Osoaviakhim. As early as the thirties, several tours were organised, covering the whole of the USSR as well as those taking place in the individual states. These events were good experience for sports fliers and useful to designers. The victorious machines were mostly serially produced for military and civilian training.

With preparations for the summer 1941 race, Osoaviakhim reached the peak of their pre-war activity. Osoaviakhim provided the Red Air Force with thousands of fliers and parachutists able to pass directly from their civilian jobs into the war without the need for any preliminary training.

The post-war structure of Osoaviakhim remained unaltered until 1948 when three independent units were formed for sport, pre-military training and co-operation with (1) the Army (2) the Navy and (3) the Air Force. The third organisation was given the name DOSAV (*Dobrovolnoye Obshchestvo Sodejstvija Aviacii* = Voluntary Society for Co-operation with the Air Force). In 1952 the three were combined to form DOSAAF,

the letters AAF standing for '*Armii, Aviacii i Flotu*' that is, 'with the Army, the Air Force and the Fleet'.

In the aircraft park of DOSAAF, military machines predominated. After the war the Po-2 and UT-2, later the Yak-18, Yak-11 and Yak-12, were the planes mostly used for sailplane towing. For parachute descent, An-2 were the most common. There were few sports planes with good qualities and performances, least of all for aerobatics, but the need was satisfied at the beginning of the sixties when DOSAAF bought several Czech machines of the 'Trener' class – mainly the types Z-326 'Trener-Master', Z-326A 'Akrobat' and machines of the Z-526 family.

Several design competitions were launched in the fifties and sixties which produced a mass of projects but no machines. Only in recent years has there been a revival of interest in the construction of light sports planes in the aviation clubs of DOSAAF, and especially in the technical aviation institutes like MAI, KhAI, KAI etc. For the young engineers and workers this is a good opportunity to gain experience in practical air-

Mignet's Pou du Ciel inspired this ZAOR version by B N Sheremetyev.

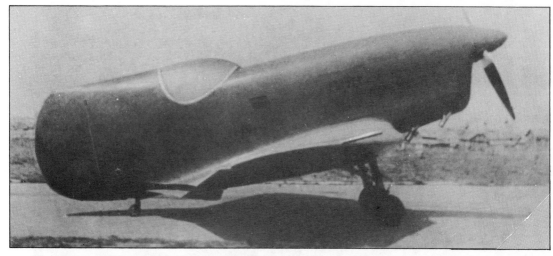

The tailless BICh-21 (SG-1) was designed by Chereanovskii for an air race planned by Osaoviakhim. Reaching 417kph on test flights it became one of the race favourites, but Germany's invasion on June 22, 1941, bought an end to the aircraft and the race.

craft construction.

We can devote only a short section to the construction of sailplanes as this book is concerned with powered aircraft. Sailplanes, their performances and history, deserve a book to themselves.

First glider group in the USSR was founded in 1919 under the direction of N J Shukovskii. The members were workers and engineers from Moscow aircraft plants. The gliding group of the Red Air Force was, however, more active and in Spring 1923 organised a gliding championship in Moscow. Meanwhile the ODVF was created and arranged regular Soviet championships at Koktebel, near Feodosia in the Crimea. In November 1923 nine gliders were to be seen here; after a year the number had risen to forty-eight. In 1925 Soviet glider pilots flew their own machines in Germany, over the Rhone.

At this time, glider pilots usually had to design and build their own or else the aircraft were produced in clubs, schools, factories, military units etc. The pilots were mostly professional fliers. In 1927 the first ten systematically trained sailplane fliers took part in the gliding championship of the USSR.

Difficulties arose because of the large number of different models, and when they came to training it was discovered that flying qualities were uneven and the aircraft were not always completely stable. Moreover, production was expensive. First attempts at standardisation were made in 1927 when the Tolstych IT-4 and Gribovskii G-2 were designated standard training gliders and aviation clubs produced them from uniform designs. In 1930 sailplane plants were opened in Gorkii, near Moscow. Primary-type gliders in particular were produced here, such as O K Antonov's US-3 (2,000 examples), the Antonov glider for advanced training, PS-1 'Upar' (140 examples), Sheremetyev's two-seat Sh-10

and other models.

The best pilots were given the most powerful sailplanes, like Gribovskii's G-9, Yemelyan's two-seat KIM-3 'Stakhanovets' and Antonov's machines known under the name of Red Front (RF). In addition there were innumerable amateur and club designs, most of them with good qualities and noteworthy technology. In the golden period of Soviet pre-war sailplane technology (1932-6) 33 sailplane types were built.

Shortly after the war, membership of clubs greatly increased, but technical equipment was still greatly neglected. Not until after 1948 did clubs receive the new high-performance A-9 sailplanes, Antonov's two-seater A-10 and Yemelnanov's two-seat Ye-8. In the second half of the fifties, Soviet glider aviation had run into a crisis, both materially and in the methodological field, for there was no industrial base for production and training no longer satisfied requirements of the time. In this situation, help was sought and found in Czechoslovakia.

Two-seat trainer LF-109 'Pionyr' was taken on in 1958 and redesigned in the Institute of Aviation Engineering KAI Kasan to make an all-metal machine. The aviation industry then produced it in quite large numbers as KAI-12 'Primorets'. The Czech industry also made large-scale deliveries of the all-metal L-13 'Blanik'.

Single-seat performance machines were next for production in the Soviet Union, most notable being the A-13 and A-15, both all-metal and both Antonov designs. The A-13 was also motorised. In 1961, AM Lyulka's small TS-31M jet engine of 55kp thrust was mounted on top of the fuselage and pilot Litvinchev set up two international records in February 1962. In the lightest class of jet aircraft (C-1-a with weight up to 500kg) speed over a 3km base was 196kph and over a 15km base, 186kph.

UPDATE

Military Trainers and Sports Aircraft

ALTHOUGH A NUMBER of Czechoslovakian light sports planes and trainers have been exported to the Soviet Union, the Yakovlev bureau, led by Y Yankevich, produced some more developments of the famous Yak-18 family. The last version mentioned was the aerobatic Yak-18PM with inwards retracting undercarriage main wheels and rearwards retracting nosewheel. Final version of the Yak-18 family of aerobatic aircraft was the PS variant, which is similar to the -18PM but with rearwards retracting tailwheel undercarriage, retaining the same aft positioned cockpit.

For the Eighth World Aerobatic Championship held at Kiev in 1976, the Yakovlev bureau produced Yak-50 which is powered by one 360hp Vedeneyev M-14P radial engine, a development of the -14B26 as installed in the Kamov Ka-26 helicopter. Yak-50 won several prizes in 1976 and is deployed in schools and airclubs of DOSAAF.

It is a single-seat, aerobatic low-wing monoplane, spanning 9.5m. Like the -18PS it has a tailwheel.

Powered by the same engine but equipped with a two-seat cabin and nosewheel, is the Yak-52, which will replace Yak-18s as a standard primary trainer. This fully aerobatic trainer was developed by the Arsenvev branch of the Yak bureau and is in production by the Romanian aeronautical industry. The nosewheel retracts rearwards and the main wheels forwards, but they are left fully exposed in retracted position.

From the Yak-52 two-seat trainer a single-seat aerobatic variant was test flown by A Sidinin. It retains the -52's semi-retracting nosewheel undercarriage and the same engine. Two-world-

Yak-50, produced for the 1976 World Aerobatic Championship.

Being introduced as the new standard primary trainer is Yak-52.

Yak-55 proved a world beater in aerobatics during 1982.

UPDATE

Military Trainers and Sports Aircraft

records have already been reported by FAI: V Makogov climbed to 3,000m in 5 minutes 5 seconds and M Molchanyuk reached 6,000m in 13 minutes 54 seconds. Designation is Yak-53.

During the World Aerobatics Championship in Spitzberg, Austria, from August 8-22, 1982, the Soviet delegation won 6 gold, 6 silver and 4 bronze medals flying Yak-55. This is also a single-seater powered by the M-14P. Span is 8.2m and length 7.48m.

Another newcomer is the Sukhoi Su-26, a neat looking single-seat aerobatic aircraft which spans 7.8m with a length of 6.82m. It is powered by the M-14P and made its first flight in June 1984.

During the 1985 Paris Salon the S-42, designed by junior engineers at Sukhoi OKB, was announced. No details were given other than that it was an aerobatic trainer.

During the summer of 1972 students at the Riga 'Lenin-Komsomol' Institute of Aviation Engineers developed a two-seat sport-amphibian powered by one Avia M-332 in-line engine. Fuselage was taken from the 'Progress' motor-boat and the wing, mounted on struts in parasol position, is similar to the 'Primoryez' training glider wing. First flight took place from Riga waters on September 6, 1974, which showed that a planing step was needed for improved take-off. Span is 13.2m, length 8.1m, wing area 20.2 sq m, empty weight 600kg, gross weight 900kg, maximum speed 160kph, practical ceiling 4,000m and range 500km. The 142hp Avia M-32 engine is placed above the cockpit in the wing of the RKIIGA-74, as this plane is designated.

A very interesting single-seat aerobatic aircraft was shown at the Economic Achievement Exhibition at Moscow in October 1967. From a distance this small, sturdy aircraft resembled a Lavochkin fighter. It was designed by the student design bureau at the Moscow Aviation Institute 'Ordshonikidze' and designated MAI-SKB-3PM 'Kvant'. It has one 360hp Vedeneyev M-14P, which also powers the Yak-50 series of aerobatic/trainer aircraft. Wing-span is 7.5m, length 5.7m and maximum speed 430kph.

A flying-boat trainer, the KhAI-30 'Professor Nyeman', was designed by the student design bureau (SKB) at Kharkov Aviation Institute for Initial Training at DOSAAF. It is powered by two engines, seats two and cruising speed at 570kg weight is reported to be 150kph.

The Riga 'Lenin-Komsomol' Institute of Aviation Engineers developed a single-seat, low-wing sport monoplane called 'Enthusiast'. It is powered by an in-line engine, take-off weight is 700kg, maximum speed 250kph and ceiling 4,500m.

Military trainers, which are usually trainer versions of basic models, have in the past been allotted reporting names beginning with 'M' for 'Miscellaneous. The Il-28UT 'Mascot', MiG-15UTI 'Midget' and MiG-21UTI 'Mongol' are examples. Following a new policy of giving trainer versions of basic aircraft their normal reporting names with a suffix, the MiG-23UM is called 'Flogger-C', the MiG-25U 'Foxbat-C', the Tu-22U 'Blinder-D' and the Yak-36U 'Forger-B'. The Czech L-39 'Albatros', which is deployed in great numbers in Soviet flying schools, has not been named in the reporting system, contrary to the older L-29 which received the name 'Maya'.

Fighter-like in appearance, this MAI-SKB-3PM single-seat aerobatic aircraft named Kvant was exhibited in Moscow in 1967. It was the work of a student design bureau.

A MiG-23U fighter trainer of the Czechoslovakian Air Force.

Above: MiG-25U which carries Western reporting name 'Foxbat-C'.

Below: Training version of the Tu-22 is designated Tu-22U and reports as 'Blinder-D'.

THE PILOT and graduate engineer, N I Petrov was first to fly the Moscow – Petersburg (Leningrad) route after the October Revolution. The flight was on April 1, 1918, and Petrov took one passenger over a distance of 600km in 4 hours 10 minutes. Fifty years later, 17 aircraft flew daily over this route, among them the Tu-124 which transports 50 passengers. The duration of flight – 45 minutes.

Almost fifty aircraft a day are engaged in flights from Moscow to the Far East. In the full tourist season, 22 aircraft a day are in service, flying the summer guests from Moscow to Sochi in the Crimea, and from there to the whole seaside area of the Black Sea. In 1972, Aeroflot transported 82.5 million passengers, besides 2.09 million tons of mail and cargo to become the world's largest air transport company.

The beginnings of aviation transport in the USSR were meagre, but the Soviet government and Lenin himself supported in every way possible development of the civilian aviation-sector.

In March 1919 Russia managed to establish air links with the newborn Hungarian Republic. Moreover, an increasing number of attempts were made to use aircraft for internal communications. In January 1920 an experimental route was opened between Sarapul and Yekaterinburg using the four-engined biplane 'Ilya Muromets'. Military fliers first opened up the Moscow – Gzhatsk – Smolensk line in 1920, main task being the transport of mail.

Autumn 1920 was an important time for development of civil aviation. A special government commission was set up to deal with problems arising in the design of commercial aircraft, whether for domestic or international use, plus political and economic implications. The first result was a law of January 1921 dealing (1) with air transport in the air space over the USSR (2), the legal prescriptions for civil aviation in the country, (3) the inviolability of Soviet air sovereignty etc.

In May 1921, the Moscow – Kharkov line was opened, again, using the 'Ilya Muromets'. A total of 43 flights carried 60 passengers and two tons of mail until October 1921 when the connection had to be interrupted because of unfavourable weather and failure of the machine itself. In 1922 air traffic on the line ceased completely.

Perhaps it was more important to have quick, reliable air links with Europe and the rest of the world than inter-state communications. The USSR was too weak to establish these international links alone, but close collaboration with Germany found expression in a common air transport company, Deruluft (German-Russian commercial air company). The government ratified its foundation on November 24, 1921; Soviet share was 250,000 gold roubles.

Route was from Moscow to Koenigsberg, in East Prussia, and in the early days it was necessary to make intermediate landings at Smolensk and Velikiye Luki. On April 30, 1922, the first Deruluft aircraft landed at Moscow's Khodynka airport. It was the high-wing Fokker

CHAPTER 31

Pre-War Commercial Aircraft

F.III (RR-1) monoplane of which the Soviets bought 20 examples.

Transport on the Deruluft line was reliable, safe and of particular significance for Soviet economy and politics. In 1929 the route was extended to Berlin. It is surprising that Deruluft was able to continue working in Germany for some time after Hitler had seized power. Not until April 1, 1937, did the Germans let the contract lapse and Deruluft was dissolved. The USSR then opened another route to Stockholm, having already established a link with Prague.

In Summer 1923 there were some 37 flights between Moscow and Nishnii-Novgorod on the occasion of the summer fair. Main task on this line was the transport of Moscow daily newspapers on the same day.

Yet up to that time everything achieved in the field of air transport was mere improvisation; there was no plan, no central direction and no supervisory office for civil aviation which could guarantee and regulate the technical and operational requirements. The necessary organisations were first called into being by the Council for Defence and Work on February 9, 1923, in a decree "concerning the foundation of the Supervisory Committee for the Air Lines in the main administrative sector of civil aviation and concerning the organisation of the Council of Civil Aviation".

The Council for Civil Aviation made a start that same year and in 1924 the sector began to be more active. Several regional joint stock companies for air transport were founded with share capital from some of the larger industrial undertakings, central authorities and a wide selection of individual shareholders. Thus Dobrolet came into being with a capital of five million roubles. This company first worked on the Moscow – Gorkiy – Kasan line but also linked towns of the Crimean Peninsula and built up a network from Tashkent to the Republics of Central Asia.

Dobrolet had regular flights to the capital of the Mongolian People's Republic, Ulanbatar, from the Siberian town Ulan-Ude. In 1928 Dobrolet extended the route from Moscow to Novosibirsk, giving the Soviet capital a fast link with Siberia and Mongolia. The route was flown with Dornier Merkur aircraft.

In the Ukraine city of Kharkov was a company called Ukrvosdukhput (UVP) with a private capital of two million roubles. Routes from here led to Orel and Moscow, Poltava, Kiev and Odessa, Rostov, Baku and Tbilisi etc. Ukrvosdukhput soon took over the smaller company Zakavia, which worked behind the Caucasus. There were other smaller companies, like Severoput for transport in the North and Arctic.

In 1930 the individual commercial companies were combined into the central state organisation Transavia and from Transavia developed the present company, Aeroflot, in 1932. Aeroflot was placed under the main administrative sector of civil aviation. Smaller organisations were then founded for specialised transport and auxiliary work, such as Lesookhrana for the monitoring of forests and their protection from fire; Aviaarktika for transport to the Arctic; and Aeropyl for agricultural aviation.

The table below provides a general view of Soviet air transport between 1921 and 1940. Aeroflot used four international routes towards the end of the thirties: Ulan-Ude – Ulanbatar, Tashkent – Kabul, Moscow – Prague (since 1935) and Moscow – Stockholm (since 1937). There were four main domestic lines: Moscow – Leningrad (600km), Moscow – Tashkent (3,050km), Moscow – Tbilisi (3,025km) and above all, Moscow – Vladivostok (8,190km). This last route was opened in 1936-7 and was, at that time, the most heavily used in the world.

Even when times were most difficult, the Soviet government still provided enough money for the purchase of foreign aircraft, so that companies were able to keep up-to-date and efficient. Thanks to these supplies, the civil sector was able to develop rapidly in the USSR. For example, 20 Junkers F-13 were purchased and a further five built in the Dobrolet plants. Some ten Junkers W-33 were imported and 17 built in the Soviet Union. under designation PS-4 (*Passashirskii Samolet* = passenger transport 'plane.) In addition, there were a number of Dornier Komet and Merkur, plus 66 Dornier Wal flying boats (60 purchased aircraft and 6 Soviet-built) some of which were used for transport. Single examples of the British De Havilland biplane DH-34 and Vickers Vernon were also purchased.

From this brief survey of the most important foreign models purchased we can see that the Soviet clients had a good knowledge of foreign aviation technology. They bought aircraft for use and for their own designers and workers to learn something.

From the beginning, Soviet designers made every effort to develop their own commercial aircraft. They produced interesting designs but these mostly suffered from inadequate workmanship and, above all, unreliable engines. Moreover, factories were not equipped even for the shortest series runs and not until the country had become industrialised, after 1928, were there more possibilities. By then the aviation industry was overburdened and construction of commercial aircraft remained a subsidiary concern.

The founding of KOMTA (*Komissiya po Tyasheloj Aviacii* = Commission for Heavy Aviation) was a piece of pioneer work in development

Soviet Air Transport 1921-1940			
Year	Distance (km)	Passengers	Cargo (kg)
1921	750	60	2,000
1922	1,250	319	21,430
1923	1,610	1,433	27,885
1924	4,400	2,618	48,000
1925	4,984	3,398	76,000
1926	6,392	4,035	85,000
1927	7,022	7,079	170,381
1928	11,427	7,500	200,500
1929	18,461	11,200	321,987
1933	53,182	42,700	1,967,385
1934	68,050	63,000	4,200,000
1937	106,040	211,800	46,000,000
1938	114,130	287,200	54,400,000
1940	138,800	358,700	59,920,000

Economics did not permit the country to cater for this upsurge in civil transport with home built planes. Until the beginning of the thirties Soviet airlines were mostly served by foreign-built aircraft. From the following table we can see that not until 1930 did the number of home-built aircraft catch up with, and indeed overtake, the purchased number.

Aircraft	1923	1929	1930	1931	1932	1933	1934	1935
Soviet built (in %)	0	39	52	63	69	87	96	99
Purchased	100	62	48	37	31	13	4	1

of Soviet commercial aircraft. KOMTA was formed by the Higher Council of Political Economy in Spring 1920 under the presidency of N J Shukovskii. It was to decide on the conditions necessary for introduction of regular air transport with heavy multi-seat aircraft and, at the same time, procure an appropriate model. KOMTA also originated the experimental Sarapul – Yekaterinburg line in January 1920 on which an Ilya Muromets of the Sarapul heavy bomber unit was used.

The engineers of this unit also submitted a project for Ilya Muromets-style heavy transport. But KOMTA considered an aircraft with the lines of Muromets outdated. After several studies and wind tunnel experiments, they decided to build a big triplane for two pilots and six to eight passengers, driven by two 280mhp Fiat engines. Main parts were built in the Sarapul plants, being mostly Muromets components or something similar. The aircraft was assembled in Moscow and pronounced to be in flying condition in March 1922.

V M Remesyuk, commander of the bomber unit, began flight tests. The aircraft could hardly get off the ground, because centre of gravity was located too far rearwards. After reconstruction, when the engines were put a metre further forward, new flight tests were begun under A M Cheremukhin, A I Tomashevskii and B N Kudrin. The aircraft flew up to the beginning of the Summer of 1924, reached 130kph and 600m ceiling. As it seemed to have no prospects it was given to the training branch.

Clearly required was a different concept and the cornerstone of Soviet aviation technology was a simple high-wing monoplane, AK-1, test flown by Tomashevskii on February 8, 1924. AK-1 was designed by V L Alexandrov and V V Kalinin at TsAGI using scientific methods. Models were tested in the wind tunnel and even released from high towers.

The strut-braced, high-wing monoplane was of composite construction with an open cabin for pilot and mechanic in front of the wing and enclosed cabin for two passengers in the fuselage. Engine was the water-cooled Salmson RB-9, a nine-cylinder radial engine of 160/170mhp. The thorough preliminary work undertaken proved worthwhile. AK-1 had excellent flying qualities, its flight tests did not take long and the plane was sold to Dobrolet on June 15, 1924, for use from Moscow to Kasan via Novgorod. On this route AK-1 covered over 11,000km and was also able to undertake a long distance flight in 1925 from Moscow to Peking, a distance of 7,000km.

During 1924 several transport prototypes were constructed. Another TsAGI plane was ANT-2, designed and built under the direction of A N Tupolev. It was a high-wing monoplane and can still be viewed today in the aviation museum of the Monino Academy near Moscow. The machine really deserves to be preserved for future generations to see, because it was the first all-metal aircraft of Soviet design and built of Soviet materials (Koltschug aluminium).

In October 1922 a committee had been formed at TsAGI for the construction of all-metal aircraft. This committee was under Tupolev. Dural sheet deformation, instability etc were problems first examined in practice when six big skids with propeller drive and a hydroplane with all-metal propeller were constructed.

Design of ANT-2 began in May 1923. It was a cantilever, high-wing monoplane of corrugated sheet metal with high flat fuselage and low undercarriage. Pilot was in an open seat in front of the wing; the two passengers sat opposite each other in a fuselage cabin. Engine was a three-cylinder, 100mhp Bristol Lucifer.

N I Petrov test flew the aircraft on May 26, 1924. Flying qualities were good on the whole, and only the rudder-fin unit had to be slightly enlarged. ANT-2 was not suited for regular transport for there was no possibility of servicing the Lucifer engine and the payload was too low. But it prepared the way for a better, all-metal, home-built transport plane.

Other machines of 1924 were less important. J E Groppius built a six-seat biplane GAZ No. 5 in the State aircraft plant – also called GAZ No. 5. This had a particularly spacious fuselage, stretching from the upper to the lower wing, and engine was a 300mhp Hispano-Suiza 8Fb. Pilot Yefremov tested the biplane in Summer 1924 and found it too unwieldy, its climbing speed too low and requiring an over-long take-off run. Nevertheless the machine was flown for a few months by Dobrolet. Speed was 165kph and range 750km.

D P Grigorovich offered his strut-braced, high wing monoplane PL-1 or SUVP to Ukrovsdukhput (*Samolet dlya UVP* = aircraft for Ukrvosdukhput). It was an all-wood aircraft with an especially thick wing section and Bristol Lucifer engine. Construction was protracted until spring 1925 but PL-1 flew well and was in service for a long time with Ukrvosdukhput.

The first really useable machines were produced in 1925, machines which justified series production. In the first days of March, Aircraft Plant No. 1 in Moscow received the order from Aviatrust to design and build a transport machine

KOMTA's big triplane could carry six to eight passengers in theory but in practice could barely get off the ground. It eventually achieved 600m and was relegated to training duties.

Above: AK-1 was the first successful passenger aircraft in Russia, undertaking a 7,000km Moscow-Peking flight in 1925.

Below: First all-metal aircraft of Soviet design was Tupolev's ANT-2 which first flew in 1924 and is now preserved at the Monino Academy, near Moscow. It did not enter service but paved the way for later models.

Dubrolet flew the GAZ No.5 for a few months despite its unwieldy nature and unusually long take-off run. Six passengers could be accommodated.

for three passengers and two crewmen. Deadline was only three months, for the aircraft was to take part in a planned Moscow – Peking long distance flight.

A A Semenov was responsible for the preliminaries and subsequent design work. N N Polikarpov directed the construction and because of this was at one stage incorrectly described as the designer. It was actually ready in 90 days and test flown on June 10, 1925, by A I Shukov, but did not take part in the long distance flight.

The all-wood machine was called PM-1 (P for *Passashirskii* = passenger plane and M for *Maybach* Mb-IVa engine of 260mhp). Qualities and performances were so good that there was no need for any change. Speed was 170kph, range 800km and work began on a production run of 10 machines. PM-1 made a flight from Moscow to Leningrad where it was to join the Deruluft line to Berlin. But during flight the engine mounting broke, the machine was damaged in an emergency landing and pilot N P Shibanov injured. As there were no more engines available, the production run of PM-1 was halted.

A further reason for stoppage was the success of another transport aircraft which had its origins in Kiev. Here K A Kalinin had been at work since 1923 as director of the design department of aircraft repair plant Remvosdukhtzavod No. 6. He and his assistants began the high-wing monoplane in their free time but later it became an official task.

Kalinin was an obstinate defender of the elliptical wing form which had good aerodynamics. He used it not only on the K-1 but on almost all of his later machines. The K-1 wing was in wood and the fuselage made of welded tubular steel, which was still available in the plant having been taken from the damaged Voisin biplanes as was the 170mhp Salmson RB-9. A new feature was the enclosed pilot's cockpit, which had two seats. In the fuselage were seats for three passengers.

The K-1 was airborne on July 26, 1925, and in

September was flown to Moscow where government tests were successfully completed. But the engine, which already had many years of service behind it, caused difficulties. In the end a 240mhp BMW-IV was mounted and performance rose considerably.

Directors of the aviation industry decided to give Kalinin opportunities for development of his aircraft. In Kharkov the experimental plant GROS was founded and Kalinin was appointed its chief designer. At GROS (*Grashdanskoje Opitnoje Samoletostrojenije* = Experimental Aircraft Plant of Civil Aviation) Kalinin worked under favourable conditions and with support of the Ukrainian government.

Next aircraft to appear was K-2, on the same lines as K-1 and with BMW-IV engine, but of all-metal construction. The wings had tubular steel spars and dural skin; fuselage had a tubular steel airframe and sheet metal skin. The aircraft was

The all-wood SUVP (PL-1) of D P Grigorovich flew for some time with Ukrvosdukhput.

PM-1, produced in 90 days, worked well but ran out of engines.

Below: K A Kalinin, an advocate of the eliptical wing, saw a few of his all-metal Ka-2 aircraft into service, carrying four passengers at a maximum of 170kph.

Equipped with ski undercarriage, this ambulance version was one of several variants of K-4. Most were used for passenger flights but some undertook aerial mapping duties.

Above: K-5 could carry eight people in addition to its crew and some 260 examples were built up to 1934.

too complicated and heavy, but a few K-2s were built and put into service on the Ukrvosdukhput lines. They carried four passengers, maximum speed was 170kph and range 650km.

The high-wing K-3 monoplane of 1927 was a great novelty, being the first Soviet aircraft built specifically for ambulance service. The plane was of composite construction with a BMW-IV engine and there was enough room for two stretchers and the doctor or, alternatively, four seated patients. On the left of the fuselage was a loading hatch. Stretchers, and the rest of the medical aircraft equipment, were the work of the 'Father' of Soviet ambulance aviation, Dr A F Linhart, born in Czechoslovakia.

The 'K' line reached a mature stage of structural engineering with model K-4 of 1928. Out of 22 machines built in 1930 most were used as commercial planes with a pilot, four passengers and BMW-IV engines. A few were equipped as ambulance machines, having the same capacity as K-3 and 300mhp M-6. A prototype was shown at the 1929 international aviation exhibition in Berlin.

Several K-4 were also equipped for aerial photography or, rather, aerial mapping. This activity was very important in the USSR, providing up-to-date data for large scale planning in agriculture, water conservation, traffic organisation, architectural planning, plans for the increase in the size of towns etc. In 1925 a few Dobrolet machines photographed the immediate 570 square kilometres round Tver and 400 square kilometres round Moscow. In 1927 Ukrvosdukhput took up the same activity and aerial mapping became systematically pursued. Two cameras were installed inside the K-4 fuselage and operated by two or three technologists. These photographs could not be developed until after landing.

Growing demands on the aerial mapping service induced V B Shavrov to design a special aircraft, Sh-5, with excellent vision and a spacious cabin where photographs could be developed during flight. Service designations of the 1929 project were FS-1 and FS-2 (*Foto Samolet =* photographic plane). FS-1 was to be a landplane and FS-2 a seaplane, but they were to have the same design. In March 1931 TsKB took over the real design work, combining them into a single amphibian with work designation TsKB No. 28/29.

Sh-5 was a cantilever, high-wing monoplane in composite construction with two M-22 engines in nacelles above the fuselage. The thickly glazed cabin could also take twelve passengers. Belly of the fuselage was boat-shaped and the outrigger floats were supplemented by a retractable undercarriage.

Sh-5 was constructed in central plants of the civil aviation sector, but work was very slow and a prototype could not be test flown on skid undercarriage until March 19, 1934. By this time the design had become very outdated and most aerial mapping was accomplished by military planes, ending the need for special aircraft.

It is interesting to note that Ukrvosdukhput originally preferred the German Dornier models to Kalinin's 'K' series and the first to arouse interest was K-4. In fact there was soon a fast growing demand for K-4 which could not be fully satisfied owing to lack of BMW-IV engines.

Such demands prompted Kalinin to build a larger K-5 aircraft in 1929, capable of carrying eight passengers or a corresponding load. The design was still wood/tubular steel with dural sheet covering of the front part of the fuselage. Prototype and the first one hundred production machines had 450mhp M-15 radial engines which proved faulty and short lived. So in 1930 the 480mhp M-22 was introduced and reliability improved.

Up to 1934 260 machines were built and several examples were used up to the Summer of 1941. Their operating speed was 160 to 170kph and range 800km.

After a while the performances of M-22 and M-15 became inadequate. Kalinin looked for a suitable engine that was both light and powerful. In 1934 he decided to try the 680mhp in-line M-17F, a heavy engine which provoked stability problems that forced either a reduced range or fewer passengers. Nevertheless some ten K-5s with M-17F were reconstructed and used for many years.

K-6, with 420mhp Gnome-Rhone Jupiter IV engine, came in 1930. This was derived from K-5, designed for the transport of mail and the matrices of daily newspapers. Two crew members were housed in a narrow fuselage and the machine reached 210kph. K-6 was not put into production.

While Kalinin's work on the whole provided good aircraft for domestic routes, the inter-

Left: Shavrov designed the Sh-5 amphibian with aerial mapping in mind but it could also accommodate 12 passengers. Progress in other areas quickly made it obsolete.

national line needed even better aircraft. In October 1927 the design department AGOS-TsAGI received an official order for a three-engined transport plane. ANT-9 was completed in April 1928 and in July 1928 the Council for Civil Aviation had scheduled development and series production in the context of the Five Year Plan.

Photographs of the ANT-9 prototype, taken in Red Square on May 1, 1929, were disseminated over the whole world. It was an all-metal, high-wing monoplane in dural and corrugated sheet with cantilever wing, enclosed two-seat cockpit and nine seats in the main cabin. Three Gnome-Rhone Titan engines, each of 230mph, were in the nose and in nacelles on the wing.

Flight tests of 'Kryla Sovetov' (Wing of the Soviets) were begun immediately after the festival when M M Gromov flew the route Moscow – Odessa – Sevastopol – Odessa – Moscow. Between July 16 and August 8 he effected a Moscow – Berlin – Paris – Rome – Marseilles – London – Paris – Berlin – Warsaw – Moscow flight of 9,037km with eight passengers. Actual flying time was 53 hours at an average speed of 170.5kph.

Twelve production machines were built with Soviet 300mhp M-26 engines, but these proved most unreliable and on some aircraft were replaced by the American 365mhp Wright J-4 Whirlwind or Gnome-Rhone Titan.

Deruluft were given two ANT-9 with Whirlwind engines in 1932. German technologists covered the corrugated metal wing surface with fabric and this helped to improve performances a little. The ANT-9 with Titan engines reached 185kph and had 900km range while with Whirlwind the figures were 205kph and 700km.

As it became clear that engine difficulties could not be eliminated, a drastic reconstruction was undertaken. On the fuselage was mounted the wing of heavy reconnaissance plane, ANT-7, together with two M-17 engines, and the nose was given a new shape. This model became PS-9 and 60 examples were constructed by 1934. PS-9 reached 235kph, had an operating speed of 200kph and range of 700km. They were still in operation during the war for front-line transport around Stalingrad and Kursk.

Two PS-9 aircraft of 1934 deserve special attention. One of them, with registration number SSSR-L-183, which was in service until 1942 achieved a total of 5,205 flying hours; the second was called 'Crocodile'. They were connected with a peculiar institution in Soviet aviation, the 'Agitation' Squadron 'Maksim Gorki'.

In September 1932 the Central Committee of the Communist Party of the USSR decided to create a squadron bearing the name of the writer, Gorki, in honour of the 40th anniversary of his first story. The squadron was called 'Agiteskad-rila Maksima Gorkogo' and director was Mikhail Koltsov, a well-known journalist. The squadron were to fly into the furthest parts of the country to execute their mission, organising cinema performances, lectures, public functions etc. On May 5, 1933, Soviet Press Day, the first machines flew to their posts.

Among the squadron were two PS-9 which were given the names of newspapers, one representing a popular satirical newspaper, 'Crocodile'. In order to fit the aircraft to its task, the fuselage nose was redesigned by Shavrov in the shape of a crocodile along with a certain amount of fuselage re-modelling. PS-9 'Crocodile' thus became very well-known among Soviet aircraft.

Flagship of the squadron was, for a time, the giant five-motored, high-wing monoplane, ANT-14, called 'Pravda' after the newspaper of the Party. With the ANT-14 Tupolev wanted to give the civil aviation sector a high-capacity aircraft capable of transporting 36 passengers and a five-man crew over the main routes. Work proceeded at a particularly fast rate, designers taking over, in scarcely modified form, the wing of a four-engined ANT-6 bomber. The wing was mounted on a large, new fuselage which had a cross-section like that of the carriage of an express train. In the nacelles and fuselage nose were a total of five Gnome-Rhone Jupiter VI engines, each of 480mhp. On top of the fuselage was an observation dome.

Construction of ANT-14 was completed in Summer 1931, and M M Gromov made the first flight on August 14. The aircraft was particularly good and required minimal modification. Maximum speed was 220kph, operating speed 195kph, service ceiling 4,000m and range 900km. With its 40.39m span and 17,530kg flying weight it was one of the largest transport planes of the time.

But it soon became evident that ANT-14 was far in advance of actual transport requirements. On none of the Soviet routes could full use be

ANT-9 in its original three-engined form (above) and with twin M-17 engines, designated PS-9 (below).

Below: Complete with specially modified nose and paintwork, PS-9 'Crocodile' carried out work for the 'Agitation' Squadron 'Maksim Gorki'.

Above: A giant on skis – Tupolev's ANT-14.

Below: ANT-14 'Pravda', a 36-passenger aircraft which served for a time as flagship of the 'Maksim Gorki' organisation.

made of a plane with ANT-14's cabin capacity. Most Soviet civil planes of the time were able to carry a maximum of ten, so no further machines of this type were built and the prototype was given to the 'Agitation' Squadron.

ANT-14 was mainly used on tours over Moscow and shortly before the outbreak of war had given 40,000 people on 1,000 flights the chance to see their capital from the air. But long years of propaganda service were not terminated. In 1942 the fuselage of ANT-14 was used as a cinema hall in one of Moscow's culture parks.

Simultaneously with the foundation of 'Maksim Gorki' it was decided to build a giant flagship, a real flying propaganda combine. The aircraft was to bear the name 'Gorki'. Of course, the design and construction of a giant like this required money, so the squadron organised a collection throughout the country. In a short time eight million roubles were collected, of which one million were obtained during a ten-day stop by ANT-14 in Leningrad.

Who else could design a giant aircraft like this but Tupolev and his group in KOSOS-TsAGI? Tupolev was given the official commission on March 10, 1933, but the real design work was directed by V M Petlyakov. A year later, on March 30, 1934, the aircraft was completed and ready at Tushino airfield. After a series of checks Gromov first test flew the aircraft on June 17, 1934, for a period of 35 minutes. His second flight on June 19 passed over Red Square where a reception was taking place to celebrate liberation of the crew from the ice-bound steamer, Chelyuskin.

ANT-20 showed influence of the ANT-16 bomber in its general design, but had a span of 63m – 9m greater. On the wing leading edge were six tractor M-34FRN engines of 900mhp and over the fuselage were two engines in tandem arrangement.

The aircraft was built in plant No. 22 at Fili, the former Junkers aircraft plant. Several factories and institutions contributed to the design production of accessories and interior equipment. It was an honour to them to work for the largest aircraft in the world. 'Maksim Gorki' was the first all-metal aircraft of the Soviet Union which had a basic construction of Soviet materials and equipment.

Flying the giant was relatively easy, thanks to electro-servo drive. Normally the crew consisted of eight men while in the fuselage and wing section were cabins where up to 72 people could be comfortably accommodated. But passenger flying was certainly not the only task given to ANT-20. For advertising work it had equipment unmatched by any plane before or since. There was an offset printing machine, a complete photographic and film laboratory, a projection cabin for films and transparencies including the facility to project during flight onto clouds or artificial mists, electric fluorescent writing on the underside of the wing, a gigantic loudspeaker, 'Golos s neba' (Voice from the Sky) which could cover 12sq km, and a telephone installation for twelve. The current was generated in a unit driven by a 30mhp benzine engine.

On advertising flights there were always about twenty people on board ANT-20. During the flight newspapers were made, printed and thrown out as the aircraft flew over various localities. Not surprisingly 'Maksim Gorki' always aroused a great deal of attention. The people at large saw a symbol of Soviet success in technology and reconstruction of the country.

It was a national tragedy when, on May 18, 1935, a special transmission announced the loss of ANT-20.

The aircraft had on board several TsAGI employees and their families. Although it was strictly forbidden, a TsAGI pilot, N P Blagin, approached the giant in his I-5 fighter and began to perform aerobatic stunts at a dangerously close range. Suddenly his I-5 hit the wings of ANT-20 and both machines fell to the ground. All 49 people aboard including the pilot and captain I C Shurov, were killed. Blagin also died.

Under the impact of this catastrophe the country was spontaneously swept by a new wave of enthusiasm. People were anxious to remove the damage as quickly as possible and build several giant machines. Within a few weeks 35,000,000 roubles were collected. Sixteen new machines were to be built, the first was to bear Gorki's name, the others the names of international revolutionaries and leaders of the Soviet Government and Party.

But the overloaded aircraft industry was not

Ill-fated ANT-20 'Maksim Gorki' was the largest aircraft in the world when it first flew on June 17, 1934. It was often escorted by two I-4 fighters (left) and was brought down when an I-5 collided with the leviathan in 1935.

capable of meeting such a large order straight away. Moreover, after 1937, official views changed and such propaganda work was no longer considered necessary. Of the machines designed only one was built, the ANT-20bis, completed in 1938, flown by Gromov and E I Shvarts in Spring 1939. Director of design was B A Saukke, for Tupolev was under arrest at the time. Saukke modernised the aircraft, rejecting a tandem engine arrangement and in its place installing six more powerful AM-34FRNV, each of 1,000/1,200mhp. Behind the engines, in each wing, was a cabin for the technician in charge of engine maintenance during flight. ANT-20bis reached 275kph, its service ceiling was 3,500m and range 1,300km.

After flight tests the machine was given to Aeroflot, being designated PS-124 and transporting 64 passengers on the Moscow – Mineralnije Vodi (Caucasus) route. In December 1940, 1,200mhp AM-35 engines were mounted. After the outbreak of war, PS-124 served for military air

transport in Central Asia, and this assignment continued until November 1942 when the aircraft was destroyed in a crash landing. Total length of flying time was 272 hours.

With the Tupolev machines we have reached the first years of the war; now we must go back to trace other developments. At this time mostly lighter models were designed and built, two to six passengers being the most common specification.

The all-steel machines designed and built by graduate engineer A I Putilov occupied an important place. Putilov was one of the oldest of Tupolev's assistants who left TsAGI in 1929 to enter the Military Aviation Academy. There, in the laboratory, he was able to carry out the first experiments with electric spot and seam welding using Soviet stainless steel Enersh-6 (18% chromium and 8% nickel).

In the laboratory was an American welding machine on which the first samples from Soviet metal plants were tested. Attempts to replace

Built to replace ANT-20, the refined ANT-20bis (PS-124) could hold 64 passengers and flew until 1942 when it was destroyed in a crash landing.

269

STAL-2, first aircraft from the Department for Test Plane Construction, had an airframe entirely made from stainless steel.

Two versions of the larger STAL-3 – with M-17 engine (above) and with the more common M-22 (below).

dural and aluminium by super refined steel were backed by the highest authorities in the country, even by the so-called Small Economic Council of the People's Commissioners. Aluminium and dural had to be imported and were expensive, so attempts to use other raw materials were always encouraged.

Experiments in 1930 changed aviation design. In this year the Inspectorate of the Civil Air Force founded a group OOS (*Otdel Opytnogo Samoletostrojenija* = Department for Test Plane Construction) under the direction of Putilov. The group started to build their aircraft in Moscow in the former Dobrolet aircraft hangar on Central Airfield.

The first was the strut-braced, high-wing monoplane STAL-2 for a pilot and four passengers, with 300mhp Wright J-6 Whirlwind engines. The whole airframe was made of stainless steel, mostly sheet sections spot or seam welded. Production took a long time and required a great number of individual parts, but the aircraft was expected to last for almost an eternity.

First STAL-2 was successfully test flown on October 11, 1931, and immediately ordered into series production. Progress in Tushino plant No. 81 was too slow, owing to complicated construction. Stainless steel production in the 'Sickle and Hammer' plant was also very laborious and expensive – it was even said that steel was as expensive as silver.

At the beginning of 1932 a new rolling mill arrived from Krupp's in Germany, after which steel sheets could be delivered more quickly and cheaply. All the same, in order to ensure that there were no hitches in delivery, a number of Swedish 18-8 steel sheets were bought, the equivalent of Soviet Enersh-6. So we can see how, at that time, the difficulties in Soviet production were quickly overcome by large-scale foreign aid.

The first production STAL-2 arrived in 1934; first they had 300mhp M-26 engines, then improved MG-31s of the same horsepower. By 1935, 111 examples had been built and delivered. An international public were able to study STAL-2 during an aircraft exhibition in Milan in 1935 and they remained in service until about 1940.

Production continued with the larger, high-wing monoplane STAL-3. This machine had a 480mhp M-22 engine and was able to transport two pilots and six passengers. It had plain flaps, Townend Ring, brakes on the main wheels and other novelties. Maximum speed was 260kph, 60kph more than STAL-2. Between 1935 and 1936 a total of 79 machines were built, some with in-line M-17. These machines served on Aeroflot routes up to Summer 1941, and for some time afterwards in the military air transport role.

When the STAL aircraft with their stainless steel airframes were introduced, people believed that they now had indestructible models which would require no maintenance. The experts were doomed to be disappointed; STAL machines needed the same maintenance as other aircraft. Not only did the fabric covering decay and the screws and other parts rust, but the stainless steel also rusted at weld spots.

Within the STAL-2 class one could find a whole string of rivals. In 1931 Yakovlev designed a light, high-wing monoplane of composite construction with wooden wings and tubular steel fuselage. But this four-seat AIR-5, with its Wright J-4 Whirlwind and 192kph, remained a prototype for the Civil Air Force were more interested in their own STAL-2.

In 1932 Yakovlev built a lighter version, AIR-6, with 100mhp M-11 engine and three-seat cockpit. This was just right for the short Aeroflot routes and between 1934/36, 468 were built. Twenty of the machines were ambulance aircraft, each with a cabin for a stretcher. In 1934 a group of AIR-6 made a flight in stages from Moscow to Irkutsk and back, altogether more than 11,000km.

The AIR-6A variant of 1933 was given two wooden floats designed by Shavrov. On May 23,

Yakovlev's AIR-5, with Wright J-4 Whirlwind engine, remained a sole prototype.

Yakovlev's AIR-6 was ideal for short Aeroflot routes and between 1934/36 a total of 468 examples were built, including some for ambulance work.

A S Moskalev made his name with SAM-5, a cantilever, high-wing transport constructed in 1933 with a mixture of smooth and corrugated metal sheets.

SAM-5bis was a re-designed SAM-5 in wood instead of metal.

1937, J V Pismennii and V P Kuznetsov set up an international record for light seaplanes when they flew 1,297.1km between Kiev and Batumi in 10 hours 25 minutes at an average speed of 124.3kph. Usually the maximum speed of AIR-6 was 162kph and of AIR-6A 150kph, ranges being 650 and 600km respectively.

Third light transport of that time was the cantilever, high-wing monoplane SAM-5. With this, A S Moskalev joined the ranks of well-known Soviet aircraft designers. He began as an amateur but his work attracted such attention that in 1932 he found himself employed in the newly built Voronesh Plant No. 18. In 1937 and 1938 he also worked as a director of *Aviatekhnikum in Voronesh* (Aviation Commercial School) and later directed his own design bureau No. 31.

SAM-5 was built in 1933 under very unfavourable circumstances in makeshift buildings at Voronesh. Most of the men concerned gained their first experience with light metals on this machine. Moskalev's fuselage was very spacious with room for a pilot and five passengers and covered with 0.3mm dural sheet. Fuselage skin was smooth whereas the wings and controls had 0.3mm corrugated sheet metal covering. This construction proved to be particularly light; empty weight was 626kg and fully loaded the machine weighed 1,100kg. It reached 175kph and all the pilots who flew with SAM-5 were enthusiastic. But imprecise work in the plant meant that the aircraft had its troubles.

Moskalev realised that the newly constructed factory was not yet in a position to build all-metal aircraft on a larger scale as few experts were working there. So in 1934 he redesigned SAM-5 in wood, thus producing SAM-5bis, characterised by two wing struts on each side of the fuselage. Engine was the familiar M-11.

All pilots were enthusiastic about SAM-5bis, including P M Stefanovskii who completed government tests in 1935. The People's Commissariat of Heavy Industry, a body of which, at that time, the aviation industry was part, enabled Plant No. 18

to test the qualities of SAM-5bis on several occasions. N D Fixon and A S Busunov averaged 133kph on the 1,600km Voronesh – Moscow – Kharkov – Voronesh circuit on September 21, 1936. A month later, on October 20 and 21, the same crew flew 3,200km in 25 hours 5 minutes, averaging 128kph via Sevastopol to Genichesk, Mariupol, Rostov, Stalingrad, Astrakhan, Stalingrad, Sysran, Kaszan and Gorkii. SAM-5bis's take-off weight was 1,500kg of which 620kg was fuel.

In spite of these successes, the SAM-5bis was only given a small production run of 37 aircraft in the Aviatekhnikum, Voronesh. Almost all were delivered in the ambulance variant form with a long loading hatch on the port side of the fuselage. SAM-5bis often flew with six people on board and in general its lifting capacity was surprisingly good with an M-11 engine. The machine normally raised a payload which was 45.7% of its take-off weight.

SAM-5-2bis made its appearance in 1936. Again, this was an all-wood machine, a little smaller than its predecessor, but with improved aerodynamics, cantilever wing and undercarriage. The cabin held five and with an M-11, SAM-5-2bis was able to reach 205kph. Service ceiling was 4,280m.

On September 23/24, 1937, A N Gusarov and V L Glebov set up a new FAI long distance record with this aircraft, covering the 3,513km from Moscow to Krasnoyarsk in 19 hours 59 minutes. A year later V V Borodin reached 8,000m altitude, but his machine had a 200mhp MG-21 engine. In Summer 1939 V K Kondrafev climbed to 8,400m in a SAM-5-2bis fitted with a 200mhp M-11FN, blower and metal propeller. By making use of warm air currents he later managed 8,900m. Moskalev wanted to mount oxygen injection for the engine and reach a full 10,000m but these preparations were interrupted by the war.

The Red Air Force ordered an ambulance variant of SAM-5-2bis in 1938, equipped for a pilot, doctor and two stretchers. The prototype was tested thoroughly and 200 aircraft were ordered. Suddenly the Commissariat of the Aviation Industry countermanded the order. M M Kaganovich had expressed strong reservations about Moskalev's work and made his aversion felt at every stage. Nor was there any use made of designs deriving directly from SAM-5-2bis.

In 1940 the SAM-14 was produced. It had an in-line 140mhp MV-4 engine, slats, plain flaps and clean qualities, but the commissariat showed no interest. In 1943 Moskalev built the SAM-25, an especially clean-lined, cantilever high-wing monoplane with M-11F. The machine was in every respect better than the U-2 biplane, but again failed to win support.

Prototype SAM-10 was test flown in June 1938. This was a low-wing version of SAM-5-2bis with a new, in-line MM-1 engine of A A Bessonov supposed to reach 220mhp. Most of the structural parts were directly taken over from SAM-5-2bis, but new features were the fully glazed cabin and trouser-leg undercarriage. The government test

SAM-5-2bis was smaller than its predecessors but aerodynamically superior. The aircraft was capable of 205kph and attained a service ceiling of 4,280m.

A low-wing version of SAM-5-2bis appered in the form of SAM-10, first flown in June 1938 with a new, in-line MM-1 engine.

report of August 1938 recommended it for use on short Aeroflot routes. The machine reached 336 kph with MM-1 which unfortunately was only available in two experimental versions and series engines could not be delivered early enough.

Moskalev hoped to win support for SAM-10bis by using the existing 220mhp MV-6. These were copies of the Renault Bengali 6Pei but in winter 1939 production was interrupted for the engines were not equal to the exacting conditions of service in the USSR. There were no engines and therefore no aircraft could be built.

We can see that much attention was paid to the design of light transport aircraft. Unfortunately not all the possible models won enough support for series production though some of those disregarded were excellent. There were various reasons for this state of affairs, some of a personal nature, but mainly the plants were overburdened with military orders.

Success or failure of a factory was judged by ability to reach a certain target production of aircraft. So the plants usually postponed, or even refused, the smaller scale civil machines which were therefore built in smaller plants, less adequately equipped. For the aviation industry it was more convenient to reconstruct military machines as transports, but these were not so efficient, economic nor practical as purpose-built aircraft. Nevertheless, a large number were used in civil aviation, as the military sector were assiduous suppliers of discarded machines.

Of military aircraft reconstructed for civil use, U-2 trainers were the most numerous as it was possible to make full use of their great lifting capacity. In 1933 the U-2SP variant was produced, a three-seater with two open seats behind the pilot. SP stood for *Specialnogo Primeneniya* (Special Purposes) which originally signified liaison and transport over short routes. Later SP came to have the meaning *Svyasnoj Passaskirskii* (Liaison and Passenger Plane) with addition of the letter L for *Limusen* (Limousine).

Full designation U-SPL was given to a new design put into production from 1935 onwards. The two rear passenger seats were enclosed, with a window. Between 1934 and 1939 some 861 U-2SP were built, including the SPL version. Moreover, numerous individual reconstructions were made in Aeroflot plants and elsewhere. For example, the big oil company, Bashneft, reconstructed their U-2SP to make a limousine. The engine was given a Townend ring and wheels were provided with drop-shaped spats.

In cargo, mail and passenger transport, the reconstructed reconnaissance R-5 won particular fame. After removal of equipment and armament, the military land or floatplane version R-5A was quite simply used to transport 400kg of mail and cargo in the rear seat. After more thorough reconstruction, two passengers plus their luggage could also be transported in the open or closed cabin.

One cannot say the machines were comfortable, and even the operating speed of 165kph was not the most favourable. But even this spelled progress for transport in the less developed regions. These civil machines were designated P-5 and P-5a when in a twin float version and were in service up to about 1943.

Besides these basic variants, smaller numbers of reconstructed R-5s had enclosed cabins and various attachments so that better use could be made of the aeroplane's lifting capacity. Usually the three seats were beneath a transparent enclosure.

In 1936 A N Rafaeljants, chief designer at Aeroflot's repair plant in Bykovo, developed the modernised variant PR-5. A four-seat passenger cabin was sunk into the fuselage and to the front and on top was a drop-shaped, fully enclosed pilot's cockpit. Centre of gravity difficulties, caused by the passenger cabin being too far rearwards, were solved with a different wing stagger.

Reconstructed U-2 military trainers saw civil use, among them the U-2SP (left) and U-2 'Bashneft' three-seater with enclosed cabin (below).

Two passengers plus luggage could be carried in the R-5 Limuzin, a modified R-5 reconnaissance aircraft. Other versions transported mail or cargo.

A specialised R-5 with detachable under-wing containers.

PS-43, civil variant of the licence-built Vultee V-11, were used for military liaison or freight carrying.

Among numerous civil versions of warplanes was PS-40, created from the SB-2 medium bomber.

Then they ran a short production run of PR-5bis in Bykovo and the plane was successfully flown by Aeroflot.

The R-5, which was not so efficient in military service, proved better in civilian role than more modern R-Zs. This machine also had a civil version designated P-Z, but they had to be written off after two years.

In order to fully use the lifting capacity for mail, designer D S Markov mounted aerodynamic freight tanks under the lower wings of P-5. These were built in fairly large numbers. Tanks were also designed for more voluminous loads and called *kasseta* (caskets). They had the shape of a wing section, were closely attached to the lower wing and supported loads through their own lift. Thus, up to 1,300kg could be carried in a casket.

P I Grokhovskii, of Leningrad, designed a casket in 1936 in which seven stretchers could be accommodated. Under the lower wing of a P-5 two such G-61 caskets were mounted and Grokhovskii himself piloted the aircraft in December 1936 to a record lift of 16 people. Smaller caskets proved their worth in 1934, when used to rescue crew from the Chelyuskin, which was locked in Polar ice.

In mail service a few reconstructed, all-metal R-3 biplanes succeeded as P-3. For cargo transport, demilitarised TB-1 bombers were also used, designated G-1. These machines had an incredible life of several thousand flying hours and after reconstruction could take passengers. Later, after repairs had been made and the airframe was barely safe, only cargo, such as sulphur from the mines near Ashkhabad, was allowed.

Similarly, the TB-3 was delivered in various civil versions and put into service as G-2. As this machine did not have to execute combat manoeuvres it could be heavily overloaded. Flying weight could reach as much as 22,000kg with four M-34RN engines in comparison with 18,600kg of the standard heavy bomber.

Further civil versions of military machines included P-6 which was a commercial variant of the heavy reconnaissance R-6 (ANT-7). It had a cabin for six passengers. High-speed medium SB-2 bombers had their civilian counterpart in the PS-40, and SB-2bis in PS.41. It was even planned to build the four-engined TB-7 in a commercial variant, PS-42, for the transport of 70 people but this aircraft was not built. PS-5 did appear, developed from the reconnaissance plane, R-10.

When the Red Air Force rejected the single-engined combat aircraft, BSh-1 (Vultee V-11G), Aeroflot put them into service as PS-43, carrying mail and cargo on the Moscow – Kiev and Moscow – Tashkent routes. During the war, and for some time afterwards, PS-43 were in the liaison service for staff of larger military units. The USSR also bought a commercial V-1A from Vultee. This aircraft was designed for six passengers and with it S A Levanevskii made a transit flight in August 1936 from the USA to Moscow.

Most purpose-built Soviet commercial planes were, at the time of design or flight testing, modern and technically mature machines with good performances. But by the time they reached service a very long time had often elapsed and the designs had become outdated.

When Kalinin's last high-wing monoplane in the 'K' series was being built, American plants had already delivered modern cantilever transports with semi or fully retractable undercarriage and speeds of 300kph. These machines had all modern methods for augmentation of lift, such as plain flaps, and even variable pitch propellers were not unusual. Soviet aviation technology had to make up leeway.

It is remarkable that on several occasions, Soviet designers conceived transport aircraft equal to the models of their Western colleagues. First in this sphere was I G Neman, of the Kharkov

Institute KhAI, who in 1932 was planning an elegant, all-wood, low-wing monoplane KhAI-1 with 480mhp M-22 engine. The machine was equipped for a pilot and six passengers and had retractable undercarriage.

B N Kudrin test flew the aircraft on October 8, 1932, and conducted subsequent tests on which a speed of 300kph was reached – faster than production I-5 biplane fighters. But the aircraft was not put into production until 1934 and final machines from the series of 43 were released as late as 1937. They reached 324kph and were in service principally on the Moscow – Simferopol route.

Yakovlev's low-wing monoplane, AIR-7, was flown at about the same time as prototype KhAI-1. AIR-7 reached 332kph but several models of various classes were needed in order to bring Aeroflot up-to-date.

The success of KhAI-1 inspired the scientific and technical company AVIAvnito to issue a design competition in 1934 for single-engined, high-speed transports for five to six passengers, and two-engined models for ten to twelve passengers or a corresponding cargo. AVIAvnito demanded all the modern design details like variable camber flaps, semi- or fully retractable undercarriages, hydraulic-pneumatic suspension, variable pitch propellers etc.

Name of the company was *Vsesojusnoje Nauchno Issledovatelskoje Tekhnicheskoje Obshchestvo* (VNITO) = Scientific and Technical Research Company of the Whole Union. This acronym was written with small letters, preceded in capitals by the specialised department with which this section of the company was concerned, in this case Aviation, i.e. AVIA.

The organisation received several competition projects. Some were tentatively built before final recommendation, some were under construction, others were still at drawing board stage. In every case, single-engined machines were less successful than the twin-engined ones, and even the best remained a prototype.

The STAL-11 of A I Putilov, a cantilever, low-wing monoplane test flown in Autumn 1936, had a retractable undercarriage or fixed skids. While the fuselage frame consisted of Enersh-6 stainless steel sheet sections covered with a skin of prepared birch plywood, the wing was entirely of wood, also with plywood skin, and all surfaces were absolutely smooth. Although preparation was complicated and expensive, empty weight of the machine was extremely low at 1,380kg.

STAL-11 was designed for a pilot and four passengers, reaching 430kph with an 860mhp M-100 engine, well up to international standard. Range was 1,000km and service ceiling 8,000m. Flight testing continued until 1937, but no uniform concensus of opinion was reached about the aircraft's qualities.

V K Tairov's low-wing monoplane OKO-1 met a similar end. This came from the OKO design bureau of aircraft plant No. 43 in Kiev, an all-wood machine with monocoque fuselage intended for six passengers and pilot. A 750mhp

M-25 engine was chosen and the fixed undercarriage given a trouser-leg fairing. During tests which took place after a first flight in October 1937, OKO-1 reached 347kph and range was 1,700 – 2,000km. Performances were not so good as STAL-11, but OKO-1 was certainly simpler and cheaper to produce. However, the model was not accepted.

Among the machines not built was an interesting design from D A Romejko-Gurko. It was a low-wing monoplane with a cabin for four passengers situated well to the rear. An M-34 engine was to be located in the middle of the fuselage, roughly the location of the centre of gravity, to drive a propeller in the nose by remote control. The committee of AVIAnito declared that passengers were too close to the engine, and centre of gravity was too far back.

Tupolev also designed a single-engined transport machine, ANT-43, for a pilot and six passengers. It was to be an all-metal, low-wing monoplane, something in the style of the I-14 fighter, with Gnome-Rhone 14Krsd of 810mhp. The design group used a new method for construction of ANT-43 in 1936; stencils for production of the structural parts were transferred directly onto sheet metal without any designs being drawn. This worried the directors of TsAGI who would not release the aircraft for flight.

Of the twin-engined machines assessed by AVIAnito, two dated from before the time of competition. In 1933 studies were being made of two-engined commercial machines in the Institute of Civil Aviation. Frenchman Andre Laville, who was working at the Institute, designed an aircraft of 300kph while the Italian, R L Bartini, reckoned on 400kph for his own design. Bartini's machine was to be produced in the design bureau of the Tushino plant; Laville's was assigned to repair plant No. 89.

Laville's ZIG-1 (*Zavod Imeni Goltsmana*) was test flown in November 1935 with skid undercarriage. It was a low-wing monoplane in all-metal construction with two 680mhp M-17F engines. Much attention was paid to reliability, the possibility of single-engined flight, low landing speed etc. The aircraft had two pilots and twelve passengers, reached 284kph, but operating speed was under 250. ZIG No.89 plant built eight production machines which were flown by Aeroflot as PS-89, most of them on the Moscow-Simferopol line.

Right: Well up to international standards was the 430kph STAL-11 which could operate on fixed skids or retractable undercarriage.

278

Elegant wooden monoplane ChAI-1 went into production in 1934, serving travellers on the Moscow – Simferopol route.

Although cheap to produce and simple to maintain, OKO-1 with its monocoque fuselage did not prompt any enthusiasm among the selectors.

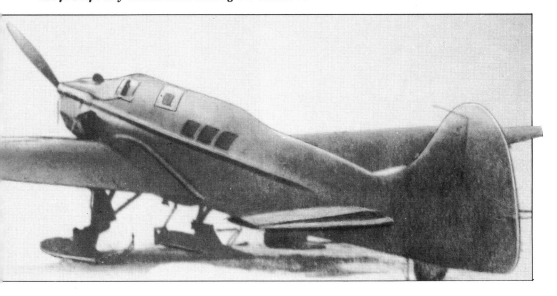

Frenchman Andre Laville designed ZIG-1 (PS-89) with reliability in mind and eight production examples were operated by Aeroflot.

STAL-7 was enthusiastically received after test flights during 1935 when it achieved 450kph at 3,000m and a range of 2,000km. The DB-240 bomber was a direct derivative.

Although fast and reliable, limited cabin space made the PS-35 version of ANT-35 uneconomic and production was halted after 11 had been built.

Bartini's STAL-7 was more modern and efficient. He had originally intended to give the machine a basic airframe of fabric covered tubular steel. But according to building precepts of the time, every transport machine had to have a bomb bay, so that in emergency it could be used as a bomber. Inclusion of the bay caused difficulties; the airframe was not stiff enough and the load bent it, so plans switched to a light metal monocoque construction.

The prototype STAL-7 was test flown in Spring 1935 by N P Shibanov, achieving unbelievably high performance and qualities. At 3,000m the machine reached a full 450kph, service ceiling was 10,000m and range 2,000km. A double dihedral wing had nacelles containing M-100 engines (Hispano-Suiza 12 Ybrs each of 760mhp) and the cabin was equipped for twelve passengers.

Such excellent flying qualities inspired a grandiose scheme – STAL-7 was to make a trip round the world with Shibanov and his crew. The prototype was equipped with additional equipment and 27 spare tanks containing 7,400 litres. In Autumn 1937 everything was ready for flight, but at the beginning of 1938 Bartini was arrested and then the machine was heavily damaged in a take-off accident.

Repairs took a very long time and not until August 28, 1939, were Shibanov, V A Matvejev and N A Bajkusov able to make an experimental flight prior to their round the world attempt. The aircraft flew over a triangle, Moscow–Sverdlovsk–Sevastopol–Moscow (5,068km), at an average speed of 404.936kph, exciting the interest of Stalin who ordered design of a long-range bomber from STAL-7. Further work was then conducted by V G Yermolayev which resulted in the DB-240 bomber.

Of the two-engined machines assessed by AVIAvnito, most successful was the all-metal, low-wing monoplane, ANT-35, of A A Arkhangelskii from the KOSOS TsAGI design bureau. Arkhangelskii used experience garnered from construction of the SB-2 bomber, so ANT-35 was given a flat sheet covering, M-85 engines (the French Gnome-

Rhone 14K of 800mhp) retractable undercarriage and a cabin with ten passenger seats.

M M Gromov began flight tests on August 20, 1936, and by September had flown over the 1,266km Moscow–Leningrad–Moscow route in a record 3 hours 38 minutes, averaging 400kph.

First production machines were assigned to Aeroflot in 1937 under designation PS-35. They had 1,000mhp M-62IR engines which raised maximum speed to 432kph, and were promptly put into service on the important Moscow–Riga–Stockholm, and Moscow–Prague lines. Later they were used on internal lines like Moscow – Lvov or Moscow – Odessa until 1941.

The aircraft were fast and reliable, easily manoeuvred and had modern equipment. Nevertheless, criticisms were made, in particular that the PS-35 were uneconomic to run with a cabin capacity that could not be increased. Only 11 series PS-35 were built.

Aeroflot's technical stipulations for ANT-35 design proved inadequate so demands for ANT-50 were better. This machine, designed in 1937, was intended for ten passengers and two M-34 engines, but was not built.

Aeroflot were given few machines out of all those designed and tested. Apart from the PS-89 and PS-35, commercial lines were served very much as before, for the KhAI-1 were no substantial help. For an infinite number of reasons, the Soviet Civil Aviation sector in the second half of the thirties possessed no aircraft comparable to the American Douglas DC-2 or DC-3.

Without doubt, DC-3 were the best commercial aircraft of the time and it was natural that the Soviet government should choose this plane when seeking to remedy the situation at Aeroflot by purchase of license rights in 1938.

Towards the end of 1939, the first production Soviet-built DC-3 left Khimki plant No.84, near Moscow. The aircraft were designated PS-84 and put into service from 1940 onwards on Aeroflot's main lines.

The design of DC-3 underwent some modification as service stipulations were different in the USSR and climatic requirements more rigid. B P Lisunov made some modifications while the plane was being prepared for construction. The whole airframe was strengthened, door of the main cabin moved from the port to the starboard side, span slightly reduced from 28.96 to 28.81m, wing area dropped from 91.7 to 91.3sq m, and Soviet 900mhp M-62 engines mounted.

These modifications increased empty weight from 7,460kg on the American model to 7,700kg. The engines were less powerful, and therefore speed fell to 280kph, but according to the length of route and nature of the territory, 14-28 passengers could be taken. Although PS-84 did not achieve the performances of DC-3, they maintained their good qualities and did not sacrifice any of the aircraft's well-known reliability.

At the beginning of 1941, PS-84 was given new designation Li-2, from the name of the designer, Lisunov. Li-2 had further subdivision according to interior equipment. Li-2P were the standard 2,300kg payload passenger planes with 14-28 cabin seats; Li-2G coped with up to 2,500kg payload and served for the combined transport of passengers and cargo. On routes which crossed quite high mountains, Li-2V were used, their M-621R with RK-19 superchargers increasing service ceiling from 7,100 to 8,000m. Li-2V also proved their worth in the meteorological service. All Li-2 built during or after the war were given ASh-62IR engines, named after the designer A D Shvetsov.

PS-84 modernised connections on the main lines, but better machines were also desired for subsidiary lines. Several projects were made, only two carried out, and none put into production.

Yakovlev designed the AIR-19, an elegant, low-wing monoplane in composite construction, driven by two 220mhp MV-6 engines. AIR-19 carried a pilot and six to eight passengers over 870km at a maximum speed of 256kph. Production of MV-6 engines was halted in 1939 and this was one of the reasons why AIR-19 could not be built.

As regards engines, A N Rafaelyants's all-wood, low-wing monoplane RAF-11 was better off. Designed in the Bykovo repair plant, it was to have two 300mhp radial MG-31 engines, carry five people and reach 289kph. The original version of 1938 was too heavy but RAF-11bis was better. This was built in 1940, driven by 330mhp MG-31F engines and capable of 294kph. The airframe was adaptable and authorities wanted to use the machine as a trainer for bomber crews as well as a passenger plane. Series production was to begin in 1941 but war created more urgent needs.

In the chapters about military aircraft we came across some types which had no counterpart in Western countries. The same applied in the civil sphere. One such individualistic aircraft was the powered cargo glider, 'Planerlet'. These were relatively large machines designed to carry 1,000kg payload or ten passengers. Each was driven by a single 100mhp M-11 engine and had to be towed into the air, after which they were able to continue under their own power to the target airfield.

Originator of the concept was L E Malinovskii, director of the Scientific-technical Administrative Sector of Civil Aviation. From his name the abbreviation LEM was formed, which became the designation of a few powered gliders. According to Malinovskii's plans, these machines were to help transport where there were no roads nor railway lines. He did not have to aim at speed and high performances; in areas where a beast of burden or a two-wheeled cart were the only means of transport, an aircraft with 100kph operating speed and 1,000kg payload constituted a fabulous advance. This system only needed a network of bases and P-5 towing planes – a network similar to relay stations of the old horse post.

In 1936 and 1937 several types of powered gliders were designed and built under the initiative of Malinovskii and with the backing of AVIAvnito. Models with large, slim wings of 20-30m span were required and only two had a classical design: LEM-3 (or LIG-6) designed by J V Dormachev of the Leningrad Institute of the Civil Air Force LIG, and the SK-7 by S P Korolev, later chief designer of Soviet space rockets. LEM-3 was able to take 700-800kg cargo, SK-7 a pilot, five passengers and mail, altogether 600kg.

There were other machines in the Planerlet class. D A Romejko-Gurko produced his large GMK-1 with 30m wing span, M-11 in pusher arrangement and provision for up to 1,000kg in the gondola-shaped front of the fuselage. I K Antonov contributed an incomplete flying wing, LEM-2/OKA-33, on which the M-11 engine was in the centre of the leading edge. Cargo compartments were in the centre section and on the wing were twin tail booms. LEM-2 was able to carry 1,000kg.

Cargo glider G-31 'Yakov Alksnis' was built in Leningrad, a machine with 28m wing span designed by P I Grokhovskii. In the wing centre section were narrow cabins to accommodate stretchers. G-31 was an exception among aircraft of this category in that it had a 700mhp M-25 engine.

Another Planerlet was KhAI-3, from Kharkov, which was known as 'Sergei Kirov'. It was a tailless machine of 22.4m span; on the wing were two narrow parallel nacelles, each containing six seats in tandem arrangement – first seat was for the pilot, the others for passengers. Originally it was intended to mount the M-11 on a frame over the fuselage, but on the machine actually constructed it was built straight onto the wing leading edge. The designer, A A Lazarev, gave his aircraft excellent stability. He also designed the KhAI-8 version with two M-11, one in the nose of each nacelle, but it was not built.

All the aircraft of the Planerlet series built were tested and some pronounced excellent by the Government Commission. Unfortunately, plans

Right: Antonov's twin-boom, powered glider LEM-2 (OKA-33).

Below: Powered glider LEM-3 (LIG-6) was able to take 700-800kg of cargo.

RAF-11 proved too heavy when it appeared in 1938. The improved RAF-11bis model looked set for a substantial series when war halted production.

Above: KhAI-3 'Sergei Kirov' was a tailless planerlet with parallel passenger compartments on each wing.

Left: R-Zet aircraft were commonly used as glider tugs. A towing cable passed through the tube extending from the rear of the cockpit.

Below: Although it did not progress beyond prototype stage, Grokhovskii's G-37 of 1934 was an advanced idea for container transport.

for more extensive use were dropped.

There were other unusual designs for civil aircraft. P I Grokhovskii, director of a special design bureau in Leningrad, experimented a lot with unusual air transport designs, especially cargo and weapon carriers. One of his ideas was the use of large, detachable cargo containers mounted under the fuselage. After landing the container could be exchanged for a fresh, pre-loaded one with which the aircraft then took off. We find the same idea employed at Fieseler in the Fi-333 project, later on the American Fairchild XC-120 'Packplane' and in several other instances. But the concept was not carried out in the USSR until 1934, on an aircraft designated G-37.

G-37 was an all-metal design which had adapted the wing and M-17 engines from the commercial PS-9. In the centre of the wing was a small cabin for the crew and on the engine nacelles, twin tail booms. The aircraft sat on a high undercarriage with trouser-leg fairing and cargo containers were to be mounted under the wing centre section. V P Chkalov test flew the G-37 and was very pleased with it, travelling from Leningrad to Moscow at an average speed of 250kph. In spite of the clear advantages, G-37 remained at prototype stage.

But at least G-37 was built and tested. A design of A I Putilov, STAL-5, worked on between 1933-1935, did not get so far. Putilov wanted to create a tailless aircraft for 18 passengers, powered by two 860/900mhp M-34F engines. The entire airframe was to be built of Enersh-6 stainless steel sections with covering of artificially saturated plywood, fabric covered on the wing tips. As well as the commercial variant there existed a military example, KhB (*Khimicheskii Bojevik* = Chemical Warrior). This aircraft was equipped for gas attacks.

At the beginning of 1934 a single-seat model construction of STAL-5 was completed, driven by two 45mhp Salmson engines. With this model they wanted to investigate stability and other qualities of the future aircraft. V V Karpov and J G Paul made several flights in 1935, but they were not satisfied with the qualities, least of all stability. Meanwhile they built the main spar of the real STAL-5 out of Enersh-6 steel. But Putilov's group had more work in connection with STAL-11 and so the tailless STAL-5 was abandoned for ever.

This is a short survey of Soviet commercial machines built up to summer 1941. In this branch much was done, much planned, much built, but there were also a lot of technical losses and failures. The whole result was a series construction of DC-3.

CHAPTER 32

Military Transport Aircraft

THE SOVIET ARMED FORCES decided early on large scale mechanisation. It was thought possible to create, in the near future, a fully mechanised army capable of effecting fast operations at full combat strength, regardless of terrain or distance. Though industrialisation of the country during early Five Year Plans provided the right conditions, the 'thirties saw only limited progress towards this goal.

But in one branch the USSR's mechanisation outstripped that of all other world powers – the branch of parachute and airborne troops. Mass training of sport parachutists at Osoaviakhim produced thousands of well prepared paratroopers whose operational efficiency was tested from time to time in army practices.

In 1930 a parachute detachment of one officer and eight men was dropped during manoeuvres to surprise, attack and capture 'enemy' headquarters. Five years later, during the big exercise near Kiev, G-2 (TB-3) aircraft dropped 700 soldiers! That created a sensation and the world did not know that in the same year a whole division of infantry had been transported by air from Moscow to Vladivostok in the Far East.

In White Russia in 1936, 1,200 parachutists with full equipment dropped 170km behind the Front and transports landed with 2,500 men from the airborne troops, 150 machine guns and 18 light guns. One year later there were already 2,200 parachutists on the East Front of the USSR and in 1939, in the Ukraine, as many as 3,000.

Heavy TB-3 bombers were able to carry the light armoured T-27 car of 1.7 tons under the fuselage, delivering it with a big parachute. P I Grokhovskii designed the whole jettison gear and devoted his attention to all possible methods of air transport for heavy weapons. For example he built transport platforms to take cargo trucks of up to 2.5 tons under the TB-3 and his cargo containers were put into service on TB-1 machines.

The semi-bulbous shaped containers were mounted close to the underside of the fuselage and dropped by parachute. Several people descended in a cargo tank by way of experiment. in 1934.

Between 1936 and 1938 efforts concentrated on dropping four-ton T-37 and T-38 fighting tanks from a TB-3 directly onto water. In these experiments there was direct co-operation with the tanks' designer S J Kotin.

It was a particularly strenuous assignment for the TB-3 pilot A N Tyangunin because he had to fly only a metre above the water with a tank under the fuselage, yet all his tests were successful. Fuel for the tank was to be stored in the fuselage of the carrier-based aircraft which would serve as a supply centre. But this type of transport was never actually used.

The Red Air Force also devoted a lot of attention to cargo gliders and at the beginning of the 'thirties, in co-operation with Osoaviakhim, embarked on the large scale training of pilots. Double and triple tow were tried, one R-5 taking three sailplanes on a 2,755km staged flight from Leningrad to the Crimea.

In 1936 an R-5 was flown with one sailplane from Moscow to the Crimea in unusual circumstances. The flight of 1,450km lasted 8 hours and was completed non-stop, thanks to spare fuel in the sailplane being taken on during flight through a tube attached to the towing cable.

In 1934 the first Soviet cargo sailplane, N Groshev's G No.4, made its appearance. Pilot Simonov made several aerobatic manoeuvres with the sailplane carrying 250kg in sandbags and a year later it was tested in tow on the R-5 for passenger and cargo transport.

Considering the successes of Soviet paratroopers and airborne troops, it may seem surprising that more extensive use of the unit was not made during the Second World War. Reasons were a total lack of transport machines and air supremacy problems which allowed little opportunity to use airborne troops in the early period.

But there were airborne actions during the war and they began during the battle of Moscow. Transport and bomber aircraft supplied the front within three days with 5,500 soldiers and 13,000kg on munitions in September and October. On December 15 a group of 415 men was dropped to stop the German retreat at Klin and Teryayeva Sloboda in the Moscow region. During the liquidation of encircled Germans near Medynsk a paratroop landing of 2,000 men was prepared for January 2, 1942. Because of heavy frost and snow only 416 men could be parachuted, but they did fulfill their duty. Between January 18 and 23, 1942, 1,643 men were parachuted in the area of Znamenka and Shelanye together with grenade launchers, machine guns and anti-tank guns to demoralise the German rear as preparation for a Soviet attack. A further 2,300 men descended from 66 transport aircraft on January 27, 1942, in the region of Vyazma and Smolensk. During the battle in that region, a total of 7,015 men were transported by air together with their arms and ammunition.

Innumerable air supply actions for partisans behind German lines were undertaken by all

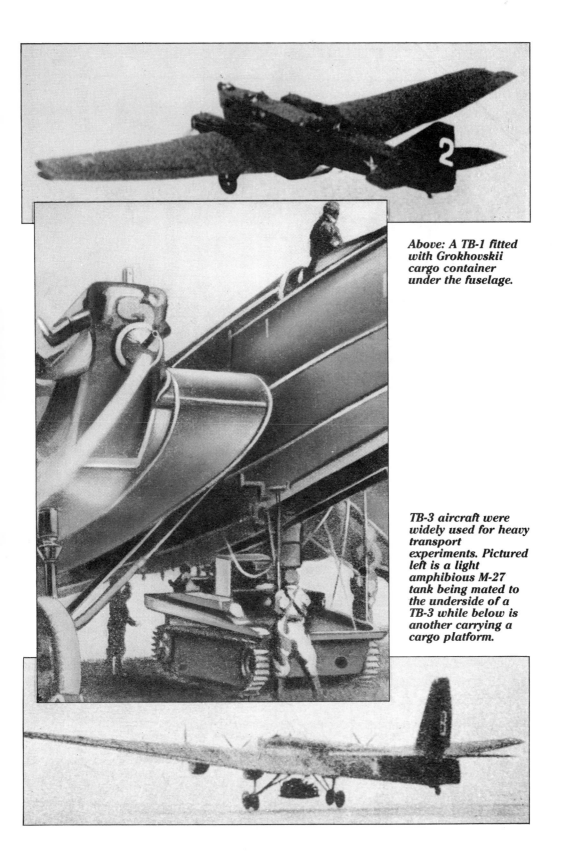

Above: A TB-1 fitted with Grokhovskii cargo container under the fuselage.

TB-3 aircraft were widely used for heavy transport experiments. Pictured left is a light amphibious M-27 tank being mated to the underside of a TB-3 while below is another carrying a cargo platform.

Paratroopers leap from a heavy TB-3 bomber. Russia was ahead of other nations in this method of deployment during the 1930s.

Two versions of U-2L, a common term for limousine variants of the U-2. Above is an example by Zusman and below a modification by Kulik which is fitted with landing flaps.

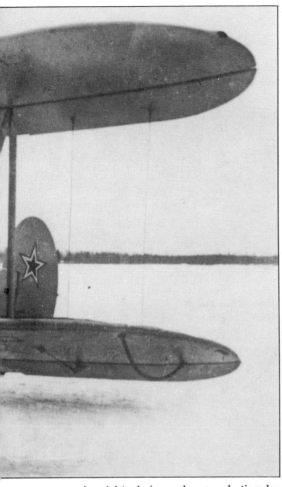

means of aerial techniques: by parachuting, by gliders or by landing small or bigger aircraft on improvised airfields, mostly during night and in bad weather.

As a preparation for the big battle at Kursk the Soviet transport group supplied the front with light anti-tank bombs of 2.5kg, named PTAB. They were sown in great numbers over a concentration of German tanks.

The big offensives in White Russia needed an air transport of 46,000 men and 3,500 tons of supplies while in September 1943 the Red Army made big paratroop landings of three brigades to secure the bridge-head on the western bank of the Dnyepr.

In the final stages of war in the Far East, against Japan, airborne operations played a decisive part at Mukden, Port Arthur and Dairen. There were landings of 50 to 500 men to occupy Japanese aerodromes, railway stations, barracks and stores. Soviet military aviation transport made 5,000 take-offs to supply the paratroopers at their battlepoints.

Over 20,000 pilots, navigators and mechanics of Aeroflot joined combat and transport units of the Red Air Force in summer 1941. Among the transport groups were also guard units, like the 10th Guard Air Transport Division which was equipped with Li-2 aircraft. During the war, air-

craft transported 330,000 wounded, 300,000 tons of military material, 2,000 tons of blood, 1,700,000 tons of medicaments and 2,550,000 passengers.

The transport sector also played an important part during the siege of Leningrad. Aircraft brought 53,000 inhabitants and 9,000 wounded soldiers out of the city and took in 4,235 tons of rations, 1,660 tons of weapons and ammunition, 128 tons of mail and 312 tons of blood. Return flights also extracted 2,463 tons of non-ferrous metal from the city, important raw material for Soviet war production.

Volume of civil air traffic diminished considerably in the first year of war, reaching only 74% of the volume of 1940, sinking still further to 60% in 1942. Then a fresh impetus brought the figure up to 78% of the pre-war level in 1943 and in 1944 the volume of air traffic was some 48% greater than in 1940.

Some assignments of war-time air traffic were unique. In January 1942 eleven G-2 machines, the transport variant of TB-3, were put into service exclusively to supply ball bearings for the armoured tank industry. Light U-2 biplanes were also given a special assignment. Working in the Far East, they transported molybdenum ore from mines to the nearest railways which then hauled it to foundries in the Ural.

Altogether U-2 biplanes contributed a lot to air transport and to making connections between important spots, proving brilliantly successful as a means of communication with the larger partisan units. U-2 was used in all its variants, particularly U-2VS (*Vijskovaya Seriya* = Military Series) which had three open seats.

The U-2 was often reconstructed, usually in the repair plants or at army airports. For example, designer M M Kulik sought to improve the short take-off and landing abilities. He equipped the upper wing with slats, put flaps on the trailing edge of the bottom wing and added a transparent enclosure over the seats. An interesting variant, U-2GN made its appearance in 1944 (*Golos's Neba* = Voice from the Sky). These machines had an efficient loudspeaker and were used in propaganda operations against German posts.

As the load capacity of U-2 was not normally fully exploited, several designers reconstructed them as new limousines, all bearing the common abbreviation U-2L. N N Polikarpov's reconstruction was given the designation U-2ShS (*Shtabnoi – Svasnoi* = Staff and Liaison Aircraft). It had a spacious cabin for a pilot and four passengers and several were built in 1944. A N Rafaelyants's U-2L (RAF-2) made its appearance in 1943. In the fuselage of this variant all space was utilised between the two wings. All these reconstructions had 145mhp M-11 series engines; on U-2ShS the engine was an M-11F and on U-2L an M-11D.

But the most important wartime transport aircraft were Li-2. These machines, when operated in the vicinity of the Front or in enemy-threatened sectors, had a machine gun turret with a flexible ShKAS on top of the fuselage. There were also openings in the cabin windows

Above: Yakovlev's NBB light transport, prototype of the Yak-6.
Below: Built almost entirely from wood was Shcherbakov's TS-1 or Shche-2.

Below: Most important wartime transports were PS-84 or Li-2, fitted with machine gun turrets.

Best of a number of cargo gliders commissioned shortly before the war was O K Antonov's RF-8, designated A-7 by the Red Air Force.

through which soldiers could fire. Li-2 of the 10th Guard Air Transport Division alone were said to have shot down 21 German aircraft.

In addition, 709 American Douglas C-47 Skytrain were obtained by the Lease/Lend agreement and proved a great help to the Soviet air transport sector. In photographs the C-47 is easily recognisable by the rather long engine nacelle, with oil cooler and a door on the port side of the fuselage.

Soviet-built planes were always light models for transport to and from the Front and supply of rations to partisan units. These aircraft could only use such material as was available in sufficient quantities and had to be simple assemblies. Wood, fabric and steel were the main constituents.

In 1942 two prototypes for such machines made their appearance. A S Yakovlev designed the low-wing monoplane Yak-6 from light night bomber NBB. It was driven by two 140mhp M-11F, reached 180kph and had a range of 800km. Yak-6 carried two pilots and six passengers or a corresponding load. Most had female pilots.

Yak-6 were also used as trainers for bomber crews with a flexible machine gun on the fuselage and practice bombs under the wing. Another version was used for training radio operators, navigators etc. Yak-6 was put into production in 1943.

Another machine of this period and type was designed by A J Shcherbakov, designated TS-1 (*Transportnii Samolet* = Transport Plane). It was also called Shche-2 after its designer. The relatively large, high-wing monoplane for ten people was built almost entirely of timber – even the fuselage was a plywood monocoque construction. With M-11E engines it reached a maximum speed of 150kph and a range of 640km. The life of Shche-2 was so long that it was still in service after the war with Aeroflot and in other East European countries, being particularly favoured for parachute training.

Shortly before the outbreak of war, several designers were commissioned to produce new cargo gliders capable of carrying 10 infantrymen with armament and equipment. The best was O K Antonov's RF-8, a simple cantilever, high-wing monoplane with narrow fuselage. The Red Air Force called it A-7 and obtained 400 during 1942. These were mostly towed by SB-2 bombers, for taking supplies to partisans. Together with A-7, other types were tested: Vorobyev 'Orol' and Gribvski G-11, the latter also going into series production.

Antonov was then given a very interesting task – he was to try out new methods for the aerial

Above: The MP was a powered glider converted from the BDP (S-1) and fitted with two M-11F engines.

Right: One of the most bizarre machines ever to fly was Antonov's 'Krylya Tanka', a T-60 tank fitted with wings. It was towed behind a TB-3 bomber and released to make its own landing with the caterpillar tracks in motion.

Below: Polikarpov's BDP (S-1) combat glider which could carry 20 fully equipped soldiers.

Below: Anti-tank cannon being loaded into a KTs-20 glider.

Above: A development of the KTs-20, Tsybin's Ts-25 glider could carry 25 men or 2.2 tons of equipment.

Left: Up to 3.5 tons could be carried by Yakovlev's Yak-14, a lateral hinged glider which saw a production run of 413.

Below left: Ilyushin's all-metal Il-32 had a substantial capacity but proved too costly to enter series production.

transport of armoured cars. A new armoured vehicle was designed which, besides its own steering gear, also possessed the standard aircraft steering gear. Following Antonov's design wooden biplane wings and tail were added and thus the KT came into being (*Kryla Tanka* = Wings for the Tank).

Test pilot S N Anokhin took a quick course in tank driving and in the spring of 1942 was able to test the KT with a T-60 tank of 5,800kg in the air near Moscow. The KT was towed behind a TB-3 bomber like a cargo glider and released before landing. Shortly before landing, the pilot had to start up the engine and set the caterpillar track in operation so that this unique aircraft could touch down more easily. Although the first landing was

by no means flawless it was evident that once necessary improvements had been made there was a future for the idea.

In 1943 the Red Army made preparations for launching possible glider attacks. For such operations larger cargo gliders than A-7 were required with capacity for anti-tank guns, trench mortars, jeeps etc. So the KTs-20 was produced designed by D N Kolesnikov and P V Tsybin. This was a simple, strut-braced, high-wing monoplane with hinged nose.

Polikarpov designed and built the BDP(S-1) in 1943 (*Bojevoj Dessantnii Planer* = Combat Glider for Airborne Operations) with a complement of 20 soldiers. The BDP (S-1) was a cantilever high-wing monoplane with clean lines.

A S Moskalev designed SAM-23 at the same time. This was the heaviest cargo glider in the USSR, a cantilever, high-wing monoplane with twin tail booms and spacious, gondola-shaped fuselage. The tail could be opened upwards so that a jeep could enter along with 16 men. SAM-23 was given a short series run.

Powered cargo gliders were also built and tested. Shortly before his death Polikarpov prepared the MP-1, a modified BDP (S-1) with two 145mhp M-11F engines and dropable bicycle undercarriage. MP-1 was first tested in October 1944, after the designer's death. It flew well, had 172kph maximum speed and a range between 700 and 930km. The Red Air Force took no further interest in machines like these so MP-1 had no successors. Moskalev's design for a powered version of SAM-23 was not carried out.

Big airborne operations of the Allies in Italy, France and in the Far East naturally had some influence on Commanders-in-Chief of the Red Air Force. But strong airborne Soviet combat units with cargo transport gliders were not built until after the war. Two main types of cargo gliders were used. One was the Ts-25 of V P Tsybin. This was a development of the war-time KTs-20 and could carry 25 men or 2.2 tons.

The other was Yakovlev's larger Yak-14, a high-wing monoplane with lateral hinged fuselage nose which left the entire cross-section of the hold free for cross-country vehicles, weapons or cargo of up to 3.5 tons. Alternatively 35 soldiers could be transported. A Yak-14 in composite construction was also produced and in all 413 aircraft of all versions went into service.

During the test period of Yak-14 its rival was also in the air – this was Ilyushin's Il-32, a robust high-wing monoplane in all-metal construction. It was rejected because the production of an all-metal cargo glider was too complicated and too costly in view of the fact that they were liable to be expended.

Ts-25 and Yak-14 could be towed at relatively high speeds in the region of 300kph and in the 'fifties were very widely used by the Soviet Air Force and in the air forces of some Eastern states. The emergence of more modern, high-capacity transports eventually made them obsolete.

CHAPTER 33

General Purpose Aircraft

A STILL YOUTHFUL Soviet Union was one of the first countries to tackle large scale treatment of fields, woods and other cultivated areas from the air. Originally the aircraft were mostly concerned with pest combat, but later they extended to fertilising and even sowing. In the thirties, Soviet agricultural aviation was best in the world.

In 1920 the first articles appeared about aerial fertilising and pest control. About a year later, at the assembly of Soviet entomologists, N N Bogdanov-Katkov spoke about combatting locusts from the air, and in February 1922 military fliers I A Valentej and V M Vishnev applied to the People's Commissary for Agriculture with a plan. The Council of the People's Commissaries approved the proposal and permitted formation of an experimental group for agricultural aviation at Khodynskoje Pole, the later Central Airport of Moscow. This group had three Voisin biplanes with which they carried out tests over the grounds of Petrov Agricultural Academy (later Academy of Timirjatsev) under the direction of Professor V F Boldyrev.

The year 1925 saw earnest efforts being made. P A Sviridenko launched the first operations against locusts in the northern area of the Caucasus with a Junkers F-13 and shortly afterwards V P Averin attacked this major enemy of Soviet agriculture in the Ukraine. They utilised the knowledge gained in 1926 when a campaign was launched against the breeding places of locusts on the rivers in Dagestan. At the same time the aircraft were put into service against night moth in the woods near Gorki.

In 1927-9 further operations were launched against locusts and night moths, and in Siberia, in the vicinity of Bakal Lake, attacks were made on other pests. Pilots V A Nabokov and B I Rukavishnikov achieved great success in the control of the malaria mosquito by means of Paris Green. By the late twenties and the thirties this danger was almost eliminated.

All these actions were organised by the commercial air companies Ukrovosdukhput and Dobrolet. At the beginning of 1930 a special organisation for agricultural aviation was set up – the All Union Association for the Combatting of Agricultural Pests (OBV) from which developed the Trust for Agricultural Aviation *(Trest Selskokhozjajstvennoj Aviacii)* TSKhA. In 1932 TSKhA had a research institute in Moscow and branches in Krasnodar, Poltava, Tbilisi (Tiflis), Leningrad, Saratov and Chimkent. TSKhA lasted only three years before being combined with the Institute to form part of Aeroflot.

In the twenties Soviet agricultural aviation suffered from lack of suitable aircraft, mostly using the German Junkers F-13. Later came the light biplane Khioni No 5, known by the name *Konjok Gorbunok* (Humpbacked Little Horse), an animal from a Russian fairy tale.

The aircraft was a design of V N Khioni from repair plant No. 7, earlier a branch of Anatra. It was, in reality, a combination of various components of the Russian Anade machine plus a new fuselage and 100mhp Fiat engine. The aircraft was a two-seater and displayed excellent qualities during test flights in spring 1923. Originally intended as a trainer, it was found of more use in the agricultural sector. In the front pilot's compartment there was a chemical tank and a primitive dusting arrangement. Thirty aircraft of this type were built and flew for many years without difficulties.

By way of experiment, three American Wilson biplanes were reconstructed for agricultural purposes. These aircraft, captured in 1919 in Orenburg, were not so successful as the Khioni No. 5. In 1929 Soviet agricultural aviation had 27 aircraft at its disposal, but of very varied design.

Not until 1931 was it possible to equip agricultural units with a fairly large number of good aircraft when production was begun of the U-2AP variant *(Aeroopylitel* = Scatterer from the Air). This was equipped with a tank for 200-250kg of chemicals in the rear cabin and had a four-blade impeller for the dusting arrangement. Under the fuselage was an apparatus of sheet metal which directed the discharge of powder over a 10m swathe. One U-2AP aircraft was capable of treating an area of 17 hectares per hour.

By 1932 the first 260 machines had been delivered and the aircraft was constructed with varying modifications up to 1945. Some 1,235 examples were built by 1940. These machines could also be equipped for dispensing liquid chemicals or seedcorn and some, which had to operate from small airfields with very soft ground, were given auxiliary wheels of steel plate which increased the wheel width to 25cm.

U-2AP formed the backbone of the agricultural aviation sector and its performances were incredible. The aircraft was known by the nickname *Kukuruznik,* meaning something like Maizer or Maize Plane; in forestry protection it was called *Lesnik* (Forester). But as more demands were made during the thirties it became

Agricultural aircraft Konjok Gorbunok, named after an animal in a Russian fairy tale.

increasingly clear that aircraft carrying only 250kg of chemicals were in many cases uneconomical and greater capacity was required.

So A G Bedunkovich, from the Institute of Civil Aviation in Leningrad (LIG), designed a fairly large biplane, LIG-10, in 1936/37. The aircraft was also known as SKh-1 *(Selskokhozjajstvennii =* Agricultural). The machine had a fuselage of steel; wings and controls were of wood and the wings folded back. The cabin was originally capable of taking 400kg and, after reconstruction, 600kg of chemicals or the same weight in seed-corn. In other variants provision was made for either six passengers, three stretchers and a doctor, or a corresponding load.

After flight tests in 1937 and 1938, which gave excellent results, further examinations were made of individual variants. In the winter war against Finland (1939-40) SKh-1 proved its worth as an ambulance plane and a series production was ordered. But no aircraft could be delivered until 1941. SKh-1 had a 330mhp MG-31F radial engine, reached 182kph and was able to land at 65kph. Take-off run was 210m.

U-2AP accomplished all the tasks of agricultural aviation in the thirties and the extent of surfaces treated from the air rose as follows:

1924/1925 – 1,300 hectares;
1927/1928 – 32,000;
1932/1933 – 120,000;
1940 – 904,000.

Even after the war, U-2AP were still used in agriculture along with the more modern Po-2A. Agricultural operations were now more broadly based. The Po-2A, with M-11K engines of 115mhp, were constructed from 1946 to the end of the forties and given V F Stepanov's AOD-S3 dusting arrangement which had a swath width of 30m and could treat up to 30 hectares per hour. Such performances in the immediate post-war period were certainly good, but the old cry for larger machines could not be silenced. Po-2A either had to take off several times when covering a wide area or operate in fairly large numbers. In either case their use was uneconomic so a substitute was urgently required.

Large biplane LIG-10 was a multi-role aircraft designed by A G Bedunkovich.

The U-2/Po-2 had another speciality – ambulance service. Thanks to the Kalinin K-4 this facility was started early and U-2 ambulance variants helped build the world's first regular and large-scale air ambulance service. Specially important was the work in those regions previously not very accessible to a doctor. Moreover, the work involved not only the actual transport of sick or wounded people to hospital, but also regular preventative visits by the doctor, standby services in the case of an epidemic, transport of medicine, blood plasma, etc.

The ambulance variant of U-2, U-2S-1, made its appearance in 1932 as a three-seater, the pilot sitting in an open cockpit. To the rear was a closed cabin for the doctor and behind a space for the patient. The stretcher lay on top of the fuselage, between wings and tail, beneath an aerodynamic cowl which could be folded to the right. The doctor was able to speak with the patient during flight or even treat him, provided he only had to handle the upper part of the body. Some 100 U-2S-1 were built, also known under the designation SS *(Sanitarnii Samolet = Ambulance Aircraft)*.

In 1939 a further variant, U-2S-2, made its appearance. It was like U-2S-1 but had a more powerful 120mhp M-11D engine. U-2S-3 dates from 1940 and is characterised by further structural improvements. All U-2S variants were used in fairly large numbers during the war.

Caskets were also used for the transport of wounded and aircraft carrying them were designated SKF. A J Shcherbakov designed the units in 1941. They were mounted under and in front of the lower wing, each accommodating one patient in a half-sitting, half-lying position. In the fuselage was the man accompanying the patient, or, a further casualty.

G I Bakshayev's caskets of 1944 were more comfortable. They were long cylindrical pods of wood and fabric, one mounted on either side of the fuselage on the lower wing. In them the stretcher bearing the patients could be inserted.

After the war ambulance aircraft were again built in the version U-2S-3, this time designated Po-2S. They were in service for many years but it was evident that potential of the basic U-2 or Po-2 construction was exhausted and new aircraft were urgently needed.

In 1948 O K Antonov, who was still in Novosibirsk, began to design a modern agricultural and general purpose aircraft, SKh-1. A technically ambitious aircraft, the cabin was to be very versatile, capable of carrying not only chemical tanks but a few passengers plus light loads or cargo.

A lot was required of the machine: short take-off and landing runs, low slow-speed flight with full manoeuvrability, a robust construction not demanding much servicing, good flying qualities etc. There were several possible ways it could be designed and Antonov chose a modern biplane layout to achieve his aims by relatively simple technical means.

The first prototype was ready in 1948. It was a robust machine with high, all-metal, monocoque fuselage which took up the whole space between the two strut-braced wings. There were retractable slats and ailerons on the upper wings and, originally, variable camber flaps on all. The large cabin had an entrance door on the left side which could be exchanged for a wider one.

The prototype was driven by a seven-cylinder ASh-21 of 730mhp which proved too weak. So 1,000mhp ASh-621R were adopted, the same as mounted in Li-2. Characteristics were the V-509A

propellers with four sabre-like blades, known to the fliers as 'Sabre Dance'. It first flew on August 31, 1947.

Production aircraft were given the designation An-2 and between 1949 and 1962 approximately 5,000 examples were built and delivered in several forms. Agricultural variant An-2Skh carries a tank for 1,400 litres of liquid chemicals or 1,200kg in dust. The aircraft can fly absolutely safely at 5m altitude over fields or at 10m over woods.

The distributive apparatus or pumps for liquid were originally driven by an eight-blade fan which was replaced in 1946 by an improved four-blade, variable pitch VD-10. When powdered chemicals were used an area of 50-60m was covered and the aircraft was able to treat 100

Three forms of the U-2S ambulance variant – U-2S-1 for stretcher transport (below); U-2S-2 with containers by Bakshayev (left); and U-2S-3 with twin Shcherbakov containers (bottom).

hectares per hour. When substances were sprayed from jets on a tube under the trailing edge of the lower wing, working area was 60m, rising to 80m when an emulsion was used and 100m with an oil solution.

An-2 was quite a step forward. In 1948, 2,153,000 hectares were treated and two years later 2,557,200. Then An-2 launched their attack. During 1953 it was possible to treat 4,323,000 hectares; three years later, 8,520,300; in 1962 the figure was 20,792,400; and in 1963 it reached 25,645,200. The figures given are for pesticide treatment, not fertilising or sowing. These comprise a further 40 to 50% of the recorded yearly achievements.

Among numerous An-2 shapes were the high altitude research aircraft An-2ZA (below) with separate observation cabin for scientists, and the original An-2 (bottom), prototype of which first flew on August 31, 1947.

In 1964 a new variant, An-2M, was introduced, distinguished in particular by a broad trapezoidal rudder and AV-2 propeller with straight blades. There was an important collective reconstruction of apparatus. The tank now took 1,960 litres or 1,500kg and distributive system was no longer driven by a fan blade but directly via the engine crankshaft. Dosage when granulated amounted to 60kg per second, when powdered 37kg and when liquid 28 litres per second. On An-2SKh it was only 19.8 litres and moreover An-2M could operate with one pilot.

In service with Aeroflot the passenger variant, An-2P and twin-float An-2V (design name An-4), proved their worth. The cabin was adapted for either seven to fourteen passengers or 1,240kg cargo. Since An-2P only needed 150m take-off and 170m landing distance it was realised at an early date that they could be used in remote areas.

An-2V were given floats 7.5m long with low waterline so that they could operate in shallows of 80cm. Four men replaced wheels with floats in 20 hours; the reverse procedure takes 8 hours. Up to 1968, An-2P and 2V carried more than 100 million passengers, so their participation in the air transport sector must not be underestimated.

For pure cargo work is the An-2T, variants being An-2TP with 12 collapsible seats along the sides of the cabin and An-2TD for 12 parachutists, An-2S takes six stretchers.

In 1966 forest fire combat units in Karelia and other regions with large areas of timber and water were given new An-2PP float planes. On the underside of the floats are openings with covers. The aircraft is flown close over the surface of the water and gathers, by ram effect, 630 litres of water in each float. Then the machine flies over the burning area of forest and discharges the water all at once.

Another interesting variant is An-2ZA (*Zond Atmosfery* = Atmospheric Probe), serial number An-16. The An-2ZA has ASh-621R-TK with TK-19 superchargers which maintain their 850mhp up to 9,500m and on top of the fuselage, just in front of the rudder, is an observation cabin for scientists. Variant An-2NAK or An-2K was built for artillery observation.

Series production of An-2 was also pursued from 1959 in Poland and China. There are, however, areas of service in which An-2 are too big to operate efficiently and economically. Po-2 biplanes took on such operations before they became the sphere of the high-wing monoplane, Yak-12.

Yakovlev had designed a four-seat machine for post-war civil and military service in 1944. He did not want his aircraft to be used merely for sport and touring purposes, but also for liaision, staff service, transport of wounded, artillery observation and light air transport – in other words, all tasks fulfilled at the time by U-2.

Two versions of a four-seat aircraft made their appearance, both with wooden wing, steel fuselage and M-11MF engines of 145mhp. These were the strut-braced, high-wing monoplane Yak-10 with fixed undercarriage and the cantilever, low-wing monoplane Yak-13 with retractable undercarriage. Both were tested in 1947 and authorities showed more interest in Yak-10, regarding the low-wing example as too much of a sports plane, ill adapted to other uses.

In 1947 Yakovlev's plant built 40 production Yak-10 which were subject to intensive experimentation. Some were Yak-10V for export, some Yak-10S for óne stretcher and even Yak-10G on twin floats. As a result of tests with different Yak-10 versions Yakovlev changed the design and the high-wing mono plane Yak-12 made its appearance in 1947 with improved aerodynamics and technology.

The new Yak-12 were put into military and civil service in 1949, reaching 200kph with one M-11FR engine of 160mhp. But one cannot say they were particularly welcomed. The engines were obviously inadequate for the Yak-12 to achieve the performances required, especially take-off and climb. Several variants were produced, like the Yak-12S with one stretcher, Yak-12SKh for agricultural work and Yak-12GP on twin wooden floats.

In 1950 Yakovlev thoroughly revised the whole design. He mounted the nine-cylinder AI-14R of 260mhp and carried out several aerodynamic and technical modifications. Thus he was able to support a full crew of four on the new Yak-12R and also attain the desired take-off and climb

performances. It is true that the aircraft, with fixed slats, only had a maximum speed of 184kph, but the take-off run with four people was reduced to 75m (on Yak-12 with three people the run was 110-150m) and landing speed dropped to 75kph.

Yak-12R achieved prompt success and were used on quite a large scale in place of Po-2. In 1955 Yak-12M appeared on the scene. This aircraft was more modern, the wing had an all-dural frame, fabric covered, and there was a long vertical fin on top of the fuselage. Yak-12M have also been serially produced in Poland where the aircraft was used as a basis for their own agricultural aircraft, PZL-101 Gawron.

The agricultural variant of Yak-12M carries a tank for 475 litres or 380kg of chemicals, covering a swathe width of up to 35m. It can easily be reconstructed for other purposes. When used as an ambulance aircraft it can carry one or two stretchers introduced through a narrow loading hatch on the side of the cabin which can also take 300kg of cargo. Two men can reconstruct the touring aircraft as the agricultural variant in three hours or less and it takes only 25-30 minutes to convert into the ambulance version. The machine is also delivered as a waterplane with two floats.

By way of experiment, Yak-12M was also tested as a biplane with detachable lower wing. Purpose was to see if take-off and climb performances could be maintained on overloaded machines, and if a higher payload and lower operating speed could be achieved with agricultural aircraft. Designation was Yak-12B and engine was an AI-14RF of 300mhp, but results were not favourable.

For passenger transport over short distances, official journeys, ambulance service etc, Yakovlev designed the variant Yak-12A in 1957. This aircraft has trapezoidal wings with no slats, lift struts instead of dihedral struts and simpler undercarriage strut-bracing. These modifications increased the speed to 215kph and range to 1,070km. Yak-12R had a range of 500km and Yak-12M, 765km.

Aeroflot and the Soviet Air Force had another light, general-purpose aircraft at their disposal, Antonov's two-motored, high-wing monoplane known as An-14 *Pchyelka* (Little Bee).

In the early fifties Aeroflot were showing great interest in the idea of a general-purpose aircraft with performances somewhere between An-2 and Yak-12M. There was large scale canvassing for such an aircraft and even Czech designers were given an opportunity to produce projects. Engineeer Karel Tomas offered his high-wing monoplane L-18, which had two engines, twin tail booms and a gondola shaped fuselage. But Aeroflot preferred the home-built An-14.

An-14 was test flown on March 15, 1958, in Kiev. The first flight was extensively covered and the whole development reported in newspapers. But the optimistic reports were premature and Pchyelka was not put into production until 1966.

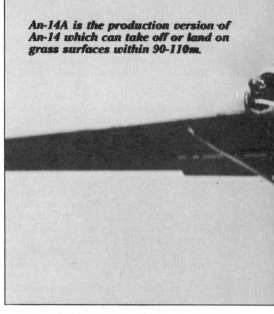

An-14A is the production version of An-14 which can take off or land on grass surfaces within 90-110m.

Reasons for the delay were complex. Antonov thinks the main trouble was that Aeroflot were not sure what they wanted. The company originally asked for an aircraft for a pilot and three passengers, later for an aircraft for five passengers, then seven. This gave rise to difficulties and slowed up design work. On the other hand, the main difficulty could have been in the actual design. The rear part of the fuselage was constantly being modified, which shows that designers were having to cope with problems of stability and structural engineering.

An-14 was put into production in its variant form, An-14A. The original 260mhp AI-14R engines were replaced by AI-14RF, each of 300/330mhp. The slim wing is no longer rectangular but tapered, with double slotted flaps and automatic slats. Fuselage lines are purer, but still show the original gondola shape cabin with a door in the tapering part which leads to the tail booms. In the cabin are eight seats, one for the pilot and seven for passengers. The cabin can speedily be reconstructed for other purposes although it would seem that the agricultural variant was discarded.

There are twin rudders with two big rectangular surfaces forming the outboard fins of the dihedrally placed elevator. A tricycle undercarriage has wheels of the same dimension, main wheels being attached to a wing stub on the under side of the fuselage where the wing strut also terminates.

Operating speed of An-14A is 175 to 180kph and the range with full 720kg load, 470km. With 630kg the range extends to 680km while take-off and landing runs are 90 to 110m on grass.

In the end Antonov reached the expected performances and qualities. But it would seem that he is no longer satisfied and there are reports of a new An-14M variant which has two GTD-550 turboprops, each of 700mhp, originally built for the Mil Mi-2 helicopter.

Above: R version of a successful Yak-12 range by Yakovlev.
Below: An early Yak-12 which entered civil and military service in 1949.

CHAPTER 34

Post-War Transport Aircraft

AT THE 1948 fairs in Poznan, Prague and Budapest, Soviet transports and trainers were exhibited for the first time. As well as Po-2 and Yak-18, Yakovlev's light transport aeroplane, Yak-16 could be seen here along with Ilyushin's medium transport, Il-12. The Soviet Union had embarked on a new stage in the development of their civil aviation sector. The industry hoped to provide transport aircraft of all classes, both for home use and export.

With Il-12 S V Ilyushin made his debut in the sphere of civil design; he had begun work on a modern transport aircraft as early as 1944 so that it should be ready for post-war demand. The whole country was engaged in reconstruction and the demands on air transport grew from month to month. Plans continued to build the licensed Li-2, but its performances were no longer adequate.

Parallel with Ilyushin, R L Bartini worked on the design of his T-117 transport. Bartini went further than Ilyushin, who only foresaw a standard cabin. Bartini was already planning to build the T-117 with a pressurised cabin, but since the construction was more complicated and the Soviet civil sector required new aircraft quickly, authorities decided on the simpler Il-12.

Ilyushin intended the Il-12 to have 300kph operating speed and a range of 1,500km when the 27-seat cabin was fully utilised. Originally Ilyushin planned to use heavy-oil, in line vee Charomskij ACh-31 engines of 1,900mhp from which an extremely low consumption was expected. He had gained some experience with them when developing the Il-6 bomber and the Il-12 prototype flew with twin ACh-31 on August 15, 1945, piloted by the Kokkinakki brothers. But the engines were not reliable enough and Ilyushin switched to fourteen-cylinder ASh-82FN engines, each of 1,520/1,850mhp, and new four-blade propellers with feathered pitch, the first of their kind in the USSR. On January 9, 1946, the brothers V K and K K Kokkinaki test flew the Il-12 with ASh-82FNs and series production was begun in the same year. So Aeroflot was able to put the first Il-12 into service on their main routes in 1947.

The Il-12 was of all-metal construction. The cabin with monocoque fuselage usually took 27 passengers, but on shorter routes it might take as many as 32 plus a crew of five. The aircraft had a tricycle undercarriage and in the technical description there was mention of 365kph maximum speed at low altitude and 407kph at 2,500m. Operating speed was said to be 350kph at 2,500m with payload of 3,000kg. With 32 passengers on board the range was 1,300km, with 27 passengers 2,000km and with 16 in the cabin 3,000km. The aircraft in regular service had lower performances but they were still higher than the minimum required.

However, after a few months in service with Aeroflot the aircraft demonstrated several inadequacies. The machine had been put into service far too soon and circumstances now exacted their revenge. Pilots complained about poor functioning of the de-icer on the wing leading edge, on the tail unit and on the propeller blades. These were basically trivial matters which could easily be rectified during the service period by the mounting of a more efficient system. But there were more serious defects.

With only one engine working the aircraft was extremely difficult to fly. Take-off at high temperatures or from airfields in an elevated situation required an unexpectedly long ground run, the machine climbing slowly and with difficulty. Failures like these could only be eliminated by redesign and this was not possible. So a simpler solution was sought – the number of passengers

Rivals as an early post-war transport were Ilyushin's Il-12 (below) and Bartini's T-117 (right). The simpler Il-12 went into production whereas T-117, which envisaged a pressurised cabin, remained at design stage

was reduced to 18! Qualities were thus improved, but the Il-12 was now very uneconomic. The Soviet economic system being what it was, nobody worried about this at the time; the main thing was to have a fast model which could be built in large numbers and an estimated 3,000 examples were produced between 1946 and 1949.

As well as the passenger version, Il-12T cargo transports were built with a fairly large door and up to 3,500kg payload. The Il-12 also found a place with the military air transport sector as the Il-12D. They were able to transport 26 fully equipped airborne infantrymen or 37 paratroopers. In the ambulance version 16 stretchers and six seated wounded could find accommodation. Il-12 were also used for towing freight gliders.

Thanks to the Il-12, the air transport sector were able to put their Five Year Plan into effect. This was the first post-war Plan and the fourth overall. During 1946 the distance covered by Aeroflot rose to 190,000km, 1.1 million people were transported plus 60,000 tons of mail and freight. By the end of this Five Year Plan in 1950 the figures were 300,000km, 1,603,700 passengers and 181,650 tons of mail and freight.

Moscow was connected with all the capitals of individual states and regions of the USSR as well as with all the capitals of allied states. The authorities had extended the network of domestic lines and modernised airfields.

The fifth Five Year Plan was more ambitious, aiming to double air transport during 1951-1955. In the final year of the Plan the distance covered had reached 321,450km, 2,523,500 passengers travelled on the Aeroflot 'planes and 258,720 tons

Tupolev's Tu-70 was derived from the Tu-4 bomber and, like many civil developments at this time, retained many military features, such as a glazed nose.

Above: From Tu-70 came the high-capacity military transport, Tu-75.

Below: Ilyushin's Il-18 of 1947 could cruise at 400kph with 66 passengers.

of mail were transported.

It was certainly not easy for Aeroflot to fulfil the demands as there were no real high-capacity aircraft available and everything had to be transported by Il-12, Li-2 and the smaller Po-2 biplanes. But it is interesting to note that prototypes existed in 1946 and 1947.

A N Tupolev's bureau designed a transport version of their giant bomber Tu-4. This was Tu-70. The wings, tail, propulsive unit and the undercarriage were taken over from the bomber. Only the fuselage was new, more spacious and equipped for 48-72 passengers plus a crew of eight. The engines were ASh-73TK, each of 2,000/ 2,400mhp.

Test pilot F F Opadchii first flew the machine on November 27, 1946, about three months after the first Tu-4 bomber took off. During flight tests in 1947 the Tu-70 reached a maximum spped of 563kph and a range of 4,900km. About half a year after the Tu-70 a further high-capacity aircraft, the Ilyushin Il-18, made its appearance. This had four ASh-73TK engines. V K Kokkinaki test flew the machine on July 30, 1947. In the fuselage were cabins for a crew of six and 66 passengers with 900kg luggage and freight. The Il-18 reached an unexpectedly high speed of 588kph and at the most economic operating speed of 400kph the range was as much as 6,200km.

Both machines had things to offer Aeroflot, but both were ahead of their time. They required concrete runways and there were few of these at Soviet civilian airfields. The whole system of air transport needed to be refashioned and modernised and at that time the means were not available.

The Tu-70 in particular might have been an economic machine, for its production could have been run simultaneously with the bomber version. Unfortunately neither Tu-70 nor Il-18 could be put into service and Aeroflot had to give up the idea of high-capacity transport aircraft for the time being.

In 1950 a military high-capacity transport was developed. It had the basic characteristics of Tu-70 and was called Tu-75. On the underside of the fuselage, behind the wing, was a hinged loading ramp; over this ramp self-drive cross-country vehicles could be taken, while other cargoes could be taken in with a hoist. The whole payload was 10 tons. A typical cargo was one cross-country GAZ vehicle, two jeeps, one aircraft engine and other material.

The pilot Marunov test flew Tu-75 in summer 1950. But full use was not made of the machine. The Soviets only began to build up their strategic air transport sector a few years later.

A S Yakovlev had made two attempts at creating a light transport aircraft – first in 1944 when he built the two-engined, low-wing monoplane Yak-8. The Yak-8 was in composite construction with a spacious fuselage for two pilots and eight passengers. The engines were M-11M, each of 150mhp and the undercarriage was retractable. Maximum speed was 180kph, the operating speed 150kph and the range 1,350km. The M-11M engines were obviously too weak for such tasks and Yak-8 remained at the prototype stage.

Yakovlev's second machine, Yak-16, could be seen in 1949 at international fairs. It was a modern-looking, all-metal, low-wing monoplane with two seven-cylinder ASh-21 engines each of 680/750mhp and controllable-pitch, two-blade propellers. There were two men in the crew and accommodation for ten to twelve passengers. Maximum speed was 310kph operating speed 290kph and range 1,000km. Yak-16 was a modern machine for its time, though Aeroflot showed no interest in it. The single prototype was used for crew training.

So Ilyushin's Il-12 remained the characteristic aircraft of the first post-war Five Year Plan. During the next Plan, Il-14 was produced. Basic design remained the same but the designers tried to eliminate the disadvantages of Il-12 while improving performance and flying qualities. We cannot be sure whether they achieved these aims on the first variant Il-14P (*Passashirskii* = Passenger Plane) but V K Kokkinaki test flew the prototype on September 20, 1950 and soon the first production aircraft were in service.

Principal aim in the design of Il-14P was absolute reliability under unfavourable conditions. The machine was capable of taking off with only one engine running, even from elevated airfields. The de-icing system was modernised, as was equipment for coping with bad weather conditions or night flying. But economy had to be sacrificed to achieve this really unique reliability. In the cabin of Il-14P there were only 18 seats, a single passenger taking 660kg of the flying weight. On Il-12 it was 412kg and on the Li-2 only 314kg.

Engines, also, were dependable. They were ASh-82T, each of 1,900mhp and with automatic four-blade propellers. Exhaust gases were conducted in jets on the upper side of the wing where they produced a measurable static thrust.

Soon Il-14P could be introduced to the Aeroflot lines, other East European states and to China, Vietnam etc. In 1955 the Czechoslovakian Avia plants in Prague-Letnany took on licensed construction of Il-14P as later did the VEB aircraft company in Dresden.

Because of Il-14P's poor operating economics the machine was rebuilt as Il-14M (*Modifikatsiia* = Modification) in 1955. Fuselage was made a metre longer, the airframe stiffened, and there was now accommodation in the cabin for 24 passengers. Il-14M soon replaced the earlier 14P models, cruising at 320kph and able to carry 2,000kg payload over 1,500km.

Il-14 of Czechoslovakian origin were also rebuilt. Since Avia and her main customer, the air company CSA, were still not satisfied that this machine was economical, it was further amended. Main improvements were in the cabin and interior equipment. Twenty-two passengers could now be transported, a number that was gradually increased to 32, 36, 40 and 41. In addition, photographic versions (Il-14F) and transports (Il-14T) were also designed and built.

Up to 1960, when aircraft production was halted at Avia, over 200 machines had been built, about 50 being the 14P version. The Dresden plant built 80.

The Il-14 marked an important stage in the development of Soviet aviation technology, especially in the transport sphere.

The sixth Soviet Five Year Plan (1956-60) proceeded under the influence of international political detente after the years of 'Cold War'. In the documentation of this Plan are the following observations: Aeroflot is to double the volume of freight transport and more than triple (3.8 times) passenger transport. High capacity aircraft are to be put into service on the main lines and main airfields of the country are to be redesigned.

Such grandiose projections could only be achieved through better aircraft technology. And better technology was achieved! The Soviet Government had been preparing for this "great leap forward" since 1953 when Tupolev's bureau had been commisioned to design a jet transport aircraft for 50 passengers with an operating speed of 800kph and range of 3,000km.

Soviet commercial aviation was about to pass over several phases of development, progressing in one bound from piston aircraft of the medium and light categories, direct to large capacity jet aircraft with high subsonic speeds.

Tupolev used the Tu-16 jet bomber as a basis, retaining the wings, tail unit, undercarriage and, to a large extent, the outfit of the crew's cabins. The fuselage was new, having a circular section and pressurised cabin for 50 passengers. Propulsive units were also taken over from the bomber — Mikulin's AM-3, detuned a little to 8,700kp in order to increase the life. Even so, they lasted only a few hundred hours. Short engine life and relatively high fuel consumption were real handicaps, but such things had to be tolerated for the sake of having an aircraft into service promptly.

June 17, 1955, was an historic day for modern Soviet civil aviation as J T Alashejev test flew the prototype Tu-104. A few weeks later it took part in the Tushino air parade, strangely arousing no interest in the Western Press. Apparently the similarity of Tu-104 to the Tu-16 bombers in silhouette misled the journalists and observers. In no other way can one explain the great surprise caused by the arrival of Tu-104 in London on March 22, 1956.

Britain had introduced the world's first jet commercial aircraft, de Havilland's DH106 Comet. This had been in service from 1952-1954 with tragic consequences as a result of which civil jet air transport had been halted in Britain for a period.

Competition from the other side of the Iron Curtain was unexpected and reaction ranged from admiration to mockery. It was possible to criticise the lace coverings of the seats, Victorian outfit of the cabin, or hint about the military appearance of the crew's quarters. But on one point they were all agreed – the machine was very well made. Here was a serviceable jet commercial aircraft, produced by a country from which such quick results were unusual.

The London visitor was a machine of the pilot series with which the potential of domestic and international jet communications were tested. Aeroflot was given the first group of Tu-104s in May 1956 and crews immediately began their training. Now the ground aids had to be tested and constructed, preparations made for the electronic control system, service and maintenance, etc. However, only fifteen months elapsed between the maiden flight of Tu-104 and take-off of the first production machine from Vnukovo, near Moscow, on the first regular flight to Irkutsk. September 15, 1956, marked the beginning of the jet transport era in the USSR.

Tu-104's passenger cabin was set out for a pressure difference of 0.5kg/sq cm, which meant that at altitudes of 10,000-12,000m there was a pressure corresponding to an altitude of 3,000m. At first there were difficulties with the pressure equipment and ram air induction, so every seat was equipped with auxiliary oxygen apparatus.

The cabin was, of course, air-conditioned and had soundproofing. Nevertheless, the level of engine noise was high, especially in the rear, and this proved tiring. TU-104's engines were mounted too close to the cabin, an unpleasant legacy of the original military model. The crew consisted of five – two pilots, a navigator, radio operator and flight mechanic. There were also two hostesses whose headquarters were in the centre of the fuselage near the kitchen.

Service characteristics of the first Tu-104 were really too military and the cabin capacity too low.

So a Tu-104A variant was constructed in 1956. It was better equipped and could take 70 passengers – 16 first-class in the front and 54 tourist class in the rear. Tu-104A had more economic AM-3M-500 engines of 9,700kp static thrust, but an hour's flying time at 780kph at 10,000m still consumed a full 4,800kg of fuel. Life of the engines climbed to over 1,500 hours.

In 1957 Czech aviation company CSA took on the first Tu-104A and put it into service on their international lines – a year before Aeroflot. Capacity was still a problem and so the variant Tu-104V was produced in spring 1962. By redesigning the interior and reducing auxiliary cabins they managed to create enough room for 100 passengers.

Il-14 represented a development of Il-12 and was an attempt to achieve maximum reliability under all conditions. First variant was the passenger carrying Il-14P (below) while another was the Il-14F photographic aircraft (bottom).

Even before the production of Tu-104V they were managing to transport 100 passengers per flight. In 1956 Aeroflot was demanding an aircraft capable of transporting this number and Tupolev responded with model Tu-110, tested in 1957. The fuselage was some 1.2m longer and contained two cabins. Main difference from Tu-104 was in the mounting of four Lyulka AL-5 engines, each of 5,000kp thrust, in pairs close to both sides of the fuselage.

The greater total thrust improved performance. Maximum speed was now 1,000kph (on Tu-104 it was 950kph), economic operating speed over routes of 3,000-3,300km was 800kph and over shorter routes 900kph. But Aeroflot found Tu-110 to be inadequate and did not order a series. Instead, a new variant of Tu-104 was taken on.

This was Tu-104B of 1958 which also had a fuselage some 1.2m longer and two AM-3M-500 engines. Many tentative alterations were made, especially modifications of the plain flaps, interior outfit of the cabin etc. The fuselage of variant 'B' had more work space so that not only could 100 passengers be accommodated, but also 2,000kg freight and 2,000kg luggage and mail. Payload therefore rose from 5,200kg on the first Tu-104 to 9,000kg on Tu-104A and 12,000kg on the Tu-104B. Another variant, Tu-104E, was like the 'B' but had reconstructed engines which ran more economically.

Following an old custom in Soviet aviation, attempts were made to set up international records with new machines. The Tu-104 was no exception. Between 1957 and 1960, Tu-104 variants set up 22 international records, mostly group achievements which were valid for several weight categories.

In the late fifties the Tu-104 became a major symbol of Soviet civil aviation and a means of communication between the USSR and other countries. For Czech company, CSA, the plane was also of great importance, making CSA one of the most modern companies using jet commercial aircraft. Moreover, the Tu-104 was an object of prestige in the old battle between West and

Tu-104A (top left) was followed by Tu-110 (below left), an almost identical aircraft but with a fuselage 1.2m longer and four engines instead of two.

entrance ramp. The door was a means of exit for parachutists and, when it was fully opened, heavy loads could be dropped by parachute or driven out after landing. Take-off weight was between 35 and 40 tons and the two turboprops were N D Kusnetsov's NK-4, each of 5,100mhp.

Among Soviet fliers this machine was known as 'Kit' which means 'Whale'. The An-8 was first shown to the public in 1956 during the flying day at Tushino. Since then An-8 have worked in military transport units and Aeroflot, especially in Siberia where they mostly transported machines for road construction etc.

The aircraft constituted a good basis for further development, particularly as the military and Aeroflot now demanded machines with similar qualities but stronger, with great capacity and four-engined. Antonov's work therefore ran in two parallel courses – he was engaged in a civil plane and a military transport. November 1955 saw the start of a large commercial aircraft, An-10, and on March 7, 1957, J I Vernikov and V P Vasin were able to test fly the prototype, named Ukrayina.

It was a gigantic high-wing monoplane of 38m span and 34m length, and its rudder rose 9.8m. The conspicuously slim wings were adequate to lift 50 tons take-off weight and 12 tons payload, under-slung with four NK-4 turboprop engines, each of 4,000mhp with four-blade propellers. Multiple wheel landing gear was used.

Fuselage was equipped for 75 passengers who had comfortable seating accommodation plus lavatories, cloakrooms, bar etc. Crew compartments retained the same 'military' shape as those of Tu-104.

In July 1959 the production An-10 with 84 seats were put into service on Aeroflot routes, being used particularly between Simferopol (on the Crimean peninsula) and Moscow or Kiev. They could operate from the same airfields as Il-12 and Il-14, requiring 700-800m take-off run but a shorter landing distance, thanks to the brake propellers. This was 500 to 650m according to weight.

But the instability of An-10 gave its creators much cause for concern. The rudder, in conjunction with the giant fuselage, lost a lot of effectiveness, particularly as it was located in the shadow of the wing. A lot of experimentation followed. The vertical fin was lengthened so it ran well into the top of the fuselage; two auxiliary fins were mounted; alternatively two (later three) keel surfaces were mounted under the tip of the fuselage. Finally, the wing tips beyond the engines were given a negative dihedral which at last stabilised the machine.

East for technical superiority.

Besides these high-speed passenger liners the Soviet commercial sector required aircraft which could be put into service on proposed grass runways. It seemed impossible to use jets for this purpose and turboprops were considered more suitable.

The year 1957 marked the appearance of commercial turboprop aircraft in the USSR. Premier Krushchev had cancelled some of the military orders, thus releasing the necessary means for modernisation of the civil sector. Moreover, the design groups were now given more time to take part in such tasks.

O K Antonov's Kiev design bureau had a lead over others having designed during 1952-1953 a high-capacity transport for vehicles, weapons or other big loads. This was An-8, test flown in 1955 and built in quite large numbers for the Air Force and Aeroflot.

An-8 was an all-metal, high-wing monoplane with spacious fuselage tapering upwards on the underside to form a cargo door with drop

An-10A entered Aeroflot service during 1960 and continued until 1972 when a crash prompted withdrawal.

Cargo version of the An-10 was An-12, characterised by a tail gun turret on the military model.

Ilyushin's second aircraft with designation Il-18 was his 'Moskva' of 1957, an airliner for 84 passengers.

At the 'Expo-58' international exhibition in Brussels, new variant An-10A was given a gold medal. This aircraft had accommodation for 100 passengers and was put into service with Aeroflot in 1960. The machines, like most An-10, flew with improved, economic AI-20 and AI-20K engines of 4,000mhp which had been designed and built by A G Ivchenko at his plant in Zaporoshiye.

An-10A achieved 680kph maximum and 600kph operating speed. With 15,000kg payload its range was 1,200km plus fuel reserve for an hour; with 10,000kg load the aircraft could fly 3,000km and the greatest range was 4,000km. An-10A were also tried in Arctic and Antarctic regions, equipped with ski undercarriage.

Interior of the cabin could be modified and the partition walls removed to accommodate up to 117 passengers. The cabin was, of course, pressurised and air-conditioned, pressure corresponding to zero height being maintained up to 5,000m and at greater heights relating to 2,350m.

In spring and summer 1960, An-10A completed several noteworthy flights, including a 2,000km Moscow-Melitopol-Moscow run at an average speed of 723kph. On another occasion the pilot made an experimental flight with 100 people in the cabin and only one engine running and on April 29, 1961, the type set an FAI record of 730.616kph over a 500km route. As regards An-10A's service in Aeroflot, a report tells us that during 1965 a full 2.5 million passengers were transported on these planes.

In 1969 An-10s and An-10As flew over 132,465km. The long service was suddenly interrupted by a fatal crash of an An-10A near Sharkov in May, 1972. In 1973 the An-10A did not return to service.

Antonov tried to make still better use of the cabin capacity, projecting the prototype An-16, a model derived from An-10A. Its cabin took up to 130 people, but neither An-16 nor An-10V were put into regular service.

Cargo version of An-10 was An-12, occupied in the tactical transport of heavy weapons straight to combat zones or, in the civil sector, carrying heavy machines. Fuselage had roughly the same lines as An-8 but was bigger. The actual cargo compartment was 2.6 x 3.5 x 13.5m and had pressure equipment as well as a small cabin for 14 people immediately behind the crew's quarters. Floor of the compartment was reinforced and took a load of 1,500kg per sq m, while the door was so designed that armoured cars, cannon etc. could be dropped by parachute.

Characteristic for this machine is the tail gun turret with two NR-23 weapons. The large fuselage certainly reduced speed a little, but maximum was still a high 640kph and operating speed 580kph. Range with 10 tons payload and an hour's reserve reached 3,400km.

Quite a number of An-12 joined the cargo sector of Aeroflot, helping in the construction of oil pipelines, industrial and energy plants in the Siberian regions etc. From February 1966 Aeroflot flew An-12 on a regular cargo connection between Moscow and Paris. Maximum payload of the civil An-12 is 20 tons and one of the heaviest single loads carried was an 11,600kg dredger. There was originally a lavatory in the gun turret position but this section was later made more streamlined and the WC transferred elsewhere.

An-12 also went into service in Egypt, India, Indonesia, Iraq and individual machines were delivered to small African states.

On July 4, 1957 another machine of this class made its appearance when V K Kokkinaki successfully test flew the four-engined Il-18 'Moskva'. It was the third 'Moskva' by Ilyushin and his second machine with number 18. Ilyushin designed the Il-18 as a speedy and very economic commercial plane for 75 passengers, to be used on medium or fairly long routes. The lines were particularly fine and for the first time military glazing of the nose was discarded in favour of a meteorological radar antenna. All compartments of the fuselage had pressure balance and air conditioning; pressure at 2,400m could be maintained up to 10,000m. Fuel tanks were built as an integral part of the wing.

Engines of the prototype were Kuznetsov's 4,000mhp NK-4, each with four-blade reversible-pitch propellers. On the first fifty machines NK-4 engines alternated with AI-20; all 400 subsequent machines were given the AI-20.

Plant and governmental tests were carried out on three aircraft of the pilot series at the same time. In autumn 1957 Kokkinaki flew 9,000km from Moscow to Petropavlovsk with an intermediate landing in Irkutsk and during all tests the first Aeroflot crews, ground personnel and others were familiarised with the machines. This hastened the introduction of Il-18 which took off for a regular Moscow-Adler-Alma-Ata flight on April 20, 1959. These Il-18 of the first series took 84 passengers, but later as many as 111.

Modern technology made it possible to save considerable time and work. The first fifty machines each required 300,000 working hours; later the figure sank to 50,000 hours and 82,000 hours for the rather more complicated Il-18E.

Il-18 was built in several variant forms. The standard version is Il-18V with 90 seats (alternatively 110 seats in the tourist class). Engines are AI-20K each of 4,000mhp while the more modern Il-18E has four 4,350mhp AI-20M. The cabin is either one through room or divided into tourist and first class. In the first case 110 people can be transported in summer and 90 in winter; when the divided cabin is used 122 people are carried in summer and 110 in winter. Discrepancy between the seasons is explained by the fact that the passengers' heavy winter coats take up more hanging space! Electronic apparatus, radar etc met international requirements, so Il-18E could readily be put into service on all world routes.

The long distance variant Il-18D has the same

Special variant Tu-114D had a Tu-20 bomber-size fuselage and was produced in 1958 for extra long flights with relatively few passengers or just mail and freight. Engines culminated with the 15,000mhp NK-12MV turbines, driving four-bladed, contra-rotating propellers.

engines and number of passengers, but fuel supply is some 32% greater. Range of the 18D is 6,500km, the 18E 5,200km and the 18V 4,800km; with 13,500kg payload the ranges of the V, E and D variants are 3,000, 3,200 and 3,700km respectively, while operating speeds are between 600 and 675kph.

Il-18 have high-pressure cabins (0.59kg/sq cm) and cargo space under the cabin is also pressurised. Pressure corresponding to an altitude of 2,400m is maintained up to 10,000m.

During testing Kokkinaki set a few records with Il-18 prototypes, especially speed records with payloads on closed circuits. On August 19, 1959, he flew with 15 tons load over a distance of 2,000km at a speed of 719.496kph; on February 2, 1960, he carried 10 tons over 5,000km at 693.55kph. Noteworthy, too, were the altitude performances. Kokkinaki and crew reached 13,154m with 10 tons on November 15, 1958;

Below: Tu-114 was the largest commercial aircraft in the world at the time of its appearance in 1957.

12,471m with 15 tons on November 14, 1959; 12,118m with 20 tons on November 25, 1959.

Soviet women pilots also used Il-18 to make record flights. Lyubov Ulyanova's crew reached 13,513m in October 1967 and in 1969 Ulyanova's team achieved 702kph over 5,000km and raised the long distance record over a closed circuit to 8,027km.

Il-18 still serve on some long lines of Aeroflot. In 1978, nineteen years after introduction, this type opened a regular connection of Moscow with the Molodoshnaya Station in the Soviet Sector of the Antarctic.

A few days before the 40th anniversary of the October Revolution, in 1957, the largest Soviet turboprop aircraft of the time and the largest commercial aircraft in the world made its first flight. It was the Tupolev Tu-114 called 'Rossiya'.

As in the case of Tu-104, designers were able to take over the well-tried structural parts of a bomber, this time Tu-20. Thus it was possible to shorten development time to eighteen months. For the Tu-114 a new fuselage was designed which had two decks and conspicuously fine lines. On the upper deck, behind the five-seat crew compartment, are the cabins for passengers and other auxiliary rooms. The lower deck comprises two large luggage and cargo compartments, each of which has the volume of a freight car. A staircase leads to the kitchen where two cooks are employed. Number of passengers varies in accordance with the service of the aircraft. On particularly long routes the Tu-114 carry 100-120 passengers, on medium flights 170 and on short routes 220. With mail, cargo and luggage this constitutes a payload of 15-30 tons.

In the standard version toilets are located behind the crew compartment followed by a cabin for 42 passengers. Behind this cabin are cloakrooms, a dining room with 48 seats, entrance room and an auxiliary kitchen where the food delivered from below is prepared. The rear compartment contains four separate cabins, each containing six first class armchairs, a cabin for 54 passengers, toilets, cloakrooms and washrooms.

Under the sweptback wings are four long engine nacelles with N D Kuznetsov's propeller turbines. On the first machines these were NK-12, each of 12,000mhp take-off performance. Production aircraft in service from 1961 onwards were given NK-12M, of 14,000mhp, and later 15,000mhp NK-12MV. In every case the turbines drive two contra-rotating, four-blade propellers.

Tu-114 was designed with regard to use on long distance flights within the USSR, especially between Moscow and Khabarovsk. On this route an express train transported an average 360 travellers in 10 carriages and the journey lasted 168 hours. Two Tu-114, each carrying 170 passengers, could transport 340 in just under nine hours for about the same price. Over longer distances, such as Moscow to New York or Tokyo, 120 passengers could be carried without intermediate landing; between Moscow and resorts on the Black Sea 220 people were regularly taken on board.

Machines of the Tu-114 pilot series undertook some noteworthy long distance flights in 1959. Tirana and Budapest were visited to see if connections were practicable and a Tu-114 was exhibited in summer 1959 at the Aerosalon in Paris. Tu-114 made its first flight to the USA on July 28, 1959, when Krushchev's second-in-command, F R Kozlov, was taken to New York. Tupolev was at that time a member of the delegation and excited a lot of attention from journalists. Tu-114 completed the 8,191km crossing in 11 hours 6 minutes averaging 740kph. The return flight, supported by a tail wind, took only 9 hours 48 minutes.

In America, Kozlov paved the way for Krushchev's visit. Krushchev also used the Tu-114, landing on September 15, 1959, at Andrews Airport, near Washington. The pilot on all long distance flights was A P Yakimov.

In 1960 a number of record flights were undertaken by the crew of I M Sukhomlin. On March 24 the Tu-114 set an FAI record of 871.38kph over 1,000km closed circuit with 25 tons load, simultaneously breaking six other payload records. On April 1 Sukhomlin took off with 25.2 tons payload on a flight over 2,000km to average 877.212kph. A third series of records were set on April 9 when with 25 tons load an average of 857.277kph was maintained over 5,000km.

In summer 1961 the attack was resumed, this time on the altitude category. On July 12 Tu-114 lifted 30,035kg to an altitude of 12,073m, at the same time beating records for 25 and 30 tons payload. And on April 21, 1962, Sukhomlin set four new standards with payloads of 1,000, 2,000, 5,000 and 10,000kg over a 10,000km closed circuit at a speed of 737.352kph. Final tally was 31 FAI records.

Tu-114 were put into service on the regular Moscow-Khabarovsk line on April 24, 1961. From 1963 onwards they flew the Moscow-Havana connection heading north, refuelling in Arkhangelsk and then completing a gigantic arc over the North Sea and Atlantic. The flight took 19 hours 40 minutes.

From summer 1966 Tu-114 also operated between Moscow and Tokyo. In the early days of this connection Japan Air Lines had no suitable machines, so Aeroflot loaned them a Tu-114.

Besides the standard Tu-114 a special variant, Tu-114D, was seen in 1958 with a Tu-20 bomber size fuselage. This was built for extra long flights carrying a small number of passengers or just mail and freight. In spring 1958 the prototype flew 8,500km non-stop from Moscow to Irkutsk and back at 10,000-12,000m, averaging 800kph. When the aircraft landed there was still enough fuel in the tanks for a further 2,000km.

Reconstructed in a similar way was the news plane, Ilyushin Il-20. Transport of newspaper matrices from the capital to the most important towns was always one of the most favoured assignments and a desire to speed up this service led Aeroflot to reconstruct some Il-28 bombers at the beginning of the fifties. While uneconomic to run, they proved worthwhile from a propaganda standpoint. But overall modernisation of the commercial sector soon rendered this specialised branch superfluous.

In 1958 the extent of the whole Aeroflot network amounted to 349,200km; 8,231,500 passengers used the services of this company which also transported 445,640,000 tons of mail, freight and luggage. Air transport amounted to a total of 941,500,000 ton-kilometres in this year, 25.3 times more than in 1940.

The Sixth Five Year Plan was changed by the 21st Assembly of the Communist Party of the USSR into a Seven Year Plan to cover 1959-1965. As regards air transport it declared: "Transport by air, after the introduction of high-speed jet and turboprop high capacity machines, will become one of the chief methods of transport for travellers. The volume of passenger air transport will be increased some sixfold during the Seven Year Plan. To ensure the operation of heavy aircraft, 90 airports will be redesigned or rebuilt; the whole commercial network will receive new, modern safety and navigational equipment. The network of the local lines will be increased".

This Plan postulated a yearly increase in air transport of 31%, growth in the last year being equal to the whole volume of air transport in 1958. Yearly increase averaged 15% during the fifties and 25% by about 1960.

Jet and turboprop aircraft were a particular help to modernisation. In 1959 only 10% of such planes were to be found in the commercial sec

tor; in 1962, 200 fast, high-capacity jets transported 60% of all travellers and for the final year of the Plan forecast figure was 80%. To meet this target there had to be a prompt supply of economic jet and turboprop transports which would take over the role of piston engine machines on short routes of 500-2,000km.

Among these new aircraft, Tupolev's Tu-124 occupies first place. Its prototype was test flown in June 1960. Passengers used to call the machine 'Little Tu', and Tu-124 does look like the child of Tu-104. It has the same forms, the same general lines, but is about 25% smaller.

All the same, it is not a direct miniaturisation of Tu-104, much having been altered. Instead of civil versions of military engines it made use of D-20P bypass jet engines of 4,500kp thrust designed by Solovyev. These were specially made for the plane and were, like all bypass jets, very economic and less noisy than ordinary engines.

The prototype Tu-124 started off with 44 passengers in the pressurised cabin, but first production models designed for Aeroflot and foreign customers had 56 seats and were designated Tu-124V. Other well known variants are: Tu-124K, a plane for mixed transport taking 36 passengers and cargo up to a full payload of 6,000kg; Tu-124K-2, designed merely for cargo transport with reinforced cabin floor and a large cargo door. If desired, a small cabin for 22 passengers can be mounted.

Tu-124 were able to fly from the same grass airfields as Il-14, powerful, double-slotted variable camber flaps shortening take-off run to 1,360m and 10m obstacles being cleared after 2,120m. Efficient braking surfaces under the fuselage and several spoilers on the wing replaced parachute brakes on the Tu-104 and shortened landing run to 930m.

Maximum speed of Tu-124 was 970kph, economic speed 800kph and altitude 8,000-11,000m. Range was 1,200km when travelling at 800kph at 10,000m with 6,000kg payload. Maximum range with 3,500kg payload reached 2,100km.

Aeroflot put its Tu-124 into service on domestic lines in 1962 and Moscow-Tallin was the first flown on October 2. They did not set any international records, but acquired fame for reliability.

Tu-124 had priority in flying on the regular Aeroflot lines, but O K Antonov's turboprop made the first flight overall. First order for a short-range aircraft came in 1958, Aeroflot requiring a cabin for 32-40 people, but during the design period these requirements were altered to 44 then 48. First prototype was in fact built with 48 seats and test flown in April 1960. During the next twelve months a further prototype and five machines of the pilot series were built.

An-24 was a high-wing monoplane with low-set fuselage so that no entrance steps were needed at the airport. Fuselage section comprised two circular arcs, allowing a spacious, high-pressure

Tu-124's D-20P bypass jet engines were specially designed for the aircraft.

Antonov's short-range liner, the An-24, was first flown in April 1960.

Above: An-26 evolved from the An-24 via the An-24RT with auxilliary jet engine.

Below: The main parts of An-26 went into construction of An-32, a 'high and hot' aircraft with powerful AI-20M engines.

cabin. Under the wing Ivchenko AI-24 turboprops of 2,550mhp were located in two relatively high nacelles into which the main undercarriage also retracted.

Development of the plane after its first flight was very slow and difficult. An-24 suffered from poor directional stability, the same 'illness' as its elder brother, An-10. The problem was solved by forming a negative dihedral of the wing tips, an anhedral of the horizontal stabiliser and addition of auxiliary vertical fins above and below the fuselage tip. All this required time and the government test of An-24 was not completed until September 1962. A year later they were put into regular service between Moscow-Voronesh-Saratov and other routes.

An-24 are produced in several variants, most common of which is the An-24V for 50-52 passengers and payload of 5,700kg. About four aircraft are produced monthly, each requiring about 40,000 working hours. Antonov has introduced superior technology – metal bonding, glass-fibre, plastics, etc.

At the Paris Aerosalon in 1967, variant An-24RV was displayed. This has S K Tumanskii's light jet engine RU-19-300 in the rear of the right-hand engine nacelle, producing 900kp static thrust and designed to give an increase in power for aircraft taking off in high temperatures or elevated airfields.

Variant An-24T is intended for freight or mixed transport. It has a cambered fuselage tail and from the underside a loading ramp can be lowered. An-24RT has the same equipment but with the RU-19-300 jet.

Antonov used the An-24RT as a basis for the An-26, a more sophisticated transport with the facility to load and unload cars of the jeep type through a rear-loading ramp. It has AI-24T engines of 2,820mhp plus an auxiliary RU-19-300 jet engine in the right hand engine nacelle. An-26 was flight tested in 1968 and delivered to the first users one year later.

In 1977 Antonov used the main parts of An-26 to construct the "high and hot" transport aircraft An-32. Its engines are the big AI-20M of 5,180mhp with four-blade propellers taken over from the Il-18 aircraft and positioned on top of the wing. The reason for using such very powerful engines was to achieve good take-off characteristics from high airfields in hot weather, making use of the RU-19-300 unnecessary. Maximum payload is 5,000 to 6,000kg and 3,000kg can be lifted from an airfield at 4,500m above sea level. An-32 was tested in May 1977 and shown in Paris in the same year. The Indian Air Force uses An-32 in the Himalayas.

An-30 is another version, this time developed from the An-24RV. Its role is aerial mapping for which it uses different sorts of cameras covering the scale from 1:10,000 to 1:150,000. Four cameras are standard, there is a darkroom for developing film during flight and other special equipment. An-30 was first shown at Hanover in 1974 and is recognised by its intensively glazed fuselage nose.

Similarity with the An-24 family remains in the newest transport type from Antonov's design bureau – the An-72. This interesting high-wing monoplane, shown in Paris in 1979, uses the so-called Coanda effect. It produces more lift and shortens take off by distributing the whole jet efflux of its twin 6,500kp Lotarev D-36 bypass engines on the upper surface of the wing and mighty camber changing flaps, like the American Boeing YC-14 prototype. An-72 has room for 10,000kg of freight, 52 passengers or 24 stretcher cases etc. It was shown in Aeroflot colors, but military transport is certainly possible.

All the variants of An-24 were put into service and exported. During 1965, 25 machines were sold abroad; in 1966 the number had risen to 50. An-24 is to be found not only in Socialist states but also in some Arab countries and Asia.

At the beginning of the first Seven Year Plan, Aeroflot had at its disposal the two-engined jet

An-72, seen here at Farnborough in 1984, uses the Coanda effect to increase lifting capacity. and shorten take-off runs.

An-30, developed from the An-24RV, is used for aerial mapping and carries four cameras.

aircraft Tu-104, four-engined turboprop machines An-10, Il-18, Tu-114 and, in smaller numbers, An-12, plus several piston-engined Il-14 or alternatively Il-12 and Li-2. Nor must we overlook the multiple purpose biplane An-2. During the first half of the Plan, Tu-124 and An-24 were added to the number.

There was a suitable machine for each route, whatever its length and character. Those times were long past when every flight was made with a two-engined piston aircraft and helicopters had also made their own impression.

But even more efficient machines had to be designed, machines which met the demands of modern technology. Propeller turbines diminished in favour of the more economic and technically superior bypass engines, but were kept for special purposes when full use could be made of their advantages.

Later Soviet jets are characterised by aerodynamically undisturbed wings and engines on the rear of the fuselage. This brilliant concept was produced by France in 1953 with the SE-210 Caravelle.

At the beginning of 1961 Tupolev's bureau under the direction of Leonid Selyakov, redesigned and reconstructed the Tu-124 transport with engines located to the rear. The prototype Tu-124A was ready in December 1963 for its first flight. Shortly afterwards its designation was changed to Tu-134 to show that a really new machine had been produced.

Structural modifications were extensive. Front part of the fuselage was lengthened, wings were mounted directly onto the fuselage and only the characteristic undercarriage nacelles kept, located on the trailing edge. The whole rear fuselage was completely reconstructed, forming an integral part of the broad, high vertical fin, capped by the elevator.

Engines on the prototype were bypass D-20P of Solovyev;on the five-machine pilot series and subsequent production aircraft the more modern D-30 were used, each producing 6,800kp static thrust. Tests produced no difficulties and by September 1964, when the first photographs were published, the prototype already had a hundred flights behind it.

Although the Tu-134 was developed from Tu-124 and was not dissimilar in dimensions, the new interior arrangement gave 50% greater seating capacity. When the aircraft had two separate cabins, the first-class compartment took 16 passengers and the tourist section 48, a total of 64. In the version with one through cabin and better utilisation of space, 72 could be taken. Crew consisted of three plus an air hostess.

Semi-automatic landing equipment proved of particular value. The aid guided aircraft automatically to an altitude of 30m over the runway, but actual landing had to be accomplished by the pilot. Better aerodynamics and more powerful engines also improved the qualities and performance in comparison with Tu-124.

Variant Tu-134A has a fuselage 2.05m longer and takes 72-80 passengers. Tu-134 has been in service since summer 1967 on the short lines of Aeroflot and some East European states. Moscow – Stockholm was the first connection flown.

Tu-134A of 1970 received more economical D-30-2 engines with better thrust reversers and could accommodate up to 80 passengers. Originally all the Tu-134As had glazed noses but Aviogenex from Yugoslavia and Czechoslovakia's CSA ordered them with a solid nose to accommodate electronics. Tu-134As are now mostly produced with solid nose. Cruising speed of the Tu-134 is betwen 870 and 900kph, the most economical being 750kph. Range with maximum payload of 8,215kg is 2,000km and maximum 3,500km.

Aeroflot was also given the large four-engined, long-range Il-62 designed by Ilyushin. This has a pure, sweptback wing with four engines mounted in pairs at the rear of the fuselage.

Ilyushin used modern constructional methods for this giant, such as the milling of whole areas of thick dural sheet covering including the inner skin reinforcing strips. Aerodynamics were also modern. The wing has a leading edge with saw teeth which provides good take-off and landing qualities, variable camber flaps and lift spoilers. Control surfaces are similar to those of Tu-134.

First two prototypes, completed by January

The Il-62 long-range airliner has a 50m fuselage and seats up to 186 passengers.

1963, were flown with Lyulka AL-7 engines, each of 7,500kp. By 1965 the bypass Kuznetsov NK-8-3 engines, specially designed for this aircraft, were ready for mounting. They produced 10,500kp static thrust. From 1967 more economic NK-8-4 were used and in 1970 came the Solovyev D-30K, each of 11,500kp. Seven large integral tanks carry about 100,000 litres of fuel.

Il-62's 50m long fuselage has a cabin for the crew of five and adaptable passenger arrangements. In the economy variant is accommodation for 186 passengers while a combination of first and luxury classes makes it possible to give 100 passengers a particularly pleasant journey. On long-distance flights like Moscow-New York (7,700km) the Il-62 transports 150 passengers without intermediate landings at a speed of 850kph. Pressure corresponding to sea-level is maintained up to 7,000m; at 14,000m the pressure relates to 2,400m.

Flight testing of two prototypes and three machines of the pilot series took a fairly long time and there were certain technical difficulties. Production in the overloaded Kasam aircraft plant also presented problems.

One prototype was the main exhibit for a few days at the Paris Aerosalon in summer 1965 and one of the first production aircraft visited Ruzyn airport, near Prague, in spring 1967 in connection with a Czech order. In summer 1967 another machine made a noteworthy flight from Moscow to Murmansk and from there to the North Pole, Novaya Zemlya, Sverdlovsk and back to Moscow – 9,000km in 11 hours. In summer 1965 an Il-62

flew with 168 passengers from Moscow to Tashkent, covering the 2,880km in 3 hours 20 minutes. In September 1967 an Il-62 flew non-stop from Moscow to Montreal for the international show and the direct Moscow to New York route was also accomplished.

Ilyushin designed a variant some 6.5m longer for 1971 and called it Il-62M. This plane can accommodate 204 passengers and is driven by D-30KU by pass engines. Long range variant Il-62MK was introduced in 1978 and takes 195 passengers.

We remarked that an Il-62 was exhibited at the 1965 Aerosalon in Paris. The machine that came some days later excited the attention of the whole exhibition. It was a giant transport plane, An-22, designed by Antonov who gave it the name of the giant in Greek mythology, Antaeus, written 'Antej' in Russian.

An-22 is certainly a remarkably strong machine. With a take-off weight of 250 tons, it carries 80 tons over 5,000km distance. The transport sector needed such aircraft, not only for use in the civil role.

Heavy weapons, armoured tanks, larger troop units, rocket launchers and other loads which were becoming increasingly difficult to transport by land could be swallowed by Antaeus.

Everything about An-22 is on a large scale. Wing span is 64.4m, fuselage 57.8m long and the undercarriage has fourteen wheels, arranged in pairs and retractable into the fuselage. At the rear is a drop ramp via which vehicles can be driven into the cargo compartment, 33m long,

Giant transport An-22, with 250 tons take-off weight, made a dramatic appearance in 1965.

Tu-134A seats between 72-80 and has been in service since 1967.

4.4m wide and 4.4m high.

There is room for: five 6,500kg bulldozers; or two E-656 dredgers, each of 22,100kg; or a fast hydroplane; or two fast PS-5 boats, each weighing 11,400kg; two buses of 7,840kg; an express train wagon of 49,500kg; five 12,000kg reinforced concrete arches for the construction of bridges etc. Cargo which is not self-propelled can be pulled in with a hoist or crane.

A crew of five is seated in standard, military, divided compartments. Behind is a small pressurised cabin for 29 people.

Four turboprop NK-12MV engines are used, each engine producing 15,000mhp and having two, four-blade, contra-rotating propellers of 6.2m diameter. The designer made sure of good stability this time by using a twin rudder.

Design on 'Antej' started in 1962 and the first flight took place on February 27, 1965. The journey from Moscow to Paris in June 1965 was one of its first long distance flights, covered in 5 hours 5 minutes at an average speed of 563kph. Three buses and a lot of other cargo was taken.

Maximum speed of An-22 is 680kph and range 11,000km. Considering its great dimensions and weight, the take-off run of 1,300m and landing distance of 800m are very short.

In autumn 1966 An-22 appeared in the FAI list, setting 13 international records. One hundred tons were taken to 7,848m, 100.45 tons to 2,000m and 88.1 tons to 6,600m. These were all set on October 27, 1966, and in command of the machine was I J Davydov. The same pilot beat his own record in October 1967 when he took 100.45 tons to 7,848m.

For mass transport of passengers Antonov designed a variant of An-22 with a fuselage about 15m longer. The double-decker cabin was to take 724 passengers – 423 on the top deck and 301 on the lower. Travellers were to board through twelve entrances. Much has been written about this aircraft but it seems that Aeroflot was not convinced of the necessity of such a machine.

In 1967 Tupolev took on the task of creating a substitute for Tu-104 and on October 4, 1968, the first prototype of his new Tu-154 was test flown by Youri Soukhov. The Tu-154 matches, in every respect, the new series of commercial aircraft. In order to make the machine more marketable in the West the Soviet designer dispensed with all special features and followed the well-tried Western aircraft engineering concepts.

Tu-154 has three 9,500kp NK-8-2 bypass engines, one right in the tail with the air intake at the root of the tail fin, and one each side of the fuselage. Fuselage has a standard 'civil' nose and Tupolev finally dispensed with the military navigator's cabin.

Aeroflot put the first Tu-154 into service in February 1972. Standard version takes 152 passengers tourist class; when a first-class cabin is included for 24 passengers, 104 seats are left. By making full use of interior space Tu-154 can transport 164 passengers in the economy class. A cargo variant of Tu-154 was designed with a 2.1 x 3.4m door on the starboard side and can take up to 30 tons load. With a take-off weight of 86 tons, the following performances were expected:

Tu-154 was a substitute for Tu-104 and first flew in October 1968.

with 16 tons payload a range of 4,700km; 18 tons, 3,300km; 5.2 tons, 5,800km. Greatest load is 19,000kg, best operating speed 885kph and the most economic 780kph.

A further variant of Tu-154 was planned. This was projected as Tu-154M, an airbus for 240-250 passengers. It was to have a fuselage some 13m longer and take-off weight increased to 90 tons. Engine performance was also to be increased.

Instead of developing an airbus from the Tu-154, Tupolev's bureau began to develop the original Tu-124 for higher performance and more economy. In April 1974 the Tu-154A entered Aeroflot service, powered by a trio of NK-8-2U engines. All-up weight rose to 94,000kg and the central part of the wing could accommodate more fuel. Tu-154As transport 152 passengers in Summer and 144 in Winter, again because of heavy clothing needed in the Russian Winters.

More modern Tu-154B weigh 96,000kg during take off, its emergency exits and other security measures are closer to Western standards and they are able to accommodate up to 169 passengers. More normal numbers are 36+98 tourist class passengers and eight first class seats. With 16,000kg payload the Tu-154B has a range of 3,200-3,300km. The Hungarian Malev and Bulgarian Balkan airlines are greatest users of Tu-154Bs outside the USSR. The Hungarian machines are known as Tu-154B-2.

In 1982 a new variant of the Tu-154 family appeared. It is the Tu-164 converted from Tu-154B-2. It uses the Solovyev D-30KU from the Il-62M, de-rated to 10,608kp for higher economy. The whole rear part of the fuselage, including tailplane, fin and rudder, was altered. The prototype provided for 169 passengers but series production machines are expected to take at least 180.

Il-62 was able to fly the long routes, Tu-154 the medium and fairly long ones. For short routes Tu-134 will suffice for a few years more. But for short and very short routes a new aircraft was designed.

A S Yakovlev designed his low-wing monoplane, Yak-40, to replace Ilyushin's Il-14. First flight of the prototype took place on October 21, 1966, and the machine was then shown at Paris in summer 1967. Most interesting features on the new machine were three AI-25 bypass jets each of 1,500kp – unusual on a plane of this size – and straight wings without sweepback.

Yakovlev had three preoccupations when he designed this plane – economy, reliability and operation from short grass airfields. Yak-40 corresponds to Il-14 in the number of passengers (24-31) and the range (1,000-1,600km), but operating speed is incomparably higher at 450-600kph. Take-off and landing qualities are comparable, runways of 700-750m being adequate.

Yak-40 was introduced into Aeroflot with surprising promptitude. On September 30, 1968, Aeroflot opened the Yak-40 service between Moscow and Kostrom and by 1975 it became the most used type on Soviet international lines. Some examples were exported to France, Italy, Western Germany, Afghanistan and Yugoslavia, the Italian Aerotirrena SpA near Florence serving as sales and service centre. Negotiations were conducted with the American Rockwell Co to produce and or sell Collins instrumented Yak-40ECs on the US market, but nothing materialised.

Yak-40s are widely used in East European airlines like CSA, some of the machines as cargo transport Yak-40T with 1.60 x 1.50m cargo-door on the left side in front of the wing.

Yakovlev's success with the Yak-40 inspired him to enter a heavier class of inter-city aircraft for Aeroflot, the Yak-42. Its prototype flew on March 7, 1975, powered by a trio of Lotarev's D-36 engines of 6,430kp. passenger carrying capacity was expected to be between 100 and 120. Three prototypes were built and tested, one with a straight wing, one with 11° and the third with 23° swept wing. The Yak-42 shown in Paris in 1977 with its 23° swept wing was the type destined for series production.

Aim of the Yak-42 was to replace Tu-134As on Soviet and other domestic and international lines, but it seems now that the aim will not be fulfilled. Aeroflot ceased experimental Yak-42 service in 1983 and the type will no longer be produced.

G M Beriev's high-wing monoplane Be-30 was the new Soviet aircraft for very short routes. This retained turboprop engines, always the most suitable for machines of this class, and was the first landplane to be designed by Beriev's bureau after many years' work on waterplanes. Be-30 is similar in its lines to An-24. Its well glazed cabin takes 14 or 15 passengers and two pilots and can transport 13,000kg payload 200-400km. Be-30 was to be put into service on routes of 150-300km, operating at 460-480kph.

Airframe of the first prototype was ready before the engines, so M I Mikhajlov had to test fly it on March 30, 1967, with two 740mhp ASh-21 piston engines. Since the USSR considered home design of light turboprop engines too slow, they purchased French Turbomeca Astazou XII for further tests, first aeroplane equipped with these taking off on July 18, 1968. For production aircraft turboprops were built under designation TVD-10. The TVD-10 produce 970mhp and drive three-blade propellers. The propeller drives of both engine groups are connected in such a way that should one engine fail the other can drive both propellers.

According to Press announcements, production Be-30 were put into service with Aeroflot in summer 1969. But after comparative flights between Be-30 and the Czech LET L-410 Turbolet, it was decided to halt production of Be-30 and put L-410 into production for the Eastern countries.

Be-30 can operate from short grass runways, taking-off in only 170m and landing in 130m. The little Be-30 also possesses a semi-automatic landing aid which takes the pilot down to 30m

Tu-134, with tail-mounted engines, was originally flown as the Tu-124A prototype.

-Tu-154B-2 in service with the Hungarian Malev airline.

Above: Yakovlev designed his Yak-50 to replace the Il-14 on short and very short routes.

Below: The future of Yak-42 remains in doubt. This example was seen in Paris in 1985.

Antonov's An-28 can be used for passengers, freight or treatment of crops.

above the ground. The interior can be quickly reconstructed for ambulance, photographic or cargo purposes.

In 1969 Antonov's bureau designed another multi-purpose small transport aircraft, developed from the earlier, and not too successful, An-14 Pchyelka family. Originally it was the An-14M powered by a pair of Izotov TVD-850 turboprops, each developing 820mhp. The aircraft had a roomier fuselage, making use of the extra power available. One of the later machines used even more powerful Glushenkov TVD-10A of 975mhp.

From the An-14M came a really new type which Antonov designated An-28. It is used for 15 to 20 passengers, crop-dusting with a 800kg container or for cargo up to 1,500kg which can be transported 1,000km. Development of the An-28 took some time. The first machine with TVD-10A engines was flown in 1975 and yet series production from the Polish factory PZL, at Mielec, did not begin until the 1980/81 period. Problems with the Polish production on one side and delivery of Czechoslovak L-410 UVP engines on another are certainly not favourable for An-28.

An aircraft which roused tremendous interest

was the Soviet supersonic commercial aircraft, Tu-144, of A N Tupolev, not only for its own intrinsic features but also on account of the contest for prestige will the Franco-British Aerospatiale/BAC Concorde.

Authorities had been aware for several years that a supersonic commercial aircraft was a 'sine qua non' for the big transport companies. But the gigantic costs for a plane with relatively limited market possibilities proved an obstacle to development. British-French co-operation showed how the concept could be realised and the costs met. Several American designs were subsequently announced, but nothing was known about the views of the USSR on supersonic commercial aircraft.

For that reason it was a great surprise to see a big model of Tu-144 on the Soviet stand at the Aerosalon in Paris, 1965. At a time when Concorde was at an advanced stage of development, notices under the model informed the public that Tu-144 would be flown in 1968, if not before.

Tupolev had chosen quite simple aerodynamics for his aircraft as had the creators of Concorde. A long, slim fuselage had delta wing with cambered leading edge, but in comparison with

The Be-30 was Beriev's first landplane after many years of floatplane work.

Concorde that part of the leading edge which runs into the fuselage had a higher sweep back and the outer parts less sweep. So the Soviet plane intended to achieve good qualities for slow-speed flying by more usual means than Concorde.

Engine grouping was also different. On the model one could see a gigantic box under the fuselage in which were four Kuznetsov NK-144 engines, each of 13,000kp thrust, arranged side-by-side. Concorde has two pairs of engines under the wing.

But one thing in common was the nose which could be dropped by about 12°. This was indispensable for take-off and landing with an aircraft possessing this wing form, the pilots being scarcely able to see straight ahead on these occasions. Also, the tip, in its straight position, forms a shield against overheating of the cockpit windows during supersonic flight.

The notice under the model announced that Tu-144 would transport 120 passengers at a speed of 2,500kph, operating at 20,000m and having a range of 6,500km.

A MiG-21 fighter was given a wing with the same outline as Tu-144 and used as a flying lab-oratory. After all necessary information had been assembled, the real design and construction of the wing began in Antonov's plant. Some details were altered, e.g. the engine box under the fuselage was now divided on its leading edge into two parts, each one displaying the air inlets for two NK-144 engines. Maximum thrust was increased to 17,500kp by means of a short after-burning. These afterburners were only for use on take-off, otherwise the aircraft was to fly with throttled engines, which is not only more economic but also quieter.

The aircraft had a tricycle undercarriage with twelve landing wheels. Construction was of duralumin, mostly milled out of thick plate, only the leading edges being made from titanium and stainless steel. Fuel tanks contained 87,500 litres.

Cabin was equipped in a standard fashion for 100 passengers, 18 of them in the first class with three seats in each row, 82 in the tourist class with five or four seats in a row. When space was fully utilised capacity rose to 121.

On December 31, 1968, test pilot Edvard Elyan took off in the Tu-144 accompanied by the MiG-21 test aircraft. Three prototypes were built and the first exceeded Mach 1 on June 7, 1969, earlier than the French-British machines. Mach 2 was also exceeded earlier – on May 26, 1970, whereas Concorde flew it on November 4, 1970. Highest Mach number reached was 2.28.

During test and development the Tu-144 underwent several modifications, supervised by Tupolev junior, Alexei Andreyevich Tupolev. In 1971 the SSSR-68001 prototype appeared at Paris Aerosalon together with Concorde, showing the differences between the two concepts as well as the common solutions. At that time Tu-144 could

Left: Virtually silhouetted, the Tu-144 prototype lands in company with a MiG-21 escort. First flight was on December 31, 1968.

A picture profile of the supersonic Tu-144. The pre-production model (bottom right and main picture) incorporated retractable foils slightly aft of the cockpit.

accommodate 140 passengers, 11 of them in the first class cabin. All the modifications made Tu-144 a very different aircraft when compared with the early model.

In the Spring of 1972 another prototype was flown, the SSR-77101 observed as the pre-production machine. Wing-shape, engine nacelles, fuselage, undercarriage and fin were altered quite extensively, showing the amount of problems to be solved. One of the greatest differences was the introduction of retractable 'moustaches', foreplanes situated just aft of the pilot's compartment. They were to assure more stability during take-off and landing without great angle of attack of the main wing. New NK-144 engines were expected to give a full 20,000kp thrust in series production; the types used showed 13,000/17,500kp with afterburning. Take-off weight was now at 180,000kg.

One of the pre-series machines, SSSR-77101, made its first experimental flight in Aeroflot colors in September 1972, connecting Moscow with Tashkent within 1hr 50min. In Summer 1973 the SSSR-77102 flew to Paris but crashed there on June 3, before 300,000 people. No public investigation result is known, but it was sure that the fault was not in the aircraft.

In Autumn 1974 Aeroflot pilots began training with Tupolev's instructors on the Moscow-Baku-Tashkent-Baku-Moscow route, averaging 1,923.10kph on the 2,500km Moscow-Baku leg. By summer 1975 Tu-144s had completed 1,000 flights.

Freight and post was transported regularly between Moscow and Alma Ata twice a week from December 1975; in February 1977 similar flights started between Moscow and Khabarovsk. On November 1, 1977, Aeroflot opened route No. SU499 from Moscow to Alma Ata and back with aircraft equipped for 133 passengers, 11 of them first class. The flying was absolutely safe, regular and extremely comfortable. Unfortunately the economics of the enterprise were not sound and after the 102nd flight Tu-144 operations ceased.

However, after July, 1978, date of the halt for Tu-144, information was published in the newspapers about a new Tu-144D version with more economic engines. On June 23, 1978, it had made a 6,185km flight from Moscow to Chabarovsk averaging 1,811.8kph. Unfortunately no other information is available.

Soviet air transport now uses a new type of commercial machine in the airbus category, the Ilyushin Il-86. Rumours of an airbus from the Ilyushin design bureau had been heard for many years, models and artist's impressions showing different forms of aircraft stemming mostly from the Il-62 concept.

G Novozhilov, who became responsible for Ilyushin's bureau after the 'chief' retired, realised that the rear engines concept had its limitations. He therefore developed a classic four-jet machine with engines in separate pods spread on the leading edge of the wing and therefore taking over some of the strain from the wing structure

during flight.

Il-86 is a big, low-wing monoplane with a double deck fuselage. In the lower deck there is a cloakroom and cargo compartments while in the upper section are main cabins for up to 350 passengers. The Aeroflot standard is 234 people, 28 of them travelling first class.

The prototype made its maiden flight on December 22, 1976, taking off from the old Moscow airport of Khodynka, or more exactly, Moscow Central Airport, the oldest in the capital and surrounded by buildings. Of the 1,800m long runway the Il-86 used 1,700m.

Il-86's wing has a sweep of 35° and has a special electroimpulsive shock waves de-icing device name EIPOS and developed by the Ilyushin

bureau. The same system is used also for unloading frozen coal wagons. A multiple-wheeled bogie type undercarriage is fitted with a 'third' leg retracting in the centreline of the fuselage. Engines are Kuznetsov NK-86 bypass jets of 13,000kp each.

First production machine was test flown on October 24, 1977, and in September 1978 Aeroflot began the first experimental line from Moscow to Mineralnyje Vody. Later came other towns inside the USSR. Since 1981 Il-86 have operated on important international lines like Moscow – East Berlin and later Moscow – Madrid. Il-86 is one of the most important means of fulfilling transport requirements of the 10th Five Years Plan.

Above and below: Soviet airbus Il-86, introduced to Aeroflot routes from 1978, emerged as a result of acceptance that tail-engined airliners had their limitations. They have an electroimpulse shock wave de-icing system.

Transport and Utility Aircraft

MOST OF THE AIRLINERS deployed by Aeroflot today have already been described. But with the improvement of avionics they have been further developed and are presented here in alphabetic order of designing bureaux.

O K Antonov's design bureau in Kiev won fame with the utility An-2 biplane, which is still in production at the WSK-Mielec plant in Poland. The many variants of this unique aircraft have recently been supplemented by a new version powered by a 940shp Glushenkov turboprop engine TVD-10B, the An-3. Pilot S Gorbikov and mechanic P Ignatenko carried out flight trials during 1981, and the Antonov OKB proudly claims that the An-3 has a spraying capability of 1,800kg of chemicals in two hours, whereas An-2 only sprayed 1,300kg. With the new engine, time-to-height has been halved compared to its predecessor and manoeuvrability is improved considerably. Cockpit conditions are also better. A version with the 1,450shp TVD-20 has also been reported.

The giant An-22 transport, which set a number of weight-lifting records during 1966 and 1967, was mentioned again in FAI announcements in 1972, 1974 and 1975 when various pilots attained record speeds carrying loads of up to 50 tons. On February 21, 1972, Maria Popovich attained 608.449kph over a closed course of 1,000km with 50 tons load, while S G Dedukh, Yu A Romanov and G N Pakilev clocked record speeds with various loads over 5,000km closed courses.

Four AN-22s were deployed to deliver supplies after the tragic 1970 earthquake in Peru, in the course of which one An-22 was lost. Military An-22s also supplied Syria and Egypt with military equipment during the 1973 war with Israel.

An-32, designed to operate from 'high-and-hot' airfields located at 4,000-4,500m above sea level, has competed in India with the Aeritalia G-22 and DHC-5 Buffalo, and was selected in favour of the more expensive aircraft. Some 95 will be acquired to replace C-119s and Caribous, but contrary to earlier reports they will not be assembled in India. The An-32 has been equipped with An-26 facilities and can be operated from airfields with insufficient servicing equipment since it has its own mechanical handling system. Maximum take-off weight is 26,000kg, cruise speed is 510kph and range with a 6-ton payload and 45 minutes fuel reserve is 800km. It has passenger accommodation for 39 and 30 paratroopers can be accommodated. An ambulance version has 24 stretchers and one medical attendant.

During the Le Bourget airshow of 1979 Antonov surprised the world with a new STOL short-haul transport aircraft, the An-72. This had made its first flight on December 22, 1977, and shortly afterwards received the reporting name 'Coaler'. It is Antonov's first pure jet and, as in the Boeing YC-14, the engines – two 6,500 kg thrust Lotarev D-36 turbofans – are mounted over the wing, thus eliminating foreign object damage when using unpaved strips.

The wings are fitted with wide-span, trailing-edge flaps, double-slotted inboard panels, situated in the exhaust efflux, and triple-slotted outboard panels. Full-span leading edge slats are also mounted. Lift at take-off is increased considerably thanks to the Coanda effect and the Antonov OKB claims that the aircraft can operate from snowy or unpaved strips with a length of not more than 1,000m. The bogie landing gear has eight wheels fitted on four independent legs, with low-pressure tyres.

There are 32 folding seats along the side walls in the roomy freight compartment, which is 9m long, 2.15m wide and 2.2m high. Rear loading is allowed through a pair of clamshell doors over a hydraulically actuated ramp, and a conveyer can be installed to handle containers or pallets. A 2,500kg hoist with four hooks runs the full length of the compartment.

Wing span is 25.83m, length 26.58m, maximum 10,000kg payload allows a range of 1,000km, 7,500kg gives 2,000km, service ceiling is 11,000m and maximum cruising speed 720kph. East German sources report designation An-74 for the production variant.

The Soviet equivalent of the Lockheed C5 Galaxy heavy lift transport aircraft, the An-124, was demonstrated at the Paris Air Show in 1985. The multi wheel undercarriage would suggest a rough field capability.

Given the reporting name 'Condor', and termed 'Ruslan', An-124 made its first flight on December 26, 1982. Maximum cruising speed with four Lotarev D-18T 23,000kp thrust bypass turbofans is 865kph and maximum take-off weight 405,000kg. The aircraft has a wing span of

Multi-wheel An-124 lowers its maximum 405,000kg weight to the ground.

73.3m and is 69.5m long.

In 1976 TASS issued a photograph of the Beriev Be-32 which is similar in appearance to the ill-fated Be-30 'Cuff'. According to the caption two time-to-height records were set by Ye Lakhmostov for turboprop aircraft (group II) and for landplanes (sub-class C-1): to 3,000m in 2 minutes 24.8 seconds and to 6,000m in 18 seconds. The Be-32 accommodates 18 passengers or can carry 1,900kg freight. There is no further information.

The veteran Ilyushin Il-18 was converted by Aeroflot for use as a freighter in arctic regions and the Far East. The floor was strengthened and a 3.5m wide freight door installed in the rear fuselage.

Ilyushin's long-range commercial Il-62 airliner has been in service for many years in various countries, including the People's Republic of China. The original Il-62 has since been modified

An-124 exhibited in Paris in 1985.

and is now called Il-62M-200, or Il-62M for short. Kuznetsov NK-8 engines were replaced by more powerful 11,000kg take-off thrust Solovyev D-30KU bypass turbojets and accommodation increased to 198 passengers. Range of flight with 23,000kg payload plus fuel reserve is 7,800km and maximum take-off weight 105,000kg. In its basic version the passenger cabin is laid out for 168 tourist seats.

On October 22-23, 1977, an all-women Aeroflot crew, led by I F Vertiprakhova, established a world record by flying from Sofia to Vladivostok, a distance of 10,086.669km, in 13 hours 1 minute, clocking an average speed of 774kph. The same crew had attained 953.038kph over a 5,000km closed course on September 16, 1977, and six days later 806.272kph over a closed course of 10,000km, also in Il-62M.

In 1971 Paris Airshow witnessed another Russian surprise, the Ilyushin Il-76 transport. A prototype had made its first flight two months before, on March 25, in the hands of test pilot Kuznetsov. General Designer Genrikh Vasilyevich Novozhilov, who succeeded Ilyushin in the late 60s because of Ilyushin's poor health, told Western observers that Il-76's prime mission was the hauling of gas pipeline sections to remote fields in central and Eastern Siberia.

The transport's ability to operate from unprepared runways is very obvious in the tricycle undercarriage. There are two side-by-side pairs of nose-wheels, and each bogie carries two pairs of main wheels in two rows, thus totalling 20 wheels, each fitted with low-pressure tyres. Furthermore, the navigator's cockpit is located below and forward of the pilot's cockpit to facilitate visual selection of landing sites. High-lift devices include full-span leading-edge slats and double-slotted trailing-edge flaps to provide short take-off and landing capability. For military use a rear turret with twin 23mm cannon is installed.

Il-76, which was allotted the reporting name 'Candid', is powered by four 12,000kg thrust Solovyev D-30KP turbofans. The cargo cabin is 24.5m long (including the downward-hinged loading ramp), 3.46m wide, 3.4m high and can take any load of standardised containers or pallets under ISO requirements. Maximum payload is 40,000kg, service range 5,000km, cruise speed 750-800kph and maximum take-off weight 170,000kg.

Two modified versions have been reported in the West – Il-76T with some 20% more fuel capacity and range increased to 6,700km, and Il-76M, which possibly is the military variant.

A number of impressive world records were established in 1975 when A M Tyuryumin attained a speed of 856.697kph carrying 60 tons payload over a 2,000km closed course on July 4, and 857,657kph with 70 tons over a 1,000km closed course three days later. Also on July 4, Ya I Vernikov lifted 70 tons to an altitude of 11,875m, and on the same flight also lifted the greatest payload, 70,121kg, to a height of 2,000m.

Il-76 is equipped with a cargo roller floor, two 3,000kg winches and two roof cranes with 10,000kg lifting capacity. Wing span is 50.5m, length 46.59m and wing area 300 sq m. Il-76TD is an uprated version with increased payload and range.

According to Soviet Civil Aviation authorities the Il-86, known in Western military circles as 'Camber', broke 18 international records on September 22 and 24, 1981, when a closed course of 2,000km was flown with 65,588kg payload at 956kph, and a payload of 80 tons was carried over 1,000km at 971kph.

One of the unique features of Il-86 is the arrangement whereby passengers carry their own baggage into underfloor cabins before entering one of three salons seating 111, 141 and 98 passengers respectively.

Polish and Czech aviation plants take part in the construction of Il-86, the WSK-Mielec plant producing parts of the wing, stabiliser and engine pylons. Polish part in the entire construction amounts to about 15%. Maximum cruising speed of Il-86 is 950kph, range with maximum payload 4,000km and with 250 passengers 5,000km. Wing span is 48.06m, length 59.54m and wing area 329.8 sq m.

In 1980 a light utility aircraft was reported, designed by the student design bureau at Moscow Aviation Institute with co-operation from Tashkent Aviation Institute. The design was supervised by Professor A Badyagin and Professor S Sarymsakov and is powered by an Ivchenko AI-25 turbofan of 1,500kp take-off thrust. A 315kp thrust auxiliary engine is used for take off assistance and serves as an emergency power unit in case the main engine stops. Intake for both engines is on top of the fuselage. Take-off weight of 'Semurg' (Uzbekistan word for 'Lucky Bird') is 3,200kg and maximum payload 800kg. During test flights a speed of 360kph was attained. Range is 1,000km and take-off run 150m.

We now come to the work of the greatest Soviet aircraft designer, Andrei Nikolayevich Tupolev, one of the most significant figures in aviation history. Tupolev died on December 23, 1972, and his work was continued by Leonid L Selyakov, chief-designer of the Tu-134 airliners, and Tupolev's son, Alexei Andreyevich Tupolev, who was in charge of the Tu-144 airliner.

Tu-144 SSST, the prototype of which made its first flight on December 31, 1968, has not been developed further. Scheduled service with freight only, which is customary Aeroflot practice, started on December 26, 1975, between Moscow and Alma Ata, with Moscow – Baku –Tashkent as the second flight trials route. These services were suspended in November 1976, according to Western sources, due to major engine problems. Then came the news that a new version, the Tu-144D powered by four Koliesov engines, was flying the Moscow – Khabarovsk route, still with

freight only. It was also reported in the West that no mention was made of Tu-144 in a detailed review of Soviet civil aircraft in the weekly journal Ekonomicheskaya Gazeta, which published details for the new Five Years Plan.

This report has since been confirmed by Soviet authorities who admitted that all work on the Tu-144 had ceased, it being too heavy and too inefficient.

An American firm, ICX Aviation, has been named as a possible manufacturer of Yak-40 for the US-market. ICX is reported to be interested in replacement of the three Soviet Ivchenko AI-25 bypass turbojets for three US Garrett AiResearch turbofans. A freight-version with a large load door on the port-side has been named Yak-40K.

Yak-40 which was allotted the reporting name 'Codling', has replaced the ageing Li-2 (Soviet-built DC-3s), Il-12s and Il-14s on Russia's national air routes. The fact that it has not been sold to so-called non-socialist nations, with the exception of West Germany and Italy, seems to be caused by difficulties with certification of the type in these countries. According to some sources, Yak-40 is no longer in production, about 1,000 examples having been delivered, mainly to Aeroflot.

In June 1981 a number of load-to-altitude records were claimed by the Soviets with Yak-42; in the 40 tons category an altitude of 3,000m was reached in 2 minutes 37 seconds, 6,000m in 5 minutes 11 seconds and 9,000m in 9 minutes 31 seconds; at a 45-55 tons weight the same altitudes were reached in 3 minutes 6 seconds, 6 minutes 27 seconds and 11 minutes 48 seconds respectively.

On December 14-15, 1981, Aeroflot pilot V G Mukhin flew from Moscow to Khaborovsk, a distance of 6,144.8km, non-stop. Mukhin had demonstrated Yak-40 in 18 African countries during 1973, and is also the pilot who flew the demonstration aircraft to Canada in 1976.

Range with 14,500kg payload is 900km, with 6,500kg 3,000km, maximum take-off weight 53,500kg, wing span 34.9m length 36.38m and wing area 150sq m. Reporting name in the West is 'Clobber'.

A Soviet-built heavylift Il-76M in Libyan service. It is powered by four 12,000kp D-30KP turbofans and has a range of 5,000km.

CHAPTER 35

Seaplanes for Patrol and Long-Range Reconnaissance

SOVIET AIR FORCE Day in summer 1961 brought several surprises. One was the appearance of jet flying boats with sweptback wings – the only such aircraft in the world, for the American Martin P6M Seamaster had been abandoned in 1959. The new Soviet flying boats which had been flown at Tushino were very impressive, as were the international records they established in August 1961.

The FAI were the first to record the achievements of G M Beryev's Be-10 on August 7, 1961. Nikolai Andriyevskii flew through a 15/25km base with two crew members at 912kph. On September 3, 1961, the same team flew over a closed circuit of 1,000km with 5,000kg payload at an average speed of 875.86kph. These were also records for 1,000 and 2,000kg payload. Shortly afterwards Georgii Buryanov broke further records, taking 5,000kg to an altitude of 14,062m; 10 tons to 12,733m; and 15 tons to 11,997m. Greatest load at 2,000m was 15,206kg and the culminating achievement was an altitude record for seaplanes of 14,962m.

The Be-10 marked a climax in the design activity of Soviets in this sphere. D P Grigorovich had achieved fame in the First World War through his flying boats of the series M-5 to M-15, especially M-9 which, in 1916, formed the essence of Russian naval aviation. They were also used during the civil war and continued long after the Revolution. They had 150mhp Salmson engines and reached 110kph.

Grigorovich formed a drawing office for seaplanes during 1923 in the Leningrad plant of *Krasnii Lotchik* ('The Red Flier'), resuming an interest after five years' absence. His first offering that year, M-23bis, a sequel to the M-9, had a 240mhp Fiat engine. The aircraft had poor hydrodynamic qualities and was abandoned in favour of M-24 which had the lines of M-9 but was a three-seater with 220mhp Renault engine and pusher propeller.

The prototype was tested in autumn 1923 and an issue of forty aircraft constructed. They suffered various difficulties and, after the departure of Grigorovich for Moscow, the design and engine work was changed. A further 20 M-24bis were then built, capable of 140kph with a range of 400km. Up to 1926 they constituted armament of the Soviet coastguard.

It became evident that Grigorovich had clung too hard to his experiences of the First World War and was not able to repeat earlier successes as a designer of flying boats. But he designed another two for coast guarding and close patrol reconnaissance. First was the MRL-1, designed in 1925 in Moscow and constructed in Leningrad. This, again, was a wooden biplane with American Liberty engine and pusher propeller. MRL-1 (*Morskoi Rasvedchik Liberty* = Naval Patrol Plane with Liberty Engine) reached 180kph but the ceiling of 3,000m was only moderate. The aircraft took off with difficulty, pushing a lot of water in front of itself, and could not really be considered a success.

In 1926, Grigorovich designed the MR-2 with Lorraine-Dietrich engine of 450mhp. It was a better machine and the first flight on September 23, 1926, in Leningrad went off favourably. F S Rastegayev, a former fighter pilot, was to complete the state test. He had never flown seaplanes before and crashed during the test flight, dying in the wreckage. During investigations some design errors were discovered; for example, the centre of gravity was too far back. The machine was discarded.

Before the MR-2 there was, of course, an MR-1. It was a seaplane variant of the reconnaissance biplane R-1 with double wooden floats designed by N N Polikarpov. The aircraft was tested in autumn 1926 and in the following two years 124

Below: The Be-10 represented a peak in Soviet flying boat design, a massive aircraft powered by two 6,500kp static thrust Lyulka AL-7PB engines.

Above: First of Grigorovich's series of flying boats, the M-5.
Below: Stalwart of Soviet coastguard flyers up to 1926, the three-seat M-24.

A 1928 design, MR-3 was constructed in metal but suffered poor flying qualities.

A total of 40 Ju 20 seaplanes served naval aviation, half of them constructed domestically.

ROM-1, offered by Grigorovich, failed extended tests between 1927 and 1928.

MR-1 were constructed. Engine was an M-5, a copy of the Liberty.

Biplane flying boat MR-3 was constructed in 1928 in Leningrad on the lines of MR-2. An all-metal boat with 500/680mhp MBW-VI, the machine was tested in July and August 1929 in Tanganrog and found to be decidedly bad. It was intended that the drawing office of P A Richard should redesign it at a later date, but I V Chetverikov, of the TsKB seaplane division, was ready for the job.

In 1931 MR-3bis was produced with M-17 engines, still a biplane, but now all-wood with a different form which showed better hydro-dynamic qualities. Unfortunately much money was spent in vain as the whole concept was antiquated. The prototype was tested on the Moskva but no production followed, nor was a state test ordered.

Chetverikov constructed a further specimen as a monoplane with higher fuselage, called MR-5. But it was abandoned when the designer G M Beryev produced his successful MBR-2 which possessed incomparably better qualities and performance.

At the end of the twenties Soviet naval aviation was quite weak. The M-24 or M-24bis had been antiquated for a long time and was out of use while the MR-1 were by no means excellent models. The Junkers Ju-20 low-wing monoplanes which had BMW-IIIa engines were a certain help. In 1923, 20 Junkers were assembled in Fili, using a mixture of German components and parts produced in the factory. In addition 20 completed machines came from Dessau.

Ju-20 had two all-metal floats and were armed with a moveable machine gun. They were in service until 1930 in the Baltic and Black Sea and up to 1933 in the White Sea. In September 1924, B G Chukhnovskii effected eleven flights with a Ju-20 to the island of Novaya Zemlya, the first Arctic flights in the USSR.

Italian Savoia-Marchetti SM-16bis flying boats were also utilised, 50 specimens being imported from 1923 onwards. Their engines were 300mhp Fiat A-12bis, later Lorraine-Dietrich of 400mhp, and most were stationed in the Black Sea.

Long-range reconnaissance, very important for a country with an extensive coastline, had at first to be carried out with imported aircraft. In 1926 Dornier Wal (Whale) flying boats came from Germany, at first with Lorraine-Dietrich engines, then BMW-VI. Deliveries continued and from 1930 sometimes only the airframes were bought into which were built M-17 engines. Altogether 70 flying boats and six additional machines were constructed in the Sevastopol repair plant from 1931 to 1933. Wals served mainly in the Black Sea but machines delivered after 1930 went to the Arctic areas.

A rumour went around in the Second World War that German bomber pilots reaching their target, Odessa, turned back without dropping any bombs because they had seen Dornier flying boats of "German naval fliers" in the harbour.

Grigorovich set about trying to design a special flying boat for long-range reconnaissance. The design was ROM-1 (Rasvechik Otkrytogo Morya = Reconnaissance 'Plane for the Open Sea). It was a sesquiplane, the upper wing made entirely of wood and the rest of duralumin. Twin Lorraine-Dietrich engines, each of 450mhp, were in tandem on the upper wing and crew consisted of four.

ROM-1 was completed in autumn 1927 and test-flown in Leningrad by L I Liksa. The real test flying took place in Sevastopol and lasted from November 1927 to autumn 1928, as a result of which it was decided the machine was not suitable for military service. Maximum speed was 165kph and range 950km.

Designers then modified the machine to make ROM-2, installing two BMW-VI with tractor propellers on the front edge of the upper wing. Thus they managed to correct the centre of gravity which had been pushed too far back in ROM-1. For ROM-2 they wanted to introduce a new, more readily understood abbreviation, MDR-1 (Morskoi Dalnii Rasvedchik = Naval Patrol Plane for Long-range Reconnaissance). This abbreviation was indeed reserved but not put into use as the aircraft was rejected after testing in 1929-30. Moreover, the machine later crashed during a landing.

Designation MDR-2 was given to a flying boat of AGOS TsAGI in 1931 – A N Tupolev's ANT-8. Tupolev had received an order for the flying boat in 1925, but only began the real design in 1930. The prototype first flew on January 30, 1931, with

S T Rybaltschuk at the controls, and State tests were completed between February and March without difficulties.

ANT-8 was an all-metal, high-wing monoplane with simple lines and twin BMW-VI engines with pusher propellers mounted on the struts above the wing. Tupolev considered the machine more as an experimental aircraft on which he wanted to confirm the efficacity of a keel construction. His concept proved to be sound, even though the boat part had to be reconstructed quite often. MDR-2 had two moveable DA-2 machine guns and could carry 900kg of bombs.

The machine was good from every point of view but production was not permitted for it was thought to be already antiquated and would not match up to later requirements. This decision proved to be a mistake as more modern designs were not successful.

In January 1931 TsKB decided to design a long-range reconnaissance flying boat, TsKB No. 11, using wings and controls of heavy bomber TB-5. Director of design was I V Chetverikov and the project was given naval designation MDR-3. Work proceeded fast. In December 1931 the aircraft was completed and on January 14, 1932, B L Bukhgolz test flew it in Sevastopol. Flight tests lasted until March 25.

MDR-3 was a high-wing monoplane, the wing having a duralumin frame with fabric covering while the boat was all-metal. Four BMW-VI engines were built in two tandem groups over the wing; armament consisted of four, twin DA-2 machine guns and 500kg bombs.

On test flights, good hydrodynamic qualities were demonstrated and speed reached 210kph. But the ceiling was only 2,200m and rate of climb could be described as wretched. At the end of 1932 it was decided the aircraft should be handed over to KOSOS TsAGI for correction in order to recoup the resources which had been expended. Chetverikov was not invited to participate.

Tupolev took on just the boat, built a new wing with a greater lifting surface and new tail unit with a higher single rudder. Instead of the two tandem groups, Tupolev now used three 750/830mhp M-34R engines, two in tractor and one in pusher arrangement over the wing. In the TsAGI designs these machines were called ANT-27, but military designation was MDR-4.

ANT-27 was completed in March 1934 and test flown in the first days of April. On April 15, 1934, the machine met with an accident on take-off and was completely wrecked. The design director of seaplanes at TsAGI, I I Pogosskii, was killed in the crash.

The second machine, ANT-27bis, was not completed until autumn and testing continued up to May 1935 when a licence for the model was granted. Performance was not excellent; maximum speed without armament reached 232kph and service ceiling was 5,000m. However, Soviet naval aviation could no longer be without such aircraft and 15 were ordered without regard for the fact that design was not yet perfected.

Another catastrophe with the prototype ANT-27bis in September 1935 did not alter the decision.

In 1936 five machines were delivered and a year later ten. Their military designation was MTB-1 *(Morskoi Torpedonosez-Bombardirovschchik* = Naval Torpedo-Carrier and Bomber). MTB-1 could carry up to 2,000kg of bombs or torpedoes at a maximum speed of only 225kph. Take-off weight reached 16,250kg whereas in the MDR-4 it was only 14,660kg.

In dimensions and weight the MTB-1 was big, but it was not the largest Soviet flying boat. This title belongs to another Tupolev machine, the double-hull ANT-22. This aircraft was designed according to 1929 specifications which demanded a 'flying cruiser' *(Morskoi Krejser)* – a big flying boat that could fly over a great distance to search out and destroy enemy warships. Tupolev created the design ANT-11 for the MK competition in 1929. A year later P L Bartini also designed a flying boat of this class, but Tupolev was given the task. He completed it under designation ANT-22.

It was an all-metal, high-wing monoplane of 51m span with twin boat fuselages next to one another. These ended with high ruddders and machine gun turrets while the elevator unit had a biplane construction. Everything was made of corrugated duraluminium. Over the wing were three tandem engine groups, each consisting of twin 750/830mhp M-34R with tractor and pusher propellers.

Two pilots sat in a cockpit in the front edge of the wing between the fuselages. Armament consisted of turrets with DA-2 machine guns in the nose and tail of each fuselage, which also had Oerlikon 20mm cannon behind the wing. Bomb load was 6 tons to give a normal take-off weight of 28,750kg, overweight 43,000kg. Speed was not bad for such a giant at 233kph but a low service ceiling of 3,500m made ANT-22 very vulnerable.

The aircraft first flew on August 8, 1934, and achieved the above performances. State tests in July and August 1935 were more rigorous and demanded full military armament which reduced speed to 205kph and service ceiling to only 2,250m! The machine received military designation MK-1, but was never taken on nor used. It was too heavy, although water qualities were almost ideal. T V Rybenko achieved an international record with MK-1 on December 8, 1936, taking 10,040kg to an altitude of 1,942m. Later he managed to take up 13,000kg – and that was the sum total of MK-1's activity.

So Naval Aviation was in a critical state in the mid thirties as regards heavy, long-range reconnaissance flying boats. Practically the only aircraft of this type in operation were the unsuccessful MDR-4 and despite every effort, the aviation industry was not in a position to deliver efficient and reliable machines. As in air transport, the USSR had to seek help abroad.

In 1936 and 1937 four Douglas DF flying boats and two smaller Sikorsky S-43 were bought from

Above: Tupolev's ANT-8 was sound in every respect, but met rejection due to its antiquated concept.

Right and below: Designed as a 'flying cruiser' ANT-22, with its 51m span and impressive armament, was thought to be capable of seeking and destroying enemy warships over large distances.

the United States, delivered to experts for study and then used in air transport, predominantly in Arctic regions. When, in 1938, the excellent American Consolidated 28 (PBY) flying boat was released for export, the USSR was one of the first clients, buying three finished machines and licence rights. Consolidated 28 were constructed as GST *(Gidro-Samolet Transportnii* = Seaplane for Transport).

The Soviet GST had twin M-87 two-row radial engines, each of 950mhp and at 329kph were faster than the PBY which originally possessed 900mhp engines and reached 294kph. Range was 2,500 to 3,000km. GST were in construction only in the 1939-1940 period and were given over to the Glavsevmorput and Aeroflot companies. They received M-62IR engines of 850mhp and were used as MP-7 with great success. During hostilities the USSR also got American PBY-5 machines and amphibian PBY-5A variants under Lend-Lease agreement.

Soviet drawing offices learned a lot from the American machines. G M Beryev delivered his MDR-5 or MS-4 flying boat *(Morskoi Samolet* = Seaplane) for a licence in 1938. Shape and general concept resembled the American Sikorsky S-43, but the aircraft cannot be described as an imitation. MDR-5 had twin 950mhp M-87A engines, reached 345kph at 5,250m, had 8,150m service ceiling and a range of 1,740km. Machine guns were in the nose and behind the frame on which the wing lay.

MDR-5 was not put on the production line. Nor was a design by V B Shavrov who presented a flying boat in 1937, 60% composed of parts of the DB-3 bomber. Only the fuselage was new.

In 1937 Chetverikov at last managed to achieve a success after such resounding failures. In summer at Sevastopol, test flights began with his MDR-6, continuing until the end of the year. MDR-6 had an interesting solution to existing problems. Fuselage was low and slim with a machine gun turret in the nose and on the back. The wing had a very broken M-line, and in the kinks were built twin 730mhp M-25E radial engines so that the propellers were sufficiently high above the water. M-25E engines were only provisional, for after successful state tests serial production of the MDR-6ASh or Samolet 'N' proceeded in 1939 with M-63 engines, each of 960mph, in the Taganrog plant. These provided a speed of 360kph.

Crew consisted of three and for armament there was a ShKAS in the fuselage nose and twin UBT 12.7mm machine guns in a turret on the back. In January 1941 the machine received designation Che-2 from the name of the designer. Fifty specimens were operated during the war in the Baltic and Black Seas and in the Far East.

Chetverikov was not satisfied with performance of the production machines and, above all, he wanted to increase their speed. MDR-6B-1 represented the first step in December 1940 and in July 1941 came MDR-6B-2. Both were more streamlined and had twin 1,050mhp M-105 in-line

engines. Important features were retractable wing-tips floats and twin rudders.

Everything was designed for speed and the increase achieved, 455kph at 6,000m, was a noteworthy performance. But capacity for operating in rough seas was sacrificed, propellers now being so low over the water that they were constantly rotating in the spray. Chetverikov increased the wing M-line in his prototype MDR-6B-3 of 1942 and VK-105R engines with front radiators were placed a little higher again. But this was not enough.

In the MDR-6B-4 prototype, Chetverikov was using a boat fuselage of normal size, higher than that of Che-2, with twin VK-105F engines, front radiators, triple rudder and fixed wing-tip floats. Chetverikov now sacrificed speed to ease of use. But MDR-6B-4 was not put on the production line as the aviation industry still had too much on its hands and the need for seaplanes was not so pressing. Not until 1945 was the situation more favourable for Chetverikov to continue.

MDR-6B-5 was test flown in 1946. This flying boat had a high fuselage and relatively short wings with twin 1,700mhp. VK-107A engines. The crew, which had formerly consisted of three men, now numbered four. In the nose was a moveable B-20 cannon and a further two were coupled in an electrically powered SEB turret on top of the fuselage. Take off weight was 12,000kg and maximum speed sank to 380kph. The MDR-6's long and demanding process of development came to an end with this prototype.

We now go back to about 1930 and the lighter reconnaissance flying boats, an arm of combat that had not met with any success for many years. The most widely used Savoia-Marchetti SM-16 were replaced in 1932 by another model of the same plant, SM-62bis. A pattern for this model and licence for imitations were both bought in 1930. Between 1932-1933, 22 specimens of the original design were built under licence in the USSR followed by a further 29 aircraft with slight modifications under designation MBR-4.

All these machines had Isotta-Fraschini Asso engines of 750mhp with pusher propeller, carried three crew and were mostly wood construction. They reached 220kph and range was 900km. Turrets with DA-2 machine guns were in the nose and behind the wings.

S-62bis and MBR-4 served in the Black Sea until 1936 when they were replaced by Soviet MBR-2 monoplanes. MBR-2 was a creation of Beryev, the first absolutely successful design in this arm of combat. Beryev began the design in 1931 as TsKB No. 25. Construction was completed the following year in the Menshinskii plant, Moscow, and successful testing was carried out at Sevastopol.

It was a high-wing monoplane in simple wood construction, with room for three or four crew, twin moveable machine gun turrets and 500kg bombs. The engine was set high over the fuselage, first a BMW-VI then, in production ma-

Chetverikov finally managed to save face with his MDR-6 which enjoyed a production run of 50 under designation Che-2. Examples served during World War 2 in the Baltic, Black Sea and the Far East.

Above: MDR-6B-1 was Chetverikov's first attempt to improve on the performance of MDR-6, particularly in terms of speed. All attempts failed to reach the right compromise and the series ended in 1946 with prototype MDR-6B-5 (below) which carried four crew and three B-20 cannon. Maximum speed was only 380kph.

chines, an M-17B of 500-730mhp. Characteristic were the front radiator and four-blade propeller.

The first machine with BMW-VIF reached 208kph and range was 1,150km. In the production models, with full armament, performance was somewhat lower – 203kph at 2,000m and 600km range. But their extremely good qualities in water and air remained constant and the aircraft was very popular. It could also be used in winter, if A K Belenkov's undercarriage was attached to the fuselage and wing. Wheels or skids could be interchanged according to requirements.

In 1935 Beryev modernised the MBR-2. Pilot's cockpit was roofed in, tail unit surfaces reconstructed and, most important, the aircraft received 750/830mhp M-34NB engines in a better shaped casing. Speed immediately rose to 275kph and the normal range of 650km was extended to 1,500 after incorporation of additional tanks. This version was built in large numbers,

Soviet naval aviation also showed interest in heavy bombers and torpedo carriers. We already know about the first model of this class, the MTB-1 or ANT-27bis. The MTB-2 was designed between March 1935 and spring 1937 in TsAGI as ANT-44 under the direction of Tupolev. A prototype completed its first flight on April 19, 1937, under I M Sukhomlin and in July the state tests were completed. In these tests a maximum speed of 355kph was measured with 18,500kg take-off weight and a range of 2,500km. Bomb or torpedo load reached 1,000-2,500kg.

ANT-44 was a constructive solution to the problem of attaining high performances. It was a cantilever high-wing monoplane in all metal construction with smooth surfaces and four 810mhp Gnome-Rhone 14 Krsd on the wings. In June the second ANT-44 prototype made its appearance, constructed as an amphibian flying boat with retractable undercarriage. Its four M-87 engines accomplished 840mhp each and increased speed to 351kph with fixed undercarriage.

Right: MBR-4, licence built versions of the Savoia Marchetti SM-62, numbered 51 in all and served from 1932 until 1936 in the Black Sea.

finally totalling 1,300. Beryev also tried producing a better MBR-2 with M-103 engine in 1937. Top speed of this MBR-7 version increased to 295-310kph but it was abandoned due to lack of engines.

The position of MBR-2 remained unshaken for many years after the war. Here and there were rivals, but they disappeared again without detriment. The lighter, more efficient two or three-seat MBR-5 of P D Samsonov had a great chance. Test flown in August 1935 it was a modern machine with wooden fuselage, fabric-covered metal wings and 712mhp Wright Cyclone engine with tractor propeller. All of the crew's working space was covered with a cowling.

MBR-5 was an amphibian with retractable wheels, reached 306kph and a service ceiling of 7,500m. But it was certainly a luckless aircraft. A fire broke out when the aircraft was flown at the plant, then some unimportant part broke and its flight to Sevastopol for state tests terminated with an accident. Thereupon further work on the aircraft was halted.

In September the first prototype received its retractable gear and both aircraft were then put into operation as MTB-2A but remained without successors. In January 1940 all work on the further design of ANT-44 was halted. On October 7, 1940, an MTB-2A commanded by Sukhomlin reached a record speed for amphibian aircraft of 241.999kph on a closed circuit of 1,000km with 2,000kg load. This record was only officially recognised after the war and remained unbroken until 1957.

During the Second World War, MBR-2, MDR-6 and GST aircraft constituted the chief armament of naval aviation on all coastal and water areas of the USSR. However, their participation was relatively slight.

Seaplane design after the war remained almost entirely in the hands of Beryev and in 1945, a long-range reconnaissance flying boat, LL-143 (*Letayushchaya Lodka* – Flying Boat) made its appearance in Krasnoyarsk. It had a spacious fuselage and eight-man crew. The wings had an M shape and on them were twin 2,000mhp ASh-

Above: MBR-2 replaced MBR-4 seaplanes in 1936, the culmination of a Beryev project which began in 1931.

Left: MBR-7, a modernised version of MBR-2, was much quicker but lack of M-103 engines caused early abandonment.

Below: Tupolev's ANT-44 was powered by four M-87 engines and two aircraft went into service. Further design work was halted in 1940.

72 engines. B-20 cannon were installed in the nose, on top of the fuselage and in the tail.

Series production of LL-143 began in 1949 at ganrog and aircraft of this type are still known as Be-6. When M J Tsepilov test flew this machine in 1949 he attained a top speed at 2,400m of 415kph and range of 5,000km. These excellent performances had been brought about by the introduction of several modifications and incorporation of 2,300mhp ASh-73 engines. Armament consisted of NS-23 and later of NR-23 cannon, and tail turret had already been given the Tu-4 shape. Up to 4,000kg bombs, torpedoes or anti-submarine weapons could be taken and after the incorporation of radar apparatus the Be-6 became a long-serving coastal and naval patrol aircraft.

As a result of advances in aeronautics, Beryev built a development of Be-6 at the beginning of the sixties. It was first known as M-12, later as Be-12 under the name of *Chajka* (Seagull). Fuselage was more favourably designed for travel in air and water, wings were smaller, slimmer and bore twin PTL AI-20D engines of 4,000mhp. Be-12 was intended from the outset to be an amphibian and M Mikhaylov's crew made several international record flights between October 23 and 27, 1964. A ceiling of 12,185m was reached without any load; with 1,000 and 2,000kg the performance was 11,360m and 10,100kg was lifted to 2,000m. Be-12 replaced the Be-6 as standard naval patrol planes and were often to be seen with a long radar cone on the tip of the fuselage or long MAD detectors in nose and tail.

Beryev's lighter amphibian aircraft, Be-8, was designed to serve after the war for coastal liaison and reconnaissance, light commercial use, as ambulance aircraft and for training etc. They were all-metal, high wing monoplanes with 730mhp ASh-21 engine, representing a further development of the Be-4 catapult plane. Two pilots and six passengers could be accommodated, plus a machine gun turret and bombs. Be-8 reached a cruising speed of 200kph and range was up to 1,100km. Only two examples were produced.

Beryev's group of designers had priority in the use of jet engines on flying boats in the USSR. First of such aircraft, Be-R-1 or simply R-1, designed and constructed in 1951, was test flown by M Sukhomlin and M J Tsepilov on May 30, 1952. In the wing were twin WK-1 jet engines of 2,700kp static thrust, the nose contained twin fixed NR-23 cannon and two more were in the tail, remotely controlled from a dome under the tail unit.

Be-R-1 reached 760kph at low altitude and at 7,000m was capable of 800kph. Ceiling was 11,500m and, with 1,000kg bomb load, range extended to 2,000km. Performances were certainly high but naval authorities regarded the machine as an experiment and were not convinced of its necessity.

For Beryev, Be-R-1 was the first step to a further jet flying boat, Be-10, which we have already mentioned. The Be-10, with 35 degrees wing sweepback, was first known as M-10. It had twin Lyulka AL-7PB engines, each of 6,500kp static thrust, which were built into passages between wings and fuselage, high enough so as not to suck in water or spray. Although we no longer know if Be-10 were used in large numbers, they certainly constituted a peak in the design of Soviet flying boats.

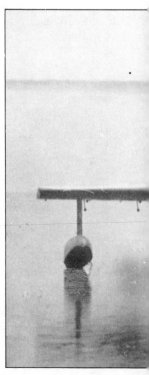

Above: One of only two examples of the Be-8, a multi-purpose amphibian that accommodated a crew of two and six passengers.

Right: Be-R-1 was the first Soviet jet powered flying boat, making its maiden flight in May 1952. Naval authorities were unconvinced of the necessity for such an aircraft.

Above: A long-serving coastal and naval patrol flying boat, Be-6 had a range of 5,000km and could carry up to 4,000kg of munitions.

Below: Developed from Be-6 was the more sophisticated Be-12 Seagull, an amphibian with greatly improved performance. It replaced ageing Be-6 as the standard naval patrol aircraft.

CHAPTER 36

Catapult Aircraft

IN THE TWENTIES, catapult planes became standard equipment for heavier warships. They were mostly float planes which were discharged by catapult and, after their mission, landed in the vicinity of the ship to be lifted aboard by means of a crane. These aircraft served, above all, for observation of the enemy fleet, as artillery spotters, transport of mail and liaison work etc.

At the beginning of the thirties the Soviet Union took several steps towards modernisation of their navy. Warships of pre-revolutionary date were reconstructed and new ones ordered from abroad. Preparations were also made for new shipbuilding in Russia. The USSR had, accordingly, to procure suitable catapult planes and turned to the German Heinkel plants which produced an excellent aircraft of this class.

The HD-55 was a biplane flying boat in wood with three-seats, a 450mhp Siemen's Jupiter engine with tractor propeller. In 1930 the USSR bought two Heinkel catapults and thirty HD-55 airframes. Soviet M-22 engines were incorporated to produce the KR-1. It had only two-seats, with the pilot under the engine and an observer/gunner behind the wing who had access to a DA-2 machine gun. The abbreviation KR stood for *Korabelnii Rasvechik* or Naval Patrol.

KR-1 reached 194kph and range was 800km. In winter it could operate by means of additional ski undercarriage and was active on warships and in the coastguard service up to 1938. G M Beriev tried to supply an indigenous substitute which could take its place and in 1937 the first KOR-1 was completed *(Korabelnii* = Seaplane). This was a two-seat biplane in composite construction with fabric covering, a central float and double wing-tip floats. The pilot had two fixed ShKAS machine guns on the upper wing while the observer had a moveable machine gun which was in a half-retracted position when not in use. KOR-1 had a maximum speed of 227kph with a 635/700mhp M-25A engine and could fly 530km.

KOR-1 served from 1937 until the beginning of the war in summer 1941. From January 1941 they were known under designation Be-2 and took part in defence of the Southern Front against the Rumanians. As landplanes were in short supply, a fixed undercarriage was assembled and Be-2 were used as light bombers.

Between 1939-1940 there was a desire to create something more modern in the category of catapult planes and Beriev was commissioned with the design. As a result he introduced the light flying boat KOR-2 in the Spring of 1941. It was an elegant, high-wing monoplane in all-metal construction with good performances. Engine was a 900mhp M-62 which gave the two-seater a speed of 362kph and 950km range. Armament was one fixed and one movable ShKAS machine gun supplemented by 400kg of bombs. In spring 1943, KOR-2 was put on the production line as Be-4, but only a few had been completed by the end of the war.

At the same time as KOR-2, A S Moskalev was designing his catapult plane SAM-16. Here was a

three-seat flying boat in wood with twin MG-31F, each of 330mph and performance estimated as about the same as KOR-2. SAM-16 was under construction in summer 1941 when the plant had to be evacuated and the unfinished machine destroyed.

In the thirties the Soviet Navy planned to construct big submarine cruisers for long voyages in the open sea. For these they also wanted reconnaissance aircraft which could be dismantled and quickly assembled to be discharged by catapult. Initative for this design came from I V Chetverikov, chief of seaplane design in the Menshinskii plant of TsKB in Moscow. He worked out the design in 1931 and delivered it to the commander's office.

Catapulted from a Soviet warship, the KR-1 was an imported Heinkel HD-55 fitted with an M-22 engine. This naval patrol aircraft had a range of 800km and could be fitted with additional ski undercarriage. The type was active up to 1938.

Above: First indigenous catapult aircraft was KOR-1, designed by Beriev and later designated Be-2. They entered service in 1937.

Below: KOR-2 (Be-4) was a more modern concept from Beriev and first flew in 1941. It was powered by a 900mhp M-62 and could carry 400kg of bombs.

Above: Designed as a reconnaissance aircraft for proposed giant submarine cruisers, OSGA-101 tested flying qualities and performance.

Below: KR-1 equipped with ski landing gear for winter work. The observer/ gunner was provided with a DA-2 machine gun.

Here they allowed themselves a lot of time for deciding about the design. Meanwhile, Chetverikov had left TsKB and was working at the Institute for Civil Aviation in the OSGA division where, under the direction of N M Andreyev, seaplanes and gliding boats were designed and built. Not until 1933 did Chetverikov get permission to prepare a submarine-based aircraft.

The machine was to be designated SPL (*Samolet dlya Podvodnoi Lodki* = Aircraft for Submarines) and the institute received 100,000 roubles for design and construction of two prototypes. OSGA had its drawing office in Moscow so it was decided first to build an amphibian version of SPL in order to ascertain flying qualities and performance. Only in the event of success was the collapsible aircraft to be built.

The small amphibian received designation OSGA-101 and was test flown in Spring 1935 by A V Krshishevskii. Constructed with an open, three-seat cockpit, the wing was cantilevered while a twin-rudder tail unit was borne by uncased tube construction. An M-11 engine was placed high above the fuselage on a braced frame.

Testing was successful, so work proceeded on the second phase under camouflage designation Gidro-1. The aircraft was completed in December 1934 and transported for testing to Sebastopol. These lasted until June 1935 with Krshishevskii as pilot and in September the state tests were completed.

SPL was smaller than OSGA-1 and had only two seats. Design was the same, but there was no undercarriage and the aircraft was collapsible. The machine could be dismantled in three or four minutes in such a way that it took a space of 2.12 by 2.35 by 7.45m, fitting into a watertight tubular hangar of 2.5m diameter and 7.5m length. Assembly took 4 to 5 minutes.

Records from the state test praised flying and water qualities of the new aircraft, the speedy hangarage and equally a quick assembly. But they criticised it on some crucial points – its stability and view from the cockpit. As at that time the authorities lost interest in cruiser-submarines there was no reason to work any further on the SPL aircraft. Prototype SPL was released and given to the sports pilots as Gidro-1, going on show at the 1935 international exhibition in Milan.

On September 7, 1937, Krshishevskii achieved three international FAI records in the class of light amphibians with OSGA-101. On a 100km course the speed reached was 170.2kph; on October 7 there followed records for distance (480km) and ceiling (5,400m). OSGA-101 and Gidro-1 remained in use for a time and then quietly disappeared.

SPL (Gidro-1), second phase of the submarine reconnaissance aircraft project, shown in assembled and folded form. It could be constructed in less than five minutes and flew well, but the submarines it was designed for were never built.

CHAPTER 37

Torpedo Aircraft

MANY TORPEDO aircraft are normal landplanes with a sufficiently long range for them to operate from coastal airfields. Geographical conditions of the USSR being what they are, the aircraft constituted an important weapon and the naval aviation sector devoted a lot of work to their design.

In Autumn 1923 they bought two British Handley-Page HP-19 torpedo bombers for pilot training. Later, the original one-seat machines were reconstructed as two-seaters and used in 1925/1926 experiments with a radio-controlled torpedo invented by V I Bekauri. These were dropped by parachute and then directed to their target by the aircraft.

Some imported K-30 Junkers were allotted to the naval aviation sector in 1926 as JuG-1. They had three Junkers L-5 engines apiece and were also partly used as torpedo bombers.

As soon as TB-1 bombers became available in fairly large numbers, attempts were made to use these in the same way by fitting floats. This had already been discussed in theory in 1926 but the first experiments did not follow until 1928. The ANT-4 aircraft 'Strana Sovetov' which flew between August and October 1929 to New York, completed part of the journey with Junkers floats taken over from the JuG-1. Junkers floats with extended noses were originally used on several of the TB-1a or TB-1P reconstructed for the naval aviation sector in 1928 and 1929. In October 1929 several British floats were bought from Short. These served as models for the design of Soviet float model 'Sh' for TB-1P.

Frenchman P A Richard designed a torpedo bomber TOM-1 *(Torpedonosez Otkrytogo Morya =* Torpedo Carrier for the Open Sea) in 1929. It was a low-wing monoplane in all duralumin construction with smooth casing, twin BMW-VI engines and double, all-metal floats. The whole appearance was strongly reminiscent of TB-1a, but more streamlined. Testing took place from August 1931 onwards in Sebastopol. The aircraft reached 210kph and pilot N I Kamov expressed great satisfaction. But as TB-1A were at this time being used in quite large numbers and had proved their worth, TOM-1 was not put on the production line.

Specifically designed as a torpedo bomber by Frenchman P A Richard, TOM-1 had twin BMW-VI engines and first flew in August 1931. It did not go into production.

Il-4T was developed from Ilyushin's DB-3 long-range bomber.

Tilted Hispano-Suiza 12 Ybrs engine in the nose of parasite torpedo bomber MP.

Still in the second half of the twenties, D P Grigorovich designed MT-1 (Morskoi Torpedonosez = Sea and Torpedo Carrier). It was to be a biplane with twin BMW-VI and make use of the fuselage of flying boat ROM-1.

One interesting design was the MM-1 (Morskoi Minonosets = Sea Mine Carrier), a monoplane with twin floats, twin tail booms and twin Lorraine-Dietrich engines in tandem over the wing. Designs MT-1 and MM-1 were not carried out.

In 1933, V V Nikitin reconstructed the reconnaissance aircraft R-5 as torpedo carrier R-5T. It was reduced to one seat and the undercarriage given a split axle so as not to hinder release of the 800kg torpedo. As R-5T was successfully test flown and state tested, they produced an issue of 50 which operated chiefly in the Far East.

TB-1P and landplane R-5T constituted the armament of torpedo units during the thirties, if one disregards the small number of MTB-1 torpedo bombers. Here and there other specialised torpedo aircraft were designed, but mostly without success.

For example, V V Myasischev constructed prototype ANT-41 of the torpedo bomber T-1 (Torpedonosets = Torpedo Carrier) in 1936. It was developed from the series of fast SB-2 bombers and possessed twin M-34FRN, each of 890mhp. T-1 did not prove satisfactory and the prototype broke into pieces in the air as a result of heavy vibrations in the tail unit. Pilot A P Chernavskii and two crew members were able to save themselves.

A completely different, but also adverse, fate was suffered by a further prototype which

Another DB-3 variant, the DB-3PT fitted with metal floats. Il-4T was considered the better option.

received designation MP (Morskoi Podvesnoi = Suspended Seaplane). N G Michelson and A I Morshchikin designed the machine in 1936 according to an interesting concept of Engineer Valko in Leningrad. Two or three MP aircraft were to be suspended under the four-motored bomber TB-3 and only shortly before reaching their target were they to separate. The TB-3 would be able to start back immediately followed by the MP after completing their attack.

Construction began in the first weeks of 1936. The machine was a low-wing monoplane with quite a low boat fuselage. Engine in the nose was a Hispano-Suiza 12 Ybrs, that could be swivelled upwards in such a way that the propeller was as far as possible from the surface of the water. The torpedo was to be stowed in an opening in the keel. Assembly took a long time and in the end Nikitin had to take over design. The idea seemed to be simple, but in reality there were major problems and uncertainty as to what would happen in the air after release of the aircraft. Not until 1938 was the aircraft described as ready for take-off. With the internal political situation as it was, when every failure could be branded as sabotage or at least negligence, nobody could summon the courage to organise flight testing. The idea was dropped and the machine handed over to the House of Pioneers in Leningrad as an exhibition piece.

In 1938 two torpedo variants were tested of Ilyushin's long-range bomber DB-3. The aircraft was provided with twin all-metal floats which had been taken over from TB-1P. This variant was designated DB-3PT, (Poplavkovii Torpedonosets = Torpedo Carrier with Floats). The machine did not fly badly but with floats and 800kg torpedoes its speed sank by about 70kph.

The landplane variant DB-3T aroused more interest and was taken on as standard armament by the naval aviation sector. After January 1941 they were known as Il-4T, serving in the Baltic and Black Seas. They flew either alone or in small groups and were even in operation in the bays of Danzig. Flights often lasted six to eight hours and took place under unfavourable weather conditions, especially in the Baltic.

After the war, Il-4T were replaced by the Tupolev Tu-2T and later the Tu-14. Both models are known to us from the chapter about bombers. In the same chapter we spoke about the visit of American Air Force commander, General Nathan F Twinning, to the test airfield at Kubinka, near Moscow, in 1956. Among the aircraft shown to him was an anti-submarine, aircraft, Tu-91.

This was a design from Tupolev's office, but few details are known. It is known that the machine possessed a PTL NK-6-TB-2 engine with twin contrarotating propellers, that the pilot's cockpit was quite far forward, and that the space under the wing served as a bay for depth-charges, torpedoes and radar apparatus. Among designers and pilots the machine was known as 'Tarzan', but it seems that Tu-91 were not built in large numbers.

CHAPTER 38

Aircraft for the Arctic

THE INTERMINABLE expanses of ice in the USSR and in its direct vicinity inspired numerous research expeditions. Their task was firstly to reconnoitre and survey these regions and then to ascertain their mineral wealth. Soon after the first steps had been taken, aircraft also ventured there. Russia had the initiative for in 1914 I I Nagurskii had sought for the lost expedition of G J Sedov on the island of Novaya Zemlya with his Maurice Farman float biplane.

In 1924 and 1925, pilots B G Chukhnovskii and O A Kalvitsa took up the challenge. Chukhnovskii in particular became an expert in Arctic flying and took part in every possible enterprise, as for example the search for General Nobile, Amundsen etc. M S Babushkin organised the first co-operation between pilots and seal hunters in the bays of the White Sea in 1921 and a year later the first aircraft entrusted with the care of an Arctic expedition had been into operation. The main party went by boat from Vladivostok into the mouth of the river Kilyma while pilots J M Koshelev and E M Lyukht flew from their base to Cape Chelyuskin.

The rescue missions of Soviet pilots were world famous. Chuknovskii, with his Ju-G-1, located crew of the airship 'Italia' which had had an accident north of Spitsbergen and directed the ice-breaker 'Krasin' to them. Dramatic too, was the rescue of the Soviet steamer 'Chelyuskin' which was trapped in ice north of the Bering Straits. In Spring 1934 pilots Lyapidevskii, Levanevskii, Molokov, Kamanin, Slepnev, Vodopyanov and Doronin distinguished themselves in this action and were first to receive the title 'Hero of the USSR'.

In 1937 the USSR began a systematic attack on the North Polar regions. First step was the foundation of polar station SP-1 which, like those that followed, depended on daily work under all conditions, care of research workers, medical service, transport service, co-operation with nomadic hunters, reindeer herdsman, fishermen, etc.

On early flights into the regions of eternal ice, aircraft of many different types proved their worth, mainly the all-metal aircraft from Germany like Junkers F-13, W-33, W-34 (designated PS-4 in the USSR), JuG-1, Dornier Wal etc. Then machines of Soviet design arrived on the scene. Moreover, there were many attempts to develop special aircraft intended from the beginning for the difficult conditions of Arctic service.

Polar pilot Chukhnovskii approached the government in 1933 for a special Arctic aircraft. He called the machine *"Severnii Samolet-Vezdekhod"* (All-purpose Aircraft for the North). Chukhnovskii was considered an authority and the government asked Italian designer R L Bartini, from the Research Institute of Civil Aviation, to carry out the job.

Bartini designed the DAR (*'Dalnii Arktitsheskii Rasvedchik* = Arctic Long-range Recon-naissance Aircraft) as a strut-braced, high-wing flying boat completely constructed of stainless steel. The wing had variable camber flaps over the whole span and ailerons were built as rotatable wing tips. Wing stubs were attached to both sides of the fuselage to increase stability. DAR was the biggest aircraft of the time built of stainless steel, and it remained so until construction of the American transport plane Budd C-93 Connestoga in the Second World War.

A further peculiarity was the power plant. Bartini had incorporated twin 760mhp Hispano-Suiza 12 Ybrs in tandem in the centre of the wing with propellers turning closely one behind the other. In addition he built a ring round the propellers which supplied an additional thrust. At that time this was called the 'Bartini Effect' and the whole

Mock-up of the originally proposed tunnel propellers for DAR.

configuration was examined in ZAGI's wind tunnel. Bartini finally gave up the arrangement which became too heavy and took 15 square metres from the wing's lifting surface, reverting to a normal tandem construction something like that in the Dornier Wal.

The landing equipment of DAR was also interesting. Bartini wanted to effect landings on ice and so designed a sort of ice-ski. On the underside of the fuselage they fitted flat,

pneumatic rubber shock absorbers to which a long slide face of plywood was attached, covered with stainless steel. These were in pairs, 5m long and 32cm wide. Chukhnovskii tried them out first on a Wal and, when satisfied, added them to the DAR.

The DAR was constructed in Andre Marti's plant in Leningrad and finished towards the end of 1935. Chuknovskii tested the aircraft in Spring 1936 and was enthusiastic about its 240kph

Bartini's DAR flying boat as it appeared in 1936. During testing it was able to stay aloft for 20 hours.

Chetverikov had little success with his ARK-3 flying boats for the Arctic. Both prototypes, ARK-3-1 (above) and ARK-3-2 (below), broke up in the air as the result of a design fault.

speed. But what really clinched matters was the long flight duration; with 9,000kg take-off weight it attained twenty complete flying hours! The government placed an order for five more machines, but as the aircraft industry administration did not regard DAR as their aircraft they took no steps to put it on the production line. This attitude was very characteristic of the times.

I V Chetverikov also designed an aircraft for the Arctic in 1933, a long range reconnaissance flying boat of modern style. But he did not get a chance to carry out the project and so turned to the organisation 'Glavsevmorput', which was in charge of all methods of transport for the North, and offered his design as an Arctic reconnaissance aircraft for iceberg patrol, passenger and goods traffic etc. 'Glavsevmorput' signed an order and Chetverikov moved to Sebastopol to construct the aircraft.

Designated ARK-3, it was a cantilever, high-wing monoplane with all-wood wings and all-metal fuselage. Over the fuselage twin M-25 engines were fitted in tandem on a frame. Plant and state tests were successfully completed in September 1936, speed reaching 308kph at

2,500m and range up to 3,000km. A few defects were still evident – form of the boat's nose and poor stability of the engine frame – but these could easily be eliminated.

As a further prototype was desired, the first machine was designated ARK-3-1. A V Yershov set an FAI record with it on April 25, 1937, climbing to 9,190m with 1,000kg load. This performance also aroused enthusiasm from the naval aviation sector which ordered five production machines. Unfortunately they did not receive any aircraft. On July 14, 1937, ARK-3-1 broke up in the air as the result of a design flaw in the covering of the fuselage tail. Exactly a year later the second machine, ARK-3-2, which had been test flown in May 1938, suffered the same fate. It had already been equipped as a long range reconnaissance aircraft for naval aviation with machine gun turrets in the nose and on top of the fuselage behind the wing.

Both clients now lost interest in this aircraft, but Glavsevmorput supported construction of another design in 1934, the ASK (*Amfibiya Severnogo Kraya* = Amphibian Aircraft for Northern Regions). This machine was the joint work of I M Sharnylskii and V J Krylov, resembling a smaller version of the giant flying boat MK-1. ASK, too, had twin boat fuselages under a cantilever wing. The pilot sat in a small nacelle in the axle of the wing, below a 480mhp M-22 engine with tractor propeller. In each fuselage was a three-seat cabin for passengers or equivalent load. An undercarriage was attached to the inner sides of the fuselages and could be pulled well up.

B V Glagolev test flew the ASK in Spring 1935 and found everything all right. Unfortunately the machine was damaged on several occasions and tested again and again on water, land and ice. But in the flood of Autumn 1937, ASK was completely destroyed and never rebuilt. Though an unlucky machine, its performance and qualities were not bad, achieving 210kph and 800km range.

In the Arctic air force many aircraft which we already know about were in use, especially the twin-motored, low-wing monoplane ANT-7 and Polikarpov's reconstructed biplane P-5, known as ARK-5. These were normal landplanes flown with ski undercarriage, but there were also special designs among the land-based group.

In 1935 A I Slokanov, director of the Aeroflot repair plant in Irkutsk, designed and built all-metal, low-wing monoplane ARK-Z-1 with M-34R engine. The machine closely resembled a Junkers W-33 but was bigger, the undercarriage could be exchanged for floats or skis and there was a cabin for six people. ARK-Z-1 flew very well, reaching 240kph and went to Moscow for state testing in October and November 1935. Result: good qualities but antiquated construction and inadequate stability. And so the Z-1 remained an isolated model.

Owing to improvements in the technical standard of aircraft, construction of specialised machines for the Arctic became superfluous. Basic all-metal aircraft with special equipment sufficed.

Commercial Seaplanes

PERHAPS IT WAS the little flying boat MP-1 (*Morskoi Passashirskii* = Seaplane and Airliner) which effected the most work in the sphere of Soviet seaplane commerce. It was a civilian version of G M Beryev's well-known MBR-2 with a comfortable cabin for six passengers who entered from above. A freight variant, MP-1T, was created quite simply by removal of the MBR-2 machine gun turret. Thanks to superior streamlining, MP-1 attained 214kph with an M-17B engine and its range was 680km.

In 1937 production was continued with model MP-1bis. This was a civilian version of the MBR-2 with an M-34B, reaching 260kph with 750km range. All MP-1 and MP-1bis proved their worth on special route such as Odessa-Batumi, the Siberian rivers etc.

With MP-1bis, woman pilot P D Osipenko set up several international records in 1937. Between May 22 and 25 she climed without any load to an altitude of 8,864m; with 500kg the aircraft rose to 7,605m and with 1,000kg to 7,009m. On July 2, Osipenko and her female crew flew the 2,416km Sebastopol – Kiev-Novgorod-Archangel route in 10 hours 33 minutes without intermediate landings, averaging 228kph.

There were at that time no other Soviet planes for maritime traffic so successful as these. Much was expected from ARK-3, designed as the commercial variant of MP-2, but it was not put into production. The GST flying boat, built under licence as MP-7 was used from 1940 onwards for passenger transport. MP-7 had M-621R engines each of 870mhp which gave her a speed of 277kph.

Some commercial seaplanes were bought abroad, such as five Savoia-Marchetti SM-55 twin-fuselaged flying boats with two 750mph Isotta-Fraschini Asso engines. They had twelve seats for passengers and were used in the Far East. After the models previously discussed (Douglas 'DF' and Sikorsky S-43) another model was brought from the USA – a Glenn Martin M-156C with four 860mhp Wright Cyclone motors and provision for 46 passengers. Martin developed M-156C for the USSR from the M-130 of 1937 and for a time there was talk of construction under licence. But it was not carried out and the one machine served under designation PS-30 for passenger and freight traffic on the Pacific coast up to 1939.

In 1939 Aeroflot began to take an interest in light amphibian aircraft for three or four passengers to establish passenger, freight and post communications along the great rivers. In response, three prototypes from different design groups made their appearance.

A.S. Moskalev constructed a four-seat, high-wing monoplane, SAM-11, in all-wood construction, making use of the wings, tail surfaces and various other parts of SAM-5-2bis. The boat fuselage was new and above it, on a frame, was a 220mhp MM-1 engine with tractor propeller. Early tests in the air were shattering. The aircraft only climbed 150m, the rudders did not work well and finally it had a serious accident.

It became evident that the engine was too spread-eagled and consequent turbulence destroyed the working of the tail units. Only after reconstruction were qualities and performances made good, top speed reaching 225kph and ceiling 4,700m. The MM-1 engine was one of only two prototypes and had not been accepted, so Moskalev reconstructed the aircraft as SAM-11bis with provision for MV-6 of equal performance. The machine was tested in autumn 1940 in Sebastopol, whereupon Aeroflot found it too heavy, uneconomical and rejected it.

In 1939 a further amphibian aircraft was tested in Leningrad, the MA-1 (*Morskaya Amfibiya* = Amphibian Seaplane) of V F Rentel. A more powerful MG-31F engine of 330mhp made it possible to raise the number of seats to six (2 pilots, 4 passengers). Top speed was 220kph and range 1,200km but, again, Aeroflot were unimpressed.

V B Shavrov's Sh-7 had the best chances. This plane was built and tested in 1940, had a duralumin boat fuselage with fabric covered duralumin frame wings. Sh-7 also got an MG-31F but had better flying qualities and construction was more carefully thought out for the production line. It carried two pilots and four passengers, reached 218kph and could fly 920km. All testing was successfully carried out to Aeroflot's satisfaction. Owing to the outbreak of war it was not put on the production line as planned, and the sole machine flew for a few months between Saratov and Astrakhan.

There was only one new post-war example of this type of aircraft – the amphibian flying boat TA (*Transportnaya Amfibiya*) conceived by Chetverikov in 1947. Designed to carry eight passengers, it was a high-wing monoplane with twin 730mhp ASh-21 and was in all-metal construction. The prototype was tested in July 1947, achieving 320kph at 1,700m with a range of 700km.

Three prototypes were built with rectangular wings, then in 1948 a TA-1 with trapezoidal wings, and finally a photogram variant TAF. None of them were introduced as Aeroflot was no longer interested in such aircraft. It was not until a few years later that a float plane version of An-2 was used in air commerce.

SAM-11's first tests were very discouraging, revealing a maximum altitude of just 150 metres. The revised SAM-11bis was better but proved uneconomical to operate.

Above: Aeroflot's changing needs brought an abrupt end to the all-metal TA-1 after five prototypes had been built and flown. Eight passengers could be carried over a range of 700km.

Below: Sole example of the Sh-7 which was about to go into production when World War 2 brought other priorities to Soviet aircraft factories.

CHAPTER 40

Light Seaplanes

AMONG LIGHT seaplanes of the USSR, V B Shavrov's small amphibian Sh-2 deserves a place of honour. What the U-2 (Po-2) biplane meant for land aviation, Sh-2 meant for marine aviation.

Its origins were modest. Shavrov built the machine with his own hands during the winter of 1928/29 in his Leningrad flat. At that time called Sh-1, it was a three-seater in wood and Shavrov got 8,000 roubles support from the organisation Osoaviakhim plus the Czechoslovakian 85mhp Walter NZ-85 engine. Sh-1 was finished in May 1929, first as a pure seaplane, then given an undercarriage which could be retracted. In August it took off from the Neva in Leningrad on a flight to Moscow, where it landed at the central airport for state tests. These were completed without complications and Shavrov returned to Leningrad with an order for the construction of a more powerful aircraft.

The new Sh-2 had basically the same design as Sh-1 but was a sesquiplane with collapsible upper wing. The underwing was continuous with the fuselage and bore wing-tip floats which also served as fuel tanks. Wheels were on the side of the fuselage and could be pulled well up and forwards mechanically. In the fuselage was an open three-seat cabin and an M-11 engine of 100mhp fitted in the centre of the upper wing. Engine, propeller, wheels, flying fittings and other details were taken over from the U-2. Skis could replace wheels if necessary.

First Sh-2 was built in Leningrad's Krasnii Lotchik plant and test flown on November 11, 1930 by B V Glagolev. After state tests in spring 1931, the aircraft was recommended for series production and manufactured up to 1934. In 1939 such aircraft were still considered useful, so construction continued in the repair plants of Aeroflot. All together over 700 machines were built.

Sh-2 proved their worth on the most diverse missions. They were used especially for training, but also served as transports in Siberia, the Arctic, Far East etc; for guarding the frontier; as reconnaissance planes for the ice breakers 'Chelyuskin', 'Krasin' and 'Lidke'; for forestry patrol; helping fishing boats in the Caspian Sea; took part in various geological expeditions; as a means of liaison etc. From 1933 onwards, sixteen speciments of the ambulance variant were delivered with an open area for stretchers.

In their operation up to 1964, the Sh-2 attained a place immediately behind the U-2. After the war, several more machines were built and equipped with more efficient engines, like M-11,

An Sh-2 with its upper wing folded for easy stowage.

Left: Over 700 Sh-2 aircraft were built and accomplished a very wide range of tasks, including ambulance work (above). Last examples were the Sh-2bis of 1946.

G, D, K, and L, most of 115 mhp. But they were almost all overloaded. Sh-2 of the year 1933 reached 145km with a range of 500km; Sh-2bis of 1946 were capable of 140kph and 700km, but take-off weight had been increased from 900 to 1,100kg. For longer reconnaissance flights the machine was able to stay in the air for up to eleven hours.

At first the marine aviation sector used MU-1 biplanes for pilot training. These were a float variant of U-1, but it is interesting to note that a similar reconstruction of the well-known U-2 never achieved success. Shavrov and Kocherigin designed floats for the U-2M or MU-2, but the aircraft performed badly and no further specimens were built.

As most Soviet seaplanes were flying boats, the designers also tried to create training aircraft of this type. D P Grigorovich designed in 1926 the wooden biplane MUR-1 driven by a 120mhp Rhone rotary engine built in between the wings with pusher propeller. In 1928 the aircraft was succeeded by the MU-2, a similar version but with M-11. Neither aircraft was successful.

In 1929 a group of designers under A S Moskalev took over MU-2 for reconstruction. The result was MU-3, an aircraft with a revised boat fuselage, smaller underwings and other modifications. In 1931 it was compared with Sh-2, designated weaker and abandoned.

V V Nikitin's flying boat for training received designation MU-4 in 1936. This, again, was a biplane with M-11 but had closed cabin for the student and teacher. It was not put into production. The same designer built a smaller copy of the American Grumman JF-1 amphibian biplane in 1937, designated NV-4. It had a central float continuous with the fuselage, retractable wheels and, of course, an M-11.

Among Soviet light seaplanes is another interesting specimen, the single-seat RV-23, *(Rekord Visoti* = altitude record*)* a 1932 design of N G Mikhelson. It was a biplane composed of U-2 parts, wing span increased from 11.4 to 17m and lifting surface from 33.15 to 51.7sqm. The larger wing received a two-part bracing. RV-23 sat on two floats, had a 710mhp Wright Cyclone engine and was also built in landplane form.

Aim of this reconstruction was to challenge the world altitude record for seaplanes. On test flights near Moscow, F F Sherebchenko reached 11,280m in September 1937 and 11,869m in October. In winter 1937, woman pilot P D Osipenko reached 13,430m with an RV-23 in Sebastopol. Then testing was given up.

Left: U-2P, a float variant of the U-2, was not successful.

Below: Although offering the comfort of an enclosed cabin for student and instructor, Nikitin's MU-4 trainer gained no support for manufacture.

IN THIS SHORT chapter we will describe various test aircraft and other special constructions not covered previously. Soviet design was characterised overall by bold experimentation, especially in the military sphere. Here, on more than one occasion, original ideas were put into practice, ideas which had no counterpart in the rest of the world or which were far ahead of their time.

Besides military aircraft there were several other Soviet test planes designed in civilian institutions, aviation clubs or originating in the work of individual amateurs. Among such machines those of B I Cheranovskii were particularly popular in the USSR before the war.

Cheranovskii was an obstinate defender of the tailless design – for all types of aircraft. He began to put his ideas into practice in 1923 when a first year student of the Military Aviation Academy. At that time he designed and built a tailless glider BICh-1 with parabolic plan-form wing. BICh-2, produced in 1924, had the same shape but it was already fit for flying. Both gliders were built by fellow students from the Academy and BICh-2 successfully completed 27 flights in the Crimea in summer 1924. On the longest flight, D I Kudrin reached 570m altitude.

The third aircraft of Cheranovskii's was a single-seat sports machine. BICh-3 may be regarded as a motorised BICh-2 with 18mhp Blackburn Tomtit engine, faired single wheel undercarriage and open cockpit. Kudrin demonstrated the little parabola several times in Moscow during 1926.

The two-seat sports machine BICh-7 of 1929 was a real success. It was a development of BICh-3 but with open, two-seat cockpit, fixed bicycle undercarriage and twin sickle-shaped rudders on the tips of the parabolic, plan-form wing. BICh-7 was absolutely stable, safe and easily manoeuvred. Unfortunately, the only engine available was a 100mhp Bristol Lucifer which suffered vibrations. BICh-7 had a slotted aileron and elevator over the whole wing trailing edge and reached 160kph.

Version BICh-7A of 1932 was even better. The aircraft had an enclosed cockpit and single vertical fin which formed an integral part of the fuselage. Both models were test flown by N A Blagin who was later responsible for the catastrophe to ANT-20 'Maxim Gorkii'. Blagin and other pilots demonstrated the BICh-7A at various sports functions.

In previous chapters we came across other Cheranovskii machines, e.g. the tailless rocket glider BICh-11 or RP-1 built to test Tsander's rocket engine O-2. The rocket was not a success, so Cheranovskii then mounted a 27mhp ABC Scorpion piston engine and after 1932 he flew the machine without problems.

Cheranovskii was anxious to persuade the authorities to use this type of construction for military machines as well. As early as 1927 and 1928 he was designing models which were tested in TsAGI's wind tunnel. BICh-5, a parabolic tailless bomber with two BMW-VI and retractable undercarriage came close to being built, but its design was too avant-garde for that time. We already know about the BICh-17 fighter with parabolic plan-form wings and two recoilless cannon.

Meanwhile, the designer was given means to produce a two-motored commercial aircraft BICh-14, at TsKB. Known originally as TsKB-10, this again was a parabolic tailless aircraft, but had two M-11 engines side-by-side on the wing leading edge and a five-seat cabin in the gondola shaped fuselage. As a preliminary Cheranovskii produced the BICh-10 design for wind tunnel testing at TsAGI.

BICh-14 was flown by J I Piontkovskii in Winter 1934, proving very unstable and the controls

The parabolic winged BICh-3, with 18mhp Blackburn Tomtit engine, was demonstrated in Moscow during 1926.

were faulty. After several reconstructions the machine was handed over for government testing in 1936. M A Njukhtikov, P M Stefanovskii and I F Petrov tried in vain to fly the machine which, apart from the faults mentioned, had promising qualities. Tests were continued until 1937 and then given up as useless.

When Cheranovskii realised that his original parabolic design had limited potential he devoted attention to other wing forms, but always retaining tailless construction. A few sailplanes followed and in 1937/38 a power plane, BICh-20 Pioner. It was a small, delta wing aircraft of 6.9m span. The single seat fuselage was short and formed an integral part of the rudder, while in the nose of the original 1937 version they mounted an old 18mhp Tomtit. This was replaced in 1938 by 20mhp Aubier-Dunne whereupon tests showed that the plane was stable, achieved a respectable 166kph and a surprisingly low landing speed of 50kph. Cheranovskii used the shape of BICh-20 as a basis for racing plane BICh-21 or SG-1.

Cheranovskii did not only work on tailless aircraft. Since 1921 he had been very interested in human powered, flapping-wing machines, testing several models and mechanisms without any practical success. In the first half of the thirties, Professors V P Vechinkin, M K Tikhonravov, B S Pyshnov, V V Golubev, worked out the theory of the Ornithopter. Cheranovskii also resumed work on the flapping-wing.

In 1934 he built BICh-16, which represented a continuation of his 1921 version. It was a flying wing with thick centre section which had the shape of a bird. In the centre sat the pilot who operated the flapping by means of pedals. The tips moved in conjunction with a slim auxiliary surface behind the wing. Undercarriage was a little more difficult because of the pilot having to use his legs, so there was only a skid to help him.

R A Pishchuchev, a true 'flyweight' at only 58kg, tested the aircraft from 1935 onwards at Podlipki, near Moscow, first in glider form with launch by elastic cable, then in its flapping-wing mode. Pishchuchev complained about instability and the aircraft was reconstructed several times before being rejected in 1938 as unsuccessful.

Cheranovskii was already devoting his attention to another flapping-wing, the BICh-18 'Muskulet' (Muscle Power Aircraft), tested in August 1937 by Pishchuchev. This aircraft, like BICh-16, was designed and built with the financial backing of the Central Committee of Osoaviakhim. It was similar to a high performance sailplane but was built in the form of a biplane. Viewed from the front, the wings had a horizontal 'X' shape and in the centre was an axis around which they could turn. The top right half wing was connected with the lower left, and vice-versa, so that the half wings always flapped symmetrically against each other and in succession. On the wing tips

Above: Flown in 1937, the BICh-18 'Muskulet' was a pedal-powered, flapping wing aircraft which demonstrated extended glide with minimal wing movements.

Right: The flapping wing BICh-16 first appeared in 1934 and was finally abandoned four years later after several reconstructions.

Above: BICh-14, known originally as TsKB-10, was Cheranovskii's attempt at a twin engined commercial aircraft. State test pilots tried in vain to fly it.

Below: Small delta BICh-20 appeared in 1937 and was later used as a basis for the racing BICh-21 or SG-1.

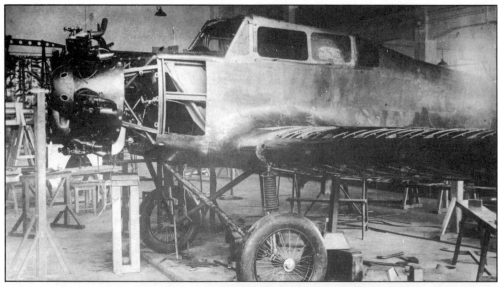

there were ailerons. The whole design was extremely light at 72kg and pedal-power was again used.

On its first flight, on August 10, BICh-18 was flown in glider form, having fixed wings and elastic cable launch. Starting from 10m altitude the aircraft glided 130m. On the fourth flight Pishchuchev made six wing movements and the glide extended to 430m. BICh-18 continued to be tested for a while and publicly demonstrated, but was eventually forgotten.

Other designers also worked on muscle power planes. In 1935, for example, Gribovskii's sailplane G-14 was flown, driven by a pedal powered propeller located over the fuselage nose. The thrust was responsible for an almost imperceptible lengthening of glide flight.

BOK was another centre for design and construction of test planes, being responsible for stratosphere aircraft designed by V A Chishevskii. We know, too, that in 1934 S S Krichevskii was at work here on test plane BOK-2. This was a single-seat, low-wing monoplane in wood construction and with M-11 engine. An interesting feature was the special slot between wing and trailing variable camber flaps. The slot and flaps were so arranged that the aircraft always flew under the most favourable aerodynamic conditions. The data collected encouraged those concerned to think of further experiments, but in 1935 the

Top left: Built from magnesium, EMAI-1 had an M-11 engine and made 600 flights between 1934 and 1938.

Left: Convertiplane LK-4 from Bedunkovich could take on four different guises.

Below: BOK-5 was Chishevskii's last design before he was arrested in 1938.

designer died and nobody continued his work.

Also out of BOK came one of the numerous Soviet tailless machines, Chishevskii's BOK-5. It was a cantilever, low-wing monoplane with tapered wing on the rear of which were ailerons and elevators. Close to the fuselage were special stabilising surfaces. BOK-5 was tested in the Scientific Institute of the Red Air Force which particularly praised the excellent stability, short take-off run of 120m and landing run of 200m. Landing speed was 85kph while maximum speed amounted to 174kph achieved with 100mhp M-11 engine. Design of a further test plane with speeds of 300 to 350kph was recommended. Chishevskii began work but was arrested in 1938 and thus his activity came to an end.

Some strange aircraft were produced by the Institute of the Civilian Air Force based in Leningrad. The design bureau was originally called *Uchebnii Kombinat* or *Leningradskii Kombinat* (Training or Leningrad Combine). The second name was then abbreviated to LK, which was sometimes interpreted as *Letajushchije Krylo* (Flying Wing).

LK-1 was the designation of a peculiar three-seater with thick wing profile built out to make a glazed cockpit. In the nose was an M-11 and a slim tail boom ended with a standard tail unit. The whole design was of timber and several parts of the airframe were of plywood. LK-1 was test flown in Summer 1934 by A J Ivanov and passed Government tests in Moscow. Twenty production aircraft were then built and used by Aeroflot in the North of the USSR.

Another interesting LK design was A G Bedunkovich's convertiplane LK-4, a two-seater of simple construction which could quickly be turned into any of four different variants. LK-4-I was a sesquiplane with wing stagger and fixed slat on the upper wing. The plane was stable and light to fly. LK-4-II had the same design only without wing stagger or slat but with excellent aerobatic qualities. LK-4-III was a high-wing monoplane, faster and better equipped for sport flying than its predecessors and LK-4-IV was a strut-braced low-wing monoplane. The LK-4 was successfully tested in all its forms during 1934 and in the following years was flown at various public functions. Series production was recommended but not carried out.

After his experience with the LK-4, Bedunkovich designed a trainer, P-3, with similar constructional qualities and an MG-31F engine. Model designation was LIG-5. With prefabricated parts it was possible to assemble either a two-seat biplane, a single-seat biplane or single-seat, low-wing monoplane to be used respectively for training R-5 crews and I-16 pilots. P-3 was completed in Summer 1936 and successfully tested at the plant. But it was destroyed while flying to Moscow in Spring 1937 for Government testing and was not rebuilt.

Various structural materials were also tried. In 1934 EMAI-1 was built in the Moscow Aviation Institute (MAI) from a design by A L Gimmelfarb

Above: Having designed and built several sailplanes, Kuzakov transformed his MAK-15 training glider in 1956 to be powered by a twin cylinder Polyakov engine.

Top right: 'Utka' (Duck) or MiG-8, an advanced concept three-seater of canard configuration, first flew at the end of 1945. It was a development exercise only and not intended for production.

Main picture: Under the leadership of Sukhanov, a small series of experimental jet-powered aircraft were evaluated from 1958. Having a distinctive circular wing planform, they were all known as 'Diskoplan'. Illustrated is the third format.

Bottom right: Designed in 1962, it is not known if the radical MAI-62 ever flew. Probably of wooden construction, power came from a pusher-mounted M-71.

Below: Vastly varying terrain gave rise to many experiments in undercarriage form. This UT-2 (Ya-20) was converted to evaluate an air cushion 'shoe' for use on all surfaces, including water.

and S O Sonshejn. It was a two-seat, cantilever, low-wing monoplane with M-11 engine and an airframe made from fabric covered magnesium. Here was tangible proof that magnesium could also be used as an aircraft construction material and in four years of testing EMAI-1 (later known as E-1 'Sergo Orjonikidse') completed 600 flights.

Less successful was the small sport aircraft E-2 Klim Voroshilov, a single-seat, mid-wing monoplane with 18mhp Tomtit engine, built from a design of M L Babad in 1934. Pilot Shukov only made one flight before further flight testing was halted because there was a suspicion of corrosion. In 1937, shortly before completion, work was also halted on the Danilov amphibian E-3. This aircraft too, was made entirely of magnesium and driven by an M-11.

P I Grokhovskii had been experimenting in 1934 with an inflatable glider which he tested in 1935 on Tushino airfield. It was a single-seat, mid-wing monoplane and all components except the tail unit and aileron were made of rubberised textiles inflated with compressed air. When assembled the machine weighed only 77kg and could be transported in a 0.5m x 1m x 1m container. Tail unit and ailerons were made of wood with fabric covering. The rubber glider was towed behind a U-2 at 60m and from that altitude flew 900m. Grokhovskii wanted to produce a motorised version but this idea never materialised. Nevertheless he had anticipated the work of Western colleagues.

After the war fewer test planes were built because aeronautical theory was now highly developed and much could be determined by calculation.

We know there was an 'Utka' ('Duck') designed by Mikoyan and Gurevich in 1945. Later his designation MiG-8 appeared. The three-seat monoplane with pusher propeller and M-11 engine had an elevator located well to the front. A I Shukov test flew 'Utka' in the last days of 1945 and was, on the whole, satisfied with its qualities. 'Utka' was intended to be a substitute for the Po-2 but was never put into production.

We mostly find the post-war test planes in institutes of aviation engineering where students could gain experience designing, constructing and flying such aircraft. There were numerous examples which are presented in the data tables.

In the second half of the fifties optimistic articles appeared about successes achieved with new designs of motorised flapping-wing aircraft. More sophisticated means at the disposal of science now allowed precise analysis of the aerodynamics and mechanics of bird and insect flight. In 1949 Komitet po Mashushchim Poletom (Committee Flapping Flight) was formed in Moscow. There were branches in Riga, Kiev, Kharkov, Kazan etc, and president was the venerable A K Shukov, who had already advocated the study of bird flight in the time of the Tzars. Noteworthy works were produced, such as the paper 'Thrust of Flapping Wing" by V V Golubev and 'Aerodynamics of the Bird Gliders' by I N Vinogradov.

Several designs were made and some were constructed. One aircraft designed by D V Ilyin, according to press reports, was to be flown in 1957 with 5mhp engine. According to Vinogradov's theories, flapping-wing flight was very economical and an aircraft for 15 people would only need an AI-14R engine of 260mhp. Towards the end of the fifties the Soviet press wrote a lot about these problems, mostly in too optimistic a vein. Unfortunately this optimism did not help matters and, as results were not very rapid, there was always a danger that the scientific work would be discredited. Results are still awaited today.

Special types of aircraft are still a theme of aeronautical research. Most experiments are kept secret and only a fraction reach the public. In 1957 photographs were published which showed a machine called 'Turbolet'. This was designed in 1954 by A N Rafaeljants with a vertically mounted 6,750kp RDK jet engine and was lifted upward by vertical thrust. It descended again when the thrust was reduced. On four long bars were small stabilising and control jets which

could be opened or shut from the cabin, so from any position a thrust vector could be created for forward, sideways or backwards flight. 'Turbolet' was demonstrated in 1957 during the Tushino air parade. Its task was to test the conditions of vertical take-off and landing.

In the Aviation Institute of Kazan, students also tried to solve the problems posed by VTOL aircraft. In 1967 a full-size mock-up of the KhAI experiment was displayed in Moscow, having been built at S P Gorbunov's plant in Kazan. The aircraft had two ducted propellers, one on each side of the fuselage, hinged to achieve any direction of thrust. A pusher propeller in the tail provided forward drive. All were driven by a Walter M-337 Czech engine of 210mhp and the designers expected a maximum speed of 320kph. Whether the aircraft was actually constructed is not known.

Above: D V Ilyin's flapping wing aircraft fitted with a 5mhp engine.

Left: 'Turbolet' was designed by A N Rafaeljants in 1954 to carry out research into vertical take-off and landing.

Below: The full-scale mock-up produced from a design by students at the Aviation Institute of Kazan to investigate VTOL characteristics.

CHAPTER 42

Helicopter Development in the 1930s

IN AUGUST 1930 the first Soviet helicopter, TsAGI-1-EA, stood ready for flight on the test field of TsAGI, near Moscow. Everyone who had contributed to the project had assembled. Among them were B N Yurjev, the outstanding aerodynamicist and father of Soviet helicopter development, G Kh Sabinin, director of aerodynamic experimental department EAO TsAGI where the helicopter had been developed, and chief helicopter designer A M Cheremukhin.

When the rotors began to turn it was certainly a big moment for Yurjev who several times before had been very near to realisation of an old dream.

Before the October Revolution Yurjev was devoting his attentions to development of a helicopter, a design that has remained the classic model type to this day – main rotor and antitorque propeller. Helicopters remained his 'hobby' after the Revolution when this pupil of N J Zhukovskii became the leading worker at TsAGI and was entrusted with design and construction of wind tunnels.

In 1925 he was at last able to inspire a group of young and enthusiastic engineers and designers to start on a helicopter in EAO-TsAGI, the department which he directed. In 1928 the group was given a fixed statute and designated as the section for special designs at EAO. At that time Yurjev left for the Academy of Sciences, but he remained the inspiring spirit and an energetic supporter.

From 1925 to 1928 the group worked prin-

cipally on theoretical problems of aerodynamics, statics and mechanics of rotor and rotor blades, their performance in different flying positions, questions of torque adjustment as well as other fundamental matters of helicopter design. So, from the beginning, TsAGI was able to establish the design on a scientific basis.

In the twenties, three main trends in helicopter design following Yurjev's concepts could be discerned. Firstly, a single engined helicopter with two contra-rotating rotors secured at the tips by two booms on both sides of the fuselage, something after the style of the Focke Fa-61. This helicopter remained in model form, as did a large, eight-motored helicopter with eight rotors intended as a combat aircraft. On both types it was planned to use the 120mhp M-2 engine, a

licensed construction of the French Gnome rotary. These were regarded as ideal for helicopters for they were self-cooling and possessed enough inertia mass to drive the rotors.

In 1928 a third, improved helicopter was designed. It was to be an aircraft with a rotor plus two dual propellers in the nose and tail for torque adjustment. At the same time a test plant was built for helicopter rotors.

Blades up to 6m long were driven by a French 120mhp Rhone engine and as a result of theoretical work, together with the favourable attitude of TsAGI, it was decided to develop the experimental helicopter TsAGI 1-EA *(Experimentalnii Avtoshir = Experimental Autogyro)*. It is not known why the word 'autogyro' was used.

TsAGI 1-EA had a long fuselage of steel tube without covering, for speed flights were not expected. Two M-2 engines were mounted at the centre of gravity, so that their shafts were perpendicular to the longitudinal axis of the fuselage, and the driving sides were placed against each other. They powered the four, rigid suspension rotors by means of clutch coupling and main reduction gear. Two pairs of propellers were used for equilibrium. The engines produced 1,470 revolutions a minute, reduced to 153 for the rotor and 1,200 for the propellers.

The first 1-EA was built in spring 1930, intensively tested and brought to the airfield in August for tethered trials. Director of the section, A M Cheremukhin, did not just learn to fly a particular machine, he actually learned how to fly a helicopter – the first to do so in the USSR. Steering devices were almost the same as we know them today.

Flight tests lasted from 1930 until 1934, the greatest successes being achieved in summer 1932. On August 1 Cheremukhin climbed to 160m, two days later to 230m and on August 5 to 285m. August 14 was a big day for the Soviet helicopter when Cheremukhin reached 605m –at a time when the Italian D'Ascanio's world record of 18m still held good! The USSR had not yet become a member of FAI; moreover the experiments were kept a close secret. In June 1934 Cheremukhin remained in the air for a full 14 minutes.

During the four experimental years all structural elements were thoroughly tested – the dynamic qualities of the rotor, wing control, transition to gliding flight, ground effect etc. A series of mistakes were also discovered, like the too rigid attachment of rotor blades, but these were the natural, pitfalls of a completely new technology.

In Autumn 1930, shortly after the first experimental flights of TsAGI 1-EA, construction of a second helicopter was begun on the same lines. It was tested in 1933 as TsAGI 3-EA and then used for the training of further test pilots. During its time of service the aircraft was kept tethered so that it could only be lifted a few metres from the ground. It was never flown freely.

Helicopter design was fundamentally changed at TsAGI in 1933 and placed on a broader scientific and technical basis. The special design section became an independent department known as OOK-TsAGI; director was A M Isakson, Cheremukhin was deputy. Two helicopter groups

Above: TsAGI-5EA was designed by Bratukhin in 1933. Obsolete engines restricted performance to maximums of 40m altitude and 13 minutes duration.

Left: TsAGI-1EA, the first Soviet helicopter, which flew in August 1930 from a test field near Moscow.

worked in OOK-TsAGI, known as brigades. Brigade A, directed by V P Lapisov, was responsible for experimental work and trial flights. Brigade B, under Ivan Pavlovich Bratukhin, was the real drawing office.

Bratukhin designed helicopter TsAGI 5-EA in 1933. It had the airframe of model 3-EA with engines and balancing propellers on nose and tail. The rotor was quite new and designed to eliminate the difficulties experienced with rigid blade retention. This consisted actually of two rotors which turned one above the other. The main rotor of 12m diameter was three-bladed, had articulated attachments to the head and was to carry most of the weight. The auxiliary rotor in the same plane had blades between the main blades, was only 7.8m in diameter and was rigidly mounted. This rotor steered the helicopter.

TsAGI 5-EA was certainly more complicated, but it worked better and was very reliable. Unfortunately the engines were already hopelessly out of date and so unreliable that the aircraft could only be flown low and slowly. During experimental flights, which lasted from autumn 1933 until the end of 1936, an altitude of 40m was reached, a range of 700m, flight duration of 13 minutes and a speed of 20kph.

Bratukhin and his fellow workers in B Brigade foresaw a good future for this composite rotor, but knew that not only more modern engines but also a more modern airframe must be used in order for higher performances to be achieved.

Design work for helicopter TsAGI 11-EA had begun in 1934. This was, in modern terminology, a composite helicopter which combined several functions. Fuselage had the lines of a two-seat aircraft and was a steel tube airframe with covering fabric. In the nose was a radiator with a three-blade fan, behind which sat an American 630mhp Curtiss GV-1570 Conqueror engine with driving shaft leading backwards to the main reduction gear. A composite rotor with two sets of three blades 15.4 and 9.2m in diameter was positioned on a frame. Torque was adjusted by two small propellers mounted on the tips of a rigid wing of 11.3sq m lifting surface in a tractor arrangement. The wing had standard ailerons and on the rear end of the fuselage was a standard tail unit.

TsAGI 11-EA was designed primarily as a pure helicopter with direct rotor propulsion. But it was also to be used as an autogyro, with the rotors freewheeling and propellers providing traction. These two methods would then be synchronised so that the machine could continually be changed from helicopter to autogyro and back again. This, however, proved too difficult.

By summer 1936 the 11-EA had been completed and tested on the ground. They had begun tethered flights on a wooden platform when it was established that the rotor blades had to have a completely all-metal construction instead of composite. Work was begun but difficulties other than technical ones soon cropped up.

In the last weeks of 1937 TsAGI was affected by the wave of arrests and among leading personalities interned were Isakson and Cheremukhin. These events had an adverse effect on those who stayed and for a long time initiative and audacity were frozen. Nobody wanted to run any risks; there was always the danger that the smallest failure could be designated sabotage.

Flight testing of helicopter 11-EA was slowed down and soon stopped. Experimental construction of helicopters was halted in the TsAGI workshops, OOK workers were transferred to other departments and helicopter design was almost brought to a halt. Even under these difficult conditions Bratukhin continued work on the Il-EA,

TsAGI-11EA was a composite helicopter which could also be used as an autogyro – in theory. In practice the transition from helicopter to autogyro proved too difficult at this stage of development.

though slowly. Flight tests showed that the auxiliary propellers took away too much of the engine performance and other problems included too great a weight, which prevented development into a composite aircraft. Under these circumstances Bratukhin decided to develop only the helicopter variant.

At the beginning of 1938 the helicopter was reconstructed as TsAGI 11-EA-PV *(Propulsivnii Variant* = Propelled Variant). Rigid wings were discarded and in their place came two 11m steel tube booms carrying two pairs of tractor and pusher propellers with the drives taken over from the tail unit of TsAGI 5-EA. A greater number of propellers at a longer distance from the longitudinal axis of the fuselage produced a smaller loss in engine performance. At the same time a new, all-metal rotor was built.

The reconstructed helicopter was ready by December 1939 and test flights began at the beginning of 1940 in the hands of engineer D I Savelyev. In October 1940, 11-EA-PV was able to take off in free flight but qualities and performances were unsatisfactory, not least because the Conqueror engine was losing power. With two people an altitude of 50m, speed of 60kph and flight duration of an hour were reached.

Test records revealed, in particular, the simple steering technique, reliability of the rotor propulsion and the high traction of the rotor (up to 1,000kp). Flight tests were interrupted in spring 1941 to mount a new engine. But they did not get that far.

Besides TsAGI models, two further helicopters were built and tested in the thirties. Engineer A H Yosifjants was occupied between 1933 and 1935 with the idea of an electric motor drive for helicopters. He accomplished several successful model tests, one in 1937 with a full scale model of 11m rotor diameter. On the blade tips of the rotor were small electric motors with mounted propellers. A certain success was achieved but everything was too heavy and complicated.

In spring 1941, Yosifjants was given the opportunity to test his ideas on the airframe of the old TsAGI 5-EA helicopter. Instead of M-2 engines, two electric motors were mounted of 2,200 revolutions a minute at 2,000mhp and 130kg weight. Current was conducted through long cables which allowed the aircraft to make short flights in the vicinity of the power source. D A Koshits, who tested the electro-helicopter, was enthusiastic, but further tests had to be halted owing to the outbreak of war.

Another helicopter made its appearance in Leningrad. Italian inventor Vittorio Isacco, who was trying in vain to make use of his ideas in France and Britain, offered his plans to the Soviet Union in 1931. Although the leading personalities at TsAGI had reservations, Isacco was invited to start building his helicopter in 1932 at the Scientific and Research Institute of Civil Aviation.

This 'Helicogir' of Isacco had a spacious fuselage for pilot and five passengers. In the nose was a 300mhp Wright J-6 'Whirlwind' engine which drove a four-blade tractor propeller. The large 24.4m diameter rotor had four blades and on the tip of each was a 130mhp de Havilland Gipsy-III engine with a small, four-blade tractor propeller. The Gipsy engines were to drive the 3,500kg 'Helicogir' without any torque.

Flight tests began in 1935, under Isacco's supervision, with shattering results. The rotor blades were not rigid enough, deformation was too great and unexpected vibrations occurred which coud not be eliminated. In the end flight tests had to be halted on grounds of safety and Isacco left the USSR soon afterwards.

TsAGI-11EA was reconstructed as TsAGI-11EA-PV in 1938, tubular booms replacing the rigid wings and two pairs of tractor/pusher propellers complementing a new, all-metal rotor. Flight tests ended in 1941.

CHAPTER 43

Age of the Autogyros

IN THE TWENTIES, the successful experiments of Spaniard Juan de la Cierva stimulated much discussion throughout the technical world. Cierva, who later transferred to Britain with his autogyro projects where he continued construction up to production stage, inspired sundry followers from numerous countries.

The USSR did not remain aloof from autogyro fever, particularly as it was wont to pay great attention to all new aviation technology and conduct practical experiments. Ample means were made available for the design of autogyros, but there were no real technical results at all. Experience only bore fruit after the Second World War when design work began on a new generation of helicopters.

Model C-8, one of Cierva's most successful autogyros, inspired designers N I Kamov and N K Skrshinskii who received support from the Central Committee of Osoaviakhim to build their first machine in 1929. This was KASKR-1, called 'Krasnii Inshener' (The Red Engineer). Fuselage of the basic training aircraft U-1, a copy construction of Avro 504, was used along with its undercarriage and controls. Short wings were added and on a frame over the fuselage was a four-blade rotor well secured by abundant bracing.

The engine, a 120mhp rotary M-2, was also taken over from U-1 but proved too weak and prevented I V Mikhejev from completing flight tests. In 1930 they obtained a 230mhp Gnome-Rhone Titan which was immediately built into the reconstructed airframe of KASKR-II. By the end of 1931 test pilot D A Koshits had completed 90 flights with this autogyro, reaching an altitude of 450m and maximum speed of 110kph.

Meanwhile TsAGI showed an ever increasing interest in autogyros. Engineers I P Bratukhin and V A Kuznetsov, of the special design section, devoted much energy to this question and after several preliminary studies decided to copy the British autogyro Cierva C-19 Mk.III. Design began in Autumn 1930 and by November 1931 the experimental TsAGI 2-EA was being tested by C A Korzinshchikov.

Not everything was quite right. There were heavy vibrations in the rotor blades, caused by insufficient rigidity of the spars, and take-off run was particularly long because the rotor could only be made to turn by aerodynamics. These and other difficulties provided a good schooling for the designers. In the end a reliable autogyro was made out of TsAGI 2-EA and in 1933 it was assigned to the Maxim Gorkii propaganda squadron. After a year the motor was worn out and the autogyro dispatched to Osoaviakhim's museum.

Elated by success of 2-EA, the authorities ordered a further design. The new autogyro was to be developed entirely at TsAGI, have a Soviet engine and be suitable for large scale production so that it could be used to train military pilots. But series production had already been arranged before the prototype had been flown.

At the same time TsAGI-4-EA was being designed. The first prototype was test flown on November 6, 1932, and the first production autogyro took off only 24 days later. This showed the boldness of conception of the Aviation Industry director, Baranov.

Autogyro TsAGI 4-EA, later renamed A-4 ,was a further development of 2-EA with steel tube fuselage and two-seat cabin. The rotor was mechanically driven at take-off by a 300mhp M-26 engine. This required about 15mhp and the rotor at take-off made 100 revolutions a minute.

As may be imagined, the first months of A-4's

With a Gnome-Rhone Titan engine KASKR-II completed 90 flights by the end of 1931.

Above: In folded mode, the light A-6 designed at TsAGI by Kuznetsov's group.

Below: TsAGI 2-EA spent some time with the Maxim Gorkii propaganda squadron. It was a copy of the British Cierva C-19 Mk.III.

existence were really dramatic. During the second flight, on November 9, 1932, Korzinshchikov discovered heavy rotor oscillations and the autogyro, in spite of maximum engine power, quickly lost its lift force and fell to the ground. The pilot was luckily not hurt.

TsAGI had to find the cause of this defect and eliminate it immediately at all costs so that production was not interrupted. Several experimental versions of the rotor were built and tested, until at last the right dimensions and shapes were found. Series production was saved. Actually some ten A-4 had gone into operation with the military aviation department, even being put under field service conditions.

Chief designer of A-4 or TsAGI 4-EA was A M Cheremukhin and construction supervisor N K Skrshinskii, who had joined the department with N I Kamov in 1931.

Almost at the same time as A-4, a light autogyro was designed at TsAGI by V A Kuznetsov's group. This was the A-6 which had the 100mhp M-11 engine, foldable three-blade rotors and foldable wings. In Summer 1933 Korzinshchikov was able to ascertain its excellent qualities. In spite of this, A-6 remained a mere test object, overshadowed by the production model A-4. A-6 underwent stability, manoeuvrability, ground resonance tests and showed especially good qualities. So, later on, another two modified versions were built.

The first of these was A-8, test flown on June 29, 1934. This aircraft was especially interesting because the rotor disc was made to tilt during rotation so the autogyro could be steered by rotor alone whatever the flying position. On A-8 the standard wings with ailerons were also kept in order to compare both steering mechanisms. Rotor steering was better in every way and on the second licensed construction, A-14, only the control surfaces were kept. Flight tests began in September 1935 and ran through without any faults, showing that a new stage had been reached in autogyro technique. At the same time A-14 represented the climax of Kuznetsov's work in this sphere.

There existed another, lighter variant of autogyro A-8, the A-13. Test flying of A-13 was begun in March 1936 but the plane was a failure and scrapped after a few months.

We have run quite quickly through the development of these autogyros, which were designed at OOK TsAGI by the so-called second development brigade under Kuznetsov. At that time the autogyro design at TsAGI was divided into six brigades. First was the aerodynamic department directed by M I Mil, the second has already been mentioned, the third under N I Kamov was concerned with design, the fourth was a brigade for structural engineering, the fifth worked on stability, and the sixth, under N K Skrshinski, was another design unit. It would seem that superabundant attention was accorded to autogyro design – more than that accorded to helicopters.

The Red Air Force wanted to use autogyros predominantly for liaison and reconnaissance in the front line as well as for artillery observation. In 1931, shortly after his arrival at TsAGI, Kamov had designed a military autogyro. Designation was originally TsAGI 7-EA, later changed to A-7.

A-7 was able to make its first flight on September 20, 1934, piloted by Korzinshchikov. It was a robust two-seater with 480mhp M-22 radial motor, short rigid wing, multipart control surfaces and covered tricycle undercarriage. The rotor, with tubular steel spars in the three blades, had a mechanical drive for jump take-off and with 1,130 engine revolutions the rotor made 195. Equipment was equivalent to that of other classic military aircraft of the time: wireless, fixed synchronised ShKAS machine gun and a flexible twin machine gun for the observer.

Test flights proceeded slowly, owing to heavy rotor oscillations and controls flutter. The autogyro was certainly one of the sensations at Tushino air parade in August 1935, but proving was by no means concluded then. Not until December 1935 could the A-7 be handed over for state tests, which were conducted in 1936 without any hitches. Between May 1937 and July

Below: A-13, a light variant of A-8, flew for a few months but was then scrapped.

A-8 broke new ground with its tilting rotor disc by means of which the aircraft could be steered.

Kamov's A-7 was one of the few successful Soviet autogyros. It was very strongly built and used a 480mhp M-22 radial engine.

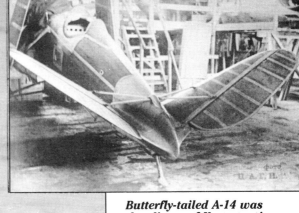

Butterfly-tailed A-14 was the climax of Kuznetsov's work in the autogyro field.

1938 test flights were made of the second improved prototype, A-7bis.

In the first weeks of 1938 there was great excitement over the rescue of I D Papanin's Soviet Arctic expedition which was trapped on a drifting iceberg. Among other methods, it was suggested that the expedition should be rescued by means of an autogyro which was to be transported on an ice breaker to the vicinity of the iceberg. The A-7 was immediately brought by rail to the harbour of Kronshtadt and loaded onto the ice breaker 'Yermak' which then proceeded to Greenland. Here news reached them that Papinin's expedition had already been rescued, so A-7 was unable to display its capacities under difficult Arctic conditions.

In the first half of 1940 five pre-production A-7bis were built and delivered to the Red Air Force. One took part in the Spring of 1941 geographical and geological expedition in Tian-Shan where it proved a valuable asset. When war broke out, all five A-7bis were assembled on an airfield near Smolensk where they were to undertake reconnaissance flights and discharge propaganda leaflets in the face of advancing German troops. But A-7bis's flights were very infrequent because Soviet fighter units could not afford sufficient protection. The autogyro unit was soon evacuated further east and later completely dissolved.

Because of the unfavourable situation in TsAGI, Kamov also left in 1939 and became chief designer in a plant which built production autogyros. Here, in 1940, he began to design wingless autogyro AK with 225mhp MV-6 engine in pusher arrangement and a two-seat cabin. AK could not be completed due to evacuation at the end of Summer 1941. Construction work on the machine continued in 1942, but the Red Air Force lost interest in machines of this class.

There remains to be discussed the sixth design brigade of OOK TsAGI under the direction of Skrshinski. Its first task was the design of a six-seat transport autogyro, A-10, with M-22 engine. The A-10 was not built, for soon after the start of design work Skrshinski transferred to other projects which seemed more important.

Skrshinski's new autogyro, the A-12, was of especial technical interest, but its creator had decidedly bad luck. The design was particularly difficult and demanding. They wanted to build an autogyro with a speed range between 45 and 300kph, 7,000m service ceiling and 35-45m take-off. Skrshinski planned that the A-12 should have particularly good aerodynamics and a 650mhp Wright Cyclone engine under a Naca-cowling. The three-blade rotor had a diameter of 14m.

A P Chernavskii began test flying on May 10, 1936, with cautious taxiing and some short jumps. A-12 was very unstable and the reason was badly designed rotor blade attachments. The mistake was eliminated by means of three springs and by May 27 Chernavskii was able to take off again. Everything was all right and on the third flight he stayed aloft for 55 minutes, reaching an altitude of 2,000m.

In one year the A-12 completed 43 flights and 18 hours of flying time with Chernavskii and Kotsyrev, yet on May 23, 1937, Kotsyrev had a fatal accident in the aircraft. That was a heavy blow from which Soviet autogyro development was not able to recover at this difficult time. The unlucky autogyro which had already reached a speed of 245kph and an altitude of 5,570m, was not repaired nor rebuilt. The cause of Kotsyrev's accident was never established. Only later was it accepted that the accident must have been caused by some fatigue fracture in the rotor blade spar.

The situation at this time was not easy for Skrshinski's group. Several commissions made a study of all the work of the sixth brigade, and subsequently all autogyros built at TsAGI were scrutinised closely. Thus several faults were discovered in stability and manoeuvrability of the autogyros, especially the wingless type.

Skrshinski tried to make use of the findings during 1938 and 1939. Several little autogyros were designed with the name A-10, the last of them adapted for jump take-off and to be given a 140mhp MV-4 engine. A-10 was not constructed, neither was A-9, a development of the A-13.

Autogyro with the highest model number before the war was A-15, designed by M L Mil in 1936 as a military machine with higher performance than A-7bis. It was a wingless model with three-blade rotor and 750mhp M-25V engine, the most powerful used on Soviet autogyros. The A-15 was two-seat and, like the A-7bis, armed.

In April 1937 the A-15 was completed and pilots Chernavskii and Ivanov began with the ground run. But after A-12's accident all flight tests were forbidden until the cause had been discovered. Tests began again in February 1938 but on the very first ground run a defect showed up in the rotor drive. Further repairs were not allowed and A-15 was at an end.

So that was the extent of autogyro development in the USSR before the war. Soviet designers did a lot and in the beginning they were given ample means. Unfortunately the results were not always satisfactory and it can even be said that, with the exception of models A-4 and A-7, there were more disappointments than successes.

In more recent years there has been an active worldwide renewal of interest in autogyros of the lighter class, for sporting, agricultural and other purposes. Ministry for the Energy Industry in the Estonian SSR issued a design competition in 1964 for a light autogyro to be used for the monitoring of overhead electricity supply cables. Students of the Kharkov Aviation Institute (SKB KhAI) designed autogyro KhAI-24 for the competition in 1965, featuring a 115mhp Czech Walter M-332 engine with propeller in the fuselage nose, a two-seat cabin and three-blade rotor. Chief design manager was B I Mysov. A full scale model was displayed in Moscow in 1966 and the autogyro was tested in 1967. Unfortunately nothing is known about the use it was actually put to.

Skrshinski's A-12 looked very promising during its first year with a top speed of 245kph. But in May 1937 it crashed, killing test pilot Kotsyrev.

Above: A model of Mil's A-15 autogyro which was built but never left the ground.

Below: Designed by students at the Kharkov Aviation Institute, KhAI-24 was intended for the inspection of overhead cables and tested in 1967.

CHAPTER 44

Bratukhin's Helicopters

THROUGHOUT the forties, Ivan Pavlovich Bratukhin was the greatest figure in helicopter design in the USSR, directing Brigade B in the OOK TsAGI helicopter group where he produced models TsAGI 11-Ea and 11-EA-PV.

In January 1940 Bratukhin left TsAGI and, with his assistants, formed the Nucleus of research and drawing office OKB-3 *(Opitno-Konstruktorskoje Bjuro)* in the Sergo Orjonikidse Moscow Aviation Institute (MAI). Between January and March OKB-3 was directed by Professor B N Jurjev, then Bratukhin succeeded him.

By July 1940 those presiding over MAI released Bratukhin's project for a helicopter called 2MG 'Omega'. The whole construction was represented in the designation – 2M meant two-engined and 'G' was for *gelikopter* (helicopter). Its fuselage had almost the classic lines of fixed wing aircraft and consisted of a steel tube framework with covering fabric. Inside was a cabin with two

Bratukhin's first two helicopters were 2MG 'Omega' (below) and G-2 'Omega II' (bottom). Ground tests of 2MG began in August 1941 and G-2 first flew in September 1944.

seats in tandem arrangement.

Standard tail surfaces included a one-section horizontal unit in 'T' shape, while on either side of the fuselage were welded steel tube booms, 7 metres in span, with air-cooled, six-cylinder 220mhp MV-6 motors at the tips. From each engine a drive shaft led to a three-blade rotor; both rotors were connected to each other so that if one engine were to fail the second would bring the helicopter to a safe landing. Both engines had cooling fans and the rotor blades were made of duraluminium.

In August 1941 'Omega' was ready and test pilot K I Ponomarjev began with ground runs on the airfield. He tried the first disengagement from the ground, tested all steering mechanism and power pack, but this was the sum total of his activities. There were some difficulties in the propulsion system and the booms were not stiff enough. There was no time for changes as MAI had to be evacuated, transferring eastward into Middle Asia. This meant over half a year's delay in the development of 2MG.

At the new plant, tethered flight tests were

made and the necessary modifications carried out. In summer 1943 Ponomarjev made the first free flights, but the test programme proceeded slowly. It was a particularly warm summer with air temperatures of 50 to 55 degrees centigrade. This meant that the engines could only operate for quite a short time – at the most, 15 minutes. Nevertheless, test results were favourable and the flying qualities conspicuously good.

MAI was able to return to Moscow at the beginning of 1944. In spite of the wartime economy and other difficulties, Bratukhin was given all the means he required for development of a helicopter which could be used in service at the Front. The Red Air Force particularly had in mind a helicopter for artillery observation.

The second prototype, G-2 'Omega-11', was completed in September 1944. Two stronger engines were mounted – pre-war nine-cylinder MG-31F radial engines each of 300/350mhp – otherwise the entire construction was the same as its predecessor. Ponomarjev was able to complete test flights between September 1944 and January 1945, then G-2 was slightly modified and tested again up to July 1945. The results were excellent: service ceiling rose from 700m on the 2MG to 3,000m, maximum speed from 115 to 150kph and load capacity from 290 to 420kg.

Two G-3 models were produced in 1945. They corresponded to the G-2 but were redesigned for serial production and possessed two American 340/450mhp Pratt and Whitney R-985 AN-1 Wasp Juniors specially bought for the production run. G-3 was designated by the Air Force as AK *(Artillerijskii Korrektirovshchik = Artillery Cor-*

rection Aircraft). Ten were ordered, but in 1945 and 1946 only five were produced.

Once again the Air Force higher command had shown uncertainty and misunderstanding. Not only were they not clear about the uses to which military helicopters could be put, but inappropriate tactical and technical specificiations were given for construction and use. This all led to a halt in production.

Two G-3 and a G-2 constituted one of the high points at Tushino air display in August 1946, but shortly afterwards the G-2 had to be abandoned as the engines' life came to an end. G-3, on account of their uncertain state, led a meagre existence flying only occasionally and just one aircraft was used for training new helicopter pilots.

Meanwhile the engine drawing office under A G Ivchenko and in close cooperation with Bratukhin, built and tested the first Soviet helicopter engines – AI-26GR variants of a seven-cylinder radial. The 420/500mhp AI-26GR possessed a reduction gear with vertical rotor drive and a horizontal drive for the synchronising shaft. In front there was also a fan drive.

The first four engines were at OKB-3's disposal in 1946 and two helicopters of the G-4 type were built for them. They had the same lines as the earlier models of Bratukhin but were bigger, with 7.7m booms.

M K Bajkalov was able to try out the first G-4 in October 1947. The programme was especially comprehensive and transition to auto-rotation was to be tested for the first time in the USSR. Unfortunately just at this stage, in January 1948, the rotors lost lift and the G-4 crashed. The second G-4, which had been flying since November 1947, was immediately grounded for modifications.

K I Ponomarjev was then able to complete the whole test programme without difficulty, even gliding flights and gliding landings with a dead engine. The most important components – gear, drive, rotor drive, shaft, clutch couplings, rotor hubs, control etc – were even submitted to a hundred-hour fatigue test. Again, a serial production was planned along with a resumption of G-3 construction. Ten machines were ordered but history repeated itself. Up to the end of 1948 four G-4 production specimens had been assembled when all work was halted.

The lines of helicopters 2MG, G-2, G-3 and G-4 all conformed to the same basic pattern. It was clear to Bratukhin that there was no future for this construction if a helicopter was required which could be successfully used as a weapon or transport aircraft. In 1945 he had begun work on a new version which, while still possessing two separate engines and rotors, was nevertheless to be laid out on more modern principles of aerodynamics and structural engineering.

The same year OKB-3 presented projects, calculations and finally design drafts for a more modern helicopter. B-5 was a robust model with broad fuselage, monocoque construction and the six-seat cabin had a convenient entrance. On the fuselage was a high wing with engines and rotors at the tips. The designer had reckoned on the fixed wing bearing about 25% of the helicopter's flying weight when the aircraft was at maximum speed in horizontal flight – an estimated 236kph.

It was a fairly long time before the new helicopter could be built. Not until 1947 were engines of sufficient power available, the AI-26GR(F) with maximum output of 550mhp.

Almost simultaneously, helicopter B-9 was prepared. It corresponded to B-5 but had more room in the cabin as it was intended as an ambulance helicopter for the transport of four wounded men on stretchers plus an escort.

In 1947, too, helicopter B-10 was produced under military designation VNP (*Vosdushnii Nabludatelnii Punkt* = Aerial Observation Point). Once again an attempt had been made to create a tactical helicopter for use on the Front and especially for artillery observation, night reconnaissance etc. B-10 had three seats, there was a flexible machine gun in the nose and another in the tail. In the fuselage beneath the wing was another cabin for various military loads or three people. The engines were two 575mhp AI-26GVF, expected to produce a speed of 218kph, service ceiling of 6,500m and range of 440km.

All three helicopters, B-5, B-9 and B-10, were to complete their plant and state tests in 1948 but a great wave of distrust again swept over leading commanders-in-chief of the Air Force. Official quarters refused to take on the helicopters. Only the B-5 had almost completed testing but performance was not found satisfactory. Today it must be admitted that OKB-3 allowed three models to be developed and built at the same time, before the findings from G-4 and other models could be studied.

The last helicopter built by Bratukhin was B-11, developed for a 1947 Military Air Force design competition. A general purpose, three-seat model was desired, appropriate for military as well as civilian tasks, not too complicated and suitable for the production line. Bratukhin used the structural design of his B-5 with the same AI-

26GR(F) engines. Fuselage was not so large, the wing had a symmetrical profile and on either side of the fuselage were two V struts. A reclining and a seated wounded person could be accommodated.

By April 1948 two B-11 prototypes were ready and flight tests took place in June. The helicopter was also flown several times with a single engine and showed good qualities, but two serious faults showed up – rotor blade stall at higher speeds and high resonant vibrations throughout the helicopter. The first prototype was pronounced unflyable in August 1948 and submitted to rigorous investigation.

Test flights of the second B-11 were resumed in a tentative way in order to better establish reasons for the flaws. The aircraft was being flown by Ponomarjev on December 13, 1948, when a blade of the right hand rotor broke. Ponomarjev and his crewman died as B-11 plunged to earth. The crash had serious consequences for OKB-3 and for Bratukhin who had to defend his work on more than one occasion in order to maintain support for new experimental work.

The first B-11 prototype was completely redesigned and reconstructed, the wing given a bigger angle of incidence, rotor heads were strengthened, vibration absorbers mounted and new emergency exits provided for the crew. AI-26GVF engines were now used.

Flight tests were begun at the beginning of 1949, but the stall occurred again. Flights continued notwithstanding, but maximum speed was only 150kph and ceiling 2,500m. Under these conditions Bratukhin's hopes were slight. He

Right: The last of Bratukhin's designs to be constructed was B-11. The first prototype was pronounced unflyable in 1948 and the second crashed, killing test pilot Ponomarjev.

B-10 was a dedicated military helicopter, armed with machine guns in the nose and tail. Distrust among Red Air Force commanders kept it out of service.

tried to further modify the B-11 in May 1950, designing new rotor blades with a profile about 15% broader, but all in vain.

Between 1948 and 1951 Bratukhin produced further designs in OKB-3. Most were two-engined and two-rotored and represented all classes of weight from the basic training aircraft to large troop transports. Bratukhin also designed a helicopter called B-12 with a main rotor and an anti-torque propeller, so following the classical design of Sikorsky. It was to be a basic training helicopter with two 150mhp M-11FR-1 or one AI-14V of 240mhp. B-12 remained on the drawing board.

Another project of Bratukhin's deserves a few words. Since 1948 he had been working in the sphere of jet propulsion and developed several rotors driven by small ramjets at the tips. By 1955 a rotor test plant was operating in the courtyard of MAI. It was really a complete engine nacelle with an AI-26GR saved from a scrapped G-4 helicopter. The reciprocating engine set the rotor in motion and only then could the ramjet engines be ignited. The tests were more than satisfactory but more time and means were needed in order to be able to exploit the findings for useable models. These were not allowed for Bratukhin's OKB-3 workers and in 1951 the drawing office was closed.

It is not easy to make a value judgement about Bratukhin's design work as a whole. We see a gigantic amount of work done which unfortunately, for various reasons, never culminated in any useable helicopters. On the other hand we must recognise Bratukhin's value as a pioneer.

Not only did he have to design helicopters, but he had to prevail on the authorities to use them in military and civilian aviation units and convince the higher commanders-in-chief of the need for helicopters in modern warfare.

In the context of Bratukhin's experiments with rotor jet propulsion we must turn our attention also to B J Sherebtsov's group in which the designers J S Braginski and J L Starinin were working. This group had been devoting its attention since 1947 to rotor drive by means of pulse ducts attached to the wing tips.

After studies and preliminary tests, several experimental rotors of 7m diameter were constructed and examined between 1948 and 1950. By attaching extension parts it was possible to increase the diameter to 8 or 9m and aeropulse engines of 9, 12 and 17kp thrust were mounted and tested.

As a conclusion to the development work a small one-seat helicopter was built, called 'Sherebtsov'. This was first tested on a moving lorry, but later the designers were able to test it in TsAGI's wind tunnel. By 1950 the machine was ready to be flown freely by pilot Smirnov, first short distances at low-level and then at increased speed and height by Tinjakov. But helicopter pulse jet was regarded as unsatisfactory and the group's experimental work ended.

In 1964, another small helicopter with pulse jet was observed once more. This was a certificate specimen by graduates of Kujbyshev's Aviation Institute. Unfortunately we have no further details about this design, which was known as VIGR-1.

CHAPTER 45

Route to a New General Purpose Helicopter

IN HELICOPTER development the USSR seemed to be lagging far behind other great powers. Great Britain and France devoted a lot of attention to helicopter technology but America had a gigantic lead over the rest of the world. Not until after the war were means made available in the USSR and then it was necessary to start again almost from scratch. It was not possible to forge links with the pre-war development – continuity had been broken.

Authorities were not always completely convinced about the potential of helicopters, but by 1947 it had become only too clear that they were going to be indispensable for both military and civilian purposes. So the technical stipulations for a three-seat helicopter were transmitted and three groups were called on to take part. I P Bratukhin built his two unsuccessful B-11 helicopters for this competition.

M L Mil's drawing office had concluded their work in 1938 with the autogyro A-15 and Mil was able to take over a new OKB in 1947, designing a GM-1 type helicopter for the competition. First prototype was finished in September 1948 and two others soon followed. Unlike Bratukhin's complicated helicopters, the GM-1 was quite simple. It had a classic form with main rotor over the fuselage and an anti-torque propeller on the tip of a fuselage boom.

M K Bajkalov, M L Gallaj and V V Vinicki tested the prototypes in autumn 1948. For Bajkalov the first test period almost had a tragic ending when the rotor lost lift, the helicopter started to oscillate, looped the loop and fell to the ground from a height of 5,000m. Bajkalov was able to save himself. The two other GM-1 successfully concluded factory flight tests, reaching a speed of 190kph, a dynamic ceiling of 6,800m and static ceiling of 3,450m.

In summer 1949, under G A Tinjakov, GM-1 passed state inspections, during which speed was kept down to 170kph lest the rotor blades should lose lift. In September 1949, a year after the first flight, all tests were successfully concluded and GM-1 was handed over to the aircraft industry for serial production. The Air Force used it under designation Mil Mi-1.

Structural design of Mi-1 was tailored for series production. The fuselage was a steel tube frame with duralumin sheet skin while the tail boom had a simple monocoque construction. In the cockpit were three seats and behind was the engine compartment housing a 575mhp seven-cylinder AI-26V. Its 2,050 revolutions a minute were reduced to 232 main rotor revolutions and 1,348 tail rotor revolutions. Further to the rear was a fuel tank of 240 litres and an auxiliary tank of 160 litres could be mounted externally.

Rotor blades were subjected to a series of changes and modifications before the designer was satisfied. Structural design of the first blades was the same as on pre-war autogyros – composite construction with spars made of three steel tubes connected by fittings. This complicated form was replaced by a tubular spar, conical in shape. Serially produced blades were of dural with pressed profile spar, but this greatly increased centrifugal forces on the rotor so hyd-

raulic boosters had to be built into the cyclic control. Life span of the most important rotor head end gear was too short in 1951, being only about 100 hours. Five years later their life was 500-600 hours, and after 1960 their term extended to over 1,000 hours.

With the Mi-1 Soviet aviation got a good, efficient and reliable helicopter. Its operation was not outstandingly economic, but it possessed a power reserve which allowed it to operate from airfields situated at higher levels, to fly over mountains or work in tropical regions. Mi-1 could be seen in several countries besides the USSR. In 1957 licensed production was begun in Poland as SM-1.

Several variants of Mi-1 were produced, each with a different sphere of activity. One basic training variant had two seats side-by-side in the front of the cabin and dual controls. It was called Mi-1U or Mi-1T when used for other training.

In 1954 a few Mi-1S ambulance variants were built. They are distinguished by two long tanks on both sides of the fuselage to each carry a wounded man. The casualty could speak by means of a communication tunnel with the doctor in the cabin during flight and could also be treated. Greater flying weight of the ambulance variant had to be compensated for by a four-blade rotor.

Agricultural variant Mi-1NCh had more uses. This could be employed in all sorts of ways in agriculture, forestry, viticulture, fruit growing, etc. On each side of the fuselage was mounted a 260 litres tank which could hold liquid or powdered chemicals.

In 1958 Mil got the task of developing a water/dry land undercarriage for Mi-1. Two versions of floating gear were tested. The first consisted of a short, inflatable rubber float fastened to every wheel of the undercarriage, but stability was poor on water. The second version was better, four long rubber floats were fastened on a framework on both sides of the fuselage so that the helicopter could touch down easily on water or land. Thus the water/dry land helicopter variant Mi-1P came into being. These were often used on whaling ships and 'Slava' was the first fleet to be fitted out with Mi-1P in the season of October 1958 to May 1959.

Aeroflot was given a passenger and taxi variant, the Mi-1A 'Moskvich'. It was a de luxe version for a pilot and three passengers in a sound insulated cabin, had hydraulic steering system and equipment for night flights. The 'Moskvich' was demonstrated in 1960 but does not seem to have been used much.

Mi-1s made a name for themselves at the beginning of their career with a series of international FAI records for Class E. Fifteen were broken, but we will only mention the most interesting: a long distance horizontal flight of 794.918km, flown by Belushkin on March 19, 1958, in five hours twenty two minutes; an altitude record of 6,700m, reached on the same day by the same pilot; speeds of 210.535kph over a 100km triangle and 196.452kph over a 500km course set by Vinicki in May 1959; in 1960 Belushkin broke his own horizontal flight record reaching 224.8kph, established a distance of 1,006.59km on a closed circuit and a record speed of 141.2kph over 1,000km.

It is easy enough to deduce that Mi-1 emerged victorious in the competition for a general-purpose helicopter. The third group taking part was that of A S Yakovlev. It is certainly surprising that a drawing office which had won fame designing fighters should now start designing this dissimilar type of aircraft. Even more surprising is the fact that Yakovlev's group were taking an interest in helicopter design before they were called on to take part in the competition.

During the war, engineer N K Skrshinskii, a designer of gyroplanes, became a member of Yakovlev's drawing office. Soon he won the chief over to the idea of a two-seat experimental helicopter and work began towards the end of 1944.

Skrshinskii designed the helicopter EG *(Experimentalnii Gelikopter = Experimental Helicopter)* with two coaxial, contra-rotating rotors. Each rotor had two wooden blades driven by a 140mhp M-11FR engine. But it was 1947 before V V Tesavrovskii was able to begin flight tests.

EG made 40 tethered and 75 free flights totalling 15 hours. It reached 180m and a maximum speed of 60kph. Tests did not proceed any further for Yakovlev's OKB were devoting all their energies to the new Yak-100 designed to compete with Mil's GM-1 or Mi-1.

Deciding on the shortest and easiest way, they took as their model the successful American Sikorsky S-51 and followed its design closely. Yak-100 had a long, thickly glazed cockpit with a pilot's seat in the middle and two others side-by-side. In the fuselage was a 425/575mhp seven cylinder AI-26GRFL driving a three-blade wooden rotor. The leading edge consisted of layers of ash and oak glued together, ribs were of plywood and the whole was fabric covered.

Only two prototypes of Yak-100 were built; the first was finished in November 1948 and the second, a two-seat variant with dual control, made its maiden flight in July, 1949. Flight tests lasted until the middle of 1950, plagued by heavy rotor vibrations caused by the centre of gravity of the blades being set too far back. After reconstruction, state tests were continued in the second half of 1950; the results were very good, but Mi-1 had won.

M L Mil adopted the classic construction of a main rotor and anti-torque propellor for his Mil-1 which provided the USSR with an efficient and reliable helicopter for a wide variety of uses.

CHAPTER 46

Heavy Transport Helicopters

THE DRAWING OFFICES of M L Mil and A S Yakovlev had been rivals in the design of a general-purpose helicopter and were destined to become rivals again. Yakovlev describes in his memoirs a dramatic consultation in the Kremlin in Autumn 1951. He and Mil were summoned by Stalin who criticised them for neglecting modern trends in helicopter technology and not designing any heavy models.

The pair were now given the task of designing heavy transport helicopters especially suited for airborne troops and tactical military operations, but which could also be used for civilian service in Aeroflot. Mil was to design a single-engined model with 1,200kg military load, Yakovlev a machine with double capacity. All this in a year – and no argument!

Mil's first prototype Mi-4 was completed in April 1952 and after all ground tests had been concluded the aircraft was given to V V Vinickii for flight testing. It was remarkable that a helicopter of this size could be ready seven months after the start of design; at the same time, serial production was begun so that by Summer 1952, the first three production models could also be test flown. Mil's group had done all that it could to meet Stalin's deadline.

Yakovlev's group had not enjoyed much sleep either. In July 1952, S G Brovtsev took off for the first time in Yak-24. The two models were fundamentally different – not only in lifting capacity and weight class but also in their general design. Mi-4 had the classic layout with a four-blade main rotor of 21m diameter and a tail rotor both driven by an ASh-82V fourteen cylinder, double row radial of 1430/1700mhp. Yak-24 had two such engines, one at either end of the box fuselage where two rotors taken over from Mi-4 were also mounted.

As regards shape, Mi-4 was a sequel to Mi-1, but the inner space was used in a different way. Engine compartment was right in the front with motor obliquely mounted and remote propulsion to the main drive under the rotor hub. Over the engine was a two-crew cabin while the main cabin was entered by a door on the left. Ten or twelve people could be accommodated here, or a corresponding load. Heavier or mobile loads, as for example, a GAZ-69 jeep or anti-tank gun, could be driven or pulled in after two hinged side doors had been opened. For observation, a glazed bathtub gunner's pit was mounted behind the engine, where machine guns could also be installed for ground attack.

Not only had Mi-4 been developed within a very short time, it also brought its designer fame and recognition.

Of course not everything was in perfect order from the start. The 21m diameter main rotor suffered heavy dynamic streses resulting in an extremely short blade life. Spar of the first production model was composed of pieces of steel tube, the diameter of which dwindled towards the tip. Otherwise the framework was wood covered with plywood. Rotor blades like these did not last for more than a hundred hours of flight. In 1954 life was extended to 300 hours and three years later Mil was able to obtain special conical steel tubes with tapering wall thickness which were good for 600 hours.

Mil's OKB had also been working on all-metal blades for the Mi-4 since 1953, but on account of various difficulties progress was quite slow. Not until 1959 were reliable blades completed and tested. These had pressed dural spars and honeycomb filling of the rear part of the blade. From 1960 onward they were installed on production machines.

Meanwhile the Mi-4 helicopters had proved their worth not only in military but also in civilian operations. In the second half of the fifties Mi-4 was among the most efficient helicopters in the world, confirmed by a whole string of international FAI records. Many are now mere history, but at the time they were astonishingly high. On April 25, 1956, R I Kapreljan lifted a load of 2,000kg to 6,017.5m; on April 26, 1956, V V Vinickii reached 6,056m with 1,000kg load and three days later B V Semskov flew over a 500km course at an average speed of 187.254kph.

As the Mi-4 were improved, so too were the records. In March 1960 G Alferov reached 7,575m with 1,012kg and K Chernobrovkin's crew lifted 2,000kg to 6,369m.

In 1958 Mi-4 won a gold medal at the World Exhibition 'Expo 58' in Brussels. At that time there began a brisk trade in Mi-4 helicopters which were sold not only to countries of East Europe but also to the Near and Far East and Africa. Individual models were even sold to west European states. The delivery of Mi-4 to India aroused great excitement for its excellent altitude performances meant that the aircraft was especially suited for service in the Himalayas.

The Mi-4, of which several thousand specimens were produced, was built in several variants. The basic military one carried up to 14 infantrymen, vehicles of up to 1,650kg weight or other loads of up to 2,000kg. During the 1956 Tushino air parade, 36 Mi-4 helicopters were responsible for the airborne landing of a unit armed with heavyish infantry weapons.

Mil's Mi-4 proved to be one of the world's most efficient and versatile helicopters, bringing fame and recognition for its designer.

Aeroflot began using the civilian Mi-4P *(Passashirskii* = Passenger Flying Helicopter) in 1954. The cabin, which had better soundproofing, held 10 passengers and 200kg luggage. From summer 1959 Mi-4P flew in the spa districts of Crimea and Caucasus. At first there were only ten lines in the USSR, but by 1960 the number had risen to 200 and from 1961 the Mi-4P service linked all Moscow's airfields to one another and with the city centre. The Mi-4L *(Ljux* = Luxury) had especially effective cabin soundproofing but could only transport six passengers.

There were variants for ambulance service which took eight stretchers and a doctor, and even flying operation theatres. Other Mi-4 helicopters were equipped as flying cranes with external stores. For example, when the trolleybus line Simferopol-Yalta was being built, Mi-4 transported 22m steel masts weighing 1,800kg.

When the television tower in Moscow-Ostankino was assembled, Mi-4 carried 1,000kg reinforced concrete slabs.

In Soviet agriculture Mi-4S were used from 1954. Dry chemical apparatus or spray bars can be mounted and 1,600 litres container is built into the fuselage. With a forward speed of 60kph Mi-4S can spray a width of 40-80m at up to 18 litres or 20kg of chemicals per second.

For service in the mountains there were the Mi-4V *(Visotnii* = Altitude). These had ASh-82FN engines with two-stage supercharger; second stage of the supercharger was switched in at about 4,600m altitude and with full load gave a service ceiling of 8,000m. Moreover, the second stage makes it possible to take off from airfields at 5,000m altitude, a good performance for a helicopter of this weight class with piston engine. All these variants of Mi-4 were equipped with a four-wheel undercarriage but could also be modified for use on either water or land.

So Mil's design was successful and its success was all the more significant in view of the time taken to design the two-engined Yakovlev machine and the difficulties encountered.

Yakovlev and N K Skrzhinskii had no luck at all in design of the 'Flying Waggon' Yak-24. They used three fundamentally different designs for three successive models without fully developing and testing the qualities of each design. Moreover, the production of a tandem helicopter, especially one the size of Yak-24, is among the most difficult tasks of aeronautical technology.

Yakovlev's prototype plant built four Yak-24 all at the same time. The first was intended for static tests, the second for vibration tests and the third and fourth for flight tests. The third prototype was completed by Spring 1952 and tested in tethered state. But it was whirled round in a storm, struck by lightning and completely burned.

The fourth Yak-24 was soon completed and able to make its first flight on July 3, 1952, with S G Brovtsev at the controls. A helicopter in this weight, size and engine class had not been built before, so flight tests proceeded quite slowly. Oscillation tests on the second prototype revealed dangerous sources and in flight the flutter was yet worse, threatening the very stability of the fuselage frame.

All scientific means available were mobilised in order to eliminate these drastic manifestations. Among other things, the rotor blades were shortened, kinetics of the rotor steerage thoroughly revised and stability of the fuselage framework improved. Vibrations were still fairly strong, but at least it was possible to complete plant tests in the last weeks of 1954 and another prototype passed through protracted state tests between Spring 1953 and April 1955.

Yak-24 was then recommended for serial production, though some problems still remained unsolved. For instance, there was dangerous instability and vibration in certain flight regimes. Cause was found to be the shape of the tail plane which had a considerable dihedral. New surfaces were built with less dihedral and large, square fin surfaces.

Yak-24 was purpose-built. In the nose was a cockpit for two pilots and a radio operator. Then came the engine compartment containing an ASh-82V double-row radial, propeller shaft being mounted towards the rear and high up. This drove the front rotor but there was also a coupling to the rear rotor and vice versa for the second engine. In the event of failure of one engine there was still enough power to continue flying.

Rotors were four-bladed and taken over from Mil's Mi-4 together with reduction gearing etc. Diameter was reduced from 21 to 20m. The helicopter rested on a four-wheel undercarriage.

Interior of the fuselage from the engine compartment in the front to the loading ramp in the rear was completely free and could take 20 fully equipped infantrymen with weapons and ammunition. Via the loading ramp, folded down from the

assymmetrically-shaped tail, various weapons could be loaded on or driven in, for example three GAZ-69 jeeps. In the floor of the hold was a big hatch above which a crane was mounted. The crane could pull up to 200kg through the opening in flight. An ambulance version of Yak-24 could accommodate 18 stretchers and a doctor.

In December 1957 the new Yak-24U was issued. On this aircraft all earlier difficulties were eliminated and all improvements to date worked in to make a technically mature helicopter. Its rotors were 21m diameter, the fuselage 400cm wider, capacity amounted to 3,500kg or 37 airborne infantrymen. Under the fuselage new, more stable mountings were attached for extra heavy external loads. Yak-24U was serially produced from 1958 onwards, and 1959 saw the introduction of gyropilots and stabilising devices from Yakovlev's OKB.

A few Yak-24U were used in the crane service of Aeroflot which also obtained some Yak-24A in 1960, adapted for the accommodation of 30 passengers. In 1961 Yak-24K arrived on the scene; they were used as VIP machines with a luxurious cabin for eight passengers.

In Soviet industrial displays abroad at the beginning of the Sixties, models of the Yak-24T with turbine engines were being shown. We have no details about the engines and do not know if this aircraft variant was actually used.

Yak-24 also achieved some international FAI records for their class. In December 1955, J F Miljetichev lifted 4,000kg to 2,902m and G S Tinjakov took 2,000kg to 5,082m. One Yak-24 was the first helicopter in the USSR to make a cross-country flight from Moscow to Leningrad.

The Yak-24 shows how dogged work and the co-operation of various scientific centres can save an almost hopeless technical failure. On the other hand, there remains the question as to whether it was worthwhile investing so much, for results certainly did not justify the outlay.

Overcoming vast problems in technology, Yakovlev produced his Yak-24 heavy transport helicopter in under two years. It is shown in its original form (above) and with modified tail surfaces (left). Rotors were four-bladed and inherited from the Mi-4 complete with reduction gearing.

CHAPTER 47

Kamov's Helicopters

IN 1945 N I Kamov resumed his work on rotating wing aircraft and, helped by a small group, designed a tiny one-seat helicopter. He was convinced of its usefulness both for military and post-war civilian purposes. In order to ensure the best possible stability, Kamov used two three-bladed rotors arranged coaxially. Rotor blades were all-wood and design of the helicopter body was extremely simple – an open steel tube framework with a seat behind the rotor axle. Power came from a motor cycle engine, the M-76 of 45mhp while two rubber pontoons formed the undercarriage.

After rather lengthy negotiations Kamov managed to win approval for the construction of three prototype Ka-8 in 1947. The fleet and mercantile navy were especially interested,for they saw a good observation aircraft also suitable for naval liaison, whaling etc, which, thanks to its small dimensions, could be easily transported on a ship. Rotor diameter was just 5.6m and weight 275kg.

What caused surprise was the fact that these three Ka-8 never needed any alterations, remaining just as they were when they left the workshop. Ka-8 were first displayed in the 1948 Tushino air parade and from then on they were frequently seen on divers missions.

As a result Kamov was once again able to open his own OKB, the fourth helicopter office in the USSR after the war. First task was to prepare the Ka-8 for production line and four Ka-10 were produced in 1949. Rotor diameter was increased to 6.12m driven by a new, flat four-cylinder AI-4V of 55mhp designed by A G Ivchenko. Maximum speed climbed from 80 to 95kph and the dynamic ceiling from 250 to a full 2,000m. For quite a long time Ka-10s were mere attractions at various public events as there were still lingering doubts about their value in real service.

It was possible to build a small series of 12 improved Ka-10M in 1954. Difference between the two model types was mainly in the technical sphere, though vertical tail surfaces were now

dual. Ka-10M were allotted to the Soviet whaling fleet but also served on ice-breakers etc.

Soon the Red Navy became more exacting, deciding that a tiny helicopter with only one open seat had limited uses. They demanded of Kamov a two-seat helicopter with robust fuselage, greater lifting capacity and the well-tried coaxial rotor system. They wanted to use them for reconnaissance, ice patrol and other tasks, predominantly in Arctic regions.

At the beginning of 1952, V V Vinickii was able to test the first prototype, Ka-15. Kamov once again proved his worth as a designer, for the machine passed its plant and state tests with hardly any trouble and could be immediately put on the production line. Ka-15 had two seats side-by-side in a closed cabin. Behind the rotor axle was an AI-14V nine-cylinder radial engine of 225/225mhp and the fuselage ended in a multiple rudder.

On both sides of the fuselage various containers could be mounted – for a stretcher, mail cargo, or, on civilian helicopters, tanks with chemicals for agricultural use. Civilian helicopters were designated Ka-15M and used mainly in Northern and Middle Asian regions of the USSR for they were especially reliable under all meteorological conditions. From 1960 onwards all Ka-15M were driven by more powerful 270/280mhp AI-14VF engines.

Ka-15M also found its way into the FAI record list. In May 1958 Vinickii averaged 162.784kph

Ka-15 was quickly into production after sailing through its tests in 1952.

Mainly a novelty at public events, Kamov's Ka-10 (left) was restricted to just four production examples during 1949. A further 12 improved Ka-10M versions (below) were manufactured in 1954 to serve on whalers and ice-breakers.

The four-seater Ka-18 drew on Ka-15 for its basic components.

over 100km and a year later achieved 170.455kph on a 500km course.

Ka-15's good lifting reserve power could be fully utilised and in 1956 Kamov used the basic parts to create a four-seater Ka-18. For all practical purposes only the fuselage was different, having a broader, longer cabin in which were two pairs of seats in tandem. Ka-18 could also be used as an ambulance aircraft, in which case the stretcher was inserted through a loading hatch in the front. From 1960 onwards it was also delivered with AI-14VF, used for military and civilian purposes, and an agricultural variant was issued with the same equipment as Ka-15M. Ka-18 received a gold medal at the world exhibition 'Expo 1958' in Brussels.

In 1964 the Soviet press announced that Kamov was designing a new helicopter especially suitable for agriculture but adaptable as a flying crane or passenger and cargo aircraft. Costs for spraying a hectare were to be kept below three roubles and bearing this in mind Kamov used a piston engine – the new AI-14VFR-26 of 325mhp.

Prototype of Ka-26 was displayed in Moscow's Sokolniki Park at the beginning of 1965 and soon the technical details and performance were revealed. Only in its well-tried coaxial rotor system did the aircraft suggest its origins. The fuselage was quite short with a two-seat cabin, pressurised to avoid penetration by chemicals. Behind the cabin was a short, thick boom containing the two AI-14VFR-26. Two parallel tail booms extended back and the helicopter stood on a four-wheel undercarriage.

All loads could be mounted on the main boom, e.g. a tank for 900kg chemicals with dry or liquid spray apparatus; a cabin pod for six passengers or 700kg load. Alternatively, a transport platform can be fixed or the space kept free for heavy external stores. Maximum speed is 175kph, range 600km (with six passengers, 400km) and flight duration is up to 10 hours.

There was widespread use of synthetic material in Ka-26's airframe. Rotor blades were exclusively glassfibre and synthetics constituted a full 30% of the airframe's empty weight. Ka-26 was also exported to the West.

A Ka-26 with cargo container removed while in the background is one with its container in place.

IN THE MIDDLE of the fifties all the great powers were planning for tactically faster and more mobile conduct of warfare. USSR commanders demanded new, powerful methods of air transport capable of carrying the heaviest of weapons to battle fronts. But such aircraft were needed in non-military operations too, delivering extra heavy cargoes into wild regions where there were neither railways nor roads.

Technical and military preparations were kept a close secret, but at the beginning of November 1957 the FAI received notifications from the USSR about new records set by a hitherto unknown heavy duty helicopter. Some of them were astonishing, like that of R I Kapreljan who had taken a full 12,004kg to 2,432m on October 30, 1957.

Soon the designation of this gigantic new aircraft was revealed; the machine was called Mi-6 and it was designed by M L Mil.

Mi-6 was the largest helicopter built to date. Its five-blade main rotor was 35m in diameter and stood 9m high. The cargo cabin, 2.65m wide, 2.5m high and 12m long, could carry 70 people up to 800km and maximum capacity was 120.

But transport of people is only a sideline of this giant. Its main use is movement of heavy military materials, excavators, large machine parts, pipeline parts etc. In the 1961 Tushino parade six Mi-6 helicopters carried a complete airborne unit with heavy weapons and transporters. Aeroflot also uses some as flying cranes or to transport heavy caterpillar tractors, oil pipelines, pylons etc.

Mil's giant Mi-6 is driven by two D-25V (TB-2MB) gas turbines designed by Solovjev. The two turbines of 4,750/550 metric shaft horse power each lie side-by-side on top of the fuselage and drive a common gear. If one of the turbines were to stop, revolutions of the second would be automatically increased. There are five crew members, concentrated in the nose.

Five prototypes were built, the first flying in September 1957 with R I Kapreljan at the controls. On flight tests of the prototypes, international FAI records were beaten a total of fourteen times. From 1959 to 1962, Mi-6 and their crews created a whole series of standards with loads of 1,000kg upwards. One impressive record was set on September 13, 1962, when Kapreljan climbed with 20,000kg to a height of 2,738m and the maximum 20,117kg load was lifted to 2,000m.

What mainly surprised people about these heavy helicopters were their speed records. In September 1962 several crews launched a real assault on the FAI list for speeds over 500 and 1,000km courses, without loads or carrying up to 2,000kg. One peak performance was 315.657kph over 500km and 300.377kph over 1,000km flown on September 15, 1962. Two years later, on September 26, 1964, the same crew under B Galickii averaged 340.15kph over 100km.

For speed flights the prototypes were given short wings on both sides of the fuselage. These cantilever wings alter automatically with the position of the rotor blades, so they always operate under the best possible angle of incidence. The wings take over part of the weight in high speed flight and thus considerably relieve the main rotor. They were fitted to the standard version of all production helicopters issued from 1960 onwards.

Mi-6 was first displayed abroad at the 1965 Paris Aerosalon. In 1966 Mi-6 visited Holland and a year later was in Paris again. A commercial variant for 80 passengers could be seen there along with a fire extinguishing version. The latter stayed in France for quite a long time but suffered an accident while fighting a forest fire in the South of France and was completely wrecked. This type of Mi-6 contains 12,000 litres of water which can be discharged within 12 seconds. Filling up over a stretch of water, without touching down, takes only two minutes.

At Tushino in 1961 another giant helicopter was demonstrated. It was reminiscent of Mi-6 but fuselage was particularly slender and the helicopter had an unusually high and wide-track four-wheel undercarriage. This was Mi-10, at that time still known by the model designation V-10.

Mi-10 is a reconstruction of Mi-6 for the transport of extra heavy loads on a platform or suspended under the fuselage. The platform is 3.5m wide, 8.5m long and takes loads up to 3.8m tall and 15,000kg in weight. Men travelling with the load are accommodated in a fuselage cabin for 28 passengers. With 12 tons load and cruising speed of 180kph, Mi-10 had a range of 200km. On both sides of the fuselage large fuel tanks of 3,600 litres can be mounted.

The Mi-10 also got among FAI records. In October 1961 the aircraft climbed to 2,326m with 15,103kg load, but this was soon beaten by Mi-6. In 1965 Mi-10 reclaimed it, lifting 25,105kg to 2,840m. Pilot Alferov set a further four records on May 28, 1965 – the heaviest load lifted to 2,000m and altitude records for 15, 20 and 25 ton loads. Two days after this achievement Kolochenko set another record when he climbed to 7,151m with 5,000kg.

On all these flights a special version of Mi-10

Left: Mil's Mi-6 was the largest helicopter built at the time of its introduction, the first of five prototypes flying in September 1957.

Centre: Mi-10 was built for the transport of particularly heavy loads suspended under its fuselage.

Below: Virtually an airliner body with rotors, Mi-12 could lift over 40,000kg and set a string of world records.

was used, without superfluous parts and with a short, simplified and covered tricycle undercarriage.

The short undercarriage, but this time in four-wheel version, featured on a further Mi-10 variant, crane helicopter Mi-10K for carrying the heaviest items over short distances. The crane pilot works from a glazed cabin under the fuselage, facing toward the rear so that he can see the loads. He steers the helicopter from here, but as a precaution there is second pilot in the main cabin. Mi-10K lifted 10,000kg under normal conditions and new 6,500 metric shaft horsepower engines were to give it capacity for 14,000kg.

Development of the Mi-6 and Mi-10 was certainly a high technical achievement. These helicopters remained unrivalled for a long period and it seemed that their position was unassailable. The American United Aircraft Corporation awarded Mil and his assistants the I I Sikorsky Prize in recognition of services to helicopter technology in 1961.

The rival to Mi-6 and Mi-10 came from Mil's own stable. On February 22, 1969, test pilot V P Koloshenko set up a string of records with this new and hitherto little known machine, V-12 or Mi-12. These were immediately reported to the FAI and, given the figures, observers were entitled to assume that this helicopter must have been the biggest in the world. Photographs released some years later confirmed the assumption.

Koloshenko reached 2,951m with a load of 31,030kg and thus became the holder of five world records – for the load categories of 15,000kg, 20,000kg, 25,000kg, 30,000kg and for the greatest load lifted to 2,000m. On August 6, 1969, Koloshenko's crew improved on this performance once again, reaching 2,250m with 40,204kg.

CHAPTER 49

Intermediate Turbine Helicopters

INTERNATIONAL progress in the development and running of small gas turbines meant a new wave of helicopter designs. Potential was greatly increased with the introduction of these light but powerful engines. It was relatively easy to master the design technique for the big turbines but little ones presented different problems and the first successes were not achieved until about 1959. Designer S P Isotov played a leading role.

If we take the first two Soviet helicopters with small gas turbines and compare them with models Mi-1 and Mi-4, it is easy to see the advantages. The new Mi-2, which directly derived from the three-seat Mi-1, accommodates six to eight people in a broad and comfortable cabin which takes up almost the entire fuselage nacelle. Engines are on the top of the fuselage, outside the work space. Mi-8, derived from Mi-4, can carry as many as 28 passengers plus crew of three while the original model could carry at most 12 passengers.

The two helicopters had already been built and tested by 1960, but not until Autumn 1961 were the Press allowed to write about them, still known under designations V-2 and V-8. The Mi-2 has its two Isotov GTD-350 gas turbines of 395 metric shaft horsepower over the fuselage in front of the rotor axle. The rotor has four blades taken over from Mi-1 with diameter enlarged from 14.36 to 14.5m. Tail boom and rotor also originate in Mi-1 and in order to have more fuselage space the fuel tanks are mounted externally.

Mi-2 went on the production line in 1964 and has seen service with Aeroflot and the military aviation department. As the Soviet aircraft industry became overloaded and the Polish industry was threatened by shortage of work, the business of production, further development and sale of Mi-2 was handed over to Polish plant WSK-Swidnik by an agreement of January 1964. Mi-1 had already been built here under licence, so the introduction of a new variant created no difficulties. Polish Mi-2 were known as 'Marabut' and development plans counted on production continuing up to 1975.

Variants for passenger transport, cargo, ambulance and agriculture were produced. The agricultural version carries chemical tanks on each side of the fuselage containing a total of 1,000 litres. It is able to spray a swathe width of 40 to 45m.

Mi-2 was on the FAI list for a short time when female pilot Tatjana Russinjan reached a speed of 253.818kph over a closed circuit of 100km on May 14, 1963.

The larger Mi-8 was presented, together with the Mi-2, to representatives of the Soviet government in September 1962. At that time it provisionally had a single gas turbine of 2,700 metric shaft horse-power designed by Soloviev and had already been flown with this engine in 1962.

On September 17, 1962, shortly before demonstration of the first prototype, the second Mi-8 made its first flight, this time equipped with two new Isotov TV-2-117 gas turbines, each of 1,500mhp. The five-blade main rotor was new, having an electric de-icing system instead of the fluid method used on Mi-4. Cabin is adapted for 24 to 28 passengers and 12 stretchers or 4,000kg. Entry is from the side and a wide cargo door in the tail accepts bulky loads. Cruising speed of Mi-8 is 200kph, range with 3,000kg is 400km and with 4,000kg load only 100km.

Mi-8 also had several records to its credit. First two were in 1965 when the aircraft reached 201.834kph on a closed circuit of 2,000km and made a flight of 2,465.736km. On August 23, 1967, a female crew under Inna Kopets created a further two records: 273 and 258kph over circuits of 500 and 1,000km respectively.

Kamov's OKB, too, made use of gas turbines for his new helicopters, but also kept the well tried coaxial rotor system. In 1961 the three man Ka-20 was demonstrated in Tushino, much bigger and more powerful than Ka-18. The spacious fuselage had two big, wagon-like doors on both sides and was equipped with two radar display panels. This machine belonged to the Red Navy and was used to combat submarines with beams either side of the fuselage carrying rocket missiles. On top are two Isotov GTP-3 gas turbines arranged side-by-side, each of 900 metric shaft horse-power.

Kamov used the successful Ka-20 design for civilian work as well. Its big cabin and simple unencumbered entry make the helicopter a good commercial aircraft, especially for cargo transport. And as the helicopter with its coaxial rotor system is especially stable when taking on a load in flight, it is especially well adapted for use as a flying crane.

Designation of the civilian machine is Ka-25, built in standard version for 12 passengers or 2,500kg cargo. The crane variant, displayed in Paris in 1967, is called Ka-25K. It is distinguished by a thickly glazed cabin under the fuselage nose. From this the pilot steers the helicopter when accomplishing crane work, on which loads of up to 2,000kg are lifted and transported. Range is up to 660km and maximum speed 220kph.

Mi-2, directly derived from Mi-1, seats six to eight people in its cabin.

Above: With its five-blade rotor Mi-8 cruises at 200kph and dates from 1962.

Below: Ka-20 retained the coaxial rotor system. This version is equipped with radar and missiles for anti-submarine work.

CHAPTER 50

Compound Helicopters

ONE OF THE BIGGEST surprises of the 1961 Tushino air parade was the demonstration of N I Kamov's giant compound helicopter, Ka-22 'Vintokryl'. This was the first sign that Soviet designers were busying themselves with machines that had short or VTO landing and take-off.

Ka-22 combines the qualities of helicopter and gyroplane with those of a classic fixed-wing aircraft. The machine is not unlike original Bratukhin helicopters, a gigantic high-wing monoplane with big cargo door in the nose and a cargo ramp in the rear. The pilot's cockpit is very high.

Tips of the 28m span wing bear large nacelles housing Solovjev TB-2 turboprops, each of 5,600mhp. These drive either four-blade propellers or the two 26m diameter rotors via complicated gear and coupling systems. On take-off, full turbine performance is transmitted to the rotors so that the machine takes off vertically, supported by the booster thrust from the turbine exhaust nozzles which are turned downwards. In transitional flight the helicopter turns into a gyroplane, power is taken from the rotors and transmitted increasingly to the propellers. The wings are thus given more and more lift and the aircraft flies like a standard fixed wing aircraft.

So the Ka-22 flies faster than a helicopter but retains its important take-off and landing qualities as well as the ability to stop in the air.

The gigantic fuselage of Ka-22 can take 80-100 soldiers or passengers and can also accommodate vehicles. As for its performances, we only know what is revealed by the official data for FAI. Shortly after its first Tushino air display on October 7, 1961, the crew of D Yefremov reached a record speed of 356.3kph over a 15/25km course. This performance provided the first entry under class E.2 for convertiplanes. The second entry was provided when Ka-22 climbed with 14,000kg to 2,588m and took a record load of 16,485kg to 2,000m on November 24, 1961.

Since this time we have learned nothing further about the Kamov Ka-22 or other designs of this kind. It would seem that the Soviets have given up this over complicated technology and are continuing with the separate design of aircraft and helicopters.

Below: The Ka-22 'Vintokryl', Kamov's design combining the qualities of helicopter, gyroplane and fixed wing aircraft.

Helicopters

TWO OKB (*Opytnyi Konstruktorskoe Byuro* =Experimental Design Bureau) are still active in the field of helicopter development, one named after Nikolai Il'ich Kamov, who died on November 24, 1973, and the other after Mikhail Leont'evich Mil, who died on January 31, 1970. Kamov was succeeded by S Mikheyev and Mil by M Tischenko.

The Kamov bureau is associated with compact helicopters of co-axial, twin-rotor layout, without long tail booms and anti-torque tail-rotor, which makes them very suitable for shipboard use.

The Ka-25 military helicopter was developed from Ka-20, which was first shown publicly at the 1961 Tushino airshow, carrying missiles. Ka-25 was developed in two versions, both allotted reporting name 'Hormone', the "Hormone-A" being a version for Anti-Submarine Warfare (ASW) with smaller chin-radome than the -B version which is reported to have a missile guidance role. Both are deployed on the carriers 'Kiev' and 'Moskva' plus other warships.

A civil flying crane conversion is designated Ka-25K. This was shown at the 1967 Paris Salon.

Empty weight of Ka-25K is 4,400kg, maximum payload 2,000kg, maximum take-off weight 7,300kg, normal cruise speed 193kph and range with standard fuel plus reserve 400km. Rotor-diameter is 15.74m and overall length 9.832m (without rotor-blades). Two 900shp Glushenkov turboshaft engines are installed, mounted side by side on top of the cabin.

Cabin of the civil variant can accommodate 12 passengers. A detachable under-nose gondola, containing a rearward-facing pilot's seat with dual controls for use during handling of freight in the crane-version, replaces the military radome. A similar gondola is found on Mi-10K of the Mil bureau.

Ka-26 has been described in detail earlier, but a development of Ka-25, the Ka-32, was shown at Moscow's Exhibition of Achievements of the National Economy. It is intended to perform reconnaissance missions and search and rescue duties in all-weather from ice-breakers, such as the atomic-powered Lenin, Sibir and Arktika. Range is 185km and a weight of 5,000kg can be carried on an external sling.

The Ka-32S was shown at the 1985 Paris Salon. According to an Avia Export brochure there are two versions, transport and naval, the latter being employed for checking ice movements in Siberian waters. Two TV3-117 engines allow a maximum speed of 250kph and 11,000kg take-off weight. Rotor diameter is 15.9m and length (without blades) 11.3m.

On January 29, 1985, N Yeremina lifted a 1,000kg load to 7,305m and 2,000kg to 6,400m with a Ka-32S. T Suyewa also reached an altitude of 8,250m and these achievements were recognised as world records by the FAI.

In late 1981 an anti-submarine helicopter, the Ka-27, now known in the West by reporting name 'Helix', was seen operating from the Soviet destroyer 'Udaloi' during exercises. Major change is a roomier cabin and twin vertical tailplane layout instead of three fins. Like the Ka-25 version, rotor blades can be folded aft for storage. A number of sensors have been reported in Western magazines. There are two versions – 'Helix-A' and 'B'.

Kamov Ka-126 is a turboshaft variant of Ka-26 and was announced by the chief designer of the Kamov-bureau, S V Mikheyev, in 1979.

Kamov Ka-27 aboard a Soviet warship. It has the NATO reporting name 'Helix'.
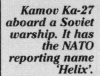

In 1959 the Mil bureau developed a small, single-seat, experimental helicopter with a two-blade rotor powered by two ramjets at the blade ends. It was called W-7. Empty weight was 730kg, flying weight 835kg and rotor diameter 11.6m.

Mi-1, -2, -4, -4, -6, -8, -10 and their various variants have been described, but Mi-12 was only mentioned briefly. This giant helicopter was first reported in March 1969, when a number of weight-to-altitude records were smashed. On February 22, 1969, it took off from Podmoskovnoe with a 31,030kg payload climbing, to a height of 2,951m. Pilot Vasily Kolochenko far exceeded his own record on August 6, 1969, by lifting 40,204.5kg to 2,255m in the same helicopter, which is powered by four 6,500shp Solovyev D-25VF turboshaft engines.

There are two cockpits, the lower one seating pilot, co-pilot, flight engineer and electrician, while navigator and radio-operator are accommodated in the top cockpit. Main cargo cabin has rails in the roof for an electrically operated, platform-mounted travelling crane with four loading points, each capable of lifting 2,500kg. There are two side-by-side five-bladed main rotors, each of 35m diameter, fuselage length is 37m and overall height 12.5m. The freight compartment is 28.15m long, 4.4m wide and 4.4m high.

Normal payload is 25,00kg (VTOL), 30,000kg (STOL), normal take-off weight 97,000kg and maximum take-off weight 105,000kg. Cruising speed is up to 240kph, service ceiling 3,500m and range with 35,400kg payload 500km. The Mi-12, reporting name 'Homer', was first shown at the 1971 Paris airshow.

A land-based ASW helicopter, the Mi-14, is clearly derived from the successful Mi-8 transport helicopter. Powerplant, rotor system and much of the airframe structure are very similar to those of Mi-8, but Mi-14 has a retractable undercarriage, chin radar, flying-boat type hull, rear-set sponsons and a small pontoon beneath the tail boom end. A MAD 'bird' is carried beneath the tail boom root. Like the Sikorsky SH-3 class the Mi-14, known as 'Haze', is capable of water landings, but with chin-radar is not likely to be normal practice. It is powered by two 2,200shp Isotov TV-3 turboshaft engines. 'Haze-A' is the ASW variant while 'Haze-B' is employed for mine countermeasures.

Also derived from Mi-8 is the civil Mi-17 light-to-medium lift helicopter, which was shown at the 1981 Paris Salon. It is powered by two 1,900shp Isotov TV3-117MT turboshafts and can lift 4,000kg inside its freight cabin and 3,000kg on a sling. The hold has a length of 5.34m, width is 2.34m and height 1.8m. Maximum take-off weight is 13,000kg but normally 11,100kg. Cruising at 240kph with normal payload gives a range of 495km, extending to 950km with extra fuel. Rotor diameter is 21.3m and length (without blades) 18.4m. Mi-17 can also accommodate 24 passengers or 12 stretchers.

A new military helicopter, first observed in 1973, is Mi-24, reporting name 'Hind', clearly derived from the Mi-8 transport helicopter but combining transport with straightforward attack capabilities. Mi-24 in its original version featured one large cockpit with flat windows. Two more variants were observed, one with straight weapon-carrying wings, whereas the other two

Ka-32 displayed among the Soviet exhibits at Paris in 1985.

A formidable weapons platform is the Mi-24 'Hind' shown in its early form (above) and the 'Hind-D' version (below) with tandem cockpits and chin turret.

Mi-14 is a land-based ASW helicopter with retractable undercarriage.

and all new versions have pronounced anhedral.

A completely redesigned version, 'Hind-D' and 'E', has two tandem cockpits with bubble canopies and a chin-turret with four-barrel gun. Aft of the turret are two more installations with sensors and/or gun-sights. The auxiliary wings carry bombs, rocket-pods and guided missiles. A cargo cabin, which is much smaller than that of Mi-8, accommodates 12 fully equipped troops. Mi-24 is powered by two 1,500shp Isotov TV-2 turboshafts, later versions are reported to have two 2,200shp TV-3s. There are reports about an A-10 designation used in connection with speed records.

The Mi-24 is a formidable weapons platform, carrying four pods each containing thirty-two 57mm unguided rockets, four anti-tank guided missiles, and one four-barrel cannon. Pilot is in the back-seat, co-pilot/gunner sitting in front and much lower. Mi-24 has been exported to a number of countries.

'Hind-D' is armed with four AT-2 'Swatter' and 'Hind-E' with AT-6 'Spiral' missiles.

Along with Mi-17 the Mil-bureau showed 1981 Paris Salon spectators the world's largest helicopter, Mi-26. Bearing the reporting name 'Halo', this heavylift helicopter is powered by two 11,400shp Lotarev D-136 turboshafts. Diameter of the eight-bladed main rotor is 32m and fuselage length (including tail rotor) 33.73m. Freight cabin extends 12m, or 15m with ramp extended. It is 3.2m wide and 3.15m high.

Mi-26's take-off weight is 56,000kg (normally 49,500kg) and up to 28,200kg can be carried internally or externally with a cruise speed of up to 295kph, range at maximum payload is 500km and at normal take-off weight 800km. An overhead crane is designed to handle a 5,000kg cargo.

A number of weight-to-altitude world records were ratified by FAI: 10,000kg to 6,400m (pilot G Karapetyan), 15,000kg to 5,500m (Petrov), 20,000kg to 4,600m (Kholupov) and 25,000kg to 4,100m (Karapetyan).

Two new attack helicopters have been reported in the West – 'Havoc' (some reports say Mi-28) and 'Hokum'.

Currently the world's largest helicopter, Mi-26 has lifted 25,000kg to 4,100m.

Tu-16s patrol against a dramatic background of cloud and snow-covered wilderness. They have a wing span of 34.8m and a range of up to 5,760km. Power comes from two 8,750kp AM-3M engines.

ALL DATA given in the following specification tables is as detailed as space allows and uses metric scales. Gaps appear among the figures where information is no longer known or not available. The following conversion factors may be useful:

- To convert metres (m) into feet, multiply by 3.281.
- To convert kilograms (kg) into pounds, multiply by 2.205.
- To convert kilometres (km) into miles, multiply by 0.6215.
- To convert kilometres per hour (kph) into miles per hour, multiply by 0.6215.
- To convert square metres (sq m or m^2) into square feet, multiply by 10.76.
- To convert tonnes (t) into tons, multiply by 1.016.
- Metric horse power (mhp) is equivalent to standard horse power.
- To convert kilograms static thrust (kp) into pounds static thrust, multiply by 2.205.

Armament abbreviations

mg = machine gun; c = cannon; hmg = heavy calibre machine gun; rc = recoilless cannon; mmg = moveable machine gun; mc = moveable cannon; mhmg = moveable heavy calibre machine guns; ms = missiles.

Designations			Crew plus passengers or load	Dimensions			Weights	
Main designation	Other designations	Year		Span	Length	Wing area	Empty	Take-off
				m	m	m²	kg	kg

Fighters

Main designation	Other designations	Year	Crew	Span	Length	Wing area	Empty	Take-off
I-1		1923	1	10.8	7.3	23.5	1,100	1,500
I-1	IL-400	1923	1	10.8	7.32 (8.2)	20	1,112	1,530
I-2bis		1924	1	10.8	7.32	23.4	1,149	1,575
I-3		1927	1	11	8.08	27.85	1,400	1,863
I-3U		1959	1	9.3		27	8,500	10,000
I-4	ANT-5	1927	1	11.4	7.28	23.8	978	1,430
I-5	VT-11	1930	1	10.24	6.78	21.25	955	1,355
I-6		1930	1	10	6.8	20.5	868	1,280
I-7	HD-37c	1932	1	10	6.95	26.7	1,296	1,729
I-8	ANT-13 Jockey	1930	1	9.03		20.09	1,000	1,424
I-12	ANT-23	1934	1	15.6	9.5	30		2,400
I-14	ANT-31	1933	1	11.2	6.1	16.8	1,100	1,455
I-142	I-14bis	1934	1	11.2	6.1	17	1,169	1,524
I-15	TsKB-3	1933	1	9.75	6.1	21.9	1,106	1,415
I-152	I-15bis	1936	1	10.2	6.2	22.5	1,320	1,730
I-153	I-15ter	1938	1	10	6.1	22.1	1,348	1,860-2,010
I-16 prototype	TsKB-12	1933	1	9	5.9	14.54	1,100	1,345
I-16 type 4		1934	1	9	5.9	14.54	1,160	1,420
I-16 type 5		1934	1	9	5.9	14.54	1,200	1,460
I-16 type 6		1937	1	9	5.9	14.54	1,260	1,660
I-16 type 10		1937	1	9	5.98	14.54	1,350	1,716
I-17 type 17		1938	1	9	5.95	14.54	1,495	1,810
I-16 type 18		1939	1	9	6.04	14.54	1,428	1,830
I-16 type 24		1939	1	9	6.04	14.54	1,475	1,878
I-16 type 24		1939	1	9	6.13	14.54	1,490	1,941
I-16P		1938	1	9	5.9	14.54	1,508	1,670
I-16TK		1939	1	9	59	14.54	1,443	1,840
I-17.1	TsKB-15	1934	1	10.2	7.3	17.75		1,655
I-17.2	TsKB-19	1935	1	10.2	7.3	17.90		1,950
I-21	TsKB-32	1936	1	10	7	18.1	1,716	2,125
I-28.1		1939	1	9.6	8.54	16.5	1,800	2,660
I-28.2		1939	1	9.6	8.54	16.5	1,850	2,720
I-28	Yak-5	1940	1	9.74	8.5	17.15		2,990
I-110		1942	1	10.2	9.91	18.73	3,285	3,980
1-180-2		1939	1	10.1	7	17.17	1,802	2,175
I-180Sh		1939	1	10.1	6.9	16.1		2,675
I-185RM(03)	I-187	1940	1	9.8	8	15.53		3,119
I-185I(ID)		1941	1	9.8	8.05	15.53	2,437	3,328
I-185(R4)		1941	1	9.8	8.05	15.53	2,595	3,485
I-190GK		1940	1	10.2				
I-207		1939	1	7	6.35	18		1,950
I-211		1947	1	12.25	11.54	25		7,450
I-211(Ye)		1942	1	13	9.2	22.44		
I-212		1947	2	16.20	12.98	33	5,130	9,250
I-215		1947	1	12.25	14.54	25		6,890

Number of engines	Type	Output or thrust	Maximum speed	Ceiling	Range	S = Series production	Guns	Bombs
		mhp/kp	kph	m	km			kg
1	Liberty	400	240	5,500	650	-	2mg	
1	M-5	400	264	6,750	650	s	2mg	
1	M-5	400	235	5,340	600	s	2mg	
1	BMW-VI Z	500	278	7,250	590	s	2mg	
1	AL-7F-1	8,400kp	3,130	18,000	1,800	-		
1	M-22	480	231	7,000	850	s	2mg	
1	M-22	480	278	7,300	660	s	2mg (4mg)	
1	M-22	480	280	7,500	700	-	2mg	
1	M-17	500/730	290	7,200	700	s	2mg	
1	Curtiss V-1570	625-700	303	8,590	250	s	2mg	-
2	Bristol Jupiter VI	420/525	300			-	2rc, 1mg	
1	Bristol Mercury VS-2	570	384	9,400	800	-	2mg, 2c	
1	M-25	715	414	9,200	800	-	2mg, 2c	
1	M-25	715	350	7,520	725	s	2mg (4mg)	200
1	M-25V	750	370	9,000	530	s	4mg	200
1	M-62R	800	444	10,700	480-900	s	4mg	200
1	M-25	480	359	7,180	720	s	2mg	200
1	M-25	715	455	9,280	820	s	2mg	200
1	M-25	715	454	9,200	820	s	4mg	200
1	M-25A	730	440	9,100	810	s	2mg	200
1	M-25V	750	440	8,270	800	s	4mg	200
1	M-25V	750	425	7,900	800	s	2c, 2mg	200
1	M-62R	800/920	464	9,470	810	s	4mg	200
1	M-62R	800/920	489	11,000	740	s	2c, 2mg	200
1	M-63	1,000	462	9,700	700	-	2c, 2mg	200
1	M-25V	750	440	9,000	550	s	2c	
1	M-25TK	750	494	11,000	800	s	4mg	
1	Hispano Suiza 12Ydrs	860	455	9,900	790	-	2c, 2mg	
1	M-100	860	491	9,700	790	-	1c, 4mg	
1	M-34RNF	1,275	550	12,000	760	-		
1	M-87A	950	545	10,500	800	-	2c, 2mg (2c, 1hmg)	100
1	M-87B	1,000	576	10,800	800	-	2c, 1hmg	100
1	M-105PD	1,220	665	12,200		-	1c, 2hmg	
1	VK-107P	1,400	610	10,000		-	1c, 2hmg	500
1	M-87B	950	540	10,250	900	-	2c	400
1	M-88R	1,000	571	11,600	900	s	2hmg, 2mg	400
1	M-81	1,200	600	10,250	900	-	2hmg, 2mg	400
1	M-82A	1,600	626	11,000	950	-	3c	400
1	ASh-71	1,700	680	11,000	835	-	2c, 2hmg	
1	M-88TK	900	490	12,400		-		
1	M-62	850	436	9,200	700	-		
2	AL-1	1,000kp				-	3c	
1	ASh-82F	1,550/1,700	670			-	2c	
2	R.R. Nene	2,270kp	1,000	14,800	3,100	-	3c	
2	R.R. Derwent	1,590kp	970		2,300	-	3c	

Designations			Crew plus passengers or load	Dimensions			Weights		
Main designation	Other designations	Year		Span	Length	Wing area	Empty	Take-off	
				m	m	m²	kg	kg	
I-220(A)	MiG-11	1942	1	11	9.5	22.44		3,730	
I-221(2A)	MiG-7	1943	1	13	9.55	22.44		3,800	
I-222(3A)	MiG-7	1944	1	13	9.60	22.44		3,790	
I-224(4A)	MiG-7	1944	1	13	9.5	22.44			
I-225(5A)		1945	1	13	9.6	22.44			
I-230(D)	MiG-11	1942	1	10.2	8.62	17.44	2,612	3,260	
I-231(2D)	MiG-3DD	1943	1	10.2	8.62	17.44	2,700	3,287	
I-250(N)		1945	1	11.05	8.75	15		3,680	
I-270(Zh)		1946	1	7.75	8.77	12	1,900	4,120	
I-302		1943	1	11.4	8	17.8			
I-320(R)		1950	1	14.2	15.77	41.2	7,367	10,265	
IP-1	DG-52	1934	1	10.97	7.23	19.98	1,174	1,740	
IP-4	DG-53	1934	1	9.6	7.08	16.36		1,549	
IP-21		1940	1	11	9	15.8		2,670	
IS-1	I-220	1940	1	8.6	6.69	20.8(13)		2,300	
I-Z	TsKB No7	1932	1	11.5	7.65	19.5	1,180	1,648	
ITP(M-1)		1942	1	10	8.95	16.45	2,960	3,570	
BI		1942	1	6.58	6.4	7	790	1,650	
2I-N1		1926	2	12	9.75	27.15	1,153	1,700	
DI-2		1929	2	11.8	8.2	31.8	1,557	2,122	
DI-3		1931	2	11.8	7.8	30.1	1,487	2,020	
DI-4		1933	2	13.3	8.5	23.9	1,448	1,949	
DI-6	TsKB-11	1934	2	10	7	23.15	1,360	1,955	
DIP	ANT-29	1935	2	19.19	13.2	55.1	3,900	5,300	
G-38		1936	3	13.6		27		4,320	
Gu-82		1941	1	9.8	8.75	17.51			
Il-1		1944	1	13.4	11.2	30	4,285	5,320	
Kr-6	ANT-7	1930	3	23.2	14.75	80	3,898	5,240	
LaGG-1	I-22	1940	1	9.8	8.81	17.51	2,968	3,380	
LaGG-3	I-301	1940	1	9.8	8.81	17.51	2,789	3,268	
LaG-5		1941	1	9.80	8.71	17.51	2,605	3,308	
La-5FN		1943	1	9.8	8.67	17.59	2,605	3,320	
La-7	La-120	1943	1	9.8	8.6	17.59	2,608	3,265	
La-9	La-130	1946	1	9.8	8.63	17.72	2,638	3,676	
La-11	La-140	1946	1	9.8	8.62	17.72	2,770	3,996	
La-15	La-174	1948	1	8.83	9.56	16.16	2,575	3,850	
La-120R		1945	1	9.8	8.75	17.59	2,770	3,470	
La-126PVRD		1946	1	9.8	8.5	17.5	2,710	3,300	
La-150		1946	1	8.2	9.42	12.15	2,059	2,961	
La-150M		1947	1	8.2	9.42	12.15	2,369	3,338	
La-152		1947	1	8.2	9.4	12.15	2,310	3,239	
La-160	Strelka	1947	1	8.95	10.06	15.9	2,738	4,060	
La-168		1948	1	9.5	10.56	18.08	2,973	4,412	
La-176		1948	1	8.59	10.97	18.25	3,111	4,631	

Number of engines	Power group		Performances				S = Series production	Armament	
	Type	Output or thrust	Maximum speed	Ceiling	Range			Guns	Bombs
		mhp/kp	kph	m	km				kg
1	AM-39	1,700	697	11,000	630		-	4c	
1	AM-39ATK-2B	1,550	690	13,000	1,000		-	4c	
1	AM-39B TK-2B	1,900	691	14,500	1,000		-	4c	
1				14,100			-	2c	
1	AM-42F	2,200	726				-	2c	
1	AM-35A	1,200	660	12,000	1,300		-	3hmg	
1	AM-39	1,700	707	11,400	1,350		-	2c	
1	VK-107R	1,700	825	11,900	1,818		-	1c, 2hmg	
1	Kholshchevniko	300 kp							
1	RD-2M-3V	1,450 kp	1,000	18,000	4.3 mins		-	2c	
1	NII-3	1,400 kp					-	4c	
2	RD-45F	2,270 kp	1,060	15,100			-	3c	
1	M-25	715	410	7,700	600-1,000		s	1mg, 2rc	
1	Wright Cyclone	640	435	8,300	600-830		-	1mg, 2rc	
1	M-105P	1,050	573	10,600	800		-	1c, 2mg	
1	M-63	900	453	8,800	600		-	4mg	
1	M-22	480	259	7,000	600		s	2rc, 1mg	
2	VK-107P	1,700	655	10,400	1,280		-	3c	
1	D-1A	1,100 kp	600	9,000			-	2c	
1	Napier Lion	450	268	7,100	800		-	2mg, 2mmg	
1	M-17	500	256	6,300	510		-	2mg, 2mmg	
1	BMW-VI Z	500	272	6,300	490		-	2mg, 2mmg	
1	Curtiss V-1570	600	266	6,440	500		-	2mg, 2mmg	
1	M-25	715	372	7,700	500		s	4mg, 1mmg	100
2	Hispano Suiza 12Ybrs	760	352				-	1mmg, 2rc	
2	Gnome Rhone K-14	850	550				-	2c, 4mg, 2mmg	
	M-82	1,300					-		
1	AM-42	2,000	580	8,600	1,000		-	2c	
2	M-17	500	240	6,050	1,000		s	4mmg	
1	VK-105P	1,050	605	9,600	556		-	1c, 2hmg	
1	VK-105PF	1,050	535	9,600	660		s	1c, 1hmg	
1	ASh-82	1,330	554	9,500	655		s	2c	
1	ASh-82FN	1,523/1,850	648	11,000	765		s	2c	
1	ASh-82FN	1,523/1,850	680	10,750	635		s	3c	
1	ASh-82FN	1,523/1,850	690	10,800	1,735		s	4c	
1	ASh-82FN	1,523/1,850	674	10,250	2,550		s	3c	
1	RD-500	1,600 kp	1,026	13,500	1,170		s	2c	
1	ASh-82FN	1,523/1,850	725				-	2c	
1	RD-1Ch3	300 kp							
1	ASh-82FN	1,523/1,850	692				-	3c	
2	PVRD-430	300 kp							
1	RD-10	850/900 kp	850	12,500	700		-	2c	
1	RD-10	900 kp	850	12,500	500		-	2c	
1	RD-10	850/900 kp	778	12,500	500		-	3c	
1	RD-10F	1,100 kp	1,050	11,000	500		-	2c	
1	R.R. Nene	2,270 kp	1,084	14,570	1,275		-	2c	
1	VK-1	2,700 kp	1,105	15,000	1,000		-	2c	

Designations			Crew plus passengers or load	Dimensions			Weights	
Main designation	Other designations	Year		Span	Length	Wing area	Empty	Take-off
				m	m	m²	kg	kg
La-190		1951	1	9.9	16.59	38.93	7,315	9,257
La-200		1949	2	12.92	17.32	40.18	7,675	10,375
La-200B		1952	2	12.96	15.9	40	8,810	11,050
La-250		1955	2	13	22			30,000
Malyutka		1944	1	6.4	6.3	10	818	2,550
MI-3	ANT-21	1933	3	20.76	12.3	55.1	3,800	5,260
MiG-1	I-200	1940	1	10.2	8.16	17.44	2,620	3,071
MiG-3		1941	1	10.2	8.25	17.44	2,595	3,350
MiG-5	DIS	1941	1	15.3	10.5	38.9		8,060
MiG-5	DIS	1942	1	15.3	10.5	38.9		8,000
MiG-7	I-222(3A)	1944	1	13	9.6	22.44		3,800
MiG-9	I-300(F)	1946	1	10	9.75	18.2	3,330	4,860
MiG-9FR		1947	1	10	9.75	18.2	3,570	5,070
MiG-15	S-01 (I-310)	1947	1	10.08	10.04	20.6	3,382-3,780	4,806-5,260
MiG-15bis	SD	1949	1	10.08	10.04	20.6	3,400	4,960-5,786
MiG-17	SI	1951	1	9.63	11.09	22.6	3.798	5.350
MiG-17P		1951	1	9.63	11.26	22.6	3,510	5,550-6,280
MiG-17F		1951	1	9.63	11.26	22.6		5,354-6,069
MiG-17PF		1952	1	9.63	11.36	22.6		5,620-6,552
MiG-19		1952	1	11.1	13.7	23		9,100
MiG-19F		1952	1	9	13.7	25	5,760	8,700
MiG-19 SM-12PM		1957	1	11.1	13.9			
MiG-19 SM-12PMU		1958	1	11.1	14			
MiG-19 SM-50		1959	1					9,000
MiG-21		1955	1	7.6	16.5			5,700
MiG-21F		1959	1	7.15	13.46	23	5,050	7,370
MK-21 Rybka		1923	1					
No 7211		1937	1	7	6.35	18		1,745
P-1 (Sukhoi)		1957	2	10	21.75	36		
Pe-3		1941	2	17.6	12.6	40.5	5,870	7,880
Pe-3bis		1941	2	17.6	12.6	40.5		8,040
Pe-3bis		1941	2	17.16	12.6	20.5	5,900	8,000
RK	LIG-7	1937	2	11.3	7.34	16.56 23.35	667	897
RK-I	RK-800	1940	1	8.2	8.8	11.9 28		3,100
SAM-13		1941	1	8		9		
Sigma	SAM-7	1936	2	9.46	7	20	940	1,480
SK-1		1939	1	7.3	8.3	9.57		2,100
SK-2		1940	1	7.3	8.3	9.57		2,300
STAL-6		1933	1	9.46	6.88	14.3	850	1,080
Su-1	I-330	1940	1	11.5	8.42	19	2,495	2,875

Number of engines	Power group		Performances			S = Series production	Armament	
	Type	Output or thrust	Maximum speed	Ceiling	Range		Guns	Bombs
		mhp/kp	kph	m	km			kg
1	AL-5	5,000 kp	1,190	15,600	1,150	–	2c	
2	VK-1	2,700 kp	1,062	15,150	2,000	–	3c	
2	VK-1	2,700kp	1,030	14,135	960	–	3c	
2	AL-7F	6,000kp	2,000			–		
1	NII-1	1,200 kp				–	2c	
2	M-17b	500	351	7,885	1,200	–	6mmg	
1	AM-35A	1,200	628	12,000	730	s	1hmg, 2mg	
1	AM-35A	1,200	640	12,000	1,195	s	1hmg, 2mg	
2	AM-37	1,400	610	10,800	2,280	–	1c, 6mg	800
2	ASh-82F	1,430	604	9,800	2,500	–	1c, 2hmg, 4mg	800
1	AM-39B-1	1,630/1,900	691	14,500	1,000	–	2c	
2	RD-20	800 kp	911	13,500	800	s	3c	
2	RD-21	1,000kp	965	13,000	800	s	3c	
1	RD-45F	2,270 kp	1,070	15,200	1,450-1,960	s	3c	200
1	VK-1	2,740 kp	1,076	15,500	1,210-2,000	s	3c	400
1	VK-1A	2,700kp	1,070	14,700	1,165-1,735	s	3c	
1	VK-1A	2,700kp	1,085	14,500	1,290	s	3c	
1	VK-1F	2,600/3,380kp	1,130	16,470	1,080	s	3c	
1	VK-1F	2,600/3,380kp	1,123	16,300	1,100	s	3c	
2	VK-5	2,950-4,000 kp	1,445	18,600	2,200	s	2c, rockets	
2	RD-9B	3,150kp	1,452	18,600	2,200	s	2c, rockets	
2	RS-26		1,720	17,400	1,700	–	rockets	
2	RMS-26		1,720	24,000	1,700	–	rockets	
1	RU-15							
2	RD-9BM	3,300kp	1,800	24,000	800	–	2c, rockets	
1	U-19	3,200kp						
1	R-37F	4,300-5,670 kp	M 2	20,000	1,300	s	2c, rockets	
1	R-11F-300	5,750kp	2,125	19,000	1,670	s	2c, rockets	
1						–	2c	
1	M-85	800	416	13,000	700	–		
1	AL-7F	10,000kp	2,050	19,500		–	3c, 50 rockets	
2	VK-105RA TK-2	1,100	523	8,600	1,500	s	2c, 2hmg, 2mg	
2	VK-105RA	1,100	530	9,100	1,500	s	2c, 3hmg, 2mg	
2	VK-105R	1,050	540	9,100	1,000	–	2c, 2hmg, 2mg	
1	M-11	100	150 144	2,900 3,100		–		
1	M-106	1,500	720			–		
2	MV-6	220	509			–		
1	M-34	730	500			–	2mg, 1mmg	
1	M-105	1,050	577			–		
1	M-105	1,050	665	10,300		–	2hmg	
1	Curtiss V-1570	600	420			–		
1	VK-105P	1,050	641	12,500	720	–	1c, 2mg	

413

Designations			Crew plus passengers or load	Dimensions			Weights	
Main designation	Other designations	Year		Span	Length	Wing area	Empty	Take-off
				m	m	m²	kg	kg
Su-3	I-360	1942	1	10.1	8.45	17	2,480	2,860
Su-5	I-107	1945	1	10.56	8.51	17	2,954	3,804
Su-7		1944	1	13.5	9.14	26		4,360
Su-7B		1955	1	9.31	16.61	34	8,620	13,960
Su-9		1946	1	11.2	10.55	26.2	4,060	5,980
Su-9		1956	1	9.4	17.30	25	9,070	13,600
Su-11		1948	1	11.8	10.55	21.4	4,495	6,277
Su-15	P	1948	1	12.87	15.44	36	7,409	10,437
Su-17		1949	1	9.95	15.25	27.5	6,240	7,390
T-405		1960	1					
T-431		1959	1					
Ta-3	(OKO-6bis)	1940	1	12.66	9.83			6,000
TI-28		1940	1	9	7.66	11.6	987	1,157
TIS(A)		1941	2	15.5	11.7	34.85	5,800	7,840
TIS(MA)		1943	2	15.5	11.7	34.85	6,410	9,080
Tu-1	ANT-63P	1945	2	18.86	13.6	48.8	9,460	14,460
Tu-28P		1957	2	19.5	28.5	78	25,000	48,000
VI-100		1939	2	17.16	12.60	40.56		7,260
VP(K)		1944	1	11		16.2	2,727	3,320
Yak-1	I-26	1940	1	10	8.48	17.15	2,330	2,847
Yak-1M		1942	1	10	8.48	17.15		2,655
Yak-3		1943	1	9.2	8.46	14.85	2,105	2,660
Yak-3U		1944	1	9.2	8.46	14.95		2,984
Yak-7-M-82		1941	1	9.74	8.17	17.15		
Yak-7B		1942	1	10	8.47	17.15	2,480	3,010
Yak-9	Yak-7DI	1942	1	9.74	8.55	17.15	2,200	2,875
Yak-9D		1943	1	9.74	8.55	17.15	2,565	3,115
Yak-9U		1944	1	9.74	8.60	17.15	2.315	3,098
Yak-15		1946	1	9.2	8.78	14.85	2,050	2,640
Yak-17		1947	1	9.2	8.78	14.85	2,430	3,323
Yak-19		1947	1	8.7	8.11	13.50	2,192	3,350
Yak-23		1947	1	8.69	8.12	13.50	1,980	3,334
Yak-25		1947	1	8.80	8.66	14.00	2,285	3,535
Yak-25		1952	2	12.34	16.65	37.12	9,850	16,000
Yak-28P		1961	2	13	22.6		11,000	18,600
Yak-30		1948	1	8.60	8.96	15	2,415	3,630
Yak-50		1949	1	8.01	11.80	16	3,085	4,100
Yak-1000		1951	1					
Ye-2A		1956	1					6,250
Ye-5		1956	1					
Ye-50		1955	1					8,500
Ye-75F		1957	1					11,380

Number of engines	Power group		Performances			S = Series production	Armament	
	Type	Output or thrust	Maximum speed	Ceiling	Range		Guns	Bombs
		mhp/kp	kph	m	km	s		kg
1	VK-105P	1,050	638	11,900	700	–	1c, 2mg	
1	VK-107A	1,700	810	11,950	650	–	1c, 2hmg	
1	Kholshchevnikov	300 kp						
1	AS-82N	1,523/1,850	590	12,750	990	–	2c	
1	RD-1x3	300 kp	705					
1	AL-7F-1-100	10,000kp	2,200	13,960	1,330	s	2c, rockets	1,700
2	RD-10	850/900 kp	900	13,000	1,140	–	3c	
1	AL-7F-1-100	10,000kp	2,337	13,600	1,125	s	rockets	
2	TR-1	1,600 kp	850	12,000	2,000	–	3c	500
2	RD-45	2,270 kp	1,032	15,000	1,208	–	2c	
1	TR-3	4,600 kp	1,250	15,500	1,080	–	2c	
1	TRD-13	9,000kp	2,032	21,270		-	rockets	
1	TRD-31	9,000kp	2,337	21,270		-	rockets	
2	M-88	1,000	580	11,100	1,160	-	4c, 2hmg	
1	MV-6	240	303			-	1mg	
2	AM-37	1,300/1,400	515	10,250	1,070-1,720	–	3c, 2hmg, 1mmg	
2	AM-39	1,700	530			–	2c, 2hmg, 1mmg	
2	AM-43B	1,900	680	10,000	2,500-3,000	s	4c, 2mmg	
2		12,500kp	1,850	20,000	4,500	s	rockets	
2	M-105	1,050	630	12,200	1,500-1,800	-	4c, 1mmg	
1	AM-39A	1,900	700	14,050		–	2c	
1	VK-105P	1,050	600	10,000	700	s	1c, 1hmg	
1	VK-105PF	1,180	650	10,770	700	s	1c, 1hmg	
1	VK-105PF-2	1,244	651	10,800	710	s	1c, 2hmg	
1	VK-107A	1,500	720	11,800	1,600	s	1c, 2hmg	
1	M-82	1,330	571	10,000	880	-	2c, 1hmg	
1	VK-105PF	1,180	570	9,900	830	s	1c, 2hmg	
1	VK-105PF	1,180	605	11,000	1,000	s	1c, 1hmg	
1	VK-105PF	1,180	600	10,000	2,000	s	1c	
1	VK-107A	1,500	698	11,900	870	s	1c, 2hmg	
1	RD-10	850/910 kp	805	13,350	510	s	2c	
1	RD-10	910kp	751	12,000	740	s	2c	
1	RD-10F	1,100 kp	904	15,000	1,000	–	2c	
1	RD-500	1,600 kp	923	14,800	1,300	s	2c	
1	RD-500	1,600 kp	953	14,000	1,600	–	2c	
2	RD-9	3,600 kp	1,140	15,500	2,500-3,000	s	2c	
2	RD-11	5,960 kp	1,180	16,750	1,180-2,570	s	2c, rockets	
1	RD-500	1,600 kp	1,025	15,000	1,500	–	3c	
1	VK-1A	2,700 kp	1,170	16,600	1,100	–	2c	
1	AL-5	5,000 kp	1,150			–		
1	R-11-300	5,100kp	1,900	18,000	2,000			
1	RD-11	5,100kp	2,000	18,000	1,400	-		
1	RD-9Ye	3,800kp	2,460	25,600	450	-	2c	
1	ZhRD-5-155	2,460kp				-		
1	AL-7F-1	8,400kp	2,300	20,000	2,000	-	rockets	

Designations			Crew plus passengers or load	Dimensions			Weights	
Main designation	Other designations	Year		Span	Length	Wing area	Empty	Take-off
				m	m	m²	kg	kg
Ye-152M		1960	1	9.15	19.8			14,500

Fighters Update

Main designation	Other designations	Year	Crew	Span	Length	Wing area	Empty	Take-off
MiG-21MF		1969	1	7.15	15.76	23	6,200	9,400
I-75F		1957	1	9.97	16.96	29	8,800	11,380
Ye-150		1958	1	8.97	19.8	28.2		
Ye-152A		1959	1	8.97	19.8	28.2		14,200
Ye-166		1960	1	8.97	18.0	29	8,500	20,000
MiG-23		1964	1	14.25/ 8.17	18.8	17° 27.26	11,000	20,000
MiG-27		1974	1	14.25/ 8.17	16.8	17°27.26	10,790	20,000
MiG-25		1964	1	13.95	23.82	56.0	20,000	35,000
MiG-29		1977	1	10	17	35	8,800	16,000
Su-11		1966	1	8.43	17.4	26.2	9,100	14,000
T-3		1956	1	8.43	16.75	24.2		
PT-7		1956	1	8.43	16.75	24.2		
PT-8		1957	1	8.43	18	24.2		
T-49		1957	1	8.43		24.2		
T-5		1958	1	8.43		24.2		
T-37		1960	1	8.43	17.75	24.2		
Su-15		1964	1	10.6	19	36	11,500	19,200
Su-17		1966	1	10.6/14	16.6	28°40.1	9,800	18,300
Su-24		1969	1	10/17.25	20.5	16° 46.4	18,100	39,500
Yak-36		1966	1	7.9	16	14.85	6,000	7,500
Yak-38		1974	1	7	15	15.8	7,700	12,000

Bombers

Main designation	Other designations	Year	Crew	Span	Length	Wing area	Empty	Take-off
ANT-58	Samolet 103	1941	3	18.7	13.2	48.8	7,626	9,950- 11,990
Ar-2	SB-RK	1939	3	18.5	12.5	48.7	4,430	6,650
BOK-1	SS	1936	2	30	12.86	78.8	3,482- 3,600	4,162- 4,800
BOK-7	K-17	1938	2	34	12.95	87	4,090	10,000
BOK-11		1939	3	34	12.95	87		5,600
TsKB-26		1935	3	21.4	14.6	65.6	4,100	9,300
TsKB-30		1936	3	21.4	14.6	65.6	4,200	9,365
DB-1	RD,ANT-25	1932	3	34	13	87.1·	4,200	11,500
DB-2	ANT-37	1935	3	31	15	84.9	5,800	9,599- 11,500
DB-2bis	Rodina	1936	3	31	15	84.9	5,855	12,500
DB-3b		1939	3	21.44	14.22	65.6	4,712	7,079
DB-A		1936	11	39.5	24.4	230	16,000	21,900
DB-LK		1938	4	21.6	9.78	56.87	6,004	9,061
DB-108VM-18		1945	4	17.8	15.02	43.16		

	Power group		Performances			S = Series production	Armament	
Number of engines	Type	Output or thrust	Maximum speed	Ceiling	Range		Guns	Bombs
		mhp/kp	kph	m	km	s		kg
2	R-11	5,600kp	3,000			-		
1	R-15	9,300kp				-		
1	R-13-300	5,100/6,600kp	2,125	17,500	1,790	s	1Gsh-23	ms
1	AL-7F	9,000kp	2,300	21,000	2,000	s		
1	R-15	9,500kp	2,900	25,000	1,500	—		
2	R-11F	5,750kp	2,500	21,000	2,300	—		
1	AL-7F	10,000kp	3,000	25,000		—		
1	AL-7F	9,000kp	2,450	18,300	2,500	s		ms
1	R-29	9,000kp	1,700	18,300	2,500	s	6 barrel c	ms
2	R-31	12,000kp	3,000	24,000	2,575	s		ms
2		7,700kp	2,655	21,300		—		
1	AL-7F	10,000kp	1,915	17,000	1,100	s		ms
1	AL-7	6,500kp	1,500			—		
1	AL-7	9,000kp				—		
1	AL-7F	9,000kp	2,000			—		
1	AL-7F	9,000kp				—		
2								
1	AL-7F	10,000kp	3,000	25,000		—		
2	R-13F	7,500kp	2,755	20,000	2,415	s		ms
1	AL-7F	10,000kp	2,300	18,000	3,000	s		ms
2	R-29B	10,000kp	1,590	18,500	6,400	s	2c	ms
2	R-11	4,000	900			—		
2			1,400		2,000	s		ms
2	AM-37	1,400	635	10,600	2,500	-	2c, 4mhmg	2,000
2	VK-105R	1,100	480	10,100	1,500	s	3mmg	1,000
1	M-34RN	727	230	10,700	1,500	-		
1	(M-34RNV)	(780)		14,100				
1	M-34FRN	890	232			-		
1	M-34FRN	890	230			-	2mmg	
2	Gnome Rhone K14	800	390	5,790	4,000	-	3mmg	1,500
2	M-85	800	390	5,760	4,000	-	3mmg	1,500
1	M-34R	900	246	3,000	12,000	-	1mmg	400
2	Gnome Rhone K14	800	342	8,000	5,000	-	3mmg	1,000
2	M-86	800/950	340	8,000	7,300	-		
2	M-86	800/950	395	8,300	1,300-4,000	s	3mmg	1,000
4	M-34RN	970	330	7,220	4,500	s	1mc, 4mmg	3,000
2	M-87B	950	488	8,500	1,270-3,000	-	6mmg	2,000
2	VK-108	1,850	660			-	1c, 1mhmg, 1mmg	1,000-4,000

Designations			Crew plus passengers or load	Dimensions			Weights	
Main designation	Other designations	Year		Span	Length	Wing area	Empty	Take-off
				m	m	m²	kg	kg
DVB-102		1943	4	25.32	19.5	78.3		14,560-17,800
Il-4	DB-3F	1940	4	21.44	14.76	66.7	5,490	7,700
Il-22		1947	5	23.06	21.05	74.5	14,950	20,000-24,000
Il-28		1948	3	21.45	17.45	60.8	12,890	18,400-21,200
Il-30		1951	4	16.5	18			
Il-46		1952	3	30	27		24,565	42,000
Il-54		1954	3	17.8	21.8			29,000
K-7		1933	11	53	28	454	24,000	38,000-42,400
K-12	BS-2	1936	3	20.9	10.3	72.7	3,070	4,200
LNB		1941	2	11.4	8.17	33.15	773	1,400
M-4	201-M Molot	1953	8	50.48	47.2	300	70,000	185,000
M-50		1960	4	37	57	195		200,000
NB(T)		1943	5	21.52	15.29	58.2	6,747	14,640
OPB		1942	1	10.4	8.28	18	2,546	3,842
PB-1		1936	2	12.5	8.8	24		
Pe-2	PB-100	1940	3	17.6	12.66	40.5	5,852	7,536
Pe-2FT		1942	3	17.6	12.66	40.5	5,950	7,770-8,520
Pe-2M		1944	3	18	12.9	41.9	6,500	9,850
Pe-2I		1944	3	18	12.9	41.9	6,500	8,983
ANT-40.1		1934	3	19	12.15	51.95	3,464	5,000
SB-2		1934	3	20.33	12.57	56.7	4,138	5,732
SB-2bis		1936	3	20.33	12.57	56.7	4,768	7,880
SB-3		1939	3	20.33	12.88	56.75	4,680	6,050
Samolet 150		1952	4	28	31.4	163	31,000	50,000
Su-10		1947	4	20.6	19.55	71.3	13,436	21,138
TB-1	ANT-4	1925	4-5	28.7	18.1	120	4,427	6,762
TB-2	L-2	1930	5	27	17.6	128	4,200	6,770
TB-3	ANT-6	1931	8	39.49	24.4	230	10,967	17,200
TB-3		1936	6	41.8	25.1	234.5	12,585	18,877
TB-4	ANT-16	1933	12	54	32	422	21,400	33,280
TB-5	TsKB No.8	1931	7	31	22.1	150	7,463	12,535
TB-6	ANT-26	1936	20	95	39	800	50,000	70,000
TB-7	ANT-42	1936	7	39.01	23.4	188.4	18,000	23,800-32,600
TB-7	Pe-8	1939	10	39.01	23.59	188.68	16,000	27,000

Power group			Performances			S = Series production	Armament	
Number of engines	Type	Output or thrust	Maximum speed	Ceiling	Range		Guns	Bombs
		mhp/kp	kph	m	km	S		kg
2	ASh-71F	2,200	460	8,300	2,230	–	1c, 2mc, 2mhmg	3,000
2	M-88B	1,100	450	10,000	3,800-4,260	s	2mmg, 1mhmg	1,500
4	TR-1	1,300 kp	718	11,100	865	–	6mc	3,000
2	VK-1	2,740 kp	902	12,300	2,000-2,400	s	2c, 2mc	3,000
2	TR-3	4,600 kp	1,000	13,000	3,500	–	6mc	3,000
2	AL-5	5,000 kp	928	12,300	4,950	–	6mc	6,000
2	AL-7	5,000 kp	1,150	13,000	2,400	s	3mc	
7	M-34F	750	225	4,000	1,600	–	3mc, 6mmg	19,000
2	M-22	480	218	7,170	700	–	2mmg	800
1	M-11D	115	131	1,500	450	s		250
4	AM-3D	8,700 kp	1,100	13,000	15,800	s	10mc	40,000
4	ND-7	14,000 kp	1,950	20,000	6,000	–		
2	ASh-82A	1,430	515	8,800	2,195-3,029	–	4mhmg	5,000
1	M-90	1,425	601	10,000	950	–		
1	M-85	800	445	9,850	1,050	–		
2	VK-105R	1,100	540	8,800	1,315	s	2mg, 2mmg	600-1,000
2	VK-105P	1,260	581	9,000	1,770	s	2hmg, 2mhmg	600-1,000
2	VK-107A	1,700	630	9,350	2,275	s	3mc	1,000-4,000
2	VK-107A	1,700	656	9,350	2,275	s	2hmg, 2mhmg	3,000
2	Hispano Suiza 12Ybrs	760	352	6,800	800	–	3mmg	600
2	M-100A	760/860	423	9,560	880-2,150	s	4mmg	600
2	M-103	860/960	450	9,300	730	s	4mmg	600
2	M-103	860-960	450	7,300	1,440	s	4mmg	600
2	AL-5	5,000	875	14,630	1,260	–	4mc	5,000
4	TR-1A	1,500 kp	940	13,000	900	–	1c, 4mc	4,000
2	M-17	680	178	4,830	1,000	s	4mmg	700-3,000
2	BMW-VI Z	500	216	6,800	1,180	–	6mmg	800
4	M-17F	715	197	3,800	2,200	s	8mmg	1,000-3,000
4	M-34RN	840/970	288	7,740	3,120	s	8mmg	1,000-4,000
6	M-34R	750/830	200	2,750	1,000	–	2mc, 10mmg	4,000-10,000
4	Bristol Jupiter	480	180	2,600		–	8mmg	2,500
12	M-34FRN	900					4mc, 16mmg	1,000-4,000
4	M-34FRN	930	403	10,800	1,000-3,000	–	8mmg	
1	HS 12Ybrs	850			3,000			
4	AM-35A	1,200	441	9,300	4,700	s	2mc, 2mhmg, 2mmg	2,000-4,000

Designations			Crew plus passengers or load	Dimensions			Weights	
Main designation	Other designations	Year		Span	Length	Wing area	Empty	Take-off
				m	m	m²	kg	kg
TB-7	Pe-8	1943	10	39.01	23.59	188.68	18,570	36,000
Tu-2S	ANT-61	1943	4	18.86	13.8	48.8	7,474	10,360-11,360
Tu-2D	ANT-62	1944	5	22.06	14.42	59.05	8,316	13,340
Tu-2DB	ANT-65	1946	4	22.06	14.42	59.12		16,450
Tu-2	ANT-67	1946	4	22.06	14.42	59.12		15.215
Tu-4		1947	11	43.08	30.19	161.7	35,270	47,600-54,500
Tu-10	ANT-68	1945	4	18.86	13.8	48.8	8,870	11,650-12,735
Tu-12	Tu-77	1947	4	18.86	16.45	48.8	8,993	14,700
Tu-14	Tu-81	1949	4	21.68	21.37	67.36	14,430	21,000-24,600
Tu-16	Tu-88	1952	6	34.8	34.8	164.65	37,200	72,000
Tu-20	Tu-95	1954	10	51.1	49.8	311.1	98,000	150,000
Tu-73		1947	4	21.71	20.32	67.36	14,340	21,100-24,200
Tu-82		1949	3	17.81	17.57	45	9,526	13,500-18,340
Tu-85		1950	16	55.94	39.1	273.6	55,400	107,000
Tu-98		1955	7					
VB-109		1945	4	17.8	14.17	43.16	7,508	9,900-11,900
Yak-28		1960	3					
Yer-2	DB-240	1940	4	23	16	72		
Yer-4		1941	4	24	16	80		14,850-18,580

Bombers Update

Su-25		1977		15.5	14.5			16,350
Tu-22		1965		28	40.5	155	40,000	85,000
Tu-22M/26		1969		34.5/26.2	42	20°170	54,000	122,000
Tu	Blackjack	1980		33.75/52	50.625			267,000

Reconnaissance and Light Bombers

An-2F	An-2NAK	1948	3	18.18	12.6	71.5	3,320	5,500
BB-1		1939	2	14.3	10.25	29	2,918	4,345
D.H.4		1921	2	12.95	9.05	40.6	1,050	1,520
D.H.9		1921	2	12.95	9.1	40.6	1,010	1,496
Ivanov	(Sukhoi)	1939	2	14.3	10.25	28.07	2,816	4,030
Ivanov	ANT-51	1937	2	14.3	9.92	29	2,604	4,000
LB-2LD		1925	4	23	16	140		6,200
LR-1	TsKB-1	1933	2	13	36.52	36.52		
R-1		1923	2	14.02	9.24	44.54	1,450	2,200
R-3	ANT-3	1925	2	13.02	9.5	37	1,377	2,128

Number of engines		Power group		Performances			S = Series production	Armament	
	Type	Output or thrust	Maximum speed	Ceiling	Range		Guns	Bombs
		mhp/kp	kph	m	km	S		kg
4	ASh-82FN	1,523/1,850	422	8,500	6,000	s	2mc, 2mhmg, 2mmg	2,000-4,000
2	ASh-82FN	1,523/1,850	547	9,500	2,100	s	2c, 3mhmg	1,000-3,000
2	ASh-82FN	1,523-1,850	531	9,900	2,790	–	2c, 3mhmg	4,000
2	AM-44TK-300	2,200	578	11,000	2,570	–	2c, 3mhmg	3,000
2	ACh-30BF	1,900	509	8,850	5,000	s	2c, 3mhmg	3,000
4	ASh-73TK	2,300	558	11,200	5,700	s	10mc	6,000-8,000
2	AM-39FN-2	1,850	641	10,450	1,740	s	2c, 3mhmg	2,000-4,000
2	R.R. Nene	2,270 kp	783	11,360	2,200	s	1c, 2mhmg	1,000-3,000
2	VK-1	2,740 kp	861	11,500	1,200-3,010	s	2c, 2mc	1,000-3,010
2	AM-3M	8,750 kp	992	12,800	4,800-5,760	s	1c, 6mc	9,000
4	NK-12MV	14,975	870	13,400	12,550	s	7mc	11,340
2	R.R. Nene	2,270 kp	872	11,500	2,810	–		
1	R.R. Derwent	1,600 kp						
2	VK-1	2,740 kp	934	11,400	2,395	–	6mc	
2	VD-4K	4,300	665	13,000	8,850-13,000	–	10mc	5,000-10,000
2	AL-7F		1,238			–		
2	VK-109	2,075	720	10,800	2,000	–	2mc	1,000-3,000
2						s		
2	VK-105	1,050	500		4,100	s	3mmg	1,000
2	ACh-30B	1,250	420	7,700	5,000	s	2mhmg, 1mc	1,000
			880			s		
2	VD-7	14,000kp	1,600	14,000	6,500	s		
2	NK-144	20,000kp	2,130		12,000	s		
					7,300	—		
1	ASh-62IR	1,000	256	4,500	700	-	2mc	
1	M-88	950	468	8,900	1,200	s	4mg, 1mmg	400-600
1	Fiat A-12	240	150	4,000	400	s	1mg, 2mmg	100
1	Mercedes	260	170	3,580	600	s	1mg, 2mmg	100
1	M-87A	950	470	8,800	1,160	–	4mg, 1mmg	500
1	M-62	830	403	7,440	1,200	–	4mg, 1mmg	300
2	Fiat	260	150			-·	4mmg	500
1	M-34N	750/815	314	9,100	800	–	2mg, 1mmg	200
1	M-5	400	185	5,000	700	s	1mg, 2mmg	400
1	Lorraine Dietrich	400	194	5,000	800	s	1mg, 2mmg	200

Designations			Crew plus passengers or load	Dimensions			Weights	
Main designation	Other designations	Year		Span	Length	Wing area	Empty	Take-off
				m	m	m²	kg	kg
R-5		1928	2	15.45	10.6	50.2	1,969	2,955-3,147
R-Z		1935	2	15.45	9.7	42.52	2,007	3,150
R-6	ANT-7	1929	3	23.2	15.06	80	3,856	6,472
R-7	ANT-10	1930	2	15.2	10.9	49	1,720	2,290
R-9	DG-58R	1937	2	12.5	8.8	24		
R-9		1936	2	12	10	24.15	1,940	2,730
R-10	KhAI-5	1936	2	12.2	9.4	26.81	2,135	2,875-3,200
S	'Sparka'	1939	2	13.8	13.2	26		5,652
SR	TsKB-27	1936	2	12	9.9	24.15	1,862	2,648
Su-2		1940	2	14.3	10.25	29	2,970	4,375
Su-2		1941	2	14.3	10.46	29	3,273	4,700
Su-4	LB	1941	2	14.3	10.79	29		4,620
Su-12	RK	1948	4	21.57	11.92	52	6,970	8,839
SS 'Aist'	OKA-38	1940	2-3	14.28	10.3	26	981	1,343
NAK		1943	2	11.4	8.17	33.15	797	1,100
Yak-4	BB-22	1939	2	14	9.37	29.4		5,200

Ground attack aircraft

Designations			Crew plus passengers or load	Dimensions			Weights	
BSh-1	Vultee V-11GB	1937	2	15.25	11.4	35.67	2,443	3,860
BSh-2	TsKB-55	1939	2	14.6	11.6	38.5	3,625	4,735
DI-6Sh	TsKB-38	1936	2	10	7	25.15	1,434	2,115
Il-2	TsKB-57	1940	1	14.6	11.6	38.5	3,792	4,988
Il-2		1941	1	14.6	11.6	38.5	4,550	5,750
Il-2 type 3		1942	2	14.6	11.65	38.5	4,525	5,873-6,360
Il-2M		1942	2	14.6	11.6	38.5	4,350	6,060
Il-8		1944	2	14.6	12.9	39	4,910	7,250-7,660
Il-10		1944	2	13.4	11.2	30	4,680	6,336-6,536
Il-10M		1951	2	14	11.8	33	5,570	7,100-7,320
Il-16		1945	2	13.4	11.2	30	4,200	6,180
Il-20	Gorbach	1948	2	17	12.59	44	7,500	9,500-9,800
Il-40		1953	2					
LSh-1	TsKB-5	1930	2	15.45	10.4	51.2		
LSh	U-2VOM	1942	2	11.4	8.14	33.1	773	1,400
LShB	S	1936	2	12	10	24.15	2,090	3,450
Pegas		1943	1	12.63	8.72	26.6	1,800	2,150-2,320
Su-6-1	SA	1941	1	13.5	9.13	26	3,727	5,250
Su-6-II	S-2A	1942	2	13.5	9.24	26	4,137	5,547

	Power group			Performances			S = Series production	Armament	
Number of engines	Type	Output or thrust	Maximum speed	Ceiling	Range			Guns	Bombs
		mhp/kp	kph	m	km	s			kg
1	M-17b	500/680	228	6,400	800	s		1mg, 1mmg (2mmg)	250
1	M-34N	850	249	6,540	800	s		1mg, 2mmg	300
2	M-17F	715	230	5,620	1,000	s		4mg	500
1	BMW-VI	680	235	5,560	1,100	-		1mg, 1mmg	300
1	M-85	800	450	9,850	1,050	-		2mg, 1mmg	200
1	M-85	800	447	8,350	1,300	-		2mg, 1mmg	60
1	M-25V	730	370	7,000	1,300	s		2mg, 1mmg	200
2	M-103	960	570		700	-		1mmg	400
1	Gnome Rhone 14K	780	460	9,000	840	-		2mmg	400
1	M-88B	1,000	460	8,400	1,190	s		6mg, 1mmg	400
1	M-82	1,330	486	8,400	1,100	s		6mg, 1mmg	400
1	ASh-82	1,250	486	1,100	8,900	-		2hmg, 2mmg	400
2	ASh-82M	2,100	550	11,000	1,000	-		1c, 3mc	
1	MV-6	173	170	4,800	700	s		1mmg	
1	M-11D	115	130	3,000	400	s		1mmg	
2	M-103	960	567	8,800	800-1,600	s		1mg, 1mmg	400
1	M-621R	750	368	7,160	913	s		4mg, 1mmg	250
1	AM-35	1,350	422	4,500	618	-		4mg, 1mmg	500
1	M-25	630/700	372	7,700	500	s		4mg, 1mmg	200
1	AM-38	1,665	435	8,500	650	-		2c, 2mg, 8rockets	400
1	AM-38	1,665	412	6,000	800	s		2c, 2mg	600
1	AM-38F	1,760	410	6,000	765	s		2c, 1mhmg, 8rockets	400
1	AM-38F	1,720	414	5,500	600	s		2c,2mg,1mmg	600
1	AM-42	2,000	472	6,400	980	-		2c, 1mhmg, 4rockets	600-1,000
1	AM-42	2,000	551	7,250	800	s		2c, (4c), 1mhmg	400-600
1	AM-42	2,000	512	7,000	800	s		4c,1mc,rockets	600
1	AM-43	2,200			900	-		2c, 1mhmg	600
1	M-47F	2,700	515	7,750	1,680	-		4c, 2mc, 8rockets	1000
2	AL-5F	2,700 kp	964	11,600	1,000	-		4c, 2mc	1000
1	M-17	500	225			-		4mg, 2mmg	100
1	M-11D	115	131	1,500	450	s		1mmg	120
1	M-85	800	439	9,810	1,300	-		4mg, 1mmg	60
1	M-11F	140	172	2,620	400	-		2c, 2mg (1hmg)	500
1	ASh-71	2,000	527	7,600	576	-		2c, 2mg, 10rockets	400
1	ASh-71F	2,200	514	8,100	973	-		2c, 2mg, 1mhmg, 10rockets	400

Designations		Year	Crew plus passengers or load	Dimensions			Weights	
Main designation	Other designations			Span	Length	Wing area	Empty	Take-off
				m	m	m²	kg	kg
Su-6-III	S-2A	1944	2	13.5	9.5	28	4,370	6,200
Su-8	DDBSh	1944	2	20.5	13.58	60	9,180	12,425
Sh-Tandem	Tandem MAI	1937	2	11	8.5	30.4		2,560
ShON	TsKB-23	1931	2	15.5	10.3	51.2	1,610	3,000
TSh-1	TsKB-6	1930	2	15.5	10.56	51.2	1,700	3,490
TSh-2	TsKB-21	1932	2	15.5	10.56	51.2	1,710	3,510
TSh-3	TsKB-24	1933	2	14.1	9.55	40		3,950
Tu-91	Tarzan	1954	2-3					
VIT-1	TsKB-44	1937	3	16.5		40.4		6,453
VIT-2	TsKB-48	1938	3	16.5	12.25	40.76	4,032	6,300

Sports and training aircraft

Main designation	Other designations	Year	Crew plus passengers or load	Span	Length	Wing area	Empty	Take-off
AIR-1	VVA-3	1927	2	8.85	6.9	18.7	335	535
AIR-2		1929	2	8.85	6.9	18.7	397	640
AIR-3		1929	2	11	7.1	16.5	392	587
AIR-4		1930	2	11	7.1	16.5	395	630
AIR-9		1934	2	10.2	6.9	15.5	530	799
AIR-9bis		1935	2	10.2	6.9	15.5	525	797
AIR-10		1936	2	10.2	6.8	15.5	516	788
AIR-11		1936	3	10.2	7.1	15.5		860
AIR-12		1936	2	12	8	17	550	
AIR-14	UT-1	1936	1	7.3	5.78	8.3	430	598
AIR-16		1937	4					
AIR-17	UT-3	1938	3	15.02		33.42		3,108
AIR-18		1937	1	7.3	6	8.3		
AIR-20	UT-2	1937	2	10.18	7.1	17.2	574	804
An-13		1961	1	12.1	6	10.5		450
ANT-1		1924	1	10.94	5.84	15	180	267
AT-1		1935	3	11.8	7.05	22	750	1,070
BICh-21	SG-1	1941	1	6.9	4.7	9	536	643
Burevestnik S-2		1924	1	10	6	15	120	220
Burevestnik S-3		1926	1	9	5.8	9.6	130	230
Burevestnik S-5		1928	1	9	5.8	9.6	145	260
DG-55	E-2	1935	2	11	7.9	12.85	1,051	1,546
G-5		1928	1	9	5.1	9	320	423
G-10		1935	1	8.4	5.6	11	335	510
G-11		1941	1+10	18	9.8	30	1,200	2,400
G-15		1934	2	11	6.25	14	670	940
G-20		1935	2	9.74	6.35	13.2	607	836
G-23		1937	2	11	6.4	15	483	713
G-23bis		1938	2	10.5	6.56	14.9		
G-27		1937	3	10.6	7	17	900	1,300
KhAI-4		1934	2	12.47	8.87	27.6	740	1,130
KhAI-17		1960	1					352
KhAI-19		1962	1	7.4	5.2	9.55	200	315

Number of engines	Type	Output or thrust	Maximum speed	Ceiling	Range	S = Series production	Guns	Bombs
	Power group		Performances				Armament	
		mhp/kp	kph	m	km	s		kg
1	AM-42	2,000	520	8,000	800	–	2c, 2mg, 1mhmg, 10rockets	400
2	ASh-71F	2,200	550	9,000	1,100	–	4c, 8mg, 1mhmg, 1hmg	800
1	M-87	930	488			–	4mg, 1mmg	200
1	M-17	500	225	6,100	730	–	4mg, 2hmg	100
1	M-17	500	200	6,000	650	–	8mg, 2hmg	100
1	M-17	500	215	6,000	650	s	8mg, 2hmg	100
1	M-34F	750/830	300	5,500	800	–	10mg, 2hmg	500
1	NK-6TB-2					–		
2	M-103	960	450	8,000	1,000	–	4c, 1mc, 1mmg	500
2	M-105	1,050	513	8,200	565	s	4c, 2mc, 1mmg	500
1	Cirrus Hermes	60	140	3,850	1,240	–		
1	Walter NZ-60	65	140	3,500	800	s		
1	Siemens	85	146	4,200	1,835	–		
1	Walter NZ-60	60	150	4,000	1,000	–		
1	M-11	100	215	6,578	750	–		
1	M-11	100	217	6,578	750	–		
1	M-11	100	200	5,700	750	–		
1	Gipsy Major	120	206	4,480	720	–		
1	M-11	100	218			–		
1	M-11G	120	257	7,120	520	s		
1	MV-6	220				–		
2	MV-6	220	273	5,000	1,000	–	1mmg	50
1	MV-4	140				–		
1	M-11E	150	230	6,500	450	s		
1	TS-31M	53 kp	196	6,000	200	–		
1	Anzani	45/60	100	2,000	180	–		
1	M-11	100	180	4,000	450	–		
1	MV-6	220	417			–		
1	Harley Davidson	9	75	300	200	–		
1	Harley Davidson	12	90	1,300	200	–		
1	Cherub	35	140	1,480	280	–		
2	Cirrus Hermes	120	296	5,000	2,200	–		
1	Tom Tit	18	150	3,000	530	–		
1	Walter Polaris	55	170	5,200	700	–		
			280			s		
1	M-11	100	183	4,500	760	–		
1	M-11	100	210	3,870	817	–		
1	GAZ-Avia M-1	76	150	2,480	400	–		
1	M-11E	150	179	7,985	450	–		
2	M-11	100	240	4,000	680	–		
1	M-11	100	154	3,950	770	–		
1	M-61K	30.5	152	2,500		–		
1	M-61K	30.5	141	2,000	600	–		

| Designations | | | Crew plus passengers or load | Dimensions | | | Weights | |
| Main designation | Other designations | Year | | Span | Length | Wing area | Empty | Take-off |
				m	m	m²	kg	kg
K-10		1932	2	10.7	7.03	18	700	1,035
KAI-1		1934	3	12.6	7.9	20.6	775	1,310
KAI-3	UPB	1935	3	12.65	7.98	20.6	825	1,400
La-5UTI		1943	2	9.6	8.71	17.37		3,210
La-7UTI		1944	2	9.8	8.64	17.59	2,625	3,293
La-9UTI		1947	2	9.8	8.64	17.72	2,554	3,285
La-15UTI	La-180	1949	2	8.83	9.56	16.16	2,805	3,730
MAK-15M		1956	1	10.85	5.05	13		311
MiG-9UTI		1946	2	10	9.75	18.2	3,584	4,762
MiG-15UTI		1952	2	10.08	10.04	20.6	3,340	4,850
NV-1		1933	1	6.4	4.25	6.85		510
NV-2	UTI-5	1935	1	8	6.15	11		700
Oktyabryonok		1936	1	6	4.12	11	120	230
OS KB-1-3 PM	Kvant	1967	1	7.5	5.7			
Po-2		1946	2	11.4	8.17	33.15	750	1,023
Sh-13		1939	1	13	5.9	12.7	397	663
S-20		1966	1	19.1	5.85	18.87		650
Tri Druga		1928	2	12	6.9	17.4	245	420
U-1		1922	2	10.97	8.3	30.1	680	930
U-2		1928	2	11.4	8.17	33.15	635	890
U-2CT		1941	2	11.4	8.17	33.15	705	964
U-3		1934	2	11	8.1	30		
U-5	NV-5	1939	2	9.84	7.62	25.53	711	974
U-5bis		1940	2	9.84	7.62	25.53	773	1,036
U-5-MG-31	LS	1940	2	9.84	7.75	25.53	880	1,400
UTB		1945	2	18.86	13.98	48.8		6,446
UTI-4	I-16UTI	1935	2	9	6.1	14.54	1,200	1,492
UTI-5	NV-2S	1936	1	8	6.3	11	560	950
UTI-6	NV-6	1939	1	7	5	14	560	753
UT-2		1938	2	10.2	7	17.2	616	856
VVA-1		1934	3	11	7.5	26		850
Yak-10	Yak-11U	1952	2	9.4	8.5	15.4	2,066	2,500
Yak-11		1946	2	9.4	8.5	15.4	2,000	2,500
Yak-18		1945	2	10.3	8.07	17	816	1,120
Yak-18U		1954	2	10.3	8.53	17	970	1,300
Yak-18A	Yak-20	1957	2	10.6	8.53	17.8	1,025	1,316
Yak-18P		1960	1	10.6	8.18	17.8	818	1,065
Yak-18PM		1966	1	10.8	8.38	17.9	825	1,100
Yak-18T		1967	4	11.6	8.35	18.5	1,200	1,620
Yak-30	Yak-104	1960	2	9.38	10.5	14.3	1,555	2,240-2,470
Yak-32		1960	1	9.38	10.14	14.3	1,460	1,930
Yak-50		1975	1	9.5	7.68	15	765	900
Yak-52		1975	1	9.5	7.68	15	1,000	1,290
Yak-53		1976	1	9.5	7.68	15	900	1,060
Yak-55		1977	1	8.2	7.48	14.3		840
Yak-200		1953	4					

Power group			Performances			S = Series production	Armament	
Number of engines	Type	Output or thrust	Maximum speed	Ceiling	Range		Guns	Bombs
		mhp/kp	kph	m	km	S =		kg
1	M-11	100	170	3,800	510	–		
2	M-11	100	218	4,000	850	–		
2	M-11	100	232	4,000	1,000	s		
1	ASh-82F	1,540	600	7,900	400	s		
1	ASh-82FN	1,850	648		675	s		
1	ASh-82FN	1,850	659	11,120	940	s		
1	RD-500	1,590kp	1,010	12,750	1,150	–		
1	Polyakov	25	150			–		
2	RD-20F	800kp	910	13,000		s		
1	RD-45F(A)	2,270 kp	1,015	14,625	1,400	s	1hmg	200
1	M-11	100	232	4,800	850	–		
1	M-11G	120	250	6,100	800	–		
1	Aubier Dunne	18	115	2,300	340			
1	A1-14P	360	420			–		
1	M-11K	115	150	3,300	500	s		
1	Salmson	40	150	2,800	3,300	–		
1		65	140			–		
1	Cherub	35	127	3,000	300	–		
1	M-2	120	137	4,500	195	s		
1	M-11	100	156	4,000	400	s		
1	M-11D	115	155	4,200	500	s		
1	M-48	200				–		
1	MG-11G	120	187	3,250	500	–		
1	MG-11F	165	203	4,500	550	s		
1	MG-31F	330	272	4,700	570	–		
2	ASh-21	700	391	7,000	900	·		
1	M-25A	650/730	389	6,400	600	s		
1	MG-31	300	350			s		
1	MG-11F	165	270	4,000	300	–		
1	M-11	100	205	3,500	500	s		
1	M-11	100				–		
1	ASh-21	615/700	460	7,100	1,280	–	1mg	
1	ASh-21	615/700	460	7,100	1,280	s	1mg	
1	M-11FR	160	248	4,000	1,000	s		
1	M-11FR-1	160	235	4,000	900	s		
1	AI-14R	260	260	5,060	750	s		
1	AI-14R	260	275	6,500	600	s		
1	AI-14RF	300	315	5,000	460	s		
1	AI-14RF	300	300	5,000	1,000	s		
1	TRD-29	850/1,050kp	660	11,500	970	–		
1	TRD-29	850/1,050kp	660	14,238	950	–		
1	AI-14P	360	300	5,500	500	s		
1	AI-14P	360	360	6,000		s		
1	AI-14P	360	300			s		
1	AI-14P	360	320			·		
2	ASh-21	615/700				–		

427

Designations			Crew plus passengers or load	Dimensions			Weights	
Main designation	Other designations	Year		Span	Length	Wing area	Empty	Take-off
				m	m	m²	kg	kg

Transport aircraft

Main designation	Other designations	Year	Crew plus passengers or load	Span	Length	Wing area	Empty	Take-off
A-7	RF-8	1940	1+9	19	11.5			
AIR-5		1931	1+3	12.8	8	23	670	912
AIR-6		1932	1+2	12.07	8.02	19.8	583	843
AIR-6A		1933	1+2	12.07	8.55	19.8	610	900
AIR-7		1932	2	11	7.8	19.4	900	1,400
AIR-19		1939	2+6 -8	15.02			2,134	2,950
AK-1		1924	2+2	14.9	10.8	37	1,100	1,600
An-2		1949	2+7 -12	18.18	12.8	71.31	3,360	5,500
An-2M		1964	2+7 -12	18.18	13.16	71.31	3,410	5,500
An-8	Kit	1955	4+10t	37	30.74	117.2		38,000
An-10	Ukrajina	1957	5+84	38	34	120	29,000	54,000
An-10A		1958	5+100	38	37	120	29,800	55,100
An-12		1957	6+20t	38	33	120	28,000	61,000
An-14	Pcholka	1958	1+7	19.8	11	43.5	4,410	6,614-7,055
An-14A		1965	1+7	21.99	11.31	41	3,600	7,000
An-22	Antej	1965	5+29 +80t	64.4	57.8	345	114,000	227,000
An-24B		1960	3+44	29.2	23.53	72.46	13,300	21,000
An-26		1960	4+5, 5t	29.20	23.8	74.98	15,020	24,000
An-28		1969	1+20	22.06	12.98	40.28	3,500	6,100
An-32		1976	5+6t	29.2	23.8	74.98	14,500	27,000
An-72		1977	3+7½t	25.83	26.58			33,000
ANT-2		1934	1+2	10	7.5	17.3	500	820
ANT-9		1929	2+10	23.7	17.01	84	3,950	6,000
ANT-14	Pravda	1931	5+36	40.39	26.5	240	11,000	17,530
ANT-20	Maxim Gorkii	1934	8+72	63	32.47	486	28,500	42,000
ANT-20bis	PS-124	1939	9+64	63	34.1	486	31,200	44,000
ANT-35		1936	2+10	20.8	14.95	57.8	4,710	6,620
BDT(S-1)		1943	2+20	20		44.72		
Ts-25		1948	2+25	25.2	16.5		2,320	4,500
G-37	ULK	1934	2+1t	23.7		80		
GAZ No5		1924	2+4	11.2	8		1,100	1,830
GMK-1		1936	1+1t	30	12.4	64	1,170	2,500
G.Nr.5		1934	1+5					
KhAI-1		1932	1+5	14.85	10.26	33.2	1,630	2,600
KhAI-3	Sergej Kirov	1936	2+10	22.4	5.8	78.6	1,100	2,250
KhAI-8		1937	2+10	22.4	5.8	78.6		
Il-12		1946	5+27 -32	31.7	21.31	100	9,000	17,250
Il-14P		1950	4+18	31.7	21.31	100	12,080	16,500

Power group			Performances			S = Series production	Armament	
Number of engines	Type	Output or thrust	Maximum speed	Ceiling	Range		Guns	Bombs
		mhp/kp	kph	m	km			kg
1	Whirlwind J-4	200	192			–		
1	M-11	100	169	4,275	850	–		
1	M-11	100	162	4,500	1,000	–		
1	M-22	480	332	5,800	650	–		
2	MV-6	220	256	5,600	870	–		
1	Salmson RB-9	160	147	2,000	480	–		
1	ASh-621R	1,000	253	4,350	905	s		
1	ASh-621R	1,000	261	4,400	950	s		
2	NK-4	4,100				s		
4	AI-20D	4,100	680	9,600	4,000	s		
4	AI-20K	4,100	680	12,000	4,000	s		
4	AI-20K	4,100	640	10,200	5,700	s		
2	AI-14R	260	250	5,000	250	–		
2	AI-14RF	330	210	5,200	470-680	s		
4	NK-12MV	15,000	680		10,900	s		
2	AI-24	2,550	500	9,000	650-2,000	s		
2	AI-24T	2,820	430	7,000	645	s		
1	RU-19-300	800kp						
2	TVD-10B	960	350	7,100	1,290	s		
2	AI-20M	3,810kp	510	9,500	2,200	s		
2	D-36	6,500kp	720	11,000	3,180	s		
1	Lucifer	100	170	3,300	560	–		
3	Bristol Titan	230	185	3,800	900	s		
5	Gn. Rh. Jupiter	480	220	4,000	900	–		
8	M-34FRN	900	220	4,500	1,200	–		
6	M-34FRNV	1,000/1,200	275	5,500	1,300	–		
2	M-85A	850	376	8,500	2,000	–		
–	–					–		
–	–	250	250			s		
2	M-17	500	295			–		
1	HS-8Fb	300	165	3,000	750	–		
1	M-11	100	130	2,500	1,000	–		
–	–					–		
1	M-22	480	324	7,200	1,135	s		
1	M-11	100	135	3,000	900	–		
2	M-11	100				–		
2	ASh-82FN	1,523/1,850	470	7,00	1,250-3,000	s		
2	ASh-82T	1,900	430	7,000	1,900	s		

Designations			Crew plus passengers or load	Dimensions			Weights	
Main designation	Other designations	Year		Span	Length	Wing area	Empty	Take-off
				m	m	m^2	kg	kg
Il-14M		1955	4+14	31.7	22.31	100	12,250	17,250
Il-18	SPD	1947	6+66	41.1	29.86	140	28,490	42,500
Il-18D		1965	5+100-122	37.4	35.9	140	33,760	64,000
Il-18V	Moskva	1957	5+100	37.4	35.9	140	34,500	61,200
Il-20		1954	3+3t	21.45	17.65	60.8	10,500	162,000
Il-32		1949	2+7t					
Il-62		1963	7+186	43.3	53.12	282.2	67,500	157,000
Il-62MK		1978	7+163-195	43.2	53.15	279.55		160,000
Il-76T		1971	4+40t	50.5	46.59	300	72,000	170,000
Il-86		1976	3-4+350	48.06	59.54	320		206,000
K-1		1925	1+3	16.76	10.72	40	1,452	1,972
K-2		1925	1+4	16.76	11.17	40	1,600	2,235
K-3		1927	1+3-5	16.76	11.25	40	1,560	2,300
K-4		1928	1+4	16.76	11.35	40	1,540	2,350
K-5		1930	2+8	20.5	15.87	66	2,275	3,750
K-6		1930	2	20	14.2	64	1,720	2,820
KOMTA		1922	2+10	15	9.7	91	2,650	3,350
Konok Gorbunok		1923	2	11.5	7.8	37	700	975
KT	A-40	1942	1	18	12.06	85.8		7,804
LEM-2		1937	2+1t	26	10.6	82	1,568	2,730
LEM-3	LIG-6	1936	1+700kg	26	13.3	82	1,050	2,000
Li-2	PS-84	1939	2-4+28	28.81	19.65	91.7	7,750	10,700-11,280
MP-1		1944	1+20	20		44.72	2,300	3,500
OKO-1		1937	1+6	15.4	11.6	35.1	2,370	3,500
PM-1		1925	2+5	15.5	11	38.5	1,350	2,360
Po-2A		1946	1+2	11.4	8.17	33.15	700	1,100
PS-9		1932	2+10	23.2	17.5	84	4,400	6,200
PS-35	ANT-37bis	1939	2+10	20.8	15.4	57.8	5,012	7,000
PS-89	ZIG-1	1935	2+12	23.11	16.24	72	5,000	7,200
RAF-11		1938	1+5	15	10.86	30	2,500	3,270
RAF-11bis		1940	1+5	15	10.1	30	2,110	3,000
SAM-5		1933	1+4	12.5	8.02	24	626	1,100
SAM-5bis		1935	1+3	12.5	8.02	24	710	1,219
SAM-5-2bis		1936	1+4	12.5	8.02	24	656	1,160
SAM-10		1938	1+4	11.49	8.5	21.86	866	1,436
SAM-10bis		1939	1+4	11.49	8.5	21.86	873	1,448
SAM-14		1940	1+5	11.49	8.46	21.86	765	1,280
SAM-25		1943	1+3	12.2	8.6	25		
SKh-1	LIG-10	1937	2+6	12.8	10.75	41.17	1,215	2,150
SK-7		1937	1+5	20.7	9	39.2	780	1,660
STAL-2		1931	1+4	16.2	9.74	31	1,030	1,800
STAL-3		1933	2+6	17.02	10.68	34.8	1,672	2,817

Power group			Performances				S = Series production	Armament	
Number of engines	Type	Output or thrust	Maximum speed	Ceiling	Range			Guns	Bombs
		mhp/kp	kph	m	km		S		kg
2	ASh-82T	1,900	416	7,000	1,500		s		
4	ASh-73TK	2,300	588	10,700	6,200		–		
4	AI-20M	4,250	650	8,000	6,500		–		
4	AI-20K	4,100	650	12,500	3,700		s		
2	VK-1	2,740 kp	935	12,600	2,500		s		
							s		
4	NK-8	10,500 kp	1,000	12,600	6,700-9,200		s		
4	D-30KU	11,000kp	1,000	13,000	9,600		s		
4	D-30KP	12,000kp	800	13,000	6,700		s	2mc	
4	NK-86	13,000kp	975	11,000			s		
1	Salmson RB-9	160	161	3,000	500		–		
1	BMW-IV	240	170	3,500	550		s		
1	BMW-IV	240	170	3,880	600		s		
1	BMW-IV	240	150	4,200	710		s		
1	M-22	480	190	4,780	800-950		s		
1	M-22	480	210	5,600	800		–		
2	Fiat	280	130	600	600		–		
1	Fiat	100	120	3,500	600		s		
							–		
1	M-11	100	125	2,800	900		–		
1	M-11	100	135	3,200	800		–		
2	M-62.IR	1,000	320	5,600	450-2,500		s		
2	M-11F	145	172	2,000	700-390		–		
1	M-25A	730	370	7,800	700		–		
1	Maybach IVa	260	170	4,000	800		–		
1	M-11K	115	140	3,900	400		s		
2	M-17	500	237	5,000	1,000		s		
2	M-62IR	1,000	372	7,200	1,640		s		
2	M-17F	680	284	4,400	1,300		s		
2	MG-31	300	289	4,200	1,000		–		
2	MG-31F	330	294	4,500	930		–		
1	M-11	100	175	3,700	1,760		–		
1	M-11	100	173	2,800	900		s		
1	M-11	100	205	3,700	515		–		
1	MM-1	220	336				–		
1	MV-6	220	262	5,910			–		
1	MV-4	140	196	3,360	550		–		
1	M-11F	145					–		
1	MG-31F	330	182	3,800	600		–		
1	M-11	100	152	4,000	860		–		
1	MG-31	300	204	5,000	750		s		
1	M-22	480	237	5,340	940		s		

Designations			Crew plus passengers or load	Dimensions			Weights	
Main designation	Other designations	Year		Span	Length	Wing area	Empty	Take-off
				m	m	m²	kg	kg
STAL-3		1935	2+6	17.02	11.3	34.8	2,000	3,100
STAL-7		1936	2+12	23	16	72	4,800	7,200-11,000
STAL-11		1936	1+4	15	12.5	31	1,830	2,700
SUPV	PL-1	1925	1+3	13.2	8.4	24.1	640	1,080
S-5		1934	2+12	24	15	73.15	3,470	5,000
Shch-2	TS-1	1942	2+8	20.48	14.27	63.9	2,270	3,400
Tu-70		1946	8+48-72	43.05	35.61	161.7		51,400
Tu-75		1950	6+10t	43.83	35.61	162.7		56,600
Tu-104		1955	5+50	34.54	38.85	174.4	41,600	76,000
Tu-104A		1956	5+70	34.54	38.85	174.4		75,500
Tu-110		1957	5+100	37.5	38.3			79,300
Tu-114	Rossija	1957	10+100-220	51.1	54.1	311.1	91,000	171,000
Tu-124		1960	3+44	25.55	30.58	119	22,500	35,600-38,000
Tu-134	Tu-124A	1962	4+64-72	29.01	34.05	127.3	27,500	44,000
Tu-134A		1970	3+64-80	29.07	37.05	127.3	29,000	47,000
Tu-144 prototype		1968	6+120	27	58			150,000
Tu-144 (series)		1972	4+117-140	28.8	65.7	438	85,000	180,000
Tu-154		1968	5+167	37.55	47.9	201.45	43,500	90,000
Tu-164		1982	5+169-180	37.55	47.9	201.45	54,000	100,000
U-2S-2		1941	1+4	11.4	8.17	33.15	862	1,415
U-2SP		1933	1+2	11.4	8.17	33.15	662	1,000
U-2ShS		1944	1+4	11.4	8.55	33.15	805	1,400
U-2L		1943	1+4	11.4	8.4	33.15	800	1,400
U-2AP		1931	1+250 kg	11.4	8.17	33.15	656	1,000
Yak-6		1942	2+6	14.00	10.35	29.6		2,350
Yak-8		1944	2+8	14.8	11.35	30	1,750	2,700
Yak-12		1946	1+3	12	8.45	23	770	1,200
Yak-12R		1952	1+3	12.6	9	23.86	1,026	1,285
Yak-12A		1957	1+3	12.6	9	23	1,059	1,588
Yak-14		1948	2+35	26.17	18.44		3,096	6,750
Yak-16		1947	2+10-12	21.5	15.6	56.2	4,465	6,050
Yak-40		1967	3+29-38	25	20.36	70	9,010-9,400	15,500
Yak-42		1974	2+120	34.2	36.38	150	14,500	52,000

Power group			Performances			S = Series production	Armament	
Number of engines	Type	Output or thrust	Maximum speed	Ceiling	Range		Guns	Bombs
		mhp/kp	kph	m	km	S		kg
1	M-17	500	257		800	s		
2	M-100	760	450	10,000		-		
1	M-100A	860	430	8,000	1,000	-		
1	Lucifer	100	130	3,500	600			
2	M-22	480	225	8,400	1,000	-		
2	M-11D	115	154	2,000	7,000	s		
4	ASh-73TK	2,300	563	10,200	4,900	-		
4	ASh-73TK	2,300				-		
2	AM-3	8,700 kp	950	11,500	2,650-3,100	s		
2	AM-3M-500	9,700 kp	1,000	12,000	4,200	s		
4	AL-5	5,000 kp	1,000	12,000	3,300	-		
4	MK-12MV	15,000	870	12,000	6,200-8,950	s		
2	D-20P	5,400 kp	970	11,500	1,200-2,100	s		
2	D-30	6,800 kp	870	12,000	2,400-3,070	s		
2	D-32-2	7,080kp	900	11,900	2,000-3,500	s		
4	NK-144	17,500 kp	2,500	20,000	2,520	s		
4	NK-144F	20,000kp	M.2.35	18,000	6,500	s		
3	NK-8-2	9,500 kp	975	12,000	3,350-6,500	s		
3	D-30KU	10,600kp	980	12,500	4,000	s		
1	M-11D	115	120	1,500	300	s		
1	M-11	100	152	4,000	500	s		
1	M-11F	145	130	1,700	350	s		
1	M-11F	145	130	1,600	300	s		
1	M-11	100	150	4,000	400	s		
2	M-11F	145	180	5,000	800	s		
2	M-11M	150	180	4,500	1,350	-		
1	M-11FR	145	160	4,000	900	s		
1	AI-14R	240	184	4,160	500	s		
1	AI-14R	260	215	4,100	1,070	s		
			300			s		
2	ASh-21	635/700	350	7,700	800	-		
3	AI-25	1,500 kp	600	8,000	1,450-2,000	s		
3	D-36	6,500kp	870	10,000	1,850-3,200	s		

Designations			Crew plus passengers or load	Dimensions			Weights		
Main designation	Other designations	Year		Span	Length	Wing area	Empty	Take-off	
				m	m	m²	kg	kg	

Seaplanes

Main designation	Other designations	Year	Crew	Span	Length	Wing area	Empty	Take-off
ANT-44D		1938	6	36.45	22.42	144.7	13,000	19,000
ARK-3-1		1936	4	20	14	58.7	3,242	4,787
ARK-3-2		1938	4	20.06	14.65	59.55	3,642	5,600
ARK-Z-1		1935	2+6	21.8	15	70.2	3,200	5,150
ASK		1934	1+6	20.8	15	66.4	2,450	3,450
Be-2	KOR-1	1937	2	11	8.67	29.3	1,800	2,486
Be-4	KOR-2	1941	2-3	12	10.5	25.5	2,082	2,760
Be-6		1949	8	33	23.56	120	18,827	28,112
Be-8		1947	2+6	19	13	40	2,815	3,624
Be-10	M-10	1960	5	22.3	31.1	111.8	24,100	46,500
Be-12	M-12	1960	6	33	29.3	120		29,000
Be-30		1967	1+14 -15	17	15	32		5,700
Be-R-1		1951	3	21.4	19.43	58		17,000
DAR		1935	4-6	27.4	19	100	4,820	7,200
GST		1939	4-6	31.72	20.68	130	6,670	12,250
KR-1	HD.55	1930	2	14	10.4	56.9	1,550	2,200
LL-143		1945	7	33	23	120	15,104	21,300
M-24		1923	2-3	15.9	9	55	1,200	1,650
M-24bis		1924	2-3	15.9	9	55	1,240	1,700
MA-1		1939	2+4	14	11.82	29.6	1,450	2,200
MBR-2		1932	4	19	13.5	55	2,475	4,100
MBR-2		1935	4	19	13.5	55	3,186	4,245
MBR-4	SM-62	1932	3	16.66	12.26	69.52	2,840	4,300
MBR-5		1935	3	15.4	11.2	32.5	2,060	3,100
MBR-7	MS-8	1939	2	13	10.59	26	2,418	3,168- 3,600
MDR-2	ANT-8	1931	5	23.2	18.5	84	4,780	7,000
MDR-3		1932	6	32.2	21.9	153	8,269	13,973
MDR-4	ANT-27	1934	6	39.4	21.9	177.5	10,500	14,660
MDR-5	MS-7	1938	5	25	15.9	78.5	6,083	8,000-9,200
MDR-6		1937	3-4	21	15.73	59.4	4,087	5,600
MDR-6	Che-2	1939	3-4	21	15.73	59.4	4,100	7,200
MDR-6B-1		1940	3-4	16.2	15.7	48	4,200	6,900
MDR-6B-5		1946	4	16.7	16.2	49.4	5,610	10,080
MK-1	ANT-22	1934	8	51.6	24.1	304.5	21,663	28,750- 33,560
MP		1938	1	8.5	8	20	2,200	3,200
MP-1		1934	2+6	19	13.5	55	2,640	4,500
MP-1bis		1934	2+6	19	13.5	55	3,119	4,640
MR-3		1929	3	15.6	11.5	53	2,030	3,080
MR-5		1930	3	15.6	11.5	53	2,050	3,100
MP-7		1940	4+20	31.7	20.65	130	6,670	11,800
MTB-1	ANT-27bis	1935	6	39.4	21.9	177.5	10,521	16,250
MTB-2	ANT-44	1937	8	36.45	22.42	144.7	12,000	18,500- 21,500
MU-2		1928	2	11.8	7.9	35.3	645	970
MU-3		1931	2	10.5	8	28	650	920

Number of engines	Power group		Performances			S = Series production	Armament	
	Type	Output or thrust	Maximum speed	Ceiling	Range		Guns	Bombs
		mhp/kp	kph	m	km			kg
4	M-87	950	355	7,100		-		
2	M-25	700	308	9,810	1,000-3,000	-	2mmg	1,000
2	M-25	700	320	9,280	1,000-3,000	-	2mmg	1,000
1	M-34R	750/830	240	3,800	1,000	-		
1	M-22	480	215	4,100	700	-		
1	M-25A	635/700	277	6,600	530-1,000	s	2mg, 1mmg	
1	M-62	900	356	8,100	1,150		2mmg	300
2	ASh-73	2,300	415	6,100	4,900	s	5mc	4,400
1	ASh-21	700	268	5,550	1,200	s	1mmg	
2	AL-7PB	6,500 kp	912	14,962	4,800	s	4mc	
2	AI-20D	4,000	600	12,185	7,500	s		
2	TVD-10	970	480		1,300	-	-	-
2	VK-1	2,740 kp	800	11,500	2,000	-	2mc, 2c	1,000
2	HS-12Ybrs	760	240	5,500	2,000	-		
2	M-87	950	329	5,500	2,600	s	6mmg	1,500
1	M-22	480	194	4,800	800	s	2mmg	
2	ASh-72	2,000	401	6,000	5,100	-	6mhmg	4,000
1	Renault	220	130	4,000	400	s	2mmg	100
1	Renault	260	140	4,000	400	s	2mmg	100
1	MG-31F	330	210	4,300	1,200	-		
1	M-17B	500	200	3,980	700-1,150	s	2mmg	200
1	M-34N	750/830	275	7,900	650-1,000	s	2mmg	200
1	IF "Asso"	750	220	4,300	900	s	2mmg	160
1	Wright Cyclone	700	306	7,500	750	-	2mmg	60
1	M-103	950	376	8,500	720-1,250	-	2mmg	500
2	M-17	500	215	5,000	1,000	-	2mmg	
4	M-17	500	215	5,000	1,000	-	2mmg	
3	M-34N	750/830	232	5,450	2,130	s	6mmg	800
2	M-87A	950	345	8,150	2,145	-	4mmg	500
2	M-25E	730	338	8,500	2,650	-	4mmg	
2	M-63	960	360	9,000	2,650	s	1mmg,1mhmg	
2	M-105	1,050	454			-		
2	M-107A	1,700	455			-	3mc	400
6	M-34R	750/830	233	3,500	1,330	-	2mc, 6mmg	6,000
1	HS 12Ybrs	850				-		
1	M-17	500	214	4,720	680	s		
1	M-34B	750/830	260	4,675	750	s		
1	M-17	500	194	4,000	750	s	4mmg	300
1	M-17	500	225	5,200	800	s	4mmg	300
2	M-62RI	850	277	5,100	1,800	s		
3	M-34R	750/830	225	4,470	2,000	-	6mmg	2,000
4	Gn. Rh. 14Krsd	810	355	6,600	2,500-4,500	-	8mmg	2,500
1	M-11	100	135	3,500	500	-		
1	M-11	100	132	2,300	400	-		

Designations			Crew plus passengers or load	Dimensions			Weights	
Main designation	Other designations	Year		Span	Length	Wing area	Empty	Take-off
				m	m	m²	kg	kg
MU-4		1937	2	12				
OSGA-101		1931	2-3	11.5	7.6	17.5	620	920
PS-30	Martin 156C	1937	5+46	47.86	28	213	14,190	28,600
ROM-1	MDR-1	1927	4	28	16	104.6	4,518	5,830
ROM-2		1929	5	26.8	17.45	108.2	4,150	6,587
SAM-11		1939	1+3	11.46	8.73	21.35	1,094	1,400
SAM-11bis		1940	1+3	11.46	8.73	21.35	1,030	1,350
SPL	Gidro-1	1934	2-3	9.68	7.45	13.4	592	800-879
Sh-1		1929	3	10.7	7.72	20.28	535	790
Sh-2		1930	3	13	8.2	24.7	660	937
Sh-2bis		1946	3	13	8.2	24.7	720	1,100
Sh-7		1940	2+4	13	9.4	23.30	1,230	1,900
T-1	ANT-41	1936	4	25.73	13.8	88.94	5,846	8,925
TA		1947	2+8	17.2	14	43	4,658	6,255
TAF		1948	4	17.8	14	43.6	4,268	5,758
TOM-1		1930	4-5	33	19	120	5,000	8,030

Experimental aircraft

BICh-3		1926	1	9.5	3.5	20	140	230
BICh-7		1929	2	12.24	4.74	30	612	865
BICh-11	RP	1933	1	12.1	3.09	20	200	
BICh-11		1933	1	12.1	3.25	20		
BICh-14	TsKB-10	1935	2+5	16.2	6	60	1,285	1,900
BICh-18	Muskulet	1937	1	8	4.48	10	72	130
BICh-20		1938	1	6.9	3.56	9	181	287
BOK-2		1935	1					
BOK-5		1937	1	9.86	4.36	23.15	596	764
Leningradskij komsomolec		1936	3	10	6.5	15.5	740	1,100
LK-1	NIAI-1	1933	2	12.47	8.87	27.6	746	1,160
LK-4	NIAI-4	1934	2	9	7	20		785
LK-4	NIAI-4	1934	2	9	7	13		721
LK-4	NIAI-4	1934	2	9.75	7	13		709
MAI-62		1962	1	4.9	5.25			440
Utka		1945	3	9.5	7.1	15	642	997

Power group			Performances				S = Series production	Armament	
Number of engines	Type	Output or thrust	Maximum speed	Ceiling	Range			Guns	Bombs
		mhp/kp	kph	m	km		S		kg
1	MG-11	165	168				–		
1	M-11	100	170	5,400	480		–		
4	Wright Cyclone	860	274	4,400	5,000		–		
2	Lorraine Dietrich	450	165	3,470	800		–	3mmg	400
2	M-17	500	180	4,500	900		–	3mmg	400
1	MM-1	220	240	4,700			–		
1	MV-6	220	240	5,600			–		
1	M-11	100	186	5,400	400		–		
1	Walter NZ-85	85	126	2,470	400		–		
1	M-11	100	139	3,850	450		s		
1	M-11D	115	140	2,860	700		s		
1	MG-31F	330	218	2,960	920		–		
2	M-34FRN	890	435	9,500	1,300		–	2mmg	800
2	ASh-21	700	320	4,400	700		–		
2	ASh-21	700	330	5,900	1,200		–		
2	M-17	500	210	5,500	1,500		–	4mmg	
1	Tom Tit	18					–		
1	Bristol Lucifer	100	165	5,000	350		–		
1	OR-2	50 kp					–		
1	A.B.C.	22					–		
2	M-11	100	220				–		
–	lidska sila				0.45		–		
1	Aubier-Dunne	20	166	4,000	320		–		
1	M-11	100					–		
1	M-11	100	174	4,850	200		–		
1	M-11	100	175				–		
1	M-11	100	157	3,950	600		s		
1	M-11	100	165	3,800			–		
1	M-11	100	174	3,800			–		
1	M-11	100	160	3,800			–		
1	M-71	80	220		800		–		
1	M-11F	110	205				–		

| Designations | | | | Dimensions | | | Weight | |
Main designation	Other designations	Year	Crew plus passengers or load	Rotor diameter	Length	Rotor disc area	Empty	Take-off
				m	m	m²	kg	kg

Autogyros

Main designation	Other designations	Year	Crew	Rotor diameter (m)	Length (m)	Rotor disc area (m²)	Empty (kg)	Take-off (kg)
A-4		1931	2	13		6.2	1,020	1,320
A-6		1933	2	11		5.9	562	815
A-7bis		1934	2	15.18		14.7	1,300	2,056
A-8		1934	2	11		5.9	595	837
A-12		1936	1	14		–	1,343	1,687
A-13		1936	2	11.5		–	559	798
A-15		1937	2	18		–	1,695	2,560
AK		1940	2	13.5		–	1,026	1,317
KhAI-24		1965	2	9.96	7.8	–		800
KASKR I		1929	2	12			750	950
KASKR II		1930	2	12			865	1,100
TsAGI 2-EA		1931	2	12		5.36	765	1,032

Helicopters

Main designation	Other designations	Year	Crew plus passengers or load	Rotor diameter (m)	Length (m)	Rotor disc area (m²)	Empty (kg)	Take-off (kg)
B-5		1947	2+6	10			2,932	4,032
B-9		1947	2+5	10				
B-10	VNP	1947	2+2-3	10			3,019	3,900
B-11		1948	3	10			3,398	4,150
EG		1947	2	10			878	1,020
G-3	AK	1945	2	7			2,195	2,600
G-4		1947	2	7.7			2,364	3,002
Helicogir		1935	1+5	24.4				3,500
Ka-8		1947	1	5.6			183	275
Ka-10		1949	1	6.12			234	375
Ka-15M		1953	2	9.96	5.9		968	1,370
Ka-18		1956	1+2-3	9.96	7.03		1,040	1,460
Ka-20		1961	2-4	15.74	9.83			
Ka-22	Vintokryl	1961	4+80-100	20	22.5			33,700
Ka-25K		1967	2+12	15.74	9.83		4,400	7,300
Ka-26		1965	2+6	13	7.76		1,950	3,160
Mi-1	GM-1	1948	1+2-3	14.34	13.25		1,798	2,296
Mi-2		1961	1+6-7	14.5			2,330	3,500
Mi-4		1952	2+12	21	16.8		4,900	6,950
Mi-6		1957	4+70-80	35	41.74		27,240	42,500
Mi-8		1961	2+28	21.29	25.28		7,161	12,000
Mi-10		1961	3+12t	35	41.89		27,000	43,450
Mi-10K		1965	3+14t	35	41.89			
Omega 2MG		1941	2	7	8.2		1,760	2,050

Power group			Performances				S + Series production	Armament
Number of engines	Type	Output	Maximum speed	Minimum speed	Ceiling in or out of ground effect	Range		
		mhp	kph	kph	m	km		
1	M-26	300	176	50	4,100		-	
1	M-11	100	142	53	2,000		-	
1	M-22	480	210	46	4,800		s	1mc
1	M-11	100	142	48	2,260		-	
1	Wright Cyclone	640	245	52	5,570		-	
1	M-11	100	151					-
1	M-25V	700	283	48	6,750		-	
1	MV-6	220	176		4,700		-	
1	M-332	115	150	40	2,200		-	
1	Rhone	110					-	
1	Gnome Rhone Titan	230	110		450		-	
1	Gnome Rhone Titan	230	160	58	4,200		-	
2	AI-26GR(F)	550	236		2,280/6,400	595	-	
2	AI-26GR(F)	550					-	
2	AI-26GRV	575	218		2,200/6,550	440	-	
2	AI-26GR(F)	550	155		2,550	328	-	
1	M-11FR-1	140	150		250/2,700	235	-	
2	Pratt & Whitney R-985AN-1	450	170		1,100/2,500	210	-	
2	AI-26GR	500	148		2,400	233	-	
1	Wright J-6	300					-	
2	ASh-82V	1,700	175		1,500/2,700	255	s	
1	M-76	44.8	80		4/250		-	
1	AI-4V	55	90		500/2,000	95	s	
1	AI-14V	255	150		/3,000	310	s	
1	AI-14V	255	145		/3,000	280	s	
2	GTD-3	900	260				s	
2	D-25	5,622	377				-	
2	GTD-3	900	220		/3,500	650	s	
2	AI-14V-26	325	170		/3,000	400	s	
1	AI-26V	575	170		/3,000	370	s	
2	GTD-350	400	210		1,450/4,000	300	s	
1	ASh-82V	1,700	185		2,000/5,500	410	s	1mh'mg
2	D-25V	5,500	320		/4,500	1,000	s	
2	TB-2-117	1,500	250		/4,500	650	s	
2	D-25V	5,500	235		/4,500	630	s	
2	D-25V	5,500	235		/4,500	630	s	
2	MV-6	220	115		150/6,000	250	-	

Designations		Year	Crew plus passengers or load	Dimensions			Weight	
Main designation	Other designations			Rotor diameter	Length	Rotor disc area	Empty	Take-off
				m	m	m²	kg	kg
Omega II		1944	2	7	8.2		1,880	2,300
TsAGI 1-EA		1930	1	11	12.8		982	1,145
TsAGI 5-EA		1933	1	12	12.8		1,047	1,210
TsAGI 11-EA		1936	2	15.4				2,600
TsAGI-11-EA-PV		1939	2	15.4				2,250
Yak-100		1943	1+2-3	14.5	13.91		1,805	2,180
Yak-24		1952	2+20	20	21.34		10,607	14,240
Yak-24U		1957	2+37	21			11,000	15,830

Helicopters Update

Main designation	Other designations	Year	Crew plus passengers or load	Rotor diameter	Length	Rotor disc area	Empty	Take-off
Ka-32S		1981	3	15.9	11.3	–	–	11,000
Mi-12		1968	3+?	67.0	37.0	–	–	105,000
Mi-14		1978	4+?	21.29	18.15	–	8,636	13,208
Mi-17		1980	3+24	21.3	18.4	–	6,790	13,000
Mi-24		1970	2+12	17.0	17.0	–	6,500	10,500
Mi-26	–	1981	4+70	32	33.73	–	28,651	56,000

Number of engines	Power group		Performances					S + Series production	Armament
	Type	Output	Maximum speed	Minimum speed	Ceiling in or out of ground effect	Range			
		mhp	kph	kph	m	km			
2	MG-31F	330	150		/3,000	300		-	
2	M-2	120	20-30		605			-	
2	M-2	120			40	0.7		-	
1	Curtiss V-1570	630						-	
1	Curtiss V-1570	630	50-60		50			-	
4	DH Gipsy III	120							
1	AI-26GRLF	575	170		2,720/5,250	325		-	
2	ASh-82V	1,700	175		2,000/4,200	265		s	
2	TV3-117	2,205shp	250	-		800		s	-
4	Solovyev D-25VF	6,500shp	240	-	3,500	500		-	-
2	Isotov TV3-117	2,200shp	230	-		650		s	
2	Isotov TV3-117 MT	1,900shp	240	-	5,000	495		s	-
2	Isotov TV2/TV3	2,200shp	290	-	-	-		s	4xms,c
2	Lotarev D-136	11,400shp	295	-	4,500	800		s	-

INDEX

In order to keep the index within reasonable proportions, many entries are inter-dependent. To find all mentions of an aircraft type it will be necessary to look up references quoted in brackets. Bold type indicates either an individual aircraft or series of aircraft from a large design bureau. Illustrations are not included in the index.

A

A- Antonov designs
A-7: (RF-8) 148, 293, 297.
A-9: 252.
A-10: 252.
A-13/15: 252.
A-x-EA: TsAGI rotorcraft
A-I-EA: 374.
A-2-EA: 378.
A-3-EA: 375.
A-4-EA: 378, 380.
A-5-EA: 376, 377.
A-6-EA: 380.
A-7-EA: 380, 382.
A-8-EA: 380.
A-9-EA: 382.
A-10-EA: 382.
A-11-EA: 376, 377.
A-12-EA: 380, 382.
A-13-EA: 380, 382.
A-14-EA: 380.
A-15-EA: 382, 388.
AIR- Yakovlev designs
AIR-1: (VVA-3) 244.
AIR-2: 244.
AIR-3: 245.
AIR-4: 245.
AIR-5: 275.
AIR-6/A: 275, 277.
AIR-7: 245, 278.
AIR-8: 245.
AIR-9/bis: 224, 225.
AIR-10: 225.
AIR-11: 245.
AIR-12: 245.
AIR-16: 245.
AIR-17: (UT-3) 227.
AIR-18: 225, 245.
AIR-19: 282.
AIR-20: (UT-2) 225.
AK-1: Alexandrov/Kalinin 262.
AN- Antonov designs
AN-2: all variants (AN-4, AN-16) 200, 251, 301, 302, 303, 321, 332, 360.
AN-3: 332.
AN-4: (AN-2V) 303.
AN-8 'Kit': 203, 313.
AN-10: 203, 313, 315, 320, 321.
AN-12: 202, 203, 315, 321.

AN-14 'Pcholka': 304, 326.
AN-16: (AN-2MA) 303, 315.
AN-22 'Antei': 322, 332.
AN-24: 318, 320, 321.
AN-26: 320.
AN-28: 326.
AN-30: 320.
AN-32: 320, 332.
AN-72: 320.
AN-74: 332.
AN-124 'Ruslan': 332.
ANT- Tulolev designs
ANT-1: 125, 242, 243.
ANT-2: 125, 188, 262.
ANT-3: (R-3, R-4) 125, 161, 188, 205.
ANT-4: (G-1, TB-1) 34, 35, 125, 286, 353.
ANT-5: (I-4) 8, 24, 190.
ANT-6: (TB-3) 35, 36, 38, 126, 127, 128, 161, 268, 286, 291, 297, 355.
ANT-7: (KR-6, P5-9) 30, 128, 190, 191, 206, 268, 277, 359.
ANT-8: (MDR-2) 339, 340.
ANT-9: 268.
ANT-10: (R-7) 190.
ANT-11: 340.
ANT-12: All variants (I-5) 10, 11, 12, 13, 14, 15, 17, 23.
ANT-13: (I-8) 12.
ANT-14: 268, 271.
ANT-16: (TB-4) 128, 271.
ANT-17: (TShB) 205, 206.
ANT-18: 206.
ANT-20: (PS-124) 129, 271, 272, 365.
ANT-21: (Mi-3) 30, 32.
ANT-22: (MK-1) 340.
ANT-23: (I-12) 26.
ANT-25: (BOK-1, BOK-7, DB-1, SS) 137, 162, 163, 164.
ANT-26: (TB-6) 129, 130.
ANT-27/bis: (MDR-4, MTB-1) 340, 344.
ANT-28: 130.
ANT-29: (DIP) 26.
ANT-31: (I-14) 17, 26.
ANT-32: 43.
ANT-34: (LK-3) 32.
ANT-35: (PS-35) 281.
ANT-36: (DB-1) 138.

ANT-37: (DB-2) 138, 139.
ANT-38: 150.
ANT-40: (SB-2, PS-40) 26, 30, 146, 147, 148, 227, 293, 355.
ANT-41: (T-1) 355.
ANT-42: (TB-7, PS-42) 132, 133.
ANT-43: 278.
ANT-44: (MTB-2/A) 344.
ANT-45: 29.
ANT-46: (DI-8) 26, 29.
ANT-47: 43.
ANT-48: 150.
ANT-49: 150, 197.
ANT-51: (S-3) 192, 195.
ANT-53: 165.
ANT-58: (Samolet 103) 151.
ANT-59: (Samolet 103U) 152.
ANT-60: (Samolet 103V) 152.
ANT-61: (Tu-2) 69, 76, 152, 155, 161, 170, 227, 355.
ANT-62: (Tu-2D/T) 155.
ANT-63P: (Tu-1) 69.
ANT-64: (Tu-2) 155.
ANT-65: (Tu-2) 155.
ANT-67: (Tu-2) 155.
ANT-68: (Tu-10) 155.
ANT-69: (Tu-8) 155.
Ar-2: Arkhangelskii (SB-RK) 148, 156.
ARK-Z-1: Slokanov, 359.
ARK-3: and variants Chet - verikov (MP-2) 359, 360.
ARK-5: (P-5) 359.
ASK: Sharnylskii/Krylov 359.
AT-1: Krylov/Vinogradov 247.

B

B- Bratukhin designs
B-5: 385, 386.
B-9: 386.
B-10: 386.
B-11: 386, 387, 388.
B-12: 387.
BB-1: (Su-2) 195.
BB-2: Grushin 195.

BB-22: (Yak-4) 45.
BDP (S1): 297.
Be- Beriev designs
Be-2: (KOR-1) 348.
Be-4: (KOR-2) 346, 348.
Be-6: (LL-143) 344, 346.
Be-8: 346.
Be-10: 336, 346.
Be-12: 'Chaika': (M-12) 203, 346.
Be-30: 324, 333.
Be-32: 333.
Be-R-1: (R-1) 346.
BI: Bereznyak/Isayev 73.
BICh- Cheranovskii designs
BICh-1: 365.
BICh-2: 365.
BICh-3: 365.
BICh-5: 365.
BICh-7/A: 365.
BICh-10: 365.
BICh-11: (RP-1) 71, 365.
BICh-14: (TsKB-10) 365.
BICh-16: 366.
BICh-17: 365.
BICh-18 'Muskulet': 26, 366, 369.
BICh-20 'Pioner': 366.
BICh-21: (SG-1) 248, 366.
BOK- Bureau Osovikh Konstrukstii designs
BOK-1: (SS) 162, 163.
BOK-2: Krichevskii 369.
BOK-5: Chishevskii 369.
BOK-7: (K-17) 163, 164.
BOK-11: 165, 197.
BOK-15: 165.
BS-2: (K-12) 150.
BSh-1: (Vultee V-1168, PS-43) 207, 210, 277.
BSh-2: (Il-2) 151, 210.
Burevestnik: Nevdachin, and P5 glider 243.

C

Che-2: Chetverikov (MDR-6) 342.

D

DAR: Bartini 356, 357, 359.
DB-A: Bolkhovitinov 143, 144.
DB-LK: Belyayev 144.
DB-1: (ANT-25/36) 137, 138.
DB-2: (ANT-37) 138, 140, 143, 144.
DB-3: (Il-4, TsKB-56) 134, 140, 141, 142, 144, 150, 355.

DB-240: (Yer-2) 143, 281.
DDBSh: (Su-8) 219.
DF-1: Fedorov 186.
DG- Grigorovich designs
DG-52: (IP-1) 24.
DG-53: (IP-4) 24.
DG-54: (IP-2) 26.
DG-55: (E-2) 248.
DG-58: (PB-1) 161, 192.
DI-1: Polikarpov 2I-NI 28, 29.
DI-2: Polikarpov 28, 29.
DI-3: Grigorovich 29.
DI-4: Laville/BNK 29.
DI-6/Sh: (Samolet 21, TsKB-11/38) 29,207.
DI-8: (ANT-46) 29.
DIP: (ANT-29) 26.
DIS: (MiG-5) 50.
DIT: (I-152) 228.
DVB- Myasishchev designs
DVB-102: 165, 166.
DVB-202: 169.

E

E-1: (EMAI-1, GF-1) 372.
E-2: (DG-55) 248.
E-3: (Danilov) 372.
EG: Skrshinskii 389.
EMAI-1: Gimmelfarb and Sonshejn (E-1) 369, 372.
Enthusiast: Riga Inst. 254.

F

FS-1: (Sh-5) 267.
FS-2: (Sh-5) 267.

G

G-1: (ANT-4/TB-1) 125, 277.
G-2: (ANT-6/TB-3) 128, 252, 277, 291.
G-3: Bratukhin 385.
G-4: Bratukhin 385, 386, 387.
G-11: Gritvski 293.

G- Gribovskii designs
G-4: 247.
G-5: 247.
G-8: 247.
G-9: 252.
G-10: 247.
G-14: 369.
G-15: 247.
G-20: 224.
G-21: 247.
G-22: 247, 248.
G-23: 247.
G-25: 247.
G-26: 247.
G-27: 227.
G-28 'Krechet': 248.
G- Grokhovskii designs
G-31: 282.
G-37: 285.
G-38: 32.
G. No.4: Groshev 286.
GF-1: Gup (E-1) 248.
Gidro 1: Chetverikov (SPL, OSGA-101) 352.
GM-1: (Mi-1) 388.
GMK-1: Romejko-Gurko 282.
Grokhovskii inflatable glider: 372.
GST: Amtorg (MP-7) 342, 344, 360.
Gu-1: Gudkov 60.
Gu-82: Gudkov (LaGG-3) 60.

H

Helicogir: Isacco 377.

I

I-1: Mikoyan 103.
I-1: Polikarpov 6.
I-1M5: (IL-400) 6, 7.
I-3: Polikarpov 9, 28.
I-3U: MiG 117.
I-4: (ANT-5) 8, 9, 11, 24, 26, 34.
I-5: (ANT-12) 10, 12, 24, 35, 38, 271.
I-5: Polikarpov, (I-190, VT-11) 10, 11, 278.
I-6: Polikarpov 11, 12.
I-7: Polikarpov 36.
I-8: (ANT-13) 12.
I-9: Grigorovich 12.
I-10: Grigorovich 12.
I-11: Polikarpov 12.
I-12: (ANT-23) 12, 26.
I-13: Polikarpov 12.
I-14: (ANT-31) 17, 18, 26, 278.

Su-22: 120, 121.
Su-24: 122.
Su-25: 123.
Su-26: 254.
Su-27: 122.
SUVP: Grigorovich 262.
SVB-1: Polikarpov 208.

T

T-1: (ANT-41) 355.
T-3: Sukhoi 110.
T-5: Sukhoi 110.
T-25: Tybin 297.
T-37: Sukhoi 110.
T-49: Sukhoi 110.
T-117: Bartini 306.
T-405: Sukhoi 112, 121.
T-431: Sukhoi 112.
TA-/TA-1: Chetverikov 360.
TB-1: and variants (ANT-4, G-1) 34, 35, 74, 125, 126, 128, 191, 277, 286, 353, 355.
TB-2: (JuG-1, R-42) 126.
TB-3: (ANT-6, G-2) 35, 36, 38, 127, 128, 129, 130, 134, 138, 143, 161, 277, 286, 291, 297, 355.
TB-4: (ANT-16) 128, 129, 130.
TB-5: (MDR-3, TsKB-8) 131, 132, 340.
TB-6: (ANT-26) 129, 130.
TB-7: (ANT-42, PS-42) 132, 133, 134, 277.
TIS(A): (SPB/D) 48, 50, 161.
TOM-1: Richard 353.
Tri Druga: Sutugin/Semenov/ Gorelov 243, 244.
TS-1: (Shche-2) 293.
TsAGI- TsAGI designs
TsAGI-1-EA: (A-1) 374.
TsAGI-2-EA: (A-2) 378.
TsAGI-3-EA: (A-3) 375.
TsAGI-4-EA: (A-4) 378, 380.
TsAGI-5-EA: (A-5) 376, 377.
TsAGI-6-EA: (A-6) 380.
TsAGI-7-EA/bis: (A-7) 380, 382.
TsAGI-8-EA: (A-8) 380.
TsAGI-9-EA: (A-9) 382.
TsAGI-10-EA: (A-10) 382.
TsAGI-11-EA/-PV: (A-11) 378, 377, 384.
TsAGI-12-EA: (A-12) 382.
TsAGI-13-EA: (A-13) 380, 382.
TsAGI-14-EA: (A-14) 380.
TSh-1: (TsKB-6) 205.
TSh-2: (TsKB-21) 205.
TSh-3: (TsKB-24) 205.
TShB: (ANT-17) 205, 206.

TsKB- TsKB series
TsKB-1: Kocherigin 191.
TsKB-3: (I-15) 12.
TsKB-5: (LSh-1) 205.
TsKB-6: (TSh-1) 205.
TsKB-7: (I-Z) 24.
TsKB-8: (TB-5) 131.
TsKB-10: (BICh-14) 365.
TsKB-11: (DI-6, MDR-3) 29, 340.
TsKB-12: (I-16) 18.
TsKB-17: (I-17) 40.
TsKB-18: (I-16) 206.
TsKB-19: (I-17) 40.
TsKB-21: (TSh-2) 205.
TsKB-23: (ShON) 206.
TsKB-24: (TSh-3) 205.
TsKB-26: Ilyushin 139.
TsKB-27: Kocherigin (SR) 192.
TsKB-28: (FS-1/2, Sh-5) 267.
TsKB-29: (I-16) 19.
TsKB-30: (DB-3) 139, 140.
TsKB-32: (Il-21) 43, 46.
TsKB-33: (I-17) 40.
TsKB-38: (DI-6Sh) 29, 207.
TsKB-43: (I-17) 43.
TsKB-44: (VIT-1) 208.
TsKB-48: (VIT-2) 208.
TsKB-55: (Il-2) 210.
TsKB-56: (DB-3) 151.
TsKB-57: (Il-2) 210, 213.

Tu- Tupolev designs
Tu-1: 69.
Tu-2: and variants (ANT-61, UTB) 69, 76, 152, 155, 158, 161, 170, 197, 227, 355.
Tu-4: 166, 168, 169, 170, 178, 346.
Tu-6: (Tu-2R) 155.
Tu-8: (ANT-69) 155.
Tu-10: (ANT-68) 155.
Tu-12: (Tu-77) 170.
Tu-14: (Tu-81) 173, 174, 179, 355.
Tu-16: (Tu-88) 178, 182, 185, 198, 202, 310.
Tu-20: (Tu-95, Tu-142) 181, 182, 189, 202, 317, 318.
Tu-22: (Tu-79, Tu-105) 172, 185, 202, 254.
Tu-22M: (Tu-26) 201.
Tu-26: (Tu-22M) 201.
Tu-28: 115, 122.
Tu-64: 166.
Tu-70: 309.
Tu-72: 172.
Tu-73R: (Tu-74) 172.
Tu-74: (Tu-73R) 172.
Tu-75: 309.
Tu-77: (Tu-12) 170, 172.
Tu-78: 172.
Tu-79: (Tu-22) 172.
Tu-80: 169.
Tu-81: (Tu-14) 172, 173.
Tu-82: 174.

Tu-85: 169.
Tu-86: 175.
Tu-88: (Samolet N/Tu-16) 178, 179, 181, 202.
Tu-89: (Tu-14R) 173.
Tu-91: 'Bychok', 'Tarzan' 122, 220, 355.
Tu-95: (Tu-20) 181, 182, 202.
Tu-98: 122, 181.
Tu-102: 122.
Tu-104: 310, 311, 312, 313, 317, 318, 321.
Tu-105: (Samolet Yu, Tu-22) 185, 202.
Tu-110: 312.
Tu-114 'Rossiya': 182, 198, 203, 317, 318, 321.
Tu-124: 260, 318, 321.
Tu-126: 203.
Tu-128: 122.
Tu-134: 321, 324, 334.
Tu-142: (Tu-20) 202.
Tu-144: 201, 326, 327, 330, 334.
Tu-154: 323, 324.
Tu-164: 324.
Turbolet: Rafaeljants 372.

U

U-1: Dux Avro 504 (MU-1) 74, 222, 364.
U-2: and many variants (Po-2) 62, 160, 217, 222, 224, 228, 247, 279, 291, 298, 299, 300, 303, 362, 364.
U-3: Mikhelson 224.
U-4: Mikhelson 224.
U-5/bis: Nikitin (LSh, U-5-MG-31) 224.
UPB: (KAI-3) 227.
US-3: Antonov 252.
UT-1: and variants, Yakovlev 225, 228.
UT-2: and variants (AIR-20, Yak-20) 224, 225, 230, 251.
UT-3: Yakovlev 227.
UTB: (Tu-2) 228.
UTI-4: (I-16UTI) 21, 228.
UTI-5: (NV-2) 228.
UTI-6: (NV-4) 288.
UTI-26: (Yak-1/7) 54, 228.
Utka: (MiG-8) 372.

V

V-2: (Mi-2) 400.
V-8: (Mi-8) 400.
V-10: (Mi-10) 397.
V-12: (Mi-12) 399.
VB-108: Myasishchyev 166.
VI-100: (PB-100, Pe-2) 155, 156, 165.
VIGR: (KAI) 387.
VIT-1: (TsKB-44) 208.
VIT-2: (TsKB-48) 208.
Vorobyev 'Oral': 293.
VP (K): Polikarpov 67.
VSI: Shcherbakov 88.
VT-11: Polkarpov/Grigorovich 10.
VVA-1: Pyshnov 247.
VVA-3: (AIR-1) 244.

W

W-7: Mil 404.

Y

Yak- Yakovlev designs
Yak-1: and variants (I-26) 45, 46, 53, 54, 57, 63, 228.
Yak-2: (BB-22) 197.
Yak-3: and variants 63, 68, 75, 80, 82, 158.
Yak-4: (BB-22, I-29, R-12) 45, 197.
Yak-5: 231.
Yak-6: (NBB) 160, 293.
Yak-7: and variants (UTS-26) 54, 57, 78.
Yak-8: 309.
Yak-9: and variants 57, 63, 64, 68, 92, 158.
Yak-10: 303.
Yak-11: 235, 236, 251.
Yak-12: 251, 303, 304.
Yak-13: 303.
Yak-14: 297.
Yak-15: 78, 80, 82, 83, 85, 170.
Yak-16: 237, 306, 309.
Yak-17: and variants 83, 84, 85, 241.
Yak-18: and variants (Yak-20) 225, 231, 234, 235, 251, 253, 306.
Yak-19: 84, 87.
Yak-20: (UT-2, Yak-18A) 225, 231, 236.

Yak-22: 195, 197.
Yak-23: 85.
Yak-24: 390, 392, 393.
Yak-25: 87, 99, 115, 181, 198.
Yak-26: 198.
Yak-28: 115, 181, 198, 202.
Yak-30: 92, 237, 241.
Yak-32: 237, 241.
Yak-36MP: 122, 254.
Yak-40: 324, 335.
Yak-42: 324.
Yak-50: 99, 253.
Yak-52: 253.
Yak-53: 254.
Yak-55: 254.
Yak-100: 389.
Yak-104: 237.
Yak-200: 237.
Yak-1000: 100.
Yak-RV: 198.

Ye- Experimental series
Ye-2A: 103, 107.
Ye-4: 107.
Ye-5: 107.
Ye-6: 107, 117.
Ye-8: 252.
Ye-33: 241.
Ye-50: 103.
Ye-66: 102, 117.
Ye-75F: 107, 109.
Ye-76: 117.
Ye-133: 109.
Ye-150: 109.
Ye-152M: 109.
Ye-166: 109, 117.
Ye-231: 118.
Ye-266: 109, 118.
Yer-2: (DB-240) 142, 143.
Yer-4: 143.

Z

Z- Vakhmistrov/Samolet/ Zveno
Z-1: 34, 35.
Z-2: 35.
Z-3: 35.
Z-5: 36.
Z-6: 38.
Z-7: 38.
ZIG-1: Laville (PS-89) 278.
ZKB-26: (TsKB-30) 140.
ZKB-29: Polikarpov 161.

NATO Names

TO AVOID confusion in reporting sightings of Soviet aircraft, the Air Standards Co-Ordinating Committee of the North Atlantic Treaty Organisation (NATO) have applied code names as follows:

B- Bomber types
Backfin – Tu-98; Backfire – Tu-22 and Tu-26; Badger – Tu-16; Bank – North American B-25 Mitchell; Barge – Tu-85; Bark – Il-2; Bat – Tu-2; Beagle – Il-28; Bear – Tu-20, Tu-95 and Tu-142; Beast Il-10; Bison – M-4; Blackjack – 'Ram-P' (Tupolev); Blinder – Tu-22; Blowlamp – Il-54; Bob – Il-4; Boot – Tu-91; Bosun – Tu-14; Bounder – M-50 and M-52; Box – Douglas A-20 Havoc; Brawny – Il-40; Brewer – Yak-28, see also Firebar; Buck – Pe-2; Bull – Tu-4.

C- Transport types
Cab – Li-2; Camber – Il-86; Camel – Tu-104; Camp – An-8; Candid – Il-76; Careless – Tu-154; Cart – Tu-70; Cash – An-28; Cat – An-10; Charger – Tu-144; Clam – Il-18; Clank – An-30; Classic – Il-62; Cleat – Tu-114; Cline – An-32; Clobber – Yak-42; Coke An-24; Colt – An-2; Condor – An-400; Cooker – Tu-110; Cookpot – Tu-124; Coot – Il-18; Cork – Yak-16; Crate – Il-14; Creek – Yak-23; Crib – Yak-8; Crow – Yak-12; Crusty – Tu-134; Cub – An-12; Cuff – Be-30; Curl – An-26.

F- Fighter types
Faceplate – Ye-2A; Fagot – MiG-15; Faithless – Ye-23; Fang – La-11; Fantail – La-15; Fargo – MiG-9; Farmer – MiG-19; Feather – Yak-17; Fencer – Su-24; Fiddler – Tu-23; Fin – La-7; Firebar – Yak-28P; Fishbed – MiG-21; Fishpot – Su-9 and Su-11; Fitter – Su-7, Su-17, Su-22 and Su-22; Flagon – Su-15; Flanker – Su-27; Flashlight – Yak-25; Flipper – Ye-152; Flogger – MiG-23 and MiG-27; Flora – Yak-23; Forger – Yak-36MP; Foxbat – MiG-25; Foxhound – MiG-31; Frank – Yak-9; Fred – Bell P-63 Kingcobra; Freehand – Yak-36; Fresco – MiG-17; Fritz – La-9; Frogfoot – Su-25; Fulcrum – MiG-29.

H- Helicopter types
Halo – Mi-26; Hare – Mi-1; Harke – Mi-10; Harp – Ka-25 see also Hormone; Hat – Ka-10; Havoc – Mi-28; Haze – Mi-14; Helix – Ka-32; Hen – Ka-15; Hind – Mi-24; Hip – Mi-8 and Mi-17; Hog – Ka-18; Homer – Mi-12; Hoodlum – Ka-26; Hook – Mi-6; Hoop – Ka-22; Hoplight – Mi-2; Hormone – Ka-25, see also Harp; Horse – Yak-24; Hound – Mi-4.

M- Miscellaneous types
Madge – Be-6; Maestro – Yak-28; Magnet – Yak-17; Magnum – Yak-30; Maiden – Su-9 and Su-11; Mail – Be-12; Mainstay – Il-76; Mallow – Be-10; Mandrake – Yak-25/26; Mangrove – Yak-27; Mantis – Yak-32; Mare – Yak-14; Mark – Yak-7; Mascot – Il-28; Max – Yak-18; May – Il-38; Midget – MiG-15; Mink – UT-2; Mole – Be-8; Mongol – MiG-21; Moose Yak-11; Mop – GST and Consolidated Catalina; Moss – Tu-126; Mote – MBR-2; Moujik – Su-7; Mug – MDR-6; Mule – Po-2.

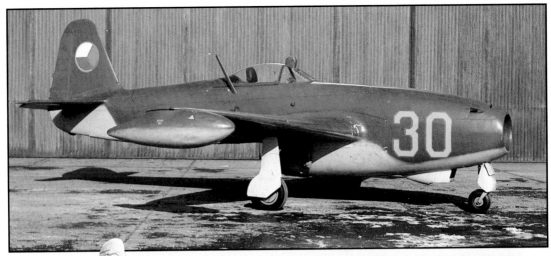

Top: Yakovlev's Yak-17 tricycle gear jet first flew in Spring 1947.

Above: Yak-23 was a further development of Yak-17 and large numbers were produced.

Below: MiG-15bis, a versatile aircraft and Korean War veteran.

Above: The variable geometry MiG-23 made its public debut in 1967.

Top right: Playing the East/West game of cat and mouse, a Phantom shepherds a giant Soviet Tu-20 reconnaissance aircraft.

Main picture: Sweeping lower over the sea a Tu-16 'Badger' is photographed after intercept.

Below: Fighter-bomber Su-7, best known aircraft from the Sukhoi Bureau.

Above: An example of the utility An-2 biplane, a master design by Antonov which first flew in 1947 and is still in production at the Polish WSK-Mielec plant.

Below: The Il-14M marked an important stage in the development of Soviet air transport when it was introduced to routes from 1955.

First Soviet jet airliner was the Tu-104, prototype of which flew on June 17, 1955. The A variant (above) appeared in 1956.

Dating from 1957, the Il-18 was originally designed for 75 passengers. The later E version illustrated could take as many as 122. Some are still in service.

Tupolev's massive Tu-114 turboprop airliner was developed in 18 months from the Tu-20 bomber, mainly for long distance internal flights.

Above: The successful Yak-40 is widely used by Soviet and Eastern European airlines.

Below: Yakovlev's heavier class inter-city aircraft, the Yak-42, lost favour when Aeroflot withdrew it in 1983.

An-10A represented a considerable improvement over the original An-10, featuring a new fin and negative dihedral of the outer wings.

Il-62M, with its four tail-mounted D-30KU bypass engines, has accommodation for 204 passengers.

Supersonic Tu-144 first exceeded Mach 2 on May 26, 1970, and after various modifications completed 102 passenger carrying flights with Aeroflot. The project is now dormant.

Soviet airbus, the Il-86, made its maiden flight on December 22, 1976. The aircraft can carry up to 350 passengers and first entered Aeroflot service in September 1978.

The Coanda effect An-72 short-haul transport has two Lotarev D-36 turbofans and can operate from 1,000m snowy or unpaved strips.

Above: Mil Mi-2 fitted with agricultural crop spraying gear.

Below: Mi-1 was the USSR's first efficient and reliable general purpose helicopter.

Above: Together with a massive array of armament, the Mi-24 'Hind' can carry 12 fully equipped troops.

Main picture: The giant helicopter Mi-12 was first reported in 1969 when it smashed a range of weight-to-altitude records. Main rotors are 35m in diameter.

Below left: Military version of the Mi-8 powered by two gas turbines.

Below: The world's largest helicopter, Mi-26 has a 56,000kg maximum take-off weight and is almost 34m in length.

Yak-50 aerobatic aircraft which house a Vedeneyev M-14P radial engine developed from the M-14B26 Ka-26 helicopter power plant.